CO-AVT-715

THE AUTHOR

Ronald E. Prather was formerly an Associate Professor of Electrical Engineering at San Jose State College and is now at Syracuse University. He received graduate degrees in Electrical Engineering and Mathematics from the University of California, Berkeley.

INTRODUCTION TO
SWITCHING THEORY:

A Mathematical Approach

INTRODUCTION TO SWITCHING THEORY:

A Mathematical Approach

RONALD E. PRATHER

Syracuse University

formerly

Associate Professor of Electrical Engineering
San Jose State College

ALLYN AND BACON, INC. BOSTON, MASS.

Library of Congress Catalog Number: 67-18974

Printed in the United States of America

TO JACQUELINE

PREFACE

Within the literature on switching theory and its application to logical design, a more or less definite class of mathematical objects has emerged; and these objects, by virtue of their proven utility, can be said to constitute a mathematical foundation for the study of digital computer logic and the design of switching systems. These objects, their role in switching theory, their application to logical design problems, and the several theories that have arisen from these applications will constitute the main body of material under investigation in this book.

It is safe to say that no two switching theorists would agree as to the exact constituents of the aforementioned class. It is equally safe to assume that Boolean algebra would be on everyone's "list." Correspondingly, this topic occupies a prominent position (Chapter 1) in the Contents. The more general concepts of "lattice" and "partially ordered set" have long been conspicuous by their absence in books of this type. This curious omission has continued in spite of the quite frequent occurrence of both structures in the technical literature of switching theory. In Chapter 1, Boolean algebra is introduced via the partially ordered set and the lattice. The additional effort entailed for having chosen this approach is negligible, but considerable advantages are thereby realized in the succeeding chapters.

The n-dimensional cube has long been recognized as an extremely useful mathematical model for the study of the analysis and synthesis of switching circuits. Chapter 2 is devoted to two representations of the cube; the first is valuable for its geometric and intuitive appeal, and the second has considerable computational advantages. These advantages become apparent in Chapter 3, where a detailed presentation of "minimization theory" is given. The presentation is based primarily on the geometrical theory of Roth-Urbano-Mueller and on several computational aids which have appeared in a publication by this author.

Chapter 4, while serving as a transition from combinational to sequential circuits, introduces the memory elements that necessarily accompany the transition. Chapter 5 is devoted to the Huffman-Mealy-Moore sequential machine model and its application to the analysis and synthesis of sequential circuits. Included are the more recent techniques of Paull-Unger-Ginsburg, which extend the earlier theory to incompletely specified machines, and the Hartmanis theory of partition pairs as applied to the state assignment problem.

The last two chapters, taken together, represent an approach to the design of switching circuits which is in considerable contrast with the more classical treatment found in Chapter 3. In Chapter 7, the essential features of the Ashenhurst-Curtis decomposition theory are developed. Together with the tree-circuit synthesis procedures of Chapter 6, this theory gives rise to an algorithm for constructing economical "multilevel" realizations of switching functions, as opposed to the "two-level" logic circuits found by the earlier synthesis techniques. Given an understanding of the methods of Chapter 3 *and* those of the last two chapters, the logical designer has a powerful capability for designing economical combinational logic circuits. If this understanding is then fused with a knowledge of the analysis and synthesis procedures of Chapters 4 and 5, he is fully equipped to participate in the effective design of sequential switching systems of a wide variety.

The opening chapter (Chapter 0) constitutes an introduction, much of which may be omitted by the reader if he has had some exposure to modern algebra. The author believes that an early introduction of the language of sets, relations, and functions permits the main body of the book to take on a preciseness and compactness that would not otherwise be possible. If the study of modern algebra were more commonly a part of the intended reader's training, Chapter 0 could be largely treated as appendix material. In the author's experience in teaching the contents of this book to seniors and beginning graduate students in Electrical Engineering, this does not yet seem to be the case.

The presence of the preliminary chapter and the mathematical stage it sets for the book as a whole ensures the fulfillment of a purpose that is not commonly met by an introductory text: The reader is brought into close contact with the literature of switching theory, exposed to the notation and mathematical concepts usually found there, and prepared— through the detailed analysis of its fundamental theory—to do research in this area should such an opportunity or necessity arise. At the same time, considerable effort has been made to ensure that the practical aspects of switching theory are given equal consideration. Through the development of algorithmic procedures, which very nearly represent computer programs, the book provides the reader with the capability for effecting the economical synthesis of large-scale digital systems. (An adequate supply of examples and problems is included to test the reader's understanding of the procedures and to develop his proficiency in implementing them.) However, it is expected that the more professionally or practically oriented student will derive as much benefit from the mathematical approach as will the potential switching theorist. It seems certain that those who will be best equipped to utilize the increasingly complex computer-aided design procedures of the coming decades will be those logical designers who have the most detailed and conceptual appreciation of the mathematical theories that foster them.

In scanning the problems that conclude each chapter, the reader will observe that certain of these bear an asterisk. This practice is employed as a warning that, by comparison, such problems are of greater difficulty— usually because they amplify or extend a portion of the text material. The asterisks that "tag" the headings in certain sections of the text have a somewhat different connotation. They label sections that may, without appreciable loss of continuity, be omitted if a shorter or less intensive course is being planned. Depending on the treatment of starred problems and sections, the book can be adapted to students of quite varied degrees of maturity and to courses of varied length.

Finally, I would like to acknowledge those persons who have influenced my thoughts in the writing of this book—whether through their teaching, advice, encouragement, or criticism: N. Balabanian, D. Carter, D. Epley, A. Grasselli, N. Gunderson, H. Huskey, W. LePage, J. Mace, B. McCormick, E. Stabler.

Syracuse, New York   RONALD E. PRATHER

CONTENTS

INTRODUCTION TO SWITCHING THEORY:

A Mathematical Approach

CHAPTER 0 | PRELIMINARIES

0.1 INTRODUCTION

In keeping with the practice generally observed when elementary set theory is employed simply as a notational convenience, we take the notion of a *set* as being an essentially undefined concept. The synonyms "set of elements," "collection of members," and "class of objects" might be listed in an attempt to convey the notion we have in mind. For our purposes, a particular set is well defined if we have at hand some definite rule for determining whether or not a given element belongs to the set under consideration.

Until we are convinced that we know what a "set" is, it will not be possible to give a clear definition of the concepts of "function" and "relation," each of which will assume an important role in the sequel. After discussing equivalence and compatibility, which are two relations of interest in their applications to switching theory, we review the principle of mathematical induction—a principle which the reader has presumably encountered in his previous training. Mathematical induction provides a technique for proving various conjectures regarding the integers. Many such conjectures will arise in the course of our discussions, so it is well that we renew our acquaintance with this often-used principle. Several immediate applications of mathematical induction are necessary at the close of this chapter, where we investigate the base conversion problem. The reader who has had some exposure to the binary number system is already aware of the need for techniques for converting numbers from binary to decimal, and vice versa. Such conversion techniques are solutions to the base conversion problem, which we will discuss in a more general setting.

As indicated in the Preface, the reader who has had an introduction to modern algebra will want to skip much of the material of this chapter, and review only selected topics of his own choosing. To the uninitiated we hasten to add that the topics taken up in this chapter (and the first portion of the next) are merely excerpts from modern algebra, chosen for their utility in the applications to switching theory. The reader is in no way invited to conclude that the topics extracted are representative or central in the study of modern algebra.

0.2 SETS

Whenever possible, we will use capital letters to act as "names" for the sets we introduce, and small letters to denote elements that may or may not belong to a particular set. If S is an arbitrary set, we indicate the fact that a is a member of S by the notation

$$a \in S$$

(read as "a is in S" or "a in S," whichever is grammatically correct in the context), while if a is not in S we write

$$a \notin S$$

If S has a finite number of elements, it is possible (though not always practical) to enumerate its members or elements. By enclosing them in braces thus,

$$S = \{a, b, c\}$$

we circumvent the need for a "rule" to determine the members of S. This notation is intended to mean that the elements a, b, and c (and only these) are members of the set S. When this practice is either not possible or not convenient, we resort to the use of a generic symbol such as x, followed by a semicolon, and a mathematical and/or English-language statement that serves as the rule for deciding which x's belong to S.

EXAMPLE 0.1

The set
$$S = \{x; \; x \text{ is an integer, } x > 5\} \tag{0.1}$$
is the set consisting of all integers that are greater than 5. Until the reader becomes accustomed to such notation, it is advisable that he interpret it in language form. He may read

(i) $=$ as "is"
(ii) $\{x$ as "the set of all elements x"
(iii)   ; as "such that" or "having the property that"
(iv)   , as "and"
(v) $\}$ as (silent)

so that the sentence of Eq. 0.1 becomes "S is the set of all elements x having the property that x is an integer and x is greater than 5." From this expression the original description of the set is readily apparent. Incidentally, it would be equally clear to write
$$S = \{6, 7, 8, \cdots\}$$
with the enumeration evident even though S is not finite.

A particular symbol $\varnothing$ is used to denote the set that has no members. For obvious reasons, this set goes by the name *empty set* (also *null* set).

A set A is said to be a *subset* of the set S if†
$$a \in A \Longrightarrow a \in S$$
In words, this definition insists that every element of A also be an element of S.

EXAMPLE 0.2

Let S be the set of Example 0.1. Now suppose
$$A = \{6, 7\}$$
Then
$$a \in A \Longrightarrow \begin{cases} a = 6 \\ \quad \text{or} \\ a = 7 \end{cases}$$
In each case we have $a \in S$, so that the statement
"whenever $a \in A$ is true, then $a \in S$ is true"
is satisfied; that is,
$$a \in A \Longrightarrow a \in S$$

†The notation "$P \Rightarrow Q$" for statements P and Q is read "P implies Q", or "whenever P is true, then Q is true," while the notation "$P \Leftrightarrow Q$" is read "P if and only if Q" or "whenever P is true, then Q is true, and conversely."

so that A is a subset of S. On the other hand, A is not a subset of S if we take

$$A = \{5, 6\}$$

EXAMPLE 0.3

If we consider the set

$$S = \{x; x \text{ is a point within the circle labeled } S \text{ in Fig. 0.1}\} \qquad \textbf{(0.2)}$$

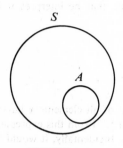

FIGURE 0.1

then certain circles A drawn on Fig. 0.1 will correspond (in the manner of Eq. 0.2) to subsets of S, while others will not. We have indicated a subset A of S on Fig. 0.1, and it is useful to keep this sort of drawing in mind whenever the word "subset" is used. Even though Example 0.2 treats sets of numbers rather than points on a sheet of paper, it is helpful to visualize the relationship of A to S in the pictorial fashion exemplified here.

Note that the empty set is a subset of any set S. (Why?) Also, S is a subset of S for any set S.

When A and B are two subsets of a set S, then we say that A is *contained* in B (written $A \subseteq B$) if

$$a \in A \Longrightarrow a \in B$$

(As with the definition of subset, this definition insists that every element of A also be an element of B.) Interchangeable with this notation is $B \supseteq A$, which is read "B *contains* A." Clearly, $A \subseteq B$ means that A is a subset of B, where the subsets A and B are themselves considered as sets. The statement $A = B$ for subsets of a set S is intended to mean that A and B have precisely the same members, that is,

$$A = B \Longleftrightarrow A \subseteq B \quad \text{and} \quad B \subseteq A \qquad \textbf{(0.3)}$$

This condition is taken as our definition of *equality* for sets. Furthermore, we write $A \subset B$ if $A \subseteq B$, but $A \neq B$ (that is, $B \nsubseteq A$), in which case we say that A is a *proper* subset of B or that B contains A *properly*.

EXAMPLE 0.4

The set S of Example 0.1 is a proper subset of

$$Z = \{x; x \text{ is an integer}\}$$

since

$$x \in S \Longrightarrow \left\{ \begin{array}{c} x \text{ is an integer} \\ \text{and} \\ x > 5 \end{array} \right\} \Longrightarrow \left\{ \begin{array}{c} x \text{ is an} \\ \text{integer} \end{array} \right\} \Longrightarrow x \in Z$$

shows that $S \subseteq Z$. But $Z \nsubseteq S$ because $-1 \in Z$ and $-1 \notin S$, so that the statement

$$a \in Z \Longrightarrow a \in S$$

is false. Similar reasoning shows that S is a proper subset of

$$Z^+ = \{x; \ x \text{ is a positive integer}\}$$

and that Z^+ is a proper subset of Z. The reader should make a drawing of the type shown in Fig. 0.1, illustrating $S \subset Z^+ \subset Z$.

0.3 COMPOSITIONS

Of the many ways in which it is possible to compose new sets out of several given sets, we will have occasion to use the intersection, the union, and the (Cartesian) product of two sets.

If A and B are two sets, the collection of elements,

$$A \cap B = \{c; \ c \in A \quad \text{and} \quad c \in B\} \tag{0.4}$$

is called the *intersection* of A and B, while the collection

$$A \cup B = \{c; \ c \in A \quad \text{or} \quad c \in B\} \tag{0.5}$$

is called the *union* of A and B. The (Cartesian) *product $A \times B$* is defined to be the collection of all pairs (a, b) for which $a \in A$ and $b \in B$; that is,

$$A \times B = \{(a, b); \ a \in A, b \in B\} \tag{0.6}$$

In $A \times B$, two elements (a, b) and (a', b') are regarded as equal if and only if $a = a'$ and $b = b'$. This should remind the reader of the definition for equality of two complex numbers. (See Example 0.7.)

EXAMPLE 0.5

If $A = \{1, 2, 4, 7\}$ and $B = \{2, 7, 8, 9\}$, then

$$A \cap B = \{2, 7\}$$

$$A \cup B = \{1, 2, 4, 7, 8, 9\}$$

Note that the properties

(i) $A \cap B \subseteq A, \ A \cap B \subseteq B$
(ii) $A \subseteq A \cup B, \ B \subseteq A \cup B$

observed here are quite generally true, as one can prove by applying the definitions of the words "intersection," "union," and "contains."

EXAMPLE 0.6

If $A = \{\text{boy, girl}\}$ and $B = \{1, 2, 3\}$,

$$A \times B = \{(\text{boy}, 1), (\text{boy}, 2), (\text{boy}, 3), (\text{girl}, 1), (\text{girl}, 2), (\text{girl}, 3)\}$$

EXAMPLE 0.7

If we take $A = B = R$, where R is the set of all real numbers,

$$A \times B = R \times R = \{(a, b);\ a \text{ and } b \text{ are real numbers}\}$$

is recognized as the Cartesian plane. This accounts for the fact that $A \times B$, for any sets A and B is frequently referred to as the "Cartesian" product of the sets A and B. Now suppose that A and B themselves are subsets of the Cartesian plane. Then it is possible to illustrate the definitions of "intersection" and "union" by means of the self-explanatory diagram of Fig. 0.2, in which $A \cup B$ consists of the points that belong to either A or B (or both).

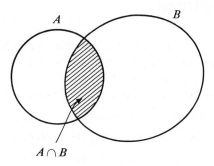

$A \cap B$

FIGURE 0.2

The three compositions introduced here have immediate generalizations to any finite number of sets $A_1, A_2, \ldots, A_n$. One defines

$$\bigcap_{i=1}^{n} A_i = A_1 \cap A_2 \cap \cdots \cap A_n \tag{0.7}$$
$$= \{a;\ a \in A_i \text{ for all } i = 1, 2, \cdots, n\}$$

$$\bigcup_{i=1}^{n} A_i = A_1 \cup A_2 \cup \cdots \cup A_n \tag{0.8}$$
$$= \{a;\ a \in A_i \text{ for some } i = 1, 2, \ldots, n\}$$

$$\prod_{i=1}^{n} A_i = A_1 \times A_2 \times \cdots \times A_n \tag{0.9}$$
$$= \{(a_1, a_2, \cdots, a_n);\ a_i \in A_i \text{ for each } i = 1, 2, \cdots, n\}$$

We wish to generalize further the concepts of intersection and union to arbitrary "indexed collections of sets," but these cannot be properly defined until we introduce the notion of a "function." This will be done in the next section.

Meanwhile, several important concepts can be described, which make direct use of the intersection and union compositions. Given two sets A and B, the first of these refers to the question: Do these two sets A and B "overlap" in the sense of Fig. 0.2? If

$$A \cap B = \varnothing$$

we say that A and B are *disjoint*, while the opposite situation,

$$A \cap B \neq \varnothing$$

is described by saying that A and B are *connected*. By the definition of the empty set, A and B need have only one element in common to be connected.

EXAMPLE 0.8

Let S be the set of Example 0.1, and for any integer $m \geq 1$,

$$Z_m = \{0, 1, 2, \cdots, m-1\}$$

Then

$$S \text{ and } Z_m \text{ are disjoint} \Leftrightarrow m < 7$$

More generally, a finite number of sets $A_1, A_2, \cdots, A_n$ are said to be disjoint (or, for clarity, *mutually disjoint*) if

$$A_1 \cap A_j = \varnothing \qquad \text{for all } 1 \leq i, j \leq n$$

If the sets $A_1, A_2, \cdots, A_n$ are each subsets of a set S, we ask: Are there elements in S which are not in any of the subsets A_i? If not,

$$S = \bigcup_{i=1}^{n} A_i$$

and we say that the subsets $A_1, A_2, \cdots, A_n$ *cover* S. A collection

$$\lambda = \{A_1, A_2, \cdots, A_n\}$$

of subsets of S (λ is a set whose elements are themselves sets), whose subsets $A_1, A_2, \cdots, A_n$ cover S (such a collection λ is called a *covering* of S) and are at the same time mutually disjoint, is said to be a (finite) *partition* of S. (See Fig. 0.3 with $n = 4$.) These have important theoretical and practical applications, as we shall see later.

As our final means for constructing new sets from old ones, we introduce a form of set subtraction. If $A \subseteq S$, we define

$$S - A = \{x; x \in S \text{ and } x \notin A\} \tag{0.10}$$

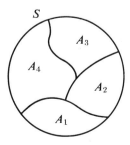

FIGURE 0.3

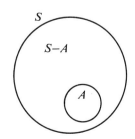

FIGURE 0.4

which is called the *difference set* (specifically, the difference of A from S). The reader may consult Fig. 0.4 in order to see that this definition is consistent with his intuition. Note the following properties:

(1) $A \cup (S - A) = S$,
(2) $A \cap (S - A) = \varnothing$,

which show that the collection

$$\lambda = \{A, S - A\}$$

is always a partition of S.

0.4 FUNCTIONS

A (single-valued) *function* α (or *mapping*, as it is sometimes called) of a set S *into* a set T is a correspondence

$$\alpha : S \longrightarrow T$$

that associates with each $s \in S$ a single element $t \in T$, which is called the *image* of s under the function α. One writes

$$t = \alpha(s)$$

or

$$s \xrightarrow{\alpha} t \quad \text{or} \quad \alpha : s \longrightarrow t$$

to express the correspondence of t with s, which the function α defines. In a pictorial fashion reminiscent of Figs. 0.1 through 0.4, we depict a function $\alpha : S \rightarrow T$, as shown in Fig. 0.5, where we have exhibited the image t of a typical element $s \in S$. Such a mapping α is said to be *onto* T if every $t \in T$ occurs as the image of some $s \in S$. A function α of S into T is said to be 1–1 (one to one) if

$$\alpha(s_1) = \alpha(s_2) \Longrightarrow s_1 = s_2$$

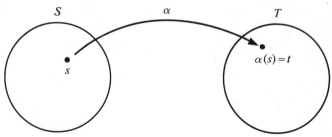

FIGURE 0.5

that is, if distinct elements of S have distinct images. (Here we have phrased the condition as if it read $s_1 \neq s_2 \Longrightarrow \alpha(s_1) \neq \alpha(s_2)$. But this is permissible because "$P \Longrightarrow Q$" for statements P and Q is equivalent to "not $Q \Longrightarrow$ not P.")

EXAMPLE 0.9

The reader is probably most familiar with functions

$$\alpha : R \longrightarrow R$$

of the real numbers, R into themselves. With such functions, the correspondence α is usually described by an expression of which

$$\alpha(x) = x^2 + 3$$

is typical. (Usually in calculus, one employs the symbol f where we have used α.) This expression gives a rule for establishing the correspondence, a part of which reads

$$2 \xrightarrow{\alpha} 7$$

$$3 \xrightarrow{\alpha} 12$$

$$\pi \xrightarrow{\alpha} \pi^2 + 3$$

Here we say that 7 is the image of 2 under the function α, 12 is the image of 3 under α, etc.

The function

$$\alpha(x) = x^2 + 3$$

has a "graph" as shown in Fig. 0.6.

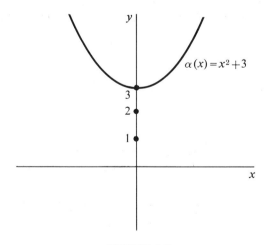

FIGURE 0.6

From its graph, it is immediately apparent that
(1) α is not onto R, since there are elements y (for example, $y = 1$) that do not occur as an image of some $x \in R$. To see this

$$\alpha(x) = 1 \Longrightarrow 1 = x^2 + 3 \Longrightarrow x^2 = -2$$

and we cannot find a real number x whose square is -2.
(2) α is not 1–1 because distinct elements $(x \neq x')$ do not necessarily have distinct images. Take $x = 1$ and $x' = -1$. Then $\alpha(x) = \alpha(x') = 4$.

EXAMPLE 0.10

If S and T have but a finite number of elements, a correspondence and hence a function $\alpha : S \longrightarrow T$ can be described by simply listing the elements of S in one column and those of T in a column to its right. From any element of S, one arrow is drawn to some element of T. If this is done for each element of S, one has exhibited a function from S into T.

Suppose

$$S = \{1, 2, 3, 4\}$$
$$T = \{a, b, c\}$$

Then the function $\alpha : S \longrightarrow T$, given by

is onto T but not 1–1, since $3 \neq 4$ and $\alpha(3) = \alpha(4)$, so that the condition

$$\alpha(s_1) = \alpha(s_2) \Longrightarrow s_1 = s_2$$

does not hold when we take $s_1 = 3$, $s_2 = 4$. On the other hand, the function $\beta : T \longrightarrow S$, given by

is 1–1, but not onto S, since the element $s = 2$ does not occur as an image. Since we consider only single-valued functions, there does not exist a function of T onto S.

Let S be a set. For each subset S' of S there is a mapping

$$i : S' \longrightarrow S$$

called the *inclusion map* and defined by

$$i(s') = s' \qquad \text{for all } s' \in S' \qquad (0.11)$$

It is clear that *inclusion maps* are always 1–1, and they are onto only if $S' = S$.

Let $\alpha : S \longrightarrow T$ and let $t \in T$. Then $\alpha^{-1}(t)$ is the subset of S, defined by

$$\alpha^{-1}(t) = \{s \in S; \alpha(s) = t\} \qquad (0.12)$$

and it is called the *inverse image* of the element t. More generally, the *inverse image of the subset* $T' \subseteq T$ is the set

$$\alpha^{-1}(T') = \{s \in S; \alpha(s) \in T'\} \qquad (0.13)$$

and conversely, for $S' \subseteq S$, we put

$$\alpha(S') = \{t \in T; t = \alpha(s) \text{ for some } s \in S'\} \qquad (0.14)$$

This set is called the *image of the subset* S'.

EXAMPLE 0.11

If $\alpha : R \longrightarrow R$ is the function

$$\alpha(x) = x^2 + 3$$

we have by Eq. 0.12,

$$\alpha^{-1}(4) = \{x \in R; \alpha(x) = 4\} = \{x \in R; 4 = x^2 + 3\}$$
$$= \{x \in R; x^2 = 1\} = \{-1, 1\}$$

and

$$\alpha^{-1}(1) = \varnothing$$

Similarly, if $\alpha : S \longrightarrow T$ is the function α of Example 0.10,

$$\alpha^{-1}(a) = \{1\}$$
$$\alpha^{-1}(b) = \{3, 4\}$$
$$\alpha^{-1}(c) = \{2\}$$

Evidently one can say that for any function $\alpha : S \longrightarrow T$,

α is 1–1 $\Longleftrightarrow$ $\alpha^{-1}(t)$ contains at most one element for each $t \in T$

as in the present example, where the fact that $\alpha^{-1}(b)$ contains two elements of S accounts for the failure of α to be 1–1.

To illustrate the concepts of "image of a subset" and "inverse image of a subset," consider this same function and the subset

$$S' = \{1, 3, 4\} \subseteq S$$

Then, by Eq. 0.14,

$$\alpha(S') = \{t \in T; t = \alpha(s) \text{ for some } s \in S'\}$$
$$= \{t \in T; t = \alpha(1) \text{ or } t = \alpha(3) \text{ or } t = \alpha(4)\}$$
$$= \{a, b\} \subseteq T$$

Thus, $\alpha(S')$ is that subset of T that consists of all elements which are images of some element in S'. Similarly, if $T' \subseteq T$, $\alpha^{-1}(T')$ is that subset of S that consists of elements whose images are in T'. For example, taking

$$T' = \{b, c\}$$

we have

$$\alpha^{-1}(T') = \{2, 3, 4\}$$

Let $\alpha : S \longrightarrow T$. We observed that

α is 1–1 $\Longleftrightarrow \alpha^{-1}(t)$ contains at most one

element of S for each $t \in T$

and it is easily seen that

α is onto $\Longleftrightarrow \alpha^{-1}(t)$ contains at least one

element of S for each $t \in T$

Hence, if α is 1–1 *and* onto T, we have

$\alpha^{-1}(t)$ contains exactly one element $s \in S$ for each $t \in T$

so that for each $t \in T$, there is a unique element $s \in S$ such that $\alpha(s) = t$. If we associate with t this element s, we obtain a mapping of T into S. We call this mapping the *inverse* α^{-1} of α. It is immediate that α^{-1} is a 1–1 mapping of T onto S. (Why?) Numerous examples of mappings that have inverses can be given; we will exhibit an entire class of such mappings in Example 0.13.

As with sets, it is important to decide on a reasonable definition for equality. We agree to regard two mappings α and β of S into T as *equal* if and only if

$$\alpha(s) = \beta(s) \qquad \text{for all } s \in S \tag{0.15}$$

Now let $\alpha : S \longrightarrow T$ and $\beta : T \longrightarrow U$. It is then possible to define a function (call it $\beta \cdot \alpha$) from S into U by associating with the element $s \in S$ the image $\beta(\alpha(s))$ in U; that is,

$$(\beta \cdot \alpha)(s) = \beta(\alpha(s)) \tag{0.16}$$

(See Fig. 0.7.) This mapping, $\beta \cdot \alpha$ is called the *composition* or *product* of α and β.

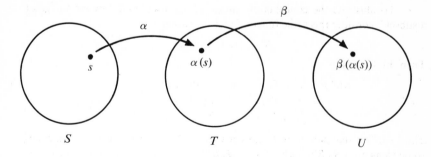

FIGURE 0.7

according to the formula

$$(\alpha \times \beta)\,(a, b) = (\alpha(a), \beta(b)) \tag{0.21}$$

for all $(a, b) \in A \times B$. The mapping $\alpha \times \beta$ is called the *Cartesian product* of α and β. More generally, when a finite number of sets $A_1, A_2, \cdots, A_n$ and mappings

$$\alpha_i : A_i \longrightarrow S_i \qquad (i = 1, 2, \cdots, n)$$

is given, we define similarly the Cartesian product mapping $\prod\limits_{i=1}^{n} \alpha_i$ according to the rule

$$\left(\prod_{i=1}^{n} \alpha_i\right)(a_1, a_2, \cdots, a_n) = (\alpha_1(a_1), \alpha_2(a_2), \cdots, \alpha_n(a_n)) \tag{0.22}$$

for all elements

$$(a_1, a_2, \cdots, a_n) \in \prod_{i=1}^{n} A_i$$

Thus we obtain a mapping

$$\left(\prod_{i=1}^{n} \alpha_i\right) : \prod_{i=1}^{n} A_i \longrightarrow \prod_{i=1}^{n} S_i$$

EXAMPLE 0.14

If

$$A = \{a, b, c\} \qquad S = \{\text{boy, girl}\}$$
$$B = \{d, e\} \qquad T = \{1, 2, 3, 4\}$$

and α, β are the mappings $\alpha : A \longrightarrow S$ and $\beta : B \longrightarrow T$ shown,

$$a \xrightarrow{\alpha} \text{boy} \qquad d \xrightarrow{\beta} 1$$
$$b \xrightarrow{\alpha} \text{girl} \qquad e \xrightarrow{\beta} 3$$
$$c \xrightarrow{\alpha} \text{girl}$$

then

$$(a, d) \xrightarrow{\alpha \times \beta} (\text{boy, 1})$$
$$(b, d) \xrightarrow{\alpha \times \beta} (\text{girl, 1})$$
$$(c, d) \xrightarrow{\alpha \times \beta} (\text{girl, 1})$$
$$(a, e) \xrightarrow{\alpha \times \beta} (\text{boy, 3})$$
$$(b, e) \xrightarrow{\alpha \times \beta} (\text{girl, 3})$$
$$(c, e) \xrightarrow{\alpha \times \beta} (\text{girl, 3})$$

is their Cartesian product. The reader can no doubt furnish his own example for the more general situation of a Cartesian product of $n > 2$ mappings.

Now let $\alpha : S \longrightarrow T$ and suppose there is a set U and mappings $\beta : S \longrightarrow U$, $\gamma : U \longrightarrow T$ such that the diagram

$$S \xrightarrow{\ \alpha\ } T$$
$$\beta \qquad \gamma$$
$$U$$

commutes; that is, $\gamma \cdot \beta = \alpha$. (According to Eqs. 0.15 and 0.16, this means $\gamma(\beta(s)) = \alpha(s)$ for all $s \in S$.) Then we say that the mapping α is *factored* or *decomposed* into the product $\gamma \cdot \beta$. Of course every function $\alpha : S \longrightarrow T$ has the *trivial* decompositions

$$\alpha = \alpha \cdot 1_S = 1_T \cdot \alpha$$

so that interest is naturally focused on the nontrivial decompositions of a function.

EXAMPLE 0.15

Let S be any set. The Cartesian product of S with itself n times is denoted

$$S^n = \overbrace{S \times S \cdots \times S}^{n}$$
$$= \{(s_n, s_{n-1}, \cdots, s_1);\ s_i \in S \text{ for } i = 1, 2 \cdots, n\}$$

The function

$$\tau_j : S^n \longrightarrow S$$

defined by

$$\tau_j(s_n, s_{n-1}, \ldots, \overset{j}{s_j}, \cdots, s_1) = s_j \qquad \text{for all } (s_n, s_{n-1}, \cdots, s_1) \in S^n \quad \textbf{(0.23)}$$

is called the *j*th *coordinate projection* of S^n onto S.

Take $n = 3$ and consider the first coordinate projection

$$\tau_1 : C^3 \longrightarrow S$$

defined by Eq. 0.23; that is,

$$\tau_1(s_3, s_2, s_1) = s_1 \qquad \text{for all } (s_3, s_2, s_1) \in S^3 \qquad \textbf{(0.24)}$$

Among the many nontrivial decompositions of this mapping, we cite the decomposition indicated by the commuting diagram

$$S^3 \xrightarrow{\ \tau_1\ } S$$
$$\beta \searrow \quad \nearrow \gamma$$
$$S^2$$

and the definitions

$$\beta(s_3, s_2, s_1) = (s_2, s_1) \qquad \text{for all } (s_3, s_2, s_1) \in S^3$$
$$\gamma(s_2, s_1) = s_1 \qquad \text{for all } (s_2, s_1) \in S^2$$

EXAMPLE 0.16

If in Example 0.15 we take $S = R$ (see Example 0.7), $S^3 = R^3$ will be ordinary Euclidean space and τ_1 will be the projection of a point $p = (z, y, x)$ onto the x axis. The decomposition of Example 0.15 is then seen first to project p onto the x-y plane and then into the x axis. (See Fig. 0.8.)

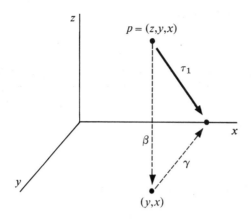

FIGURE 0.8

0.5   SEQUENCES

Let J and S be sets and

$$f:J \longrightarrow S$$

a mapping of J *onto* S. When the elements $x \in S$ are "named"†

$$x = x_\alpha$$

whenever $f:\alpha \longrightarrow x$, we say that the set S has been *indexed* by the set J. The mapping f is called the *index mapping* and J is called the *index set*. One frequently refers to the indexed set in the notation

$$S = \{x_\alpha; \, \alpha \in J\}$$

or

$$S = \{x_\alpha\}$$

if the index set is not important to the discussion. Lest this concept appear too abstract, we quickly specialize to instances with which the reader is no doubt familiar. Suppose $J = Z^+$ and $f:Z^+ \longrightarrow S$ is a mapping onto a set S. Then the elements $x \in S$ may be considered as the "terms" of an infinite sequence where

$$x = x_n \Longleftrightarrow f:n \longrightarrow x$$

†Unless f is known to be 1–1, it is conceivable that elements $x \in S$ may have more than one "name."

The ordered array enclosed in angle brackets

$$\langle x_1, x_2, \cdots, x_n, \cdots \rangle \qquad \text{(0.25a)}$$

which is also written in the forms

$$\langle x_n; n = 1, 2, \cdots, \rangle \qquad \text{(0.25b)}$$

$$\langle x_n; n \in Z^+ \rangle \qquad \text{(0.25c)}$$

or simply $\langle x_n \rangle$, is called an *infinite sequence* (or *sequence*, for brevity). Often the mapping $f: Z^+ \longrightarrow S$ is itself called a sequence. In this connection, we remark that when $f: Z^+ \longrightarrow S$ is not necessarily onto S, we say that f defines (or is) a sequence *in S*.

EXAMPLE 0.17

Let $f: Z^+ \longrightarrow Z^+$ be defined by

$$f(n) = n - (-1)^n$$

Then we obtain

$$f(1) = 1 + 1 = 2$$
$$f(2) = 2 - 1 = 1$$
$$f(3) = 3 + 1 = 4$$
$$f(4) = 4 - 1 = 3 \qquad \text{etc.}$$

so that the mapping f defines the sequence

$$\langle 2, 1, 4, 3, 6, 5, \cdots \rangle$$

EXAMPLE 0.18

Since the mappings f defining sequences are not required to be 1–1, we may very well obtain sequences whose terms are not distinct. Let $S = \{a, b\}$ and suppose $f: Z^+ \longrightarrow S$ is defined according to the rules

$$f(n) = \begin{cases} a & \text{if } n \text{ is odd} \\ b & \text{if } n \text{ is even} \end{cases}$$

Then we obtain the sequence

$$\langle a, b, a, b, a, b, \cdots \rangle$$

Note that each element of S has an infinite number of "names," that is,

$$a = x_1 = x_3 = x_5 \cdots$$
$$b = x_2 = x_4 = x_6 \cdots$$

The last example illustrates that whereas one thinks of the elements of a set as being distinct, the same is not necessarily true of the terms of a sequence. The preceding example dramatizes another distinction between sets and sequences. The elements of a set are not thought to be ordered, that is, as having a first element, a second element, etc. Quite to the contrary, the notion of being ordered is fundamental to the sequence concept. Indeed, a sequence $\langle x_n \rangle$ *inherits* its order from the index mapping f. Nevertheless, there are instances in which the notions of set and sequence might be considered as identical. Suppose S is a set for which there exists a 1–1 mapping of Z^+ onto S. (1–1 onto mappings are often called 1–1 *correspondences*.) Then S is said to be a *countably infinite set*. With such sets, the selection of a mapping

$$f : Z^+ \longrightarrow S$$

which is 1–1 and onto S gives rise to a sequence of distinct terms, the terms being elements of S. Moreover, every element of S is a term of the sequence. In this case we denote S by one of the following forms (see Eqs. 0.25):

$$\{x_1, x_2, \cdots, x_n, \cdots\} \tag{0.26a}$$

$$\{x_n; n = 1, 2, \cdots\} \tag{0.26b}$$

$$\{x_n; n \in Z^+\} \tag{0.26c}$$

or simply $\{x_n\}$, and S is said to be an *ordered* countably infinite set. At the same time we see why S might be called a sequence. Accordingly, we use the notations of Eqs. 0.25 or 0.26, depending upon whether or not we wish to emphasize the ordering of the elements of S inherited from f.

Now suppose that S is a *finite set* (a set having a finite number of elements). The integer $|S|$ is simply the number of elements in S. Thus, if

$$S = \{a, b, c\}$$

we have

$$|S| = 3$$

From Example 0.13 we see that when $|S| = n$, there are $n!$ mappings of the form

$$f : n^+ \longrightarrow S$$

which are 1–1 and onto S. Any one of these mappings may be chosen to index S, in which case S is denoted by one of the equivalent forms:

$$S = S_n = \{x_1, x_2, \cdots, x_n\} \tag{0.27a}$$

$$S = S_n = \{x_i; i = 1, 2, \cdots, n\} \tag{0.27b}$$

$$(\text{or } \{x_i : 1 \le i \le n\})$$

$$S = S_n = \{x_i; i \in n^+\} \tag{0.27c}$$

and S is termed an *ordered* finite set with n elements. (We will ordinarily denote this set by S_n.) As with countably infinite sets, we replace braces ({ }) by angle brackets ($\langle$ $\rangle$) when we wish to call special attention to the order inherited from f. If this is done, we say that the ordered array

$$\langle x_1, x_2, \cdots, x_n \rangle$$

is a *finite sequence* (with distinct terms). Arbitrary finite sequences in which the terms are not necessarily distinct are defined in an obvious manner—simply consider arbitrary mappings $f:n^+ \longrightarrow S$.

EXAMPLE 0.19

If $S = \{a, b, c\}, |S| = 3$. Suppose we take

$$f:3^+ \longrightarrow S$$

to be the mapping

$$1 \xrightarrow{\ f\ } b = x_1$$

$$2 \xrightarrow{\ f\ } a = x_2$$

$$3 \xrightarrow{\ f\ } c = x_3$$

Then S is written in the form of Eq. 0.27a as

$$S = \{x_1, x_2, x_3\}$$

We should note that a change in the order in which the elements of a set occur in its enumeration does not effect a change in the set; that is, as sets

$$\{a, b, c\} = \{b, a, c\}$$

which can be easily verified by applying the definition of set equality, Eq. 0.3.

In contrast with the definition of equality for sets, two sequences

$$\langle x_n; n \in Z^+ \rangle \quad \text{and} \quad \langle y_n; n \in Z^+ \rangle$$

are regarded as equal iff†

$$x_n = y_n \qquad \text{for all } n \in Z^+$$

(The definition is similar if finite sequences are to be compared.) Thus, the order of occurrence is important for sequences, whereas a rearrangement does not destroy the equality of sets.

Finally we are prepared to generalize the compositions of intersection and union in the following way: Let

$$S = \{A_\alpha; \alpha \in J\}$$

be a collection of sets A_α indexed by the set J. Note that S is a set whose elements are themselves sets. We write

$$\bigcap_{\alpha \in J} A_\alpha = \{a; a \in A_\alpha \ \text{ for all } \alpha \in J\} \qquad \textbf{(0.28)}$$

$$\bigcup_{\alpha \in J} A_\alpha = \{a; a \in A_\alpha \ \text{ for some } \alpha \in J\} \qquad \textbf{(0.29)}$$

to generalize Eqs. 0.7 and 0.8, respectively. It can be seen that if $J = n^+$, Eqs. 0.28 and 0.29 are identical to Eqs. 0.7 and 0.8. If, instead, $J = Z^+$, it is more common to write

---

†The reader should have encountered this abbreviation for the phrase "if and only if." It is interchangeable with the symbol $\Longleftrightarrow$.

$$\bigcap_{n=1}^{\infty} A_n = \{a; a \in A_n \quad \text{for all } n = 1, 2, \cdots\} \qquad (0.30)$$

$$\bigcup_{n=1}^{\infty} A_n = \{a; a \in A_n \quad \text{for some } n = 1, 2, \cdots\} \qquad (0.31)$$

in place of Eqs. 0.28 and 0.29.

0.6   RELATIONS

The Cartesian product, considered earlier, allows us to treat functions α of the form

$$\alpha: S \times S \longrightarrow S$$

Such mappings are called *binary compositions* in the set S, and are said to be *commutative* if

$$\alpha(s_1, s_2) = \alpha(s_2, s_1) \qquad \text{for all } s_1, s_2 \in S$$

EXAMPLE 0.20

Suppose $S = R$, the set of real numbers. Then the function $\gamma: R \times R \to R$ defined according to the rule

$$\gamma: (r_1, r_2) \longrightarrow r_2$$

is a binary composition in R. (The reader who is accustomed to viewing $R \times R$ as the set of all complex numbers would perhaps write "Im" in place of γ to stand for the imaginary part of $z = r_1 + ir_2$). Of a more complicated nature are the binary compositions in R that are ordinarily called "addition" and "multiplication." If α is the addition composition, we have

$$\alpha: (r_1, r_2) \longrightarrow r_1 + r_2$$

whereas

$$\beta: (r_1, r_2) \longrightarrow r_1 \cdot r_2$$

for the multiplication composition β. Observe that α and β are commutative compositions but γ is not.

Closely related to the notion of a binary composition in its structure is the concept of a "relation" on a set S. This has numerous and important applications to switching theory, and this is particularly true of the equivalence and compatibility relations to be discussed in the succeeding sections.

We say that a *relation* ρ is defined in a set S if there is a mapping (also called ρ)

$$\rho: S \times S \longrightarrow B$$

where $B = \{0, 1\}$.† Then, if $(a, b) \xrightarrow{\rho} 1$, we say that a is *related* to b (by the relation ρ) and we write

$$a \rho b$$

while if $(a, b) \xrightarrow{\rho} 0$, we write

$$a \rho' b$$

to denote that a is not related by ρ to b.

Hence, a relation ρ is defined in a set S if, for any ordered pair (a, b) with $a \in S$, $b \in S$, we can determine (by some rule) whether or not a is in the given relation to b. The mapping ρ is merely a convenient way of describing those elements that are related and those that are not.

EXAMPLE 0.21

Let $S = R$, the set of real numbers, and define

$$a \rho b \Longleftrightarrow a - b \in Z = \{x; x \text{ is an integer}\}$$

In this instance, it is more convenient to give a rule (as we have done) for determining which ordered pairs of elements are related than it is to describe the function

$$\rho: R \times R \longrightarrow B$$

If necessary, however, we could write

$$\rho(a, b) = \begin{cases} 0 & \text{if } a - b \notin Z \\ 1 & \text{if } a - b \in Z \end{cases}$$

to define the function ρ. Among the related and unrelated pairs of elements in R, we cite

$$3.26 \; \rho \; 7.26$$

$$4 \quad \rho' \; \pi$$

$$e \quad \rho \; (e - 1)$$

as illustration.

Some authors prefer to define a relation on S as being a subset R of $S \times S$. When a relation

$$\rho: S \times S \longrightarrow B$$

has been defined in the sense we have intended, these writers say that the subset

$$R = \rho^{-1}(1) \tag{0.32}$$

is the relation. If, on the other hand, they give a subset $R \subseteq S \times S$ as a relation, we could define

---

†Curious as it may seem, this set B is central to the theory of switching circuits and logical design. A concerted effort will be made to reserve the symbol B for denoting this set $\{0,1\}$.

$$a \rho b \Leftrightarrow (a, b) \in R \qquad (0.33)$$

Thus, for

$$\rho : S \times S \longrightarrow B$$

we take

$$\rho(a, b) = \begin{cases} 0 & \text{if } (a, b) \notin R \\ 1 & \text{if } (a, b) \in R \end{cases}$$

Therefore, since

$$\rho^{-1}(1) = \{(a, b) \in S \times S; \rho(a, b) = 1\} = R$$

the two approaches to defining relations are equivalent.

EXAMPLE 0.22

Consider $S = n^+ = \{1, 2, \cdots, n\}$ for some $n \geq 2$. Then the subset

$$R = \{(i, i); i \in n^+\} \cup \{(i, n + 1 - i); i \in n^+\}$$
$$\cup \{(1, 2), (2, 1)\}$$

of $n^+ \times n^+$ may be used to define a relation. From the tabulations:

$$R = \{(1,2), (2,1), (1,1), (2,2)\}$$
$$= n^+ \times n^+ \qquad \text{if } n = 2$$
$$R = \{(1,2), (2,1), (1,1), (2,2), (3,3),$$
$$(1,3), (2,2), (3,1)\} \qquad \text{if } n = 3$$
$$R = \{(1,2), (2,1), (1,1), (2,2), (3,3),$$
$$(4,4), (1,4), (2,3), (3,2), (4,1)\} \qquad \text{if } n = 4$$

and so on, one can determine the related elements from Eq. 0.33. This information is perhaps most conveniently displayed in the arrays

	1	2
1	1	1
2	1	1

$(n = 2)$

	1	2	3
1	1	1	1
2	1	1	0
3	1	0	1

$(n = 3)$

	1	2	3	4
1	1	1	0	1
2	1	1	1	0
3	0	1	1	0
4	1	0	0	1

$(n = 4)$

and so on. The arrays or matrices (r_{ij}) have the property

$$r_{ij} = 1 \Leftrightarrow (i, j) \in R \Leftrightarrow i \rho j \qquad (0.34)$$

and thereby contain all necessary relational information.

The preceding example suggests the following *definition:* Suppose ρ is a relation on an ordered finite set $S_n = \{x_1, x_2, \cdots, x_n\}$. Then the matrix (r_{ij}) defined by

$$r_{ij} = \begin{cases} 1 & \text{if } x_i \, \rho \, x_j \\ 0 & \text{if } x_i \, \rho' \, x_j \quad \text{(that is, otherwise)} \end{cases} \qquad (0.35)$$

is called the *relation matrix* of ρ.

Evidently our procedure for constructing a relation matrix for a given relation can be reversed. Given any $n \times n$ matrix

$$\begin{pmatrix} r_{11}r_{12} & \cdots & r_{1n} \\ r_{21}r_{22} & \cdots & r_{2n} \\ \cdot & & \cdot \\ \cdot & & \cdot \\ \cdot & & \cdot \\ r_{n1}r_{n2} & \cdots & r_{nn} \end{pmatrix}$$

with coefficients $r_{ij} \in B = \{0,1\}$, we can define a relation

$$\rho : S_n \times S_n \longrightarrow B$$

on $S_n = \{x_1, x_2, \cdots, x_n\}$, which is an ordered finite set, by setting

$$\rho(x_i, x_j) = r_{ij} \qquad (1 \le i, j \le n) \qquad (0.36)$$

Clearly, this relation has the given matrix as its relation matrix.

Before we turn to a discussion of an important class of relations, the equivalence relations, we first examine a few properties of the partitions of finite sets. At the conclusion of Sec. 0.8 we will learn that equivalence relations are intimately related to partitions, and this is our reason for introducing them at this time.

0.7 PARTITIONS

In Sec. 0.3 we agreed that a (finite) partition λ of a set S was to be a collection

$$\lambda = \{A_1, A_2, \cdots, A_n\}$$

of subsets of S having the properties

$$S = \bigcup_{i=1}^{n} A_i \qquad (0.37a)$$

and

$$A_i \cap A_j = \varnothing \qquad \text{for all } 1 \le i, j \le n \qquad (0.37b)$$

More generally, an indexed collection

$$\lambda = \{A_\alpha; \alpha \in J\}$$

of subsets of S satisfying

$$S = \bigcup_{\alpha \in J} A_\alpha \qquad\qquad \text{(0.38a)}$$

$$A_\alpha \cap A_\beta = \varnothing \qquad \text{for all } \alpha \neq \beta \in J \qquad \text{(0.38b)}$$

is said to be a *partition* of S. Thus we allow for partitions having an infinite number of subsets in the collection.

But if $|S| = n$ (S is a finite set), it is intuitively clear that every partition λ must be a finite partition. Then we agree that two partitions λ and γ of S are *equal* if they are equal as sets.

EXAMPLE 0.23

Suppose

$$S = \{1, 2, 3, 4, 5, 6, 7, 8\} = 8^+$$
$$A_1 = \{1, 2, 5, 6\}$$
$$A_2 = \{3, 7\}$$
$$A_3 = \{4, 8\}$$

Then the reader can easily see that properties (0.37a) and (0.37b) hold so that

$$\lambda = \{A_1, A_2, A_3\} = \{\{1, 2, 5, 6\}, \{3, 7\}, \{4, 8\}\}$$

is a partition of S. Note that the elements of the set are themselves sets, so that partitions are (technically speaking) sets of sets. In this connection we wish to illustrate the definition of equality for partitions by pointing out that for

$$\gamma = \{\{1, 2, 6, 5\}, \{8, 4\}, \{3, 7\}\}$$

we have $\gamma = \lambda$, since γ and λ are equal as sets.

For ease of writing, we will often replace the inner braces by over-lines, which display equally well the members of a particular subset of the partition. Replacing as we will the separating commas by semicolons, for clarity, we write the above partition λ in the form

$$\lambda = \{\overline{1,2,5,6};\ \overline{3,7};\ \overline{4,8}\}$$

Note that every set S possesses two "trivial" partitions—one whose only subset is S itself and another in which every single-element subset of S is a subset of the partition. Denoting these by I and 0, respectively, for the set S of Example 0.23 we have

$$I = \{\overline{1,2,3,4,5,6,7,8}\} \qquad\qquad \text{(0.39)}$$

and

$$0 = \{\overline{1};\ \overline{2};\ \overline{3};\ \overline{4};\ \overline{5};\ \overline{6};\ \overline{7};\ \overline{8}\} \qquad\qquad \text{(0.40)}$$

Clearly, I and 0 are respectively the smallest and largest partitions in terms of

$$|\lambda| = \text{the number of subsets (or *blocks* as they}$$
$$\text{are often called) in a finite partition } \lambda \qquad \text{(0.41)†}$$

---

†Observe that the notation $|\lambda|$ is consistent with $|S|$ as defined in Sec. 0.5.

From another point of view, I and 0 are respectively the largest and smallest partitions of S. This terminology would result from reckoning the "size" of a partition according to

$$\langle\lambda\rangle = \text{the number of elements in the largest}$$
$$\text{block of the finite partition } \lambda \qquad (0.42)$$

It is because we adopt the second point of view that the definitions given for I and 0 are natural.

EXAMPLE 0.24

For the partition λ of the preceding example we have

$$|\lambda| = 3$$
$$\langle\lambda\rangle = 4$$

How many partitions does a finite set have? In asking "How many partitions has the set $S_n = \{x_1, x_2, \cdots, x_n\}$?" we may, of course, replace S_n by $n^+ = \{1, 2, \cdots, n\}$ and arrive at the same answer. If we denote

$$\Lambda(n) = |\{\lambda; \lambda \text{ is a partition of } n^+\}| \qquad (0.43)$$

the question is reduced to that of determining the integer $\Lambda(n)$. (See Prob. 0.21.) The number $\Lambda(n)$ is of interest in discussing the so-called state assignment problem for sequential machines. (See Chapter 5.)

0.8   EQUIVALENCE RELATIONS

Let S be any set and ρ a relation on S. The relation ρ is called an *equivalence* relation (in which case the symbol $\sim$ often replaces ρ) if it satisfies the following three conditions:

Reflexive: $\qquad a \rho a \qquad$ for all $a \in S$ $\qquad\qquad$ (0.44)

Symmetric: $\quad a \rho b \Longrightarrow b \rho a \qquad$ for all $a, b \in S$ $\qquad$ (0.45)

Transitive: $\quad \left.\begin{array}{c} a \rho b \\ b \rho c \end{array}\right\} \Longrightarrow a \rho c \qquad$ for all $a, b, c \in S$ $\qquad$ (0.46)

EXAMPLE 0.25

Consider the set $S = R \times R$ (the Cartesian plane) and define for $a = (r_1, r_2)$ and $b = (r_1', r_2')$ in S;

$$a \rho b \Longleftrightarrow r_2 = r_2'$$

(This is a formal way of saying that two points in the Cartesian plane are to be related by ρ if and only if they lie on the same horizontal line of the plane.)

The reader can easily verify that ρ satisfies conditions 0.44, 0.45, and 0.46 above, so that ρ is an equivalence relation. If we pursue this example further and define for $a = (r_1, r_2) \in S$, the collection

$$\bar{a} = \{b;\, b \in S,\, b = (r'_1, r_2)\}$$

(the set of all points in the plane whose second coordinate agrees with that of a) is seen to be the horizontal line through a. Furthermore,

$$a \,\rho\, b \Longleftrightarrow b \in \bar{a}$$

The collection of all these horizontal lines (one for each $r_2 \in R$) is a partition of the set S into nonoverlapping subsets. We now demonstrate that this phenomenon is typical of equivalence relations.

Let $\sim$ be an equivalence relation on a nonempty set S. For $a \in S$ define

$$\bar{a} = \{x \in S;\, x \sim a\} \tag{0.47}$$

Since

$$x \sim a \Longleftrightarrow x \in \bar{a}$$

the set $\bar{a}$ is called the *equivalence class* determined by a. First, note that $\bar{a}$ is a subset of S and $\bar{a} \neq \varnothing$ because the reflexivity of the relation $\sim$ guarantees that $a \in \bar{a}$. In this framework, we can state two lemmas.

Lemma 0.1. $a \sim b \Longleftrightarrow \bar{a} = \bar{b}$.

PROOF. Assume $a \sim b$ and let $x \in \bar{a}$, so that $x \sim a$. Then, by transitivity, $x \sim b$, so $x \in \bar{b}$ and we conclude that $\bar{a} \subseteq \bar{b}$. We are assuming that $a \sim b$, so that also $b \sim a$ by symmetry. Now suppose $z \in \bar{b}$ and hence $z \sim b$. Then, again by transitivity, we have $z \sim a$, so that $z \in \bar{a}$, which proves that $\bar{b} \subseteq \bar{a}$. This and the preceding statements show that

$$a \sim b \Longrightarrow \bar{a} = \bar{b}$$

For the other direction of implication, suppose $\bar{a} = \bar{b}$. As we noted earlier, $a \in \bar{a}$. Also, $a \in \bar{b}$, since we are assuming that $\bar{a} = \bar{b}$. Then $a \sim b$ by definition of

$$\bar{b} = \{x \in S;\, x \sim b\} \quad \blacksquare$$

We leave to the interested reader the proof of the following easy consequence of Lemma 0.1.

Lemma 0.2. $\bar{a} \cap \bar{b} \neq \varnothing \Longrightarrow \bar{a} = \bar{b}$.

The lemma asserts that if a and b have any element in common, then they are identical. Taken together, these two lemmas imply an important characterization of equivalence relations, given in the following theorem.

Theorem 0.3. Let S be any set and $\sim$ an equivalence relation on S. Then S is partitioned by $\sim$ into equivalence classes (*blocks*) in such a way that (1) every element of S is in some block; (2) the elements within a given block are mutually equivalent; and (3) no element is in two different blocks. Conversely, any partition λ of S defines an equivalence relation $\underset{\lambda}{\sim}$ on S. One merely defines

$$a \underset{\lambda}{\sim} b \Leftrightarrow a \text{ and } b \text{ are in the same block of } \lambda.$$

It is trivial to verify that this definition satisfies the reflexive, symmetric, and transitive laws, which must prevail in order that we can rightfully call it an equivalence relation. This explains the converse assertion of Theorem 0.3. Moreover, Theorem 0.3 would seem to imply that there exists for a given set S a 1–1 correspondence between the collection of its "distinct" equivalence relations and the set

$$\Lambda(S) = \{\lambda; \lambda \text{ is a partition of } S\} \tag{0.48}$$

Here, it would be important to agree that two equivalence relations, $\sim$ and $\simeq$ on S are *equal*† (not distinct) if

$$a \sim b \Leftrightarrow a \simeq b$$

for all a and b in S.

EXAMPLE 0.26

To see the type of difficulty that could arise if we did not first take this precaution, suppose

$$S = \{1, 2, 3, 4, 5, 6, 7, 8, 9\}$$

We define two relations $\sim$ and $\simeq$ on S as follows:
(i) $a \sim b \Leftrightarrow a - b$ is a multiple of 3.
(ii) $a \simeq b \Leftrightarrow a$ and b are in the same column of the matrix

$$\begin{pmatrix} 1 & 2 & 3 \\ 4 & 5 & 6 \\ 7 & 8 & 9 \end{pmatrix}$$

From the words alone it might appear that two unrelated equivalence relations have been defined on S, but the reader will quickly observe that such is not the case. In fact, $\sim$ is not distinct from $\simeq$. Abstractly, they should be thought of as defining only one equivalence relation on S, namely, that whose associated partition is

$$\{\overline{1,4,7}; \quad \overline{2,5,8}; \quad \overline{3,6,9}\}$$

Hence, with the proper interpretation we can assert two corollaries.

Corollary 0.4 Every (finite) set S has $|\Lambda(S)|$ distinct equivalence relations.

Corollary 0.5 The set n^+ has $\Lambda(n)$ distinct equivalence relations.

†A similar definition might have been made for relations generally.

*0.9   GROUPINGS[†]

In Sec. 0.7, a (finite) partition of a set S was defined as a disjoint covering of S. By way of contrast, a (finite) *grouping*

$$\gamma = \{A_1, A_2, \cdots, A_n\}$$

of a set S is a (possibly "overlapping") covering of S; that is,

$$S = \bigcup_{i=1}^{n} A_i \qquad\qquad (0.49)$$

such that for every $i = 1, 2, \cdots, n$, we have that, for each $x \in S - A_i$, an element $a \in A_i$ exists having the property

$$\{x, a\} \nsubseteq A_j \qquad \text{for all } j \neq i \qquad\qquad (0.50)$$

The reader can provide a generalization to indexed collections of subsets A_α, as we did for partitions. Two groupings of S are regarded as *equal* when they are equal as sets.

EXAMPLE 0.27

Suppose

$$S = \{1,2,3,4,5,6,7\} = 7^+$$
$$A_1 = \{1,2,3\}$$
$$A_2 = \{3,5,6\}$$
$$A_3 = \{4,5,6,7\}$$
$$A_4 = \{1,2,4,6\}$$

Then Eq. 0.49 is clearly satisfied by

$$\gamma = \{A_1, A_2, A_3, A_4\} = \overline{1,2,3}; \ \overline{3,5,6}; \ \overline{4,5,6,7}; \ \overline{1,2,4,6}$$

but Eq. 0.50 is not. This is because (taking $i = 1$) the element

$$x = 6 \in S - A_1$$

is such that

$$\{6, 1\} \subseteq A_4$$
$$\{6, 2\} \subseteq A_4$$
$$\{6, 3\} \subseteq A_2$$

and hence the condition that an element $a \in A_i$ exists having the property

$$(x, a) \nsubseteq A_j \qquad (j \neq i)$$

does not hold when $i = 1$ and $x = 6$.

On the other hand,

---

†The terminology used in this and the following section has, in part, been suggested by Paull and Unger. See the appropriate reference in Chapter 5.

$$\rho = \{\overline{1,2,3,6};\ \overline{3,5,6};\ \overline{4,5,6,7};\ \overline{1,2,4,6}\}$$

is a grouping of S, as the reader is invited to verify.

We observe that every partition is a grouping but that the converse is not true (see the preceding example). Even so, we will borrow much of the terminology and notation used in the discussion of partitions. Thus, the subsets A_i of a grouping will be called the *blocks* of the grouping, and the notations $|\gamma|$ and $\langle\gamma\rangle$ will have the meanings of Eqs. 0.41 and 0.42, with "partition" replaced by "grouping." The number

$$\Gamma(n) = |\{\gamma;\ \gamma \text{ is a grouping of } n^+\}| \tag{0.51}$$

is of interest in the theory of "incompletely specified sequential machines." (See Chapter 5.) We will be in a position to compute this number in the next section.

*0.10 COMPATIBILITY RELATIONS

The groupings of the preceding section correspond to a type of relation on a set S in much the same way that partitions correspond to equivalence relations. This type of relation will be called "compatibility." It differs from equivalence only in that it need not be transitive. Thus, a relation ρ on a set S is said to be a *compatibility relation* (in which case we replace ρ by $\approx$) if it is

Reflexive: $a\,\rho\,a$ for all $a \in S$ (0.52)

Symmetric: $a\,\rho\,b \Longrightarrow b\,\rho\,a$ for all $a, b \in S$ (0.53)

EXAMPLE 0.28

Let S be a set of (English) words. Define for $a, b \in S$ the relation:

$$a\,\rho\,b \Longleftrightarrow a \text{ and } b \text{ contain a common letter}$$

This relation is seen to be reflexive and symmetric, but not transitive. (Every equivalence relation is a compatibility relation. We are naturally interested in those compatibility relations that are not equivalence relations, that is, not transitive.) For example, let

$$S = \{\text{cat, top, spy, rod, pick}\}$$

Then (writing $\approx$ instead of ρ) we have

$$\text{cat} \approx \text{top} \quad \text{and} \quad \text{top} \approx \text{spy}$$

but

$$\text{cat} \not\approx \text{spy}$$

Let $\approx$ be a compatibility relation on an ordered finite set

$S_n = \{x_1, x_2, \cdots, x_n\}$. Its relation matrix $((r_{ij})$ of Eq. 0.35) is then a symmetric matrix, that is,

$$r_{ij} = r_{ji}$$

for all $1 \le i, j \le n$. Thus the triangular array

$$(r_{ij}; i > j) = \begin{pmatrix} r_{21} & & & \\ r_{31} & r_{32} & & \\ \cdot & \cdot & \cdot & \\ \cdot & \cdot & & \cdot \\ \cdot & \cdot & & \\ r_{n1} & r_{n2} & \cdots & r_{n,n-1} \end{pmatrix} \qquad (0.54)$$

is sufficient to display the compatible and incompatible pairs of elements from S_n. This array is called the *compatibility matrix* of the relation $\approx$. The subset $\bar{x}_i$ of S_n, defined by

$$\bar{x}_i = \{x_j \in S_n; x_j \approx x_i\} \qquad (0.55)$$

is called the *compatibility class* determined by x_i.

EXAMPLE 0.29

Denoting

$$x_1 = \text{cat}$$
$$x_2 = \text{top}$$
$$x_3 = \text{spy}$$
$$x_4 = \text{rod}$$
$$x_5 = \text{pick}$$

in Example 0.28, we obtain the compatibility matrix

x_2	1			
x_3	0	1		
x_4	0	1	0	
x_5	1	1	1	0
	x_1	x_2	x_3	x_4

From this, the compatibility classes

$$\bar{x}_1 = \{x_1, x_2, x_5\}$$
$$\bar{x}_2 = \{x_1, x_2, x_3, x_4, x_5\} = S_5$$
$$\bar{x}_3 = \{x_2, x_3, x_5\}$$
$$\bar{x}_4 = \{x_2, x_4\}$$
$$\bar{x}_5 = \{x_1, x_2, x_3, x_5\}$$

are easily determined. Note that they are not disjoint, as were the equivalance classes of an equivalence relation.

Without loss of generality, suppose now that $\approx$ is a compatibility relation on the set $n^+ = \{1, 2, \cdots, n\}$, with compatibility matrix $(r_{ij}; i > j)$;

$$r_{ij} = \begin{cases} 1 & \text{if } i \approx j \\ 0 & \text{if } i \not\approx j \quad \text{(that is, otherwise)} \end{cases} \tag{0.56}$$

Although it might be assumed that the compatibility classes would somehow replace the equivalence classes in the theory of compatibility relations, this role is instead played by the "maximal compatibles." A subset $C \subseteq n^+$ is said to be a *maximal compatible* of the relation $\approx$ if

(A) $i \approx j$ for all $i, j \in C$.
(B) $k \in n^+ - C \Longrightarrow k \not\approx i$ for some $i \in C$.

The first condition asserts that each pair of elements in C is compatible. The second (maximality) condition insists that it not be possible to enlarge C while maintaining condition (A).

If the compatibility matrix is given, the following procedure will be seen to generate the maximal compatibles:

(1) Begin with the covering

$$\gamma_1 = \{A_1, A_2\}$$

of n^+ in which

$$A_1 = n^+ - \{1\}$$
$$A_2 = \bar{1} = n^+ \cap \bar{1}$$

as found from the first column of $(r_{ij}; i > j)$.

(2) Examine those subsets $A \in \gamma_1$ for which
   (i) $2 \in A$;
   (ii) $r_{i2} = 0$ for some $i \in A$ with $i > 2$.
   Replace such subsets A by two subsets A_1 and A_2 where

$$A_1 = A - \{2\}$$
$$A_2 = A \cap \bar{2}$$

Denote the resulting covering γ_2'. Delete subsets of γ_2' that are contained in other subsets of γ_2'. The resulting covering is denoted γ_2.

(j) Examine those subsets $A \in \gamma_{j-1}$ for which
   (i) $j \in A$;
   (ii) $r_{ij} = 0$ for some $i \in A$ with $i > j$.
   Replace such subsets A by two subsets A_1 and A_2 where

$$A_1 = A - \{j\}$$
$$A_2 = A \cap \bar{j}$$

Denote the resulting covering γ'_j. Delete subsets of γ'_j that are contained in other subsets of γ'_j. The resulting covering is denoted γ_j.

(n)   We assert that $\gamma_{n-1} = \{C_1, C_2, \cdots, C_p\}$ is the set of maximal compatibles.

Since the reader will have sufficient opportunity to explore the intricacies of this procedure, he will eventually be convinced of the validity of the above assertion without being exposed to its formal proof.

EXAMPLE 0.30

Using the compatibility matrix

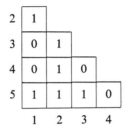

of Example 0.29, we compute

$$\gamma_1 = \{\overline{2,3,4,5}; \ \overline{1,2,5}\} = \gamma'_2 = \gamma_2$$
$$\gamma'_3 = \gamma_3 = \{\overline{2,4,5}; \ \overline{2,3,5}; \ \overline{1,2,5}\}$$
$$\gamma'_4 = \{\overline{2,4}; \ \overline{2,5}; \ \overline{2,3,5}; \ \overline{1,2,5}\}$$
$$\gamma_4 = \{\overline{2,4}; \ \overline{2,3,5}; \ \overline{1,2,5}\}$$

so that the maximal compatibles are

$$C_1 = \{2,4\}$$
$$C_2 = \{2,3,5\}$$
$$C_3 = \{1,2,5\}$$

Observe that the covering

$$\gamma_{n-1} = \gamma_4 = \{\overline{2,4}; \ \overline{2,3,5}; \ \overline{1,2,5}\}$$

is a grouping of 5^+, since

(i) $5^+ = C_1 \cup C_2 \cup C_3$.

(ii) $\{1,4\} \nsubseteq C_2, C_3$ $\{1,3\} \nsubseteq C_1, C_3$ $\{3,1\} \nsubseteq C_2, C_2$,
       $\{3,4\} \nsubseteq C_2, C_3$ $\{4,3\} \nsubseteq C_1, C_3$ $\{4,1\} \nsubseteq C_1, C_2$
       $\{5,4\} \nsubseteq C_2, C_3$

That this is by no means an accident can be inferred from the following theorem.

Theorem 0.6. Let S be any set and $\approx$ a compatibility relation on S. Then S is "grouped" by $\approx$ into maximal compatibles (blocks) in such a way that

(1) Every element of S is in some block.

(2) The elements within a given block are mutually compatible.

(3) It is not possible to enlarge any blocks while still satisfying property (2).

Conversely, any grouping γ of S defines a compatibility relation $\underset{\gamma}{\approx}$ on S. One simply defines

$$a \underset{\gamma}{\approx} b \Longleftrightarrow \quad a \text{ and } b \text{ are in the same block for some block of } \gamma$$

This relation, $\underset{\gamma}{\approx}$, is then seen to be reflexive and symmetric, and hence a compatibility relation.

Since our discussion in these last two sections has steered an obvious parallel to that of Secs. 0.7 and 0.8, the reader has probably observed the intended similarity in the wording of Theorems 0.6 and 0.3. This similarity is designed to alleviate the necessity for a complete and rigorous proof of Theorem 0.6. (See Prob. 0.22.) It is presumed that the reader could have anticipated much of the essential contents of this theorem since the instant that we removed the transitivity requirement in defining "compatibility."

If we attempt to continue our parallel discussion by asking, "How many compatibility relations exist for the set n^+?", we find a more direct answer than that given for equivalence relations. This number is (by virtue of the 1–1 correspondence between groupings and compatibility relations established in Probs. 0.22 and 0.23) the same as $\Gamma(n)$; but in contrast to the situation with equivalence relations, it will be more convenient to compute the number of compatibility relations directly. The compatibility relations on n^+ are in 1–1 correspondence with their compatibility matrices; that is, distinct compatibility relations have different compatibility matrices, and vice versa. Now a compatibility matrix for n^+ has

$$\frac{n^2 - n}{2} = \frac{n(n-1)}{2}$$

entries, and we have two choices for each entry. Thus we obtain

Theorem 0.7   The set n^+ has $2^{\frac{n(n-1)}{2}}$ distinct compatibility relations.

Corollary 0.8 $\Gamma(n) = 2^{\frac{n(n-1)}{2}}$

0.11 MATHEMATICAL INDUCTION

It is fairly certain that the reader has encountered the so-called principle of mathematical induction elsewhere in his studies. Therefore we merely state† the principle here and content ourselves with a few examples. This often-used principle is concerned with the positive integers Z^+ and with mathematical statements involving them.

PRINCIPLE OF MATHEMATICAL INDUCTION.

Suppose that for each integer $n \geq k$ there is an associated statement $E(n)$. Suppose further that:

(i) $E(k)$ is true.

(ii)   For all $n \geq k$, $E(n) \Longrightarrow E(n + 1)$.

Then the principle asserts that

$$E(n) \text{ is true for all } n \geq k$$

In words, the principle states that in order to prove that a certain statement is true for all integers greater than or equal to a certain fixed integer k, it suffices to prove two things:

(i)   The statement is true for the smallest integer (k) under consideration.

(ii)   The assumption (often called the *inductive hypothesis*) that the statement is true for some integer $n \geq k$ implies that the statement is true for the next largest integer $n + 1$.

EXAMPLE 0.31

Suppose we try to verify that for all $n \geq 1$,

$$\sum_{j=1}^{n} j = \frac{n(n + 1)}{2}$$

In this case we are dealing with the statement

$$E(n) \colon \sum_{j=1}^{n} j = \frac{n(n + 1)}{2}$$

Here, the first integer under consideration is $k = 1$. Clearly,

(i) $E(k) = E(1)$ is true, since

$$\sum_{j=1}^{1} j = 1 = \frac{1(2)}{2}$$

(ii)   Now suppose that $E(n)$ is true for *some* $n \geq k = 1$. (Note that we do not assume that $E(n)$ is true for *all* $n \geq 1$, for this is what we are trying to prove. Furthermore, we *know* from (i) that $E(n)$ is true for some $n \geq 1$ (namely, $n = 1$), so that our supposition is reasonable.) Can we then show that $E(n + 1)$ is true as a consequence? Yes, for the statement $E(n + 1)$ is simply

†It is possible to base a proof of this principle on Peano's postulates for the integers. However, the Peano postulates are perhaps more obscure than the principle that they imply. The reader may therefore adopt the view that we are taking the principle itself as a postulate.

$$E(n + 1): \sum_{j=1}^{n+1} j = \frac{(n + 1)(n + 2)}{2}$$

and we obtain it by using the inductive hypothesis in the second equality of the calculation:

$$\sum_{j=1}^{n+1} j = (n + 1) + \sum_{j=1}^{n} j = (n + 1) + \frac{n(n + 1)}{2}$$

$$= \frac{2n + 2 + n^2 + n}{2} = \frac{n^2 + 3n + 2}{2}$$

$$= \frac{(n + 1)(n + 2)}{2}$$

0.12 BINOMIAL COEFFICIENTS

If a and b are nonnegative integers, the binomial coefficients $\binom{a}{b}$ are defined by the formula

$$\binom{a}{b} = \frac{a!}{b!(a - b)!} \tag{0.57}$$

where we adopt the usual definitions

$$(n + 1)! = n!\,(n + 1)$$

$$0! = 1$$

Observe that

$$\binom{a}{b} + \binom{a}{b + 1} = \frac{a!}{b!(a - b)!} + \frac{a!}{(b + 1)!(a - b - 1)!}$$

$$= \frac{a!(b + 1) + a!(a - b)}{(b + 1)!(a - b)!}$$

$$= \frac{a!(a + 1)}{(b + 1)!(a - b)!}$$

$$= \frac{(a + 1)!}{(b + 1)!(a - b)!}$$

$$= \binom{a + 1}{b + 1}$$

and since

$$\binom{n}{n} = \binom{n}{0} = 1$$

the equality

$$\binom{a + 1}{b + 1} = \binom{a}{b} + \binom{a}{b + 1} \tag{0.58}$$

which we have derived above, allows a simple means for computing as many entries as we wish in the triangular array of Table 0.1. This array

TABLE 0.1

a \ b	0	1	2	3	4	5	6	7
0	1							
1	1	1						
2	1	2	1					
3	1	3	3	1				
4	1	4	6	4	1			
5	1	5	10	10	5	1		
6	1	6	15	20	15	6	1	
7	1	7	21	35	35	21	7	1

is known as *Pascal's triangle*.

The reader will probably agree that this is a clever device. However, we have introduced it for a definite reason. The numbers that appear in this array will be needed in Chapter 2, and the triangle of Pascal is perhaps the most efficient way to introduce them. Also, we wish to remark in passing that Eq. 0.58 can be used to effect a proof of the binomial theorem:
    For all $n \geq 0$,

$$(x + y)^n = \sum_{k=0}^{n} \binom{n}{k} x^{n-k} y^k$$

for real numbers x, y. The reader may find this an interesting exercise in the use of mathematical induction.

*0.13   POLYNOMIAL EXPRESSIONS

Although this is not the place to ask a question like, "What is a number?", we do wish to call attention to the distinction between "numbers" and "numerical symbols" that serve as names for numbers. For example, the number "twenty-nine" can be denoted by a good many symbols, of which

XXIX, 29, ⫪⫪⫪ ⫪⫪⫪ ⫪⫪⫪ ⫪⫪⫪ ⫪⫪⫪ 1111

are representative.

Of particular interest are the symbols that we call *polynomial expressions* in the base b, in which a given number x is represented in the form

$$x = \sum_{i=-j}^{p} x_i b^i \tag{0.59}$$

where b itself is an integer greater than 1 and the *coefficients* x_i are integers for which

$$0 \leq x_i < b$$

According to such systems of numerical symbols, which are most often notated in the "shorthand" form

$$x_p x_{p-1} \cdots x_1 x_0 . x_{-1} x_{-2} \cdots x_{-j}$$

the number "twenty-nine" has the representations:

11101.00 $\cdots$	if $b = 2$
1002.	if $b = 3$
131.	if $b = 4$
.	.
.	.
.	.
29.	if $b = 10$
27.	if $b = 11$
.	.
.	.
.	.

Other than the fact that we are endowed with ten fingers (which some feel accounts for the predominant use of the decimal system), there is no good reason to employ one base to the exclusion of all others. (Due to certain electronic limitations, digital computers commonly employ the *binary* system in which $b = 2$.) Of course the overwhelming reason for using such systems at all is the ease with which arithmetic operations can be performed, by virtue of the simple rules for addition and multiplication of polynomials. And since the addition and multiplication tables must have b^2 entries (this figure is reduced to $(b(b + 1))/2$ by the use of the commutative laws), one would not like to choose b so large as to overburden the memory.

In Sec. 0.15 we consider the *base conversion problem:* Given the expression for a number x,

$$x = x_p x_{p-1} \cdots x_1 x_0 . x_{-1} x_{-2} \cdots x_{-j}$$

in the base $b > 1$, where

$$0 \leq x_i < b \; (-j \leq i \leq p)$$

and given another base β, how can we determine the coefficients r_i (or "digits" as they are sometimes mistakenly called; we say mistakenly since the word "digit" implies that $\beta = 10$) for the representation

$$x = r_n r_{n-1} \cdots r_1 r_0 . r_{-1} r_{-2} \cdots r_{-m} \cdots$$

of the number x in the base β?

It could be argued, on the basis of the remarks made above, that we need concern ourselves only with the bases 2, 10. But, since there are at least two other systems (base 3, 8) that one encounters with some frequency in the literature, it seems advisable to discuss the problem of base conversion in its generality.

*0.14   EUCLIDEAN ALGORITHM

The reader is probably aware of the *Euclidean algorithm:*
Let a and b nonnegative integers and $b > 1$. Then there exist unique nonnegative integers q and r such that

(1) $a = bq + r; 0 \leq r < b$.
(2)   Furthermore, if $a > 0, 0 \leq q < a$.

If the reader needs evidence of its validity,† he will be easily convinced when we remark that one needs only to take r as the remainder that is left after dividing a by b, with q taken as the quotient. The remainder r is certainly less than b (for otherwise further division would be possible).

EXAMPLE 0.32
    If $a = 54$ and $b = 4$, upon division we obtain $q = 13, r = 2$, and we see that
(i) $54 = 4(13) + 2$.
(ii) $0 \leq 13 < 54$.

*0.15   BASE CONVERSION

The Euclidean algorithm has an immediate application to the base conversion problem, which was introduced in Sec. 0.13. Suppose the number in question, x, is a positive integer:

$$x = x_p x_{p-1} \cdots x_1 x_0.000 \cdots$$

Define the sequences $\langle r_i \rangle$ and $\langle q_i \rangle$ by $q_0 = x$, and for all $i \geq 0$,

$$q_{i+1} = \text{the } q \text{ such that} \quad q_i = \beta q + r$$
$$0 \leq r \leq \beta - 1 \qquad \text{(0.60)}$$
$$r_i = \text{the } r \text{ such that} \quad q_i = \beta q + r$$
$$0 \leq r \leq \beta - 1$$

Then these definitions give

†The proof would lead us too far afield. See Ref. 0–1, for example.

$$q_i = \beta q_{i+1} + r_i \qquad \text{for all } i \geq 0$$

and we can state the following theorem.

Theorem 0.9.   The sequences $\langle q_i \rangle$, $\langle r_i \rangle$ have the properties:
(1)   For all $i \geq 0$, $0 \leq r_i \leq \beta - 1$.
(2)   For all $i \geq 0$, $q_i > 0 \Longrightarrow 0 \leq q_{i+1} < q_i$.
(3)   If $q_0 = x > 0$, there exists a unique fixed index n for which
    (a) $q_{n+1} = 0$ while $q_n > 0$.
    (b) $q_k = 0$ for all $k \geq n + 1$.
    (c) $r_n \neq 0$.

PROOF.   Properties (1) and (2) are immediate consequences of (1) and (2) in the Euclidean algorithm, Sec. 0.14. Property 3(a) follows from (2); that is, the q_i are a monotonically decreasing sequence of nonnegative integers, so that eventually one of them (call it q_{n+1}) is zero. We take n to be the least positive integer for which this is the case, and this accounts for the uniqueness of n. Property 3(b) is obvious from the Euclidean algorithm. As for 3(c), suppose conversely that $r_n = 0$. Then

$$q_n = \beta q_{n+1} + r_n = \beta \cdot 0 + 0 = 0$$

which contradicts the choice of n. ∎

The following corollary asserts that the (finite) sequence $\langle r_i; 0 \leq i \leq n \rangle$ comprises the "digits" of the integer x when written in the base β; that is,

$$x = r_n r_{n-1} \cdots r_1 r_0 .000$$

Corollary 0.10

$$x = \sum_{i=0}^{n} r_i \beta^i \quad \text{and} \quad r_n \neq 0$$

where $0 \leq r_i \leq \beta - 1$ for all i.

PROOF.   The equality we seek is immediate if we can show that the statement

$$E(k) \colon x = \beta^{k+1} q_{k+1} + \sum_{i=0}^{k} r_i \beta^i$$

is true for all $k \geq 0$. (One then has only to take $k = $ the n of Theorem 0.9, since $q_{n+1} = 0$.) As expected, we prove this by induction. The statement

$$E(0) \colon x = \beta q_1 + r_0$$

is true by definition of q_1 and r_0.

Now suppose that for *some* $k \geq 0$, $E(k)$ is true; that is,

$$\sum_{i=0}^{k} r_i \beta^i = x - \beta^{k+1} q_{k+1} \qquad \text{for some } k \geq 0$$

Then

$$\sum_{i=0}^{k+1} r_i \beta^i = r_{k+1}\beta^{k+1} + \sum_{i=0}^{k} r_i \beta^i$$

$$= x - \beta^{k+1}q_{k+1} + r_{k+1}\beta^{k+1}$$

$$= x - \beta^{k+2}\left(\frac{q_{k+1} - r_{k+1}}{\beta}\right) = x - \beta^{k+2}q_{k+2}$$

since $q_{k+1} = \beta q_{k+2} + r_{k+1}$. In other words, $E(k) \Longrightarrow E(k+1)$, so the proof is complete except to note that the property $r_n \neq 0$ follows from Theorem 0.9. ∎

EXAMPLE 0.33

Suppose

$$x = x_2 x_1.00 = 54.00$$

with $b = 10$ (so that x is the number "fifty-four") and suppose $\beta = 4$. We have $q_0 = 54$ and

$$54 = 4(13) + 2; \quad r_0 = 2, \quad q_1 = 13$$
$$13 = 4(\ 3) + 1; \quad r_1 = 1, \quad q_2 = 3$$
$$3 = 4(\ 0) + 3; \quad r_2 = 3, \quad q_3 = 0$$

It is perhaps advisable to indicate the (short) divisions by replacing these three lines by the computations

$$\begin{array}{llll} \beta = 4 & \underline{|54} = q_0 = x & \\ \beta = 4 & \underline{|13} = q_1 & r_0 = 2 \\ \beta = 4 & \underline{|\ 3} = q_2 & r_1 = 1 \\ & 0 = q_3 & r_2 = 3 \end{array}$$

According to the definition of n in Theorem 0.9, we have $n + 1 = 3$ and $n = 2$. By Corollary 0.10 we have

$$x = r_2 r_1 r_0. = 312. \quad (\beta = 4)$$

We abbreviate this result in the form

$$54_{10} \longrightarrow 312_4$$

Next we investigate the case when $0 < x < 1$. In this discussion, it will be convenient to use the notation $[y]$ for the *integral part of* a real number y. By this we mean that $[y]$ is the unique integer for which

$$[y] \leq y < [y] + 1 \tag{0.61}$$

As an example, $[\pi] = 3$. Note, however, that $[-\pi] = -4$ (not -3).

Using this notation, suppose $0 < x < 1$ and define in this case infinite sequences $\langle d_i \rangle, \langle s_i \rangle$ by $s_0 = x$ and for all $i \geq 1$

$$s_i = \beta s_{i-1} - [\beta s_{i-1}]$$
$$d_i = [\beta s_{i-1}] \tag{0.62}$$

For these sequences, we have the following theorem.

Theorem 0.11.   The sequences $\langle s_i \rangle$, $\langle d_i \rangle$ have the properties

(1) $0 \leq s_i < 1$ for all $i \geq 0$.

(2) d_i is an integer and $0 \leq d_i \leq \beta - 1$ for all $i \geq 1$.

PROOF.   The first property follows from the definition of "integral part of" and the fact that $0 < x < 1$. It is clear that the d_i are integers. Furthermore, using the definition of d_i and Eq. 0.61,

$$0 \leq s_{i-1} < 1 \Longrightarrow 0 \leq d_i < \beta$$

as we see upon multiplication by β. ∎

The following corollary (which again is proved by induction), whose proof is left as an exercise, states that the replacement

$$d_i = r_{-i} \quad (i \geq 1)$$

yields an infinite sequence $\langle r_{-i} \rangle$ whose elements are the "digits" of x in the base β; that is,

$$x = 0.r_{-1}r_{-2} \cdots r_{-m} \cdots$$

Corollary 0.12.   For all $m \geq 1$,

$$x = \sum_{i=1}^{m} d_i \beta^{-i} + s_m \beta^{-m}$$

Note that the *error* term $s_m \beta^{-m} \to 0$ as $m \to \infty$, since property (1) of Theorem 0.11 implies that

$$s_m \beta^{-m} \leq \beta^{-m}$$

and the latter certainly tends to zero.

EXAMPLE 0.34.

Let $x = 0.x_{-1}x_{-2}x_{-3} = 0.624$, with $b = 10$, and suppose (as in Example 0.32) that $\beta = 4$. From the computation

$$
\begin{array}{rcl}
s_0 = x = & 0.624 & \\
& \underline{\times\ 4} & \\
\beta s_0 = & 2.496 & d_1 = 2 \\
s_1 = & 0.496 & \\
& \underline{\times\ 4} & \\
\beta s_1 = & 1.984 & d_2 = 1 \\
s_2 = & 0.984 & \\
& \underline{\times\ 4} & \\
\beta s_2 = & 3.936 & d_3 = 3 \\
s_3 = & 0.936 & \\
& \underline{\times\ 4} & \\
\beta s_3 = & 3.744 & d_4 = 3
\end{array}
$$

$$s_4 = \quad 0.744$$
$$\underline{\times \ 4}$$
$$\beta s_4 = \quad 2.976 \qquad d_5 = 2$$
$$s_5 = \quad 0.976$$

.

.

.

and Corollary 0.12 we learn that $0.624_{10} \longrightarrow (0.21332 \cdots)_4$.

This example, taken together with the preceding one gives

$$(54.624)_{10} \longrightarrow (312.21332 \cdots)_4$$

which illustrates the procedure to be followed in the general case where

$$x = x_p x_{p-1} \cdots x_1 x_0 . x_{-1} x_{-2} \cdots x_{-j}$$

that is, we split the problem into two parts:

$$x^{(1)} = x_p x_{p-1} \cdots x_1 x_0. \qquad (x^{(1)} \text{ an integer})$$
$$x^{(2)} = .x_{-1} x_{-2} \cdots x_{-j} \qquad (\text{with } 0 < x^{(2)} < 1)$$

where $x = x^{(1)} + x^{(2)}$; convert each $x^{(i)}$ from base b to base β according to the methods just described, and recombine the results.

It is important to note that the computations (division by β or multiplication by β) involved in Eqs. 0.60 and 0.62 are performed on the digits x_i of x in the base b. Therefore, if $\beta < b$, these procedures are quite suitable because β is expressible as a single "digit" in the base b, so that the resulting computations are "short" division and "short" multiplication. Although these procedures are applicable when $\beta > b$, they become cumbersome because β is no longer expressible as a single "digit" in the base b, so that the computations in Eqs. 0.60 and 0.62 become "long" division and "long" multiplication.

EXAMPLE 0.35

If we take $x = 312_4$ and try to use Eqs. 0.60 to compute x in the base $\beta = 7$, we must write $\beta = 13_4$ and use long division:

$$
\begin{array}{r}
13 = q_1 \\
\beta = 13\overline{)312} = q_0 = \dot{x} \\
\underline{13} \\
122 \\
\underline{111} \\
11 = r_0 \qquad r_0 = 5_7
\end{array}
$$

$$
\begin{array}{r}
1 = q_2 \\
= 13\overline{)13} = q_1 \\
\underline{13} \\
0 = r_1 \qquad r_1 = 0_7
\end{array}
$$

$$
\begin{array}{r}
0 = q_3 \\
= 13\overline{)1} = q_2 \\
\underline{0} \\
1 = r_2 \qquad r_2 = 1_7
\end{array}
$$

so that

$$312_4 \longrightarrow 105_7$$

Similarly, in converting $x = 0.22_4$ to the base $\beta = 7$, we would have to use long multiplication in Eqs. 0.62; that is,

$$
\begin{array}{rl}
s_0 = x = & 0.22 \\
& 13 \\
\hline
& 132 \\
& 22 \\
\hline
\beta s_0 = & 10.12 \qquad d_1 = 4_7 \\
\\
s_1 = & 0.12 \\
& 13 \\
\hline
& 102 \\
& 12 \\
\hline
\beta s_1 = & 2.22 \qquad d_2 = 2_7
\end{array}
$$

and so on; hence

$$0.22_4 \longrightarrow (0.424242\cdots)_7$$

Note that in performing these computations, one needs to consult the addition and multiplication tables

+	0	1	2	3		·	0	1	2	3
0	0	1	2	3		0	0	0	0	0
1	1	2	3	¹0		1	0	1	2	3
2	2	3	¹0	¹1		2	0	2	¹0	¹2
3	3	¹0	¹1	¹2		3	0	3	¹2	²1

for the base 4. (Here we have indicated "carries" with left superdigits.)

For the reasons just outlined, it is generally advisable to proceed in another way when $\beta > b$. As before, suppose

$$x = \sum_{i=-j}^{p} x_i b^i \qquad (0 \le x_i \le b - 1)$$

and that we wish to convert x to the base β; that is, we wish to determine $\langle r_i \rangle$ for which

$$x = \sum_{i=-\infty}^{n} r_i \beta^i$$

In the method to be described, we assume that the digits x_i are expressed in the base β and also that b is expressed in the base β. If $\beta > b$, these will be single-digit expressions. It is advisable to point out at the outset that the computations to be developed will be performed in the base β *into* which we are converting. Note this important distinction from the computations of Eqs. 0.60 and 0.62, which were performed in the base *from* which we were converting.

Again it is convenient to consider the integral and fractional parts of x separately:

$$x = \sum_{i=0}^{p} x_i b^i + \sum_{i=-j}^{-1} x_i b^i$$

$$= \sum_{i=0}^{p} x_i b^i + \sum_{i=1}^{j} x_{-i} b^{-i}$$

For the integral part of x, define the finite sequence $\langle t_i; 0 \le i \le p \rangle$ by

$$t_0 = x_p$$

$$t_i = t_{i-1} \cdot b + x_{p-1} \qquad (1 \le i \le p) \tag{0.63}$$

and for the fractional part of x, define the sequence $\langle \tau_i; 1 \le i \le j \rangle$ by

$$\tau_1 = b^{-1} \cdot x_{-j}$$

$$\tau_i = (\tau_{i-1} + x_{i-j-1}) b^{-1} \qquad (2 \le i \le j) \tag{0.64}$$

There will result numbers t_p and τ_j, and by their very definition we can deduce the following theorem.

Theorem 0.13. $\quad x = t_p + \tau_j$ where t_p is the integer part of x,

$$t_p = \sum_{i=0}^{p} x_i b^i$$

and τ_j, the fractional part of x,

$$\tau_j = \sum_{i=1}^{j} x_{-i} b^{-i}$$

is the representation of x in the base β.

EXAMPLE 0.36

Suppose we use this new procedure to perform the conversions of Example 0.35. For

$$x = x_2 x_1 x_0 \cdot x_{-1} x_{-2} = 312.22_4$$

From Eq. 0.63 we have

$$t_0 = x_2 = 3$$

$$t_1 = t_0 \cdot b + x_1 = 3 \cdot 4 + 1 = 15 + 1 = 16$$

$$t_2 = t_1 \cdot b + x_0 = 16 \cdot 4 + 2 = 103 + 2 = 105$$

Using Eq. 0.64, we write

$$\tau_1 = b^{-1} x_{-2} = (0.1515 \cdots) (2) = 0.3333 \cdots$$

$$\tau_2 = (\tau_1 + x_{-1}) b^{-1} = (2.3333 \cdots) (0.1515 \cdots) \approx 0.4242$$

so that, according to Theorem 0.13, we have (approximately)

$$312.22_4 \longrightarrow 105.4242_7$$

Here it is important to note that the addition and multiplication tables for the base 7 were employed. Our approximate solution to the fractional conversion was due to the impossibility of expressing $b^{-1} = 0.1_4$ as a terminating "decimal" in the base 7.

EXAMPLE 0.37

In contrast to the preceding example, suppose

$$x = x_3 x_2 x_1 x_0 \cdot x_{-1} x_{-2} x_{-3} x_{-4} = 1011.1101_2$$

and let $\beta = 10$. Then

$$t_3 = (((1 \times 2 + 0) 2 + 1) 2 + 1) = 11$$

and since $b^{-1} = 0.1_2 = 0.5_{10}$ terminates in the base 10, we obtain an exact fractional conversion,

$$\tau_4 = ((((1 \times 0.5 + 0) 0.5) + 1) 0.5 + 1) 0.5 = 0.8125$$

so that

$$1011.1101_2 \longrightarrow 11.8125_{10}$$

The binary to decimal conversion of integers will be of special interest in the subsequent chapters. Often the binary integer to be converted will be disguised as an element of

$$B^n = \{(b_n, b_{n-1}, \cdots, b_1); b_i \in B = \{0,1\}\} \qquad (0.65)$$

Then we associate with the element $(b_n, b_{n-1}, \cdots, b_1)$ the binary integer $b_n b_{n-1} \cdots b_1.00 \ldots$ and the converted integer is denoted $\partial(b_n, b_{n-1}, \ldots, b_1)$. We thereby define a function

$$\partial : B^n \longrightarrow Z_{2^n}$$

(see Example 0.8) according to the base conversion method of Theorem 0.13, that is,

$$\partial(b_n, b_{n-1}, \cdots, b_1) = \sum_{i=1}^{n} b_i 2^{i-1} \qquad (0.66)$$

The reader should not have difficulty in seeing that ∂ is 1–1 and onto. (Its inverse would represent decimal to binary conversion.) This mapping ∂ will have numerous applications.

EXAMPLE 0.38

Consider the element $(b_4, b_3, b_2, b_1) = (1, 0, 1, 1)$ in B^4. Then, according to Eq. 0.66,

$$\partial(1, 0, 1, 1) = \sum_{i=1}^{n} b_i 2^{i-1} = 1 \cdot 2^0 + 1 \cdot 2^1 + 0 \cdot 2^2 + 1 \cdot 2^3$$

$$= 1 + 2 + 0 + 8 = 11$$

which is in complete agreement with the result anticipated from a glance at Example 0.37.

PROBLEMS

0.1   Which of the following functions are 1–1? onto?
    (a) $\alpha:Z \longrightarrow Z$, where $\alpha(n) = n + 1$.
    (b) $\beta:Z \longrightarrow Z$, where $\beta(n) = 2n$.
    (c) $\gamma:Z \longrightarrow B$, where

$$\gamma(n) = \begin{cases} 0 & \text{if } n \text{ is even} \\ 1 & \text{if } n \text{ is odd} \end{cases}$$

    (d) $\delta:C \longrightarrow R$, where $C =$ complex numbers, $R =$ real numbers and

$$\delta(z) = \text{Re}(z) = \text{the real part of } z$$

    (e) $\epsilon:B \longrightarrow B$ where

$$\epsilon(b) = \begin{cases} 0 & \text{if } b = 1 \\ 1 & \text{if } b = 0 \end{cases}$$

Describe the inverse mappings in cases where the given mapping is 1–1 *and* onto.

0.2   Describe the sets:

    (a) $\alpha^{-1}(7)$ (f) $\alpha^{-1}(\{7,8,9\})$
    (b) $\beta^{-1}(7)$ (g) $\beta^{-1}(\{7,8,9\})$
    (c) $\gamma^{-1}(0)$ (h) $\gamma^{-1}(B)$
    (d) $\delta^{-1}(1)$ (i) $\delta^{-1}(Z)$
    (e) $\epsilon^{-1}(0)$ (j) $\epsilon^{-1}(B)$
where α, β, γ, δ, ϵ are as in Prob. 0.1.

0.3   Define a mapping $\alpha:Z \times Z^+ \longrightarrow Q$ which is onto Q, where $Q =$ rationals. Prove that your mapping is onto Q. Is it 1–1?

0.4   Show that $\alpha \cdot \beta \neq \beta \cdot \alpha$ and that $\epsilon \cdot (\gamma \cdot \alpha) = \gamma$ for the respective mappings of Prob. 0.1.

0.5   Determine which of the three properties, "reflexive," "symmetric," and "transitive," apply to the following relations on the set of all human beings:
    (a) "is a father of"
    (b) "is a brother of"
    (c) "is a friend of"
    (d) "is a descendent of"
    (e) "is an uncle of"

0.6   A relation ρ is said to be *circular* if

$$a \, \rho \, b, \; b \, \rho \, c \Longrightarrow c \, \rho \, a$$

Show that a relation is reflexive and circular if and only if it is an equivalence relation.

0.7 Determine which of the three properties, "reflexive," "symmetric," and "transitive," apply to the following relations on the set Z where $a \rho b$ means, respectively:
  (a) $a \le b$.
  (b) $a < b$.
  (c) $a^2 + a = b^2 + b$.
  (d) $a < |b|$.
  (e) $a|b$ (read a "divides" b, in the sense that there exists an integer q such that $b = qa$).

0.8 Prove Lemma 0.2.

*0.9 Prove (by mathematical induction) the binomial formula

$$(x + y)^n = \sum_{k=0}^{n} \binom{n}{k} x^{n-k} y^k$$

0.10 Prove (by mathematical induction) that

$$\sum_{j=1}^{n} j^3 = \left[\frac{n(n + 1)}{2} \right]^2.$$

0.11 Show that the integers q and r of the Euclidean algorithm are unique.

0.12 Prove Corollary 0.12.

0.13 Show that for all $n \ge 1$,

$$\sum_{j=1}^{n} 2^{j-1} = 2^n - 1$$

0.14 Use the algorithm described in Theorem 0.11 and its corollary to perform the indicated base conversions:
  (a) $0.8537_{10} \longrightarrow ?_4$
  (b) $0.904_{10} \longrightarrow ?_2$
  (c) $0.2541_{10} \longrightarrow ?_4$
  (d) $0.6_7 \longrightarrow ?_4$.

0.15 Use the results of Prob. 0.14 together with the Euclidean algorithm to perform the following base conversions:
  (a) $831.8537_{10} \longrightarrow ?_4$.
  (b) $127.904_{10} \longrightarrow ?_2$.
  (c) $1513.2541_{10} \longrightarrow ?_4$.
  (d) $532.6_7 \longrightarrow ?_4$.

0.16 Convert $101101_2 \longrightarrow ?_{10}$, using the Euclidean algorithm.

0.17 Repeat Prob. 0.16, using instead the method of Theorem 0.13.

0.18 Convert $127_{10} \longrightarrow ?_2$, using the method of Theorem 0.13 and noting that $1_{10} = 1_2$, $2_{10} = 10_2$, $7_{10} = 111_2$, $10_{10} = 1010_2$. Repeat, using the Euclidean algorithm.

0.19 Convert $0.63_{10} \longrightarrow ?_2$ by two different methods.

0.20 Convert $3096_{10} \longrightarrow ?_3$

*0.21 Show that (with the agreement that $\Lambda(0) = 1$) for all $n \ge 0$,

$$\Lambda(n + 1) = \sum_{k=0}^{n} \binom{n}{k} \Lambda(k)$$

Compute a table of values for $\Lambda(n)$, $1 \leq n \leq 10$. ($\Lambda(10) = 115{,}975$.)

*0.22 Show that if ρ is a compatibility relation on n^+

$$\gamma_\rho = \{A_i; A_i \text{ is a maximal compatible of } \rho\}$$

is a grouping of n^+. Conversely, if γ is a grouping of n^+, show that $\widetilde{\widetilde{\gamma}}$ is a compatibility relation on n^+.

*0.23 Show that if ρ and σ are compatibility relations on n^+,

$$\rho = \sigma \Longleftrightarrow \gamma_\rho = \gamma_\sigma$$

0.24 Which of the following coverings of 6^+ are groupings?

$$\gamma_1 = \{\overline{1,2,5}; \ \overline{3,6}; \ \overline{4,5,6}; \ \overline{1,2,4}\}$$

$$\gamma_2 = \{\overline{1,3,4,6}; \ \overline{2,5,6}; \ \overline{1,3,6}\}$$

$$\gamma_3 = \{\overline{1,2}; \ \overline{2,3}; \ \overline{3,4}; \ \overline{4,5,6}\}$$

Obtain the relation matrix $(r_{ij}; i > j)$ for the relation $\widetilde{\widetilde{\gamma}}$ in cases where $\gamma = \gamma_i$ ($i = 1,2,3$) is a grouping. Find the maximal compatibles of such relations.

*0.25 Let λ be a (not necessarily disjoint) covering of n^+ (which is not necessarily a grouping). Show that there is a natural compatibility relation $\widetilde{\widetilde{\lambda}}$ on n^+ to be associated with λ. Let γ_λ be the grouping:

$$\gamma_\lambda = \{A_i; A_i \text{ is a maximal compatible of } \widetilde{\widetilde{\lambda}}\}$$

Show that

$$\gamma_\lambda = \lambda \Longleftrightarrow \lambda \text{ is a grouping}$$

Illustrate with the coverings of Prob. 0.24.

0.26 Draw the "graph" of the function $f(x) = [x]$ in the range $-4.5 \leq x \leq 4.5$. Also draw the graph of the function $g(x) = x - [x]$ in the same range.

0.27 Let

$$\alpha : Z^+ \longrightarrow Z^+ \cup \{0\}$$

be defined as follows:

For $n \in Z^+$ we take $\alpha(n)$ to be the unique nonnegative integer such that

$$\log_2 n \leq \alpha(n) < 1 + \log_2 n$$

(This integer, $\alpha(n)$, is often denoted by $[\log_2 n]$ even though confusion is likely to arise because [ ] can be misinterpreted to mean "the integral part of," as in Prob. 0.26.)

  Show that α is onto $Z^+ \cup \{0\}$ but is not 1–1. Compute a table of values for $[\log_2 n]$, $1 \leq n \leq 17$. ($[\log_2 17] = 5$.)

0.28 Determine the maximal compatibles for the following compatibility matrices:

(a)

2	1				
3	0	0			
4	0	1	0		
5	1	1	1	1	
6	1	0	0	1	1
	1	2	3	4	5

(b)

2	0					
3	1	0				
4	1	0	1			
5	1	1	1	0		
6	0	1	0	0	1	
7	0	1	1	1	0	1
	1	2	3	4	5	6

(c)

2	0					
3	1	1				
4	0	1	0			
5	1	0	0	1		
6	1	1	1	0	1	
7	1	0	1	1	0	0
	1	2	3	4	5	6

0.29 Prove properties (i) and (ii) cited in Example 0.5.

0.30 If $S \subseteq Z^+$, min S is the (unique) smallest integer in S. Thus, if $S = \{4,5,2,8\}$, we have min $S = 2$. When the elements x of the set S are determined by the statement of a requisite property P, as in $S = \{x \in Z^+;$ x has the property $P\}$—see Eq. 0.1, for example—we often write

$$\min_{P} x = \min S = \min\{x \in Z^+; x \text{ has the property } P\}$$

Determine:

(a) $\min\limits_{x>5} x = \min S$ for S the set of Example 0.1.

(b) $\min\limits_{i \in n^+} n + 3 - i$.

(c) $\min\limits_{\pi \leq x \leq 2\pi} [x]$.

(d) $\min\limits_{\lambda \in \Lambda(n^+)} |\lambda|$.

SUGGESTED REFERENCES

0-1 G. BIRKHOFF and S. MACLANE, *A Survey of Modern Algebra* (New York: Macmillan Company), 1965.

0-2 P. R. HALMOS, *Naive Set Theory* (Princeton, New Jersey: D. VAN NOSTRAND Co.), 1960.

0-3 ROBERT R. STALL, *Set Theory and Logic* (San Francisco and London: W. H. FREEMAN and Co.), 1963.

CHAPTER 1 | BOOLEAN ALGEBRAS

1.1 INTRODUCTION

Boolean algebras constitute the fundamental mathematical structures for the study of digital computer logic. In a conventional manner, one can quickly introduce such a structure by stating a group of postulates (for example, those due to Huntington[†]). Alternatively, one can first introduce the more general concepts of "partially ordered set" and "lattice." In the latter approach, many of the postulates one would have stated for a Boolean algebra appear as theorems about lattices (and hence about Boolean algebras, since every Boolean algebra is a lattice). Since partially ordered sets and lattices occur with some frequency in the literature of switching theory and since we can make considerable use of these

[†]E. V. Huntington, "Sets of Independent Postulates for the Algebra of Logic," *Trans. Amer. Math. Soc.*, 5 (1904), 288–309.

two concepts in the sequel, there appears to be considerable justification for adopting the second of our two alternatives.

1.2 PARTIALLY ORDERED SETS

A *partially ordered set* is a mathematical structure $(X, \geq)$ consisting of a set X and a relation $\geq$ (which might be pronounced "greater than or equal to," "contains," or simply "is related to by $\geq$," depending on the immediate circumstances) which satisfies the following three conditions:

Reflexivity: $x \geq x$ for all $x \in X$ $\qquad$ **(1.1)**

Antisymmetry: $x \geq y,\ y \geq x \Longrightarrow x = y$ for all $x, y \in X$
$$\textbf{(1.2)}$$

Transitivity: $x \geq y,\ y \geq z \Longrightarrow x \geq z$ for all $x, y, z \in X$ **(1.3)**

Note the important distinction in Eq. 1.2 between a partial order and an equivalence relation (cf. Sec. 0.8).

EXAMPLE 1.1

Let $X = Z$ (cf. Example 0.4) and let $\geq$ have its usual meaning. Then, since

(i) $n \geq n$ for all $n \in Z$,
(ii) $n \geq m, m \geq n \Longrightarrow n = m$,
(iii) $n \geq m, m \geq p \Longrightarrow n \geq p$,

the integers are seen to form a partially ordered set. The same can be said for Z^+ or for the nonnegative integers.

The reader should be cautioned that the symbol $\geq$ will be used in a more general sense than he may have encountered in previous studies; that is, $x \geq y$ will *not* always mean (as it does in Example 1.1) that $x - y$ is a nonnegative real number—consider our next example.

EXAMPLE 1.2

Let $X = S_4$ (cf. Eq. 0.27). Then, to any relation ρ on S_4, there corresponds a 4×4 relation matrix (r_{ij}). Conversely, any 4×4 matrix (r_{ij}) whose entries are in $B = \{0,1\}$ defines a relation ρ on S_4 according to Eq. 0.36. If

$$(r_{ij}) = \begin{pmatrix} r_{11} & r_{12} & r_{13} & r_{14} \\ r_{21} & r_{22} & r_{23} & r_{24} \\ r_{31} & r_{32} & r_{33} & r_{34} \\ r_{41} & r_{42} & r_{43} & r_{44} \end{pmatrix}$$

then ρ is

$$\text{Reflexive} \Longleftrightarrow r_{ii} = 1 \quad \text{for all } i \tag{1.1a}$$

$$\text{Antisymmetric} \Longleftrightarrow \{r_{ij} = r_{ji} = 1 \Longrightarrow i = j\} \tag{1.2a}$$

and, by way of contrast,

$$\text{Symmetric} \Longleftrightarrow r_{ij} = r_{ji} \quad \text{for all } i, j \tag{1.2b}$$

Furthermore, ρ is

$$\text{Transitive} \Longleftrightarrow \{r_{ij} = r_{jk} = 1 \Longrightarrow r_{ik} = 1\} \tag{1.3a}$$

Consider the matrix

$$(r_{ij}) = \begin{pmatrix} 1 & 0 & 0 & 1 \\ 0 & 1 & 0 & 1 \\ 1 & 1 & 1 & 1 \\ 0 & 0 & 0 & 1 \end{pmatrix}$$

Since the right-hand sides of Eqs. 1.1a, 1.2a, and 1.3a are satisfied, (r_{ij}) defines a partial order on S_4. We will have more to say about this example as the discussion proceeds.

If $(X, \geq)$ is a partially ordered set, we can define a new relation $>$ on X by

$$x > y \Longleftrightarrow x \geq y \quad \text{and} \quad x \neq y \tag{1.4}$$

(The relation $>$ might be pronounced "greater" or "properly contains," or "is related to by $>$"). We see that $>$ cannot be a partial order on X because from the beginning we meet with failure when attempting to verify reflexivity.

EXAMPLE 1.3

Consider the partially ordered set S_4 as defined by the matrix of Example 1.2. Using Eq. 1.4, we obtain a new relation $>$ on S_4 whose relation matrix is

$$(r'_{ij}) = \begin{pmatrix} 0 & 0 & 0 & 1 \\ 0 & 0 & 0 & 1 \\ 1 & 1 & 0 & 1 \\ 0 & 0 & 0 & 0 \end{pmatrix}$$

Hence we can write

$$x_1 > x_4, \quad x_2 > x_4, \quad x_3 > x_4, \quad x_3 > x_1, \quad x_3 > x_2$$

while $a \not> b$ for all other ordered pairs of elements (a, b). Clearly, this new relation is not a partial order on S_4. Nevertheless we will soon see its usefulness in describing the original partial order $\geq$.

Partially ordered sets that have but a finite number of elements can be conveniently represented by means of their "Hasse diagram," which is obtained as follows: We say that x *covers* y for $x, y \in X$ if $x > y$ and an $x' \neq x, y$ for which $x \geq x' \geq y$ does not exist; that is,

$$x \text{ covers } y \Longleftrightarrow \begin{cases} x > y \\ \qquad\qquad \text{and} \\ x \geq x' \geq y \Longrightarrow x' = x \quad \text{or} \quad x' = y \end{cases}$$

Now let each element of the set X be represented by a small circle, so placed on an oriented sheet of paper that the circle for x is drawn above the circle for y if $x > y$. One then draws a line descending from x to y in case x covers y. When this is done for all $x,y \in X$, the resulting figure is called the *Hasse diagram*[†] of the partially ordered set X. Given the Hasse diagram of a partially ordered set (and nothing else) one can reconstruct the relation $\geq$ from the diagram; for by its construction, $x \geq y$ if and only if it is possible to climb from y to x along ascending line segments of the diagram.

EXAMPLE 1.4

Using the two preceding examples, we cannot write

$$x_3 \text{ covers } x_4$$

for although $x_3 > x_4$, we can find an element x' (say, $x' = x_1$) such that

$$x_3 \geq x' \geq x_4 \quad \text{and} \quad x' \neq x_3, \quad x' \neq x_4$$

A similar analysis of the remaining pairs (a, b), for which $a > b$, yields the relation matrix of the covering relation

$$(r''_{ij}) = \begin{pmatrix} 0 & 0 & 0 & 1 \\ 0 & 0 & 0 & 1 \\ 1 & 1 & 0 & 0 \\ 0 & 0 & 0 & 0 \end{pmatrix}$$

That is, one can write

$$a \text{ covers } b$$

for the remaining four pairs. The recipe for drawing the Hasse diagram then yields Fig. 1.1.

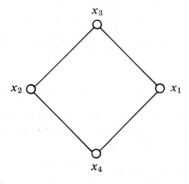

FIGURE 1.1

†Because of their effective use by H. Hasse.

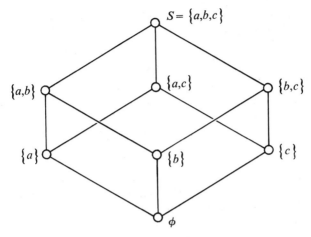

FIGURE 1.2

EXAMPLE 1.5

The Hasse diagram of Fig. 1.2 is that of the partially ordered set

$$\mathscr{P}(S) = \{\text{all subsets of } S\}$$

where

$$S = \{a, b, c\}$$

with the relation

$$A \geq B \Longleftrightarrow A \supseteq B \qquad \text{for } A, B \in \mathscr{P}(S)$$

(a reflexive, antisymmetric, and transitive relation). This example explains why $\geq$ is often pronounced "contains"; that is, the example of the set of all subsets of a given set, together with the relation $\supseteq$, is one of the first examples that comes to mind when one thinks of partially ordered sets.

EXAMPLE 1.6

For our future purposes, there is a sequence of increasingly restrictive conditions that one may place on a covering (cf. Sec. 0.3):

$$\gamma = \{A_1, A_2, \cdots, A_n\}$$

of a set S, two of which we have already encountered in our discussion of groupings and partitions. The least restrictive of these is the "set system" requirement that no block of the covering be contained within another. Thus, γ is said to be a a *set system* if $A_i \subseteq A_j \Rightarrow i = j$. It can be shown (see Prob. 1.26) that every grouping is a set system but that the converse is not generally true. Intermediate between the concept of a grouping and a partition is that of an "irredundant" covering. γ is said to be *redundant* if $\gamma - \{A_i\}$ is a covering for some $i = 1, 2, \cdots, n$. If, conversely, $\gamma - \{A_i\}$ is *not* a covering for each $i = 1, 2, \cdots, n$ we say that γ is an *irredundant covering*.

Now suppose that $X = \{\gamma_j\}$ is a collection of coverings of a set S. We can define a relation on X by setting

$$\gamma_j \geq \gamma_k \Longleftrightarrow \frac{\text{every block of } \gamma_k \text{ is contained in}}{\text{some block of } \gamma_j} \tag{1.5}$$

(In this event we say that γ_k is a *refinement* of γ_j.) This is surely a reflexive and transitive relation. It may not be antisymmetric, however. To see this, take $S = 5^+$ and

$$\gamma_1 = \{\overline{1};\ \overline{1,2,3};\ \overline{1,2,3,4,5}\}$$
$$\gamma_2 = \{\overline{1,2};\ \overline{1,2,3,4,5}\}$$

Then $\gamma_1 \geq \gamma_2$ and $\gamma_2 \geq \gamma_1$, but $\gamma_1 \neq \gamma_2$. (Note that neither γ_1 nor γ_2 is a set system If $X = \{\gamma_j\}$ is a collection of set systems of a set S, the definition of Eq. 1.5 is antisymmetric and hence a partial order.

Suppose $X = \{\gamma_1, \gamma_2, \gamma_3, \gamma_4\}$, where

$$\gamma_1 = \{\overline{1,2,3};\ \overline{4};\ \overline{5}\}$$
$$\gamma_2 = \{\overline{1,2};\ \overline{3,5};\ \overline{3,4}\}$$
$$\gamma_3 = \{\overline{1,2,3};\ \overline{2,3,5};\ \overline{3,4}\}$$
$$\gamma^4 = \{\overline{1,2};\ \overline{3};\ \overline{4};\ \overline{5}\}$$

are (irredundant) coverings of $S = 5^+ = \{1, 2, 3, 4, 5\}$. Then the definition of Eq. 1.5 makes X into a partially ordered set having the Hasse diagram of Fig. 1.3. Evidently this $(X, \geq)$ is indistinguishable as a partially ordered set from that of Example 1.2 because they have the same Hasse diagram. We say that the two partially ordered sets are "abstractly equivalent" (since the formal definition of the word "isomorphic" is deferred to Sec. 1.7).

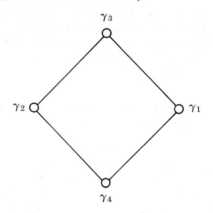

FIGURE 1.3

Note that $\gamma = \gamma_3$ is a grouping of 5^+ (since it is irredundant), while γ_1, γ_2, γ_3 are set systems (since they, too, are irredundant) which are refinements of γ. In our future discussions, a set system γ_k which is a refinement of a grouping

γ of n^+ will be called a *subgrouping* of γ. (This terminology will be useful in Chapter 5.) From the above discussion, the reader is invited to deduce that when γ is a grouping of n^+,

$$X_\gamma = \{\gamma_k; \ \gamma_k \text{ is a subgrouping of } \gamma\}$$

is a partially ordered set.

1.3   LATTICES

Let $(X, \geq)$ be a partially ordered set and $x, y \in X$. An element u is called a *least upper bound* (abbreviated l.u.b.) of x and y if

$$u \geq x, \quad u \geq y \qquad (u \text{ is an } upper \ bound \text{ for } x \text{ and } y) \qquad \textbf{(1.6)}$$

$$w \geq x, \quad w \geq y \Longrightarrow w \geq u \qquad \textbf{(1.7)}$$

EXAMPLE 1.7

In Example 1.5, suppose $x = \{b\}$, $y = \{c\}$. Then $u = \{b,c\}$ is a l.u.b. of x and y. Note that S is an upper bound for x and y, since

$$S \geq x, \quad S \geq y \qquad \textbf{(1.6a)}$$

But S is not a *least* upper bound because the statement

$$w \geq x, \quad w \geq y \Longrightarrow w \geq S \qquad \textbf{(1.7a)}$$

is false. (Take $w = \{b,c\}$ to see this.)

In a dual fashion, v is called a *greatest lower bound* (g.l.b.) of x and y if

$$v \leq x, \quad v \leq y \qquad (v \text{ is a } lower \text{ bound}) \qquad \textbf{(1.8)}$$

$$w \leq x, \quad w \leq y \Longrightarrow w \leq v \qquad \textbf{(1.9)}$$

(Note that $a \leq b$ is intended to mean $b \geq a$.)

Theorem 1.1   Let $(X, \geq)$ be a partially ordered set and $x, y \in X$. Then, if x and y have a l.u.b. u, they have only one l.u.b. Similarly, g.l.b.'s are unique when they exist.

PROOF.   Suppose u_1 and u_2 are each l.u.b.'s for x and y. Then $u_1 \geq x, u_1 \geq y, u_2 \geq x, u_2 \geq y$. From Eq. 1.7 of the definition of l.u.b., this implies that $u_1 \geq u_2, u_2 \geq u_1$, from which we conclude that $u_1 = u_2$ by the antisymmetry of $\geq$. The corresponding proof for the uniqueness of g.l.b.'s is completely dual. ∎

A *lattice* L is a partially ordered set $(L, \geq)$ in which every pair of elements $x, y \in L$

(I)   has a l.u.b., which we denote $x + y$.
(II)   has a g.l.b., which we denote $x \cdot y$.

The "uniqueness" theorem, theorem 1.1, guarantees that $+, \cdot$ are well-defined operations in the sense that two binary compositions (cf., Sec. 0.6)

$$\alpha : L \times L \longrightarrow L$$
$$\beta : L \times L \longrightarrow L$$

result when we set

$$\alpha(x, y) = \text{l.u.b. of } x \text{ and } y = x + y$$
$$\beta(x, y) = \text{g.l.b. of } x \text{ and } y = x \cdot y$$

It will be useful when discussing a lattice to reformulate conditions 1.6 through 1.9 in our new notation; that is,

$$x + y \geq x, \quad x + y \geq y \tag{1.10}$$

$$z \geq x, \quad z \geq y \Longrightarrow z \geq x + y \tag{1.11}$$

$$x \cdot y \leq x, \quad x \cdot y \leq y \tag{1.12}$$

$$z \leq x, \quad z \leq y \Longrightarrow z \leq x \cdot y \tag{1.13}$$

When we wish to emphasize the additive and multiplicative structure of a lattice $(L, \geq)$, rather than its structure as a partially ordered set, we denote L by $(L, +, \cdot)$.

EXAMPLE 1.8

The partially ordered set of Fig. 1.2 is a lattice, in which one takes

l.u.b. of A and $B = A + B = A \cup B$

g.l.b. of A and $B = A \cdot B = A \cap B$

for $A, B \in \mathscr{P}(S)$.

More generally, $\mathscr{P}(S)$ is a lattice for *any* set S.

EXAMPLE 1.9

The partially ordered set of Fig. 1.1 is also a lattice with the addition and multiplication tables

$+$	x_1	x_2	x_3	x_4
x_1	x_1	x_3	x_3	x_1
x_2	x_3	x_2	x_3	x_2
x_3	x_3	x_3	x_3	x_3
x_4	x_1	x_2	x_3	x_4

$\cdot$	x_1	x_2	x_3	x_4
x_1	x_1	x_4	x_1	x_4
x_2	x_4	x_2	x_2	x_4
x_3	x_3	x_2	x_3	x_4
x_4	x_4	x_4	x_4	x_4

EXAMPLE 1.10

Lest the reader conclude that every partially ordered set is a lattice, we observe that the one whose Hasse diagram appears in Fig. 1.4 fails to be a lattice because the pair of elements y, z does not have a g.l.b. (It does not even have a lower bound.) In Fig. 1.5, w and z have an upper bound, but do not have a l.u.b., so that neither does this Hasse diagram represent a lattice.

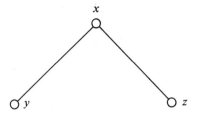

FIGURE 1.4

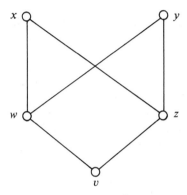

FIGURE 1.5

A subset L' of a lattice $(L, +, \cdot)$ is called a *sublattice* of L if

$$x, y \in L' \Longrightarrow x + y, \quad x \cdot y \in L'$$

That is, the sum and product of x and y must accompany every pair x, y in L'. This is another way of saying that a subset of L must itself be a lattice in order that we may call it a sublattice.

Before we derive those properties of lattices which are important for the more restricted concept of a Boolean algebra, we state the following characterizations of the relation $\geq$ (for a lattice L when viewed as a partially ordered set) in terms of the lattice operations $(+, \cdot)$.

Lemma 1.2   Let L be a lattice and $x, y \in L$. Then any one of the three conditions

$$x + y = x \qquad x \cdot y = y \qquad x \geq y$$

implies the other two.

PROOF.   For example, suppose $x + y = x$. Then $x \geq x$ and $x \geq y$ by Eq. (1.10). But $y \geq y$ from reflexivity and

$$x \geq y, \quad y \geq y \Longrightarrow x \cdot y \geq y \text{ from Eq. (1.13)}$$

Since we also have $y \geq x \cdot y$ from Eq. (1.12) we obtain $x \cdot y = y$ because of the antisymmetry of $\geq$.

The two remaining implications in the triangle

$$x + y = x \Longrightarrow x \cdot y = y$$
$$x \geq y$$

are of a similar nature and we leave them as exercises. ∎

Theorem 1.3 Let $(L, +, \cdot)$ be a lattice, and let $x, y, z \in L$. Then

P1a $x + x = x$	**P1b** $x \cdot x = x$
P2a $x + (y + z) = (x + y) + z$	**P2b** $x \cdot (y \cdot z) = (x \cdot y) \cdot z$
P3a $x + y = y + x$	**P3b** $x \cdot y = y \cdot x$
P4a $x + (x \cdot y) = x$	**P4b** $x \cdot (x + y) = x$

Conversely, given a set L with two binary compositions $(+, \cdot)$ satisfying P1 through P4, (where (P1) through (P4) are known respectively as the *idempotent, associative, commutative,* and *absorption* laws), there exists a relation $\geq$ on L, relative to which L is a lattice with $(+)$ and $(\cdot)$ as l.u.b. and g.l.b. operations.

PROOF. As an example of the style of argument used in the proof, we choose to verify P2a. Let $w = x + (y + z)$. Then, by Eq. (1.10) $w \geq x$, $w \geq y + z$, so that also $w \geq y$ and $w \geq z$, using Eq. (1.10) and transitivity. Then, since $w \geq x$, $w \geq y$, we have $w \geq x + y$. And since also $w \geq z$, we obtain $w \geq (x + y) + z$. Similarly, if $v = (x + y) + z$, we can show $v \geq x + (y + z) = w$. Together with the preceding results, we have $v \geq w$ and $w \geq v$, so that $w = v$ by antisymmetry; that is, $x + (y + z) = (x + y) + z$.

All other proofs for P1 through P4 employ similar arguments, so we content ourselves here with a discussion of the converse.

Suppose P1 through P4 are satisfied by a set with binary compositions $(+, \cdot)$. By means of Lemma 1.2 we can define a relation $\geq$ by

$$x \geq y \Longleftrightarrow x + y = x \qquad (1.14)$$

It is then necessary to verify that $\geq$ partially orders the set; that is, we must check that $\geq$ satisfies reflexivity, antisymmetry, and transitivity.

(1) $x + x = x$ by P1a above; so $x \geq x$ by Eq. (1.14).

(2) Suppose $x \geq y$ and $y \geq x$. By Eq. (1.14) this means that $x + y = x$ and $y + x = y$, and by the commutativity, P3a, we obtain $x = y$, so that $\geq$ is antisymmetric.

(3) If $x \geq y$ and $y \geq z$ we get $x \geq z$ through the use of P2a, which completes the proof that $\geq$ is a partial order. ∎

Because of the duality of P1a through P4a with P1b through P4b we can state the fundamental *principle of duality*:

> If S is a statement that is deduced from P1 through P4, then the dual statement S', obtained by interchanging $(+\ \cdot)$ in S, is also true.

The scope of this principle will be enlarged in the subject of Boolean algebra but its underlying philosophy is already apparent here.

An element 1 of a partially ordered set $(X, \geq)$ is called an *identity* if

$$1 \geq a \qquad \text{for all } a \in X$$

Dually an element 0 for which

$$0 \leq a \qquad \text{for all } a \in X$$

is called a *zero* for the partially ordered set X. If $(X \geq)$ has a zero or an identity or both we note that Lemma 1.2 then implies the corresponding addition and multiplication rules:

P5a $a + 1 = 1$ **P5b** $a \cdot 0 = 0$

P6a $a \cdot 1 = a$ **P6b** $a + 0 = a$

We leave to the reader the proof that zeros and identities are unique when they exist.

A lattice $(L, +, \cdot)$ is said to be *distributive* if

$$\textbf{(P7a)} \qquad x + (y \cdot z) = (x + y) \cdot (x + z)$$

$$\textbf{(P7b)} \qquad x \cdot (y + z) = (x \cdot y) + (x \cdot z)$$

Note that only the distributive law P7b is encountered in the more customary algebras (for example, the algebra of real numbers). P7a is further evidence of the duality of lattices.

In a distributive lattice $(L, +, \cdot)$ one can prove by induction on n that for all $n \geq 2$,

$$x \cdot \left(\sum_{j=1}^{n} y_j \right) = \sum_{j=1}^{n} xy_j \qquad (\textbf{1.15})$$

and dually,

$$x + \left(\prod_{j=1}^{n} y_j \right) = \prod_{j=1}^{n} x + y_j \qquad (\textbf{1.16})$$

Similarly, induction on m yields the more general (dual) results:

$$\left(\sum_{i=1}^{m} x_i \right) \cdot \left(\sum_{j=1}^{n} y_j \right) = \sum_{i,j} x_i y_j \qquad (\textbf{1.17})$$

$$\prod_{i=1}^{m} x_i + \prod_{j=1}^{n} y_j = \prod_{i,j} (x_i + y_j) \qquad (\textbf{1.18})$$

Now if we agree to say that a *lattice polynomial* $f(x_n, x_{n-1}, \cdots, x_1)$ in the elements $x_1, x_2, \cdots, x_n$ of a lattice $(L, +, \cdot)$ is either

(1)   One of the x_i, or *recursively*,

(2a)   A sum of two lattice polynomials, or

(2b)   A product of two lattice polynomials,

then Eqs. 1.17 and 1.18 allow us to conclude the following theorem.

Theorem 1.4   Every lattice polynomial $f(x_1, x_2, \cdots, x_n)$ in the elements $x_1, x_2, \cdots, x_n$ of a distributive lattice $(L, +, \cdot)$ may be written as

(a)   A sum of products in the elements x_i
       or, dually, as

(b)   A product of sums in the elements x_i.

EXAMPLE 1.11

In order to illustrate Theorem 1.4, suppose we discuss the *free distributive-lattice with n generators*: $x_n, x_{n-1}, \cdots, x_1$.[†] This lattice is denoted FD(n) and consists of all lattice polynomials $f(x_n, x_{n-1}, \cdots, x_1)$ in the elements $x_n, x_{n-1}, \cdots, x_1$ together with elements 0, 1 defined to have the properties:

$$0 \leq f \leq 1$$

for every polynomial f.

For definiteness, suppose we restrict our attention now to FD(3). While it may appear (due to the recursive definition of "lattice polynomials") that this lattice is infinite, the reader will soon be convinced instead that FD(3) has 20 elements. Consider the lattice polynomial

$$f(x_1, x_2, x_3) = (((x_1 + x_2)x_3 + x_2)x_1 + x_2x_3)(x_3 + x_1)$$

Using the distributivity (P7b), we write

$$
\begin{aligned}
f(x_1, x_2, x_3) &= ((x_1x_3 + x_2x_3 + x_2)x_1 + x_2x_3)(x_3 + x_1) \\
&= (x_1x_3 + x_1x_2x_3 + x_1x_2 + x_2x_3)(x_3 + x_1) \\
&= (x_1x_3 + x_1x_2x_3 + x_1x_2 + x_2x_3)x_3 \\
&\quad + (x_1x_3 + x_1x_2x_3 + x_1x_2 + x_2x_3)x_1 \\
&= x_1x_3 + x_1x_2x_3 + x_1x_2x_3 + x_2x_3 \\
&\quad + x_1x_3 + x_1x_2x_3 + x_1x_2 + x_1x_2x_3 \\
&= x_1x_3 + x_2x_3 + x_1x_2
\end{aligned}
$$

where properties P1 through P7 have been applied in reducing the polynomial; that is, by P4a,

$$x_1x_3 + x_1x_2x_3 = x_1x_3$$

and by P1a,

$$x_1x_3 + x_1x_3 = x_1x_3$$

and so on.

†See Ref. 1–1, pp. 145–146.

Thus we are forcing FD(3) to be a distributive lattice by imposing properties P1 through P7 on all "lattice polynomials."

Finally we were able to write f as a sum of products in the elements x_i as predicted by Theorem 1.4. Had we used property P7a rather than P7b, we could have written f as a product of sums in the x_i. A little reflection should convince the reader that FD(3) consists of 20 elements whose "canonical forms" as sums of products are

$$
\begin{array}{ll}
0 & x_1x_2 \\
1 & x_1x_3 \\
x_1 & x_2x_3 \\
x_2 & x_1x_2 + x_3 \\
x_3 & x_1x_3 + x_2 \\
x_1 + x_2 & x_2x_3 + x_1 \\
x_1 + x_3 & x_1x_2 + x_1x_3 \\
x_2 + x_3 & x_1x_2 + x_2x_3 \\
x_1 + x_2 + x_3 & x_1x_3 + x_2x_3 \\
x_1x_2x_3 & x_1x_3 + x_2x_3 + x_1x_2
\end{array}
$$

(Certainly a verification that the sum or product of any two of these polynomials can be reduced by P1 through P7 to one among the list would provide a most convincing proof.)

The lattice FD(5) will have important applications in our subsequent work. Although we have seen that

$$|\,FD(3)\,| = 20$$

it will probably be surprising for the reader to learn that

$$|\,FD(4)\,| = 168$$
$$|\,FD(5)\,| = 7581$$
$$|\,FD(6)\,| = 7,828,354$$

and that a general formula for $|\,FD(n)\,|$ is not known.

*1.4 LATTICE OF PARTITIONS

It is possible to define an addition and multiplication for partitions of a set S, relative to which the set $\Lambda(S)$ becomes a lattice. (Cf. Eq. 0.48.) This lattice is of primary importance in any complete discussion of the synthesis of sequential machines—a topic that we will examine in Chapter 5. If $\lambda_j, \lambda_k \in \Lambda(S)$, we write (cf. Eq. 1.5)

$$\lambda_j \geq \lambda_k \Longleftrightarrow \begin{array}{l} \text{every block of the partition } \lambda_k \\ \text{is contained in some block of } \lambda_j \end{array} \qquad (1.19)$$

Thus, $\lambda_j \geq \lambda_k$ might be read "λ_k is a refinement of λ_j." Since partitions are invariably set systems, the discussion of Example 1.6 shows that Eq. 1.19 defines a partial order on $\Lambda(S)$.

EXAMPLE 1.12

Suppose

$$S = 4^+ = \{1, 2, 3, 4\}$$

Then $(\Lambda(S), \geq)$ has 15 elements whose Hasse diagram is partially drawn in Fig. 1.6.

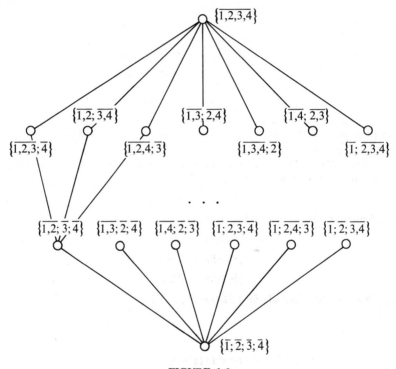

FIGURE 1.6

In order to describe the addition operation in $\Lambda(S)$, it is necessary to first introduce a set-theoretic property regarding intersections of sets. Recall that two sets A and B are said to be *connected* if $A \cap B \neq \varnothing$. More generally if A and B are two subsets from among a collection $\mathscr{C} \subseteq \mathscr{P}(S)$ of subsets of a set S, we say that A is *chain-connected* to B in $\mathscr{C}$ if there exists a finite sequence $\langle A_i; 1 \leq i \leq k \rangle$ of subsets in $\mathscr{C}$ such that $A = A_1$, $A_k = B$, and A_i is connected to A_{i+1} $(1 \leq i \leq k - 1)$. (See Fig. 1.7.) With this terminology we can describe the lattice operations $(+, \cdot)$ of $(\Lambda(S), \geq)$ in the next theorem.

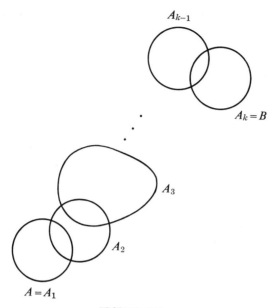

A_{k-1}

$A_k = B$

A_3

A_2

$A = A_1$

FIGURE 1.7

Theorem 1.5   Let $\lambda = \{A_1, A_2, \cdots, A_n\}$ and $\gamma = \{B_1, B_2, \cdots, B_k\}$ be elements of $(\Lambda(S), \geq)$. Then

$$\lambda \cdot \gamma = \{A_i \cap B_j; A_i \in \lambda, B_j \in \gamma, A_i \text{ is connected to } B_j\} \qquad (1.20)$$

$$\lambda + \gamma = \{A^i = \cup A_\alpha; A_\alpha \text{ is chain-connected to } A_i \text{ in } \lambda \cup \gamma$$

$$(i = 1, 2, \cdots, n)\} \qquad (1.21)$$

PROOF.   To prove that $\lambda \cdot \gamma$ is the g.l.b. of λ and γ is not difficult. But first we must show it to be a partition. Observe first that each block of $\lambda \cdot \gamma$ is of the form $A_i \cap B_j$ where $A_i \in \lambda$, $B_j \in \gamma$, are connected. Two such blocks, $A_i \cap B_j$ and $A_{i'} \cap B_{j'}$, cannot intersect, for if they are different blocks we must have $A_i \neq A_{i'}$ or $B_j \neq B_{j'}$. Therefore, $A_i \cap A_{i'} = \varnothing$ or $B_j \cap B_{j'} = \varnothing$. Hence

$$(A_i \cap B_j) \cap (A_{i'} \cap B_{j'}) = (A_i \cap A_{i'}) \cap (B_j \cap B_{j'}) = \varnothing$$

Now if $x \in S$, then $x \in A_i$ for some $i = 1, 2, \cdots, n$ and $x \in B_j$ for some j because λ and γ are partitions. Then $x \in A_i \cap B_j$, so $\lambda \cdot \gamma$ is indeed a partition of S. Now each block $A_i \cap B_j$ of $\lambda \cdot \gamma$ will naturally have the properties

$$A_i \cap B_j \subseteq A_i, \quad A_i \cap B_j \subseteq B_j$$

so that we have

$$\lambda \cdot \gamma \leq \lambda, \quad \lambda \cdot \gamma \leq \gamma$$

Furthermore, if we are given any partition ρ that satisfies

$$\rho \leq \lambda, \quad \rho \leq \gamma$$

then each block A of ρ is contained in some block (say A') of λ and in some block (say, B') of γ. We must show that A is contained in some block of $\lambda \cdot \gamma$. Now $A' \cap B' \neq \varnothing$, since their intersection must contain A. That is,

$$A \subseteq A' \cap B'$$

where $A' \cap B'$ is by definition of $(\cdot)$, a block of the product $\lambda \cdot \gamma$. Since this argument holds for any block A of ρ, we have shown that

$$\rho \leq \lambda, \quad \rho \leq \gamma \Longrightarrow \rho \leq \lambda \cdot \gamma$$

and hence that $\lambda \cdot \gamma$ is the g.l.b of λ and γ, which was to be proved. $\blacksquare$

The demonstration that $\lambda + \gamma$ is a partition and is the l.u.b. of λ and γ is left as an exercise. We do not mean to imply (as a casual glance at its definition would seem to do) that $\lambda + \gamma$ has as many blocks as λ has. It is likely that some of the unions A^i will be identical. These blocks A^i of the sum $\lambda + \gamma$ consist (as the definition asserts) of the set union of all blocks from among the union $\lambda \cup \gamma$ which are chain-connected to A_i in $\lambda \cup \gamma$, for a block A_i of λ.

EXAMPLE 1.13

Consider the elements

$$\lambda = \{\overline{1,2}; \ \overline{3,4}; \ \overline{5,6}; \ \overline{7,8,9}\}$$

$$\gamma = \{\overline{1,6}; \ \overline{2,3}; \ \overline{4,5}; \ \overline{7,8}; \ \overline{9}\}$$

of $\Lambda(S)$, where

$$S = \{1, 2, 3, 4, 5, 6, 7, 8, 9\} = 9^+$$

We have

$$\lambda \cdot \gamma = \{\overline{1}; \ \overline{\dot{2}}; \ \overline{3}; \ \overline{4}; \ \overline{5}; \ \overline{6}; \ \overline{7,8}; \ \overline{9}\}$$

and since

$$\lambda \cup \gamma = \{\overline{1,2}; \ \overline{3,4}; \ \overline{5,6}; \ \overline{7,8,9}; \ \ \overline{1,6}; \ \overline{2,3}; \ \overline{4,5}; \ \overline{7,8}; \ \overline{9}\}$$

(which, incidentally is *not* a partition), we determine $\lambda + \gamma$ by first denoting

$$\lambda = \{\overline{1,2}; \ \overline{3,4}; \ \overline{5,6}; \ \overline{7,8,9}\} = \{A_1; A_2; A_3; A_4\}$$

Now

$$A^1 = \{1, 2\} \cup \{2, 3\} \cup \{3, 4\} \cup \{4, 5\} \cup \{5, 6\} \cup \{1, 6\}$$

$$= \{1, 2, 3, 4, 5, 6\}$$

$$A^2 = \{3, 4\} \cup \{5, 6\} \cup \{1, 6\} \cup \{1, 2\} \cup \{2, 3\} \cup \{3, 4\}$$

$$= \{1, 2, 3, 4, 5, 6\} = A^1$$

$$A^3 = A^1$$

$$A^4 = \{7, 8, 9\} \cup \{7, 8\} \cup \{9\} = \{7, 8, 9\}$$

and hence

$$\lambda + \gamma = \{\overline{1,2,3,4,5,6};\ \overline{7,8,9}\}$$

1.5 BOOLEAN ALGEBRAS[†]

A lattice $(L, +, \cdot)$ is said to be *complemented* if for every $a \in L$ their exists an element $\bar{a} \in L$ such that

P8a $a + \bar{a} = 1$ **P8b** $a \cdot \bar{a} = 0$

in which case $\bar{a}$ is called a *complement* for a.

Finally we define a *Boolean algebra A* to be a lattice with a zero and an identity which is both distributive and complemented. Many of their properties P1 through P8 would have occurred as postulates if we had chosen the more direct means of introducing Boolean algebras mentioned in Sec. 1.1. The following theorem asserts the uniqueness of complements in a Boolean algebra and states two important connections between complementation and the algebraic operations $(+, \cdot)$.

Theorem 1.6 The complement $\bar{a}$ of any element a of a Boolean algebra A is uniquely determined. The mapping $a \longrightarrow \bar{a}$ is a 1–1 mapping of A onto itself. It is of period 2, in the sense that $\bar{\bar{a}} = a$, and it behaves in the following way with respect to addition and multiplication:

P9a $\overline{(a + b)} = \bar{a} \cdot \bar{b}$ **P9b** $\overline{a \cdot b} = \bar{a} + \bar{b}$

PROOF. Let A be a Boolean algebra and let a be any element of A. Suppose a has two complements: $\bar{a}$ and a'; that is,

$$a + \bar{a} = 1 \qquad a + a' = 1$$

$$a \cdot \bar{a} = 0 \qquad a \cdot a' = 0$$

Then we compute

$$a' = a' \cdot 1 = a'(a + \bar{a}) = a'a + a'\bar{a}$$

$$= 0 + a'\bar{a} = a'\bar{a}$$

$$= 0 + \bar{a}a' = \bar{a}a + \bar{a}a' = \bar{a}(a + a')$$

$$= \bar{a} \cdot 1 = \bar{a}$$

which proves the uniqueness of complements.

†G. Boole, *The Mathematical Analysis of Logic*, Cambridge, 1847; *Laws of Thought*, London, 1854 (reprinted by Open Court Publishing Co., Chicago, 1940).

By what we have just proved, there is a unique complement $(\bar{a})$ for the element $\bar{a}$ for which

$$(\bar{\bar{a}}) + \bar{a} = 1 \quad \text{and} \quad (\bar{\bar{a}}) \cdot \bar{a} = 0$$

Since the element a meets these requirements, we must have $a = \bar{\bar{a}}$ so that the map

$$a \longrightarrow \bar{a}$$

is of period 2, as claimed.

Using properties P7b and P7a, we have

$$(a + b)(\bar{a} \cdot \bar{b}) = a\bar{a}\bar{b} + b\bar{a}\bar{b} = 0 + 0 = 0$$

$$(a + b) + \bar{a} \cdot \bar{b} = (a + b + \bar{a})(a + b + \bar{b}) = 1 \cdot 1 = 1$$

so that $\bar{a} \cdot \bar{b}$ is a complement for $a + b$. By the uniqueness of complements, we must have

$$(\overline{a + b}) = \bar{a} \cdot \bar{b}$$

In a similar way one sees that $\overline{a \cdot b} = \bar{a} + \bar{b}$. ∎

By analogy with the lattice polynomials defined in Sec. 1.3, we use the term *Boolean polynomial* $f(x_n, x_{n-1}, \cdots, x_1)$ in the elements x_1, $x_2, \cdots, x_n$ of a Boolean algebra A when referring to

(1) One of the x_i, or *recursively*,

(2a) A sum of two Boolean polynomials or,

(2b) A product of two Boolean polynomials, or,

(2c) The complement of a Boolean polynomial.

EXAMPLE 1.14

If a, b, c, d are elements of a Boolean algebra A, then

$$a(\bar{b} + c\bar{d})$$

is a Boolean polynomial in a, b, c, d.

Eventually we will derive a precise generalization of Theorem 1.4 for Boolean polynomials. For the time being, however, we content ourselves with the following important extension of properties P9a and P9b to the problem of complementation of polynomials.

Corollary 1.7   DeMorgan's Theorem: To complement a Boolean polynomial having no complemented products or complemented sums, change all occurrences of $(+)$ to $(\cdot)$, and vice versa, while replacing each *literal* (x_i or $\bar{x}_i$) of the polynomial by its complement.

EXAMPLE 1.15

For the polynomial of Example 1.14 we obtain

$$\overline{a \cdot (\bar{b} + c \cdot \bar{d})} = \bar{a} + (b \cdot (\bar{c} + d))$$

illustrating the use of DeMorgan's theorem. If instead we seek the complement of the polynomial $a \cdot (\bar{b} + \overline{c \cdot d})$, we must first obtain

$$a \cdot (\bar{b} + \overline{c \cdot d}) = a \cdot (\bar{b} + c + d)$$

a polynomial without complemented products or sums. Then DeMorgan's theorem applies:

$$\overline{a \cdot (\bar{b} + \overline{c \cdot d})} = \overline{a \cdot (\bar{b} + c + d)} = \bar{a} + (b \cdot \bar{c} \cdot \bar{d})$$

Before we give examples of Boolean algebras, it is perhaps best to complete the list of their more commonly used properties. This we do in the following theorem, where it will be noted that property P11 is "self-dual" in the sense that the replacement of $(+)$ by $(\cdot)$, and vice versa, again yields the same property.

Theorem 1.8   If a, b, c are elements of a Boolean algebra A,

P10a $\overline{ac + b\bar{c}} = \bar{a}c + \bar{b}\bar{c}$

P10b $\overline{(a + c)(b + \bar{c})} = (\bar{a} + c)(\bar{b} + \bar{c})$

P11 $(a + b)(\bar{a} + c) = ac + \bar{a}b$

PROOF.   For P11:

$$(a + b)(\bar{a} + c) = a\bar{a} + ac + \bar{a}b + bc$$
$$= ac + \bar{a}b + bc(a + \bar{a})$$
$$= ac(1 + b) + \bar{a}b(1 + c)$$
$$= ac + \bar{a}b$$

For P10a, by De Morgan's theorem,

$$\overline{(ac + b\bar{c})} = (\bar{a} + \bar{c})(\bar{b} + c) = (c + \bar{b})(\bar{c} + \bar{a})$$

Now if we use the (already proved) property P11, we obtain

$$\overline{(ac + b\bar{c})} = c\bar{a} + \bar{c}\bar{b} = \bar{a}c + \bar{b}\bar{c}$$

Because of the complete duality, the proof of P10b is omitted. ∎

1.6   ISOMORPHIC ALGEBRAIC SYSTEMS

In discussing examples of Boolean algebras (or any other algebraic system, for that matter), it is advantageous to have a precise rule for deciding whether or not two examples are "essentially the same," for it very often happens that two examples arise, which from their outward or physical appearance would be considered distinct. Yet these two examples might be "abstractly equivalent." In such instances, considerable time and effort can be misspent if each example is studied separately and in detail, for the deductions one could make and the theorems one could prove by studying one example would apply equally well to the abstractly equivalent (or, as we shall say, "isomorphic") example.

First consider the case of the partially ordered set. In order that two of these $(X, \geq)$, $(Y, \geq)$ would be "abstractly equivalent," one would certainly insist that they be equivalent as sets. That is to say, there should exist a 1–1 mapping

$$\alpha : X \longrightarrow Y$$

of X onto Y. But, in addition, one would ask that the mapping α preserve the algebraic structure (here, the order relation).

Hence, we adopt the definition: two partially ordered sets $(X, \geq)$ and $(Y, \geq)$ are *isomorphic*[†] if there exists a 1–1 mapping

$$\alpha : X \longrightarrow Y$$

of X onto Y, such that

$$x \geq x' \longleftrightarrow \alpha(x) \geq \alpha(x')$$

for all $x, x' \in X$.

Guided by the preceding definition, we say that two lattices $(L, +, \cdot)$ and $(L', +, \cdot)$ are *isomorphic* if there exists a 1–1 mapping

$$\beta : L \longrightarrow L'$$

of L onto L' such that

$$\beta(x + y) = \beta(x) + \beta(y)$$
$$\beta(x \cdot y) = \beta(x) \cdot \beta(y)$$

for all $x, y \in L$ and that two Boolean algebras A and A' are *isomorphic* if there exists a 1–1 mapping

$$\gamma : A \longrightarrow A'$$

of A onto A' such that

$$\gamma(x + y) = \gamma(x) + \gamma(y)$$
$$\gamma(x \cdot y) = \gamma(x) \cdot \gamma(y)$$
$$\gamma(x) = \overline{\gamma(x)}$$

Note in the last two definitions that the 1–1 correspondences must preserve the additive and multiplicative structure, and in the case of a Boolean algebra, must preserve the complementation structure as well.

We have already seen (cf. Examples 1.2 and 1.6) two isomorphic partially ordered sets. Further examples of isomorphic algebraic systems will occur as we proceed.

[†]Often the term *order-isomorphic* is used for definiteness.

1.7   EXAMPLES OF BOOLEAN ALGEBRAS

EXAMPLE 1.16

Let $B = \{0, 1\}$ with the addition and multiplication tables

+	0	1		·	0	1
0	0	1		0	0	0
1	1	1		1	0	1

and define complements in the obvious way:

$$\bar{0} = 1; \quad \bar{1} = 0$$

Then one can easily verify that $(B, +, \cdot)$ is a lattice (by using Theorem 1.3) with a zero (0) and an identity (1) that is both distributive and complemented. Hence, B is a Boolean algebra consisting of but two elements.

EXAMPLE 1.17

Let S be any set and

$$\mathscr{P}(S) = \{\text{all subsets of } S\}$$

Take the operations $+$, $\cdot$ to be set union and intersection, respectively, as was done in Example 1.8. For $A \in \mathscr{P}(S)$, define (cf. Sec. 0.3)

$$\bar{A} = S - A$$

Then

$$(\mathscr{P}(S), +, \cdot) = (\mathscr{P}(S), \cup, \cap)$$

is a lattice. (We saw an example in Fig. 1.2 for the case $S = \{a, b, c\}$.) We have already defined a complementation structure that clearly satisfies P8, and since one can easily verify that $\cup$ and $\cap$ satisfy the distributive laws

$$A \cup (B \cap C) = (A \cup B) \cap (A \cup C)$$
$$A \cap (B \cup C) = (A \cap B) \cup (A \cap C)$$

it can be seen that $(\mathscr{P}(S), \cup, \cap)$ is a Boolean algebra.

EXAMPLE 1.18

By analogy with Example 1.11, consider for any $n \geq 1$ the set

$$S_n = \{x_n, x_{n-1}, \cdots, x_1\}$$

and let FB(n) denote the *free Boolean algebra with n generators* $x_n, x_{n-1}, \cdots,$ x_1, consisting of all Boolean polynomials (cf., Sec. 1.5) $f(x_n, x_{n-1}, \cdots, x_1)$ in the elements of S_n together with elements 0, 1 defined to have the properties

$$f + \bar{f} = 1$$
$$f \cdot \bar{f} = 0$$

for every polynomial f. As with FD(n), we impose conditions P1 through P8 on all polynomials formed. The effect of doing this is to cause certain polynomials of different appearance to be equal in FB(n).

Thus, in FB(2), the polynomials

$$f(x_2, x_1) = x_1 + \bar{x}_2$$

$$g(x_2, x_1) = ((0 + x_1) + ((x_1 \cdot 1) \cdot \bar{x}_2)) + (\bar{x}_2 \cdot (1))$$

are equal, since

$$g = (x_1 + x_1 \cdot \bar{x}_2) + \bar{x}_2 = x_1 + \bar{x}_2 = f$$

using associativity, commutativity, P6a, P6b, and finally the absorption law

FB(n) is an extremely important Boolean algebra in the applications. The reader will begin to see why this is so after considering the next example. Meanwhile, we remark that

$$\text{FD}(n) \subseteq \text{FB}(n)$$

and the former is a sublattice of FB(n). Evidently FD(n) consists of all Boolean polynomials in the elements of S_n which can be written without complementation.

EXAMPLE 1.19

Again let $S_n = \{x_n, x_{n-1}, \cdots, x_1\}$. Let it be supposed that the elements x_i are wires, each of which is assumed to be at either a "high" or "low" voltage at the discrete times $t = 1, 2, \cdots, k, k + 1, \cdots$.

If x and y are two wires that have this property, then let $x + y$ denote the output wire of an electronic circuit

which behaves in such a way that

$$x + y \text{ is a "high" voltage wire} \Longleftrightarrow \begin{cases} x \text{ is "high"} \\ \quad \text{or} \\ y \text{ is "high"} \\ \text{(or both)} \end{cases}$$

and let $x \cdot y$ denote the output wire of an electronic circuit that has the property

$$x \cdot y \text{ is a "high" voltage wire} \Longleftrightarrow \begin{cases} x \text{ is "high"} \\ \quad \text{and} \\ y \text{ is "high"} \end{cases}$$

(Since this is an extremely important example for the applications, the reader may wish to keep in mind a pair of definite circuits, of which those in Fig. 1.8 are typical.)

Whether the circuits use diodes, transistors, vacuum tubes, or some other device is not important here. In fact, to demonstrate our impartiality, we

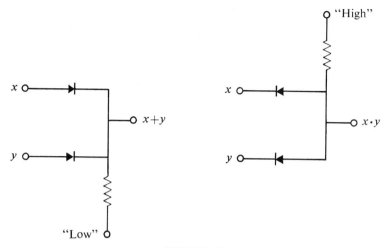

FIGURE 1.8

will make exclusive use of the *symbolic circuits* of Fig. 1.9. We refer to these two symbolic circuits as the *or circuit* and the *and circuit*, respectively.

FIGURE 1.9

Now we assume the existence of a wire (1) which is always "high" and a wire (0) which is always "low", and assume further the existence of a third symbolic circuit .This third circuit, the *inverter circuit*, (the reader will be able to supply an electronic realization) is denoted by

$$x —— \ominus \longrightarrow \bar{x}$$

and its output is "low" when its input is "high," and conversely. Then, in principle, we can construct (from S_n and an unlimited supply of our three types of symbolic circuits) an infinite collection FL(n) of single-output, n-input *logic circuits* (or *networks*) that are in 1–1 correspondence with the Boolean polynomials of the collection FB(n) in Example 1.18. To illustrate this correspondence, the polynomial

$$g(x_2, x_1) = ((0 + x_1) + ((x_1 \cdot 1) \cdot \bar{x}_2)) + (\bar{x}_2 \cdot (1))$$

of FB(2) is associated with the logic circuit of Fig. 1.10.

Suppose we denote this correspondence or mapping by

$$\rho : \text{FB}(n) \longrightarrow \text{FL}(n)$$

and agree to call two circuits $c_1, c_2 \in$ FL(n) *equivalent* ($c_1 \sim c_2$) if

$$\rho^{-1}(c_1) = \rho^{-1}(c_2)$$

where equality is taken in the Boolean algebra FB(n). Then it is clear that $\sim$ is an equivalence relation on FL(n). By Theorem 0.3, $\sim$ partitions FL(n) into nonoverlapping classes of equivalent circuits. If we let L(n) denote the resulting set of equivalence classes, the reader can easily infer from the foregoing constructions that L(n) is a Boolean algebra which is isomorphic to FB(n). We write FB(n) $\cong$ L(n) to express the isomorphism.

Before we give further important examples of Boolean algebras and discuss the structure of FB(n), it will be advantageous to examine the Cartesian product of two sets with a view toward learning which algebraic properties of the factors are inherited by their product.

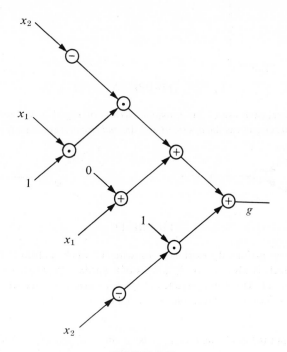

FIGURE 1.10

1.8   CARTESIAN PRODUCTS OF PARTIALLY ORDERED SETS

Let $(X, \geq)$ and $(Y, \geq)^\dagger$ be partially ordered sets. Then the set $X \times Y$ (cf. Sec. 0.3) given by

†For complete technical clarity, we should use here a different order-relation symbol (say, $\geqslant$) for Y and yet a third symbol (say $\sqsupseteq$) for the order relation in $X \times Y$. However, we expect that little ambiguity will arise from employing a common symbol $\geq$.

$$X \times Y = \{(x, y); x \in X, y \in Y\}$$

together with the order relation

$$(x, y) \geq (x', y') \Longleftrightarrow x \geq x' \quad \text{and} \quad y \geq y' \tag{1.22}$$

forms a partially ordered set $(X \times Y, \geq)$, which we call the *Cartesian product of the partially ordered sets X and Y.*

EXAMPLE 1.20

Suppose $S = \{a, b, c\}$ and $X = \mathscr{P}(S)$ is the partially ordered set of Fig. 1.2, while $Y = \{x, y, z\}$ is the partially ordered set of Fig. 1.4; that is, $(Y, \geq)$ has the relation matrix

	x	y	z
x	1	1	1
y	0	1	0
z	0	0	1

Then $(X \times Y, \geq)$ is a partially ordered set having

$$|X| \cdot |Y| = 8 \cdot 3 = 24$$

elements and the Hasse diagram of Fig. 1.11.

When combining two partially ordered sets in this fashion, it is of interest to ask whether or not certain algebraic properties that may be possessed by the original partially ordered sets X and Y are inherited by their Cartesian product. In the preceding example, it is observed from Figs. 1.2 and 1.4 that both

$$X = \mathscr{P}(S)$$

and

$$Y = \{x, y, z\}$$

have identity elements, namely, S for X and x for Y. It is not coincidental that their Cartesian product (see Fig. 1.11) has an identity element. For, generally, if X has the identity 1_x and Y the identity element 1_y, it is clear that $(1_x, 1_y)$ will be an identity element for $(X \times Y, \geq)$, since

$$x \leq 1_x \qquad \text{for all } x \in X$$
$$y \leq 1_y \qquad \text{for all } y \in Y$$

implies

$$(x, y) \leq (1_x, 1_y)$$

for all $(x, y) \in X \times Y$. By duality, one can conclude that the possession of a zero element by two partially ordered sets X and Y will ensure that their Cartesian product has a zero element.

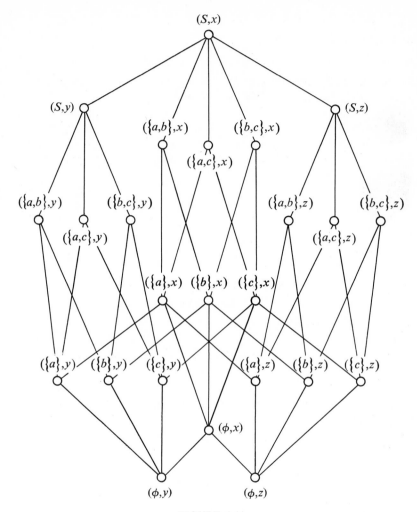

FIGURE 1.11

The two dual properties thus preserved in the construction of the Cartesian product are necessary in deducing the next theorem.

Theorem 1.9   Let $(X, \geq)$ and $(Y, \geq)$ be partially ordered sets. Then $(X \times Y, \geq)$ is a

(I)   Lattice if X and Y are lattices.

(II)   Boolean algebra if X and Y are Boolean algebras.

Furthermore

(A) $(x, y) + (x', y',) = (x + x', y + y')$.

(B) $(x, y) \cdot (x', y',) = (x \cdot x', y \cdot y')$.

And in case (II),

(C) $\overline{(x, y)} = (\bar{x}, \bar{y})$.

PROOF.   First suppose X and Y are lattices. This means that for every pair of elements x and x' in X, there exists a unique l.u.b., denoted $x + x'$, and a g.l.b., which we denote $x \cdot x'$. A similar statement can be made regarding Y. Now the element $(x + x', y + y')$ is surely an upper bound for the elements (x, y) and (x', y') in $X \times Y$, since

$$\left. \begin{array}{l} x \leq x + x' \\ y \leq y + y' \end{array} \right\} \Longrightarrow (x, y) \leq (x + x', y + y')$$

and, similarly,

$$\left. \begin{array}{l} x' \leq x + x' \\ y' \leq y + y' \end{array} \right\} \Longrightarrow (x', y') \leq (x + x', y + y')$$

Furthermore, if $(u, v) \in X \times Y$ has the properties

$$(x, y) \leq (u, v)$$
$$(x', y') \leq (u, v)$$

by the definition of the order relation on $X \times Y$, we have

$$\begin{array}{ll} x \leq u & x' \leq u \\ y \leq v & y' \leq v \end{array}$$

Since $x + x'$ is the l.u.b. of x and x', and similarly for $y + y'$, we obtain

$$x + x' \leq u \qquad y + y' \leq v$$

and hence, by Eq. 1.22,

$$(x + x', y + y') \leq (u, v)$$

which shows that $(x + x'), y + y'$ is the l.u.b. of (x, y) and (x', y'). Summarizing, we have shown that $(X \times Y, \geq)$ is a lattice with operations

(A) $(x, y) + (x', y') = (x + x', y + y')$,
(B) $(x, y) \cdot (x', y') = (x \cdot x', y \cdot y')$,

if one simply inverts the above argument to deduce the existence of g.l.b.s and their characterizations as in (B).

Now suppose that both $(X, \geq)$ and $(Y, \geq)$ are distributive lattices. Then, using (A) and (B),

$$\begin{aligned} (x, y) \cdot [(x', y') + (x'', y'')] &= (x, y) \cdot (x' + x'', y' + y'') \\ &= (x \cdot (x' + x''), y \cdot (y' + y'')) \\ &= (xx' + xx'', yy' + yy'') \\ &= (xx', yy') + (xx'', yy'') \\ &= (x, y)(x', y') + (x, y)(x'', y'') \end{aligned}$$

In a similar fashion, the dual distributive law

$$(x, y) + (x', y')(x'', y'') = [(x, y) + (x', y')] \cdot [(x, y) + (x'', y'')]$$

can be verified.

If the two lattices X and Y are complemented,

$$(x, y) + (\bar{x}, \bar{y}) = (x + \bar{x}, y + \bar{y}) = (1_X, 1_Y)$$
$$= 1_{X \times Y}$$

is the identity element of the lattice $X \times Y$. Similarly,

$$(x, y) \cdot (\bar{x}, \bar{y}) = (x \cdot \bar{x}, y \cdot \bar{y}) = (0_X, 0_Y) = 0_{X \times Y}$$

so that $X \times Y$ is complemented, with the complementation rule

(C) $\overline{(x, y)} = (\bar{x}, \bar{y})$ ∎

Now if $X_1, X_2, \cdots, X_n$ are partially ordered sets, we can use an obvious extension of Eq. 1.22 to define for elements

$$(x_1, x_2, \cdots, x_n) \quad \text{and} \quad (y, y_2, \cdots, y_n) \quad \text{in} \prod_{i=1}^{n} X_i$$

the partial order

$$(x_1, x_2, \cdots, x_n) \geq (y_1, y_2, \cdots, y_n)$$
$$\Longleftrightarrow x_i \geq y_i \text{ in } X_i \qquad (i = 1, 2, \cdots, n)$$

In so doing, the reader should anticipate the following corollary.

Corollary 1.10   Let $(X_i, \geq)$ be a partially ordered set for each $i = 1$, $2, \cdots, n$. Then $\prod_{i=1}^{n} X_i$ is a

   (I)   lattice if each X_i is a lattice.
   (II)   Boolean algebra if each X_i is a Boolean algebra.

   Furthermore

   (a) $(x_1, x_2, \cdots, x_n) + (y_1, y_2, \cdots, y_n)$
          $= (x_1 + y_1, x_2 + y_2, \cdots, x_n + y_n).$
   (b) $(x_1, x_2, \cdots, x_n) \cdot (y_1, y_2, \cdots, y_n)$
          $= (x_1 \cdot y_1, x_2 \cdot y_2, \cdots, x_n \cdot y_n).$
   (c)   And in case (II), $\overline{(x_1, x_2, \cdots, x_n)} = (\bar{x}_1, \bar{x}_2, \cdots, \bar{x}_n).$

EXAMPLE 1.21

Consider the product set

$$B^n = \overbrace{B \times B \times \cdots \times B}^{n}$$

$$= \{(b_n, b_{n-1}, \cdots, b_1); \; b_i \in B \quad \text{for all } i = 1, 2, \cdots, n\}$$

where $B = \{0, 1\}$ is the Boolean algebra of Example 1.16. Then, according to Corollary 1.10, B^n is a Boolean algebra in which

(a) $(b_n, b_{n-1}, \cdots, b_1) + (b, b'_{n-1}, \cdots, b'_1)$
$$= (b_n + b'_n, b_{n-1} + b'_{n-1}, \cdots, b_1 + b'_1).$$

(b) $(b_n, b_{n-1}, \cdots, b_1) \cdot (b'_n, b'_{n-1}, \cdots, b'_1)$
$$= (b_n \cdot b'_n, b_{n-1} \cdot b'_{n-1}, \cdots, b_1 \cdot b'_1).$$

(c) $(\overline{b_n, b_{n-1}, \cdots, b_1}) = (\bar{b}_n, \bar{b}_{n-1}, \cdots, \bar{b}_1).$

Hence, addition, multiplication, and complementation of elements of B^n are performed "coordinate-wise." Evidently $1_{B^n} = (\overbrace{1, 1, \cdots, 1}^{n})$, $0_{B^n} = (\overbrace{0, 0, \cdots, 0}^{n})$, and B^n is a Boolean algebra having 2^n elements. (That B^n has 2^n elements may be easily proved by induction.)

While it may appear that the character of this Boolean algebra is completely different from that of other Boolean algebras we have described, we will now demonstrate that it is "abstractly equivalent" to one of our previous examples. Consider the Boolean algebra $\mathcal{P}(S)$ of Example 1.17 for the set

$$S = S_n = \{x_n, x_{n-1}, \cdots, x_1\}$$

and define the mapping

$$\gamma : \mathcal{P}(S_n) \longrightarrow B^n$$

in the following way: For $A \in \mathcal{P}(S_n)$ define $\gamma(A) = b$ to be that element $b = (b_n, b_{n-1}, \cdots, b_1) \in B^n$ for which

$$\begin{aligned} b_i &= 1 \text{ if } x_1 \in A \\ b_i &= 0 \text{ if } x_1 \notin A \end{aligned} \quad (i = 1, 2, \cdots, n)$$

Then γ is onto B^n, since for any element $b = (b_n, b_{n-1}, \cdots, b_1)$ in B^n, we can find a set $A \in \mathcal{P}(S_n)$ with $A \xrightarrow{\gamma} b$. (We need only take A as that subset of S_n that contains x_i if $b_i = 1$ and does not contain x_i if $b_i = 0$.)

Furthermore γ is 1–1, for if $b = (b_n, b_{n-1}, \cdots, b_1)$, $b' = (b'_n, b'_{n-1}, \cdots, b'_1)$ and $\gamma(A) = b$, $\gamma(A') = b'$

then

$$b = b' \Longrightarrow b_i = b'_i \quad \text{for all } i = 1, 2, \cdots, n$$
$$\Longrightarrow \begin{Bmatrix} b_i = 1 \Longleftrightarrow b'_i = 1 \\ b_i = 0 \Longleftrightarrow b'_i = 0 \end{Bmatrix}$$
$$\Longrightarrow \{x_i \in A \Longleftrightarrow x_i \in A'\} \Longrightarrow A = A'$$

Moreover, the map γ preserves the operations, $(+, \cdot, -)$ of the Boolean algebras, for if $A, A' \in \mathcal{P}(S_n)$, where

$$A \xrightarrow{\gamma} b = (b_n, b_{n-1}, \cdots, b_1)$$

and

$$A' \xrightarrow{\gamma} b' = (b'_n, b'_{n-1}, \cdots, b'_1)$$

then

$$
\begin{aligned}
\gamma(A + A') &= \gamma(A \cup A') \\
&= \gamma(\{x_i; \, x_i \in A \text{ or } x_i \in A'\}) \\
&= (b_n + b'_n, \, b_{n-1} + b'_{n-1}, \cdots, b_1 + b'_1) \\
&= (b_n, b_{n-1}, \cdots, b_1) + (b'_n, b'_{n-1}, \cdots, b'_1) \\
&= b + b' = \gamma(A) + \gamma(A')
\end{aligned}
$$

and, similarly,

$$\gamma(A \cdot A') = \gamma(A) \cdot \gamma(A')$$

while

$$
\begin{aligned}
\gamma(\bar{A}) &= \gamma(S_n - A) \\
&= \gamma(\{x_i; \, x_i \notin A\}) \\
&= (\bar{b}_n, \bar{b}_{n-1}, \cdots, \bar{b}_1) = \bar{b} = \overline{\gamma(A)}
\end{aligned}
$$

These computations show that the Boolean algebras $\mathscr{P}(S_n)$ and B^n are isomorphic, and we write

$$\mathscr{P}(S_n) \cong B^n$$

Hence, whatever we learn about the Boolean algebraic properties of B^n (for example, that is has 2^n elements) applies equally well to $\mathscr{P}(S_n)$, for these two algebras are abstractly indistinguishable.

1.9   RECAPITULATION, CLARIFICATION, AND PREVIEW

It is from Example 1.19 that we can gain considerable insight as to why the subject of Boolean algebra is so useful in the study of digital computer logic. The logic circuits introduced there, together with the memory elements which we encounter in Chapter 4, extract the essential features of electronic digital computer circuitry. They mirror the behavior of the electronic circuitry with sufficient retention of information to make possible their successful use in analyzing and synthesizing digital computer circuitry.

However, the first difficulty that one encounters is contained in the simple realization that these logic circuits are quite cumbersome to manipulate. This difficulty is largely overcome by the isomorphism

$$FB(n) \cong L(n)$$

which allows us to associate with each logic circuit a Boolean polynomial (more precisely, with each class of equivalent logic circuits a collection of equal, in FB(n), Boolean polynomials). Through this association we transform logic circuits into the more manageable algebraic expressions, to which the theorems of Boolean algebra can be readily applied, often yielding improvements in an already designed digital circuit or providing insight into synthesis techniques. Examples are sprinkled throughout the coming chapters and are too numerous to refer to at this time.

A second difficulty is implied by the parenthetical remark above. That is, we will find in Sec. 1.14 that infinitely many logic circuits of FL(n) (those within a particular equivalence class of L(n)) will have the same "input-output" characteristics, so that when viewed as "black boxes" they are indistinguishable. It is a part of the logical designer's business to be able to select economical representatives within a given class of equivalent logic circuits. And it is the switching theorist's concern to define criteria for economy and to develop effective algorithms or procedures for this selection process. These problems are of such importance that several chapters are devoted to their study.

We intended to devote this section to a recapitulation and clarification of Examples 1.18 and 1.19 and (insofar as this is possible with the material developed thus far) a preview of some of the problems we will later encounter in depth. However, before proceeding to the next section, it is well to enlarge the class FL(n) of logic circuits we have described thus far. In this description, we have no doubt given the reader the impression that, aside from the inverter circuit, we are willing to admit only two-input symbolic circuits of the "and" and "or" variety. This limitation is by no means consistent with reality (that is, available electronic circuits), and we will make little attempt to adhere to it in the future. We therefore enlarge the class of symbolic circuits to include the *m-input "and" circuit* and *m-input "or" circuit* of Fig. 1.12, whose logical characteristics

$x^{(1)} + \cdots + x^{(m)}$ is a "high" voltage wire $\Longleftrightarrow$ $x^{(i)}$ is "high" for some i

$x^{(1)} \times \cdots \times x^{(m)}$ is a "high" voltage wire $\Longleftrightarrow$ $x^{(i)}$ is "high" for every i

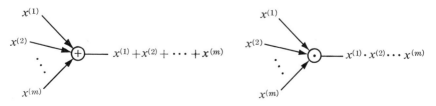

FIGURE 1.12

are obvious generalizations of those for the original *and* and *or* circuits. At the same time, we rename[†] FL(n) so as to include logic circuits that are built from these more general symbolic circuits. This convention is consistent with the observation that certain Boolean polynomials in FB(n) may be unambiguously written with several of their parentheses deleted, a direct consequence of the associativity of Boolean algebras.

EXAMPLE 1.22

To illustrate this new freedom, the logic circuit of Fig. 1.13 becomes an acceptable member of FL(2). Note that the corresponding Boolean polynomial might be written

$$0 + x_1 + (x_1 \cdot 1 \cdot \bar{x}_2) + (\bar{x}_2 \cdot 1)$$

where several parentheses have been deleted from the polynomial g of Examples 1.18 and 1.19.

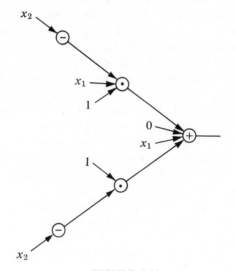

FIGURE 1.13

1.10 BOOLEAN POLYNOMIALS

In elementary calculus one introduces polynomials $F(x)$, $F(x, y)$, $F(x, y, z)$, etc., of one, two, three, or more real variables, of which

$$F(x, y, z) = 2x^2y + xy^2z$$

[†]We make an exception in Chapter 6.

is typical. Such a polynomial $F(x_n, x_{n-1}, \cdots, x_1)$ defines a function (also called F)

$$F : R^n \longrightarrow R$$

When the variables x_i assume the values

$$x_i = t_i \qquad (i = 1, 2, \cdots, n)$$

the "value" $F(t_n, t_{n-1}, \cdots, t_1)$ of this function is found by computing the real number obtained by substitution of t_i for x_i in the polynomial F.

EXAMPLE 1.23

If $F(x, y, z) = 2x^2y + xy^2z$,

$$F(2, -1, \tfrac{1}{4}) = 2(2)^2(-1) + 2(-1)^2(\tfrac{1}{4})$$
$$= -8 + \tfrac{1}{2} = -7\tfrac{1}{2}$$

is the "value" of the function when x, y, z assume the values

$$x = 2$$
$$y = -1$$
$$z = \tfrac{1}{4}$$

We write

$$F : (2, -1, \tfrac{1}{4}) \longrightarrow -7\tfrac{1}{2}{}'$$

to exhibit the correspondence that F establishes between the element (x, y, z) $= (2, -1, \tfrac{1}{4}) \in R^3$ and $-7\tfrac{1}{2} \in R$.

If $F(x_n, x_{n-1}, \cdots, x_1)$ is a polynomial in the real variables x_n, $x_{n-1}, \cdots, x_1$, the substitution of a particular value

$$x_i = t_i \in R$$

for the ith variable causes F to be transformed into a polynomial

$$G(x_n, x_{n-1}, \cdots, \hat{x}_i, \cdots x_1) = F(x_n, x_{n-1}, \cdots, \overset{i}{t_i} \cdots x_1)$$

in the remaining variables.[†]

EXAMPLE 1.24

In the preceding example, the substitution $y = 3$ causes F to be transformed into a polynomial

$$G(x, z) = F(x, 3, z) = 6x^2 + 9xz$$

in the variables x and z.

We have presented this brief excursion into the calculus of functions of real variables in order that the concept of a "Boolean function" might be better appreciated. By direct analogy to the above familiar situation,

[†]The placement of a caret (^) over a symbol serves to delete that symbol. Thus
$$G(x_n, x_{n-1}, \cdots, \hat{x}_i, \cdots, x_1) = G(x_n, x_{n-1}, \cdots, x_{i+1}, x_{i-1}, \cdots, x_1)$$

a Boolean polynomial $f(x_n, x_{n-1}, \cdots, x_1)$ defines a *Boolean function* (also called f); that is, a mapping

$$f : B^n \longrightarrow B$$

where $B = \{0. 1\}$. The *value* $f(b_n, b_{n-1}, \cdots, b_1)$ of f when the *Boolean variables* x_i assume the values

$$x_i = b_i \in B \qquad (i = 1, 2, \cdots, n)$$

is found by computing the element of B that the substitution of b_i for x_i yields in the polynomial f. Since these computations are performed in the Boolean algebra B(cf. Example 1.16), they automatically yield 0 or 1 as their result.

Completing the analogy between polynomials in n real variables and Boolean polynomials, we note that the replacement

$$x_i = b_i \in B$$

of the ith variable by an element of B serves to transform f into a polynomial

$$g(x_n, x_{n-1}, \cdots, \hat{x}_i, \cdots, x_1) = f(x_n, x_{n-1}, \cdots, \overset{i}{b_i}, \cdots, x_1)$$

in the remaining $n - 1$ variables.

In this framework we phrase our first result (the Shannon expansion theorem[†]) concerning Boolean polynomials.

Theorem 1.11   Every Boolean polynomial $f(_n, x_{n-1}, \cdots, x_1)$ can be expanded (for each $i = 1, 2, \cdots, n$) in the form

$$f(x_n, \cdots, x_i, \cdots, x_1)$$
$$= f(x_n, \cdots, \overset{i}{1}, \cdots, x_1) \cdot x_i + f(x_n, \cdots, \overset{i}{0}, \cdots, x_1) \cdot \bar{x}_i \quad \textbf{(1.23)}$$

or in the form

$$f(x_n, \cdots, x_i, \cdots, x_1)$$
$$= [f(x_n, \cdots, \overset{i}{0}, \cdots, x_1) + x_i] \cdot [f(x_n, \cdots, \overset{i}{1}, \cdots, x_1) + \bar{x}_i]$$

PROOF.   Since the two forms are easily seen to be dual, we will prove only the first expansion. First of all, we certainly have such an expansion for the particular polynomials:

$$f_1(x_n, x_{n-1}, \cdots, x_1) \equiv 0 = 0 \cdot x_i + 0 \cdot \bar{x}_i$$
$$= f_1(x_n, \cdots, \overset{i}{1}, \cdots, x_1) \cdot x_i$$
$$+ f_1(x_n, \cdots, \overset{i}{0}, \cdots, x_1) \cdot \bar{x}_i$$

$$f_2(x_n, x_{n-1}, \cdots, x_1) \equiv x_i = 1 \cdot x_i + 0 \cdot \bar{x}_i$$
$$= f_2(x_n, \cdots, \overset{i}{1}, \cdots, x_1) \cdot x_i$$
$$+ f_2(x_n, \cdots, \overset{i}{0}, \cdots, x_1) \cdot \bar{x}_i$$

[†]C. E. Shannon, "The Synthesis of Two-Terminal Switching Circuits," *Bell System Tech. Jour.*, 28 (1949).

$$f_3(x_n, x_{n-1}, \cdots, x_1) \equiv x_j = x_j \cdot x_i + x_j \cdot \bar{x}_i$$
$$= f_3(x_n, \cdots, \overset{i}{1}, \cdots, x_1) \cdot x_i$$
$$+ f_3(x_n, \cdots, \overset{i}{0}, \cdots, x_1) \cdot \bar{x}_i \qquad (j \neq i)$$

Now, by the way in which Boolean polynomials are constructed (from f_1, f_2, f_3, using addition, multiplication, and complementation), it suffices to show that if $g(x_n, x_{n-1}, \cdots, x_1)$ and $h(x_n, x_{n-1}, \cdots, x_1)$ are any two Boolean polynomials that have the expansion property with respect to the Boolean variable x_i, then the polynomials $g + h$, $g \cdot h$, and $\bar{g}$ also have the property. So suppose g and h have the expansion property. Then

$$(g + h)(x_n, \cdots, x_i \cdots, x_1)$$
$$= g(x_n, \cdots, x_i, \cdots, x_1) + h(x_n, \cdots, x_i, \cdots, x_1)$$
$$= g(x_n, \cdots, 1, \cdots, x_1) \cdot x_i + g(x_n, \cdots, 0, \cdots, x_1) \cdot \bar{x}_i$$
$$+ h(x_n, \cdots, 1, \cdots, x_1) \cdot x_i + h(x_n, \cdots, 0, \cdots, x_1) \cdot \bar{x}_i$$
$$= [g(x_n, \cdots, 1, \cdots, x_1) + h(x_n, \cdots, 1, \cdots, x_1)] \cdot x_i$$
$$+ [g(x_n, \cdots, 0, \cdots, x_1) + h(x_n, \cdots, 0, \cdots, x_1)] \cdot \bar{x}_i$$
$$= [(g + h)(x_n, \cdots, 1, \cdots, x_1)] \cdot x_i$$
$$+ [(g + h)(x_n, \cdots, 0, \cdots, x_1)] \cdot \bar{x}_i$$

and similarly for $g \cdot h$, while

$$\overline{g(x_n, \cdots, x_i, \cdots, x_1)}$$
$$= \overline{g(x_n, \cdots, 1, \cdots, x_1) \cdot x_i + g(x_n, \cdots, 0, \cdots, x_1) \cdot \bar{x}_i}$$
$$= \overline{g(x_n, \cdots, 1, \cdots, x_1)} \cdot x_i + \overline{g(x_n, \cdots, 0, \cdots, x_1)} \cdot x_i$$

where we have used property P10a in the last equality. ∎

EXAMPLE 1.25

Let

$$f(x_3, x_2, x_1) = (x_1 + x_2) \cdot \overline{(x_1 \cdot x_2 + \bar{x}_1 \cdot x_3)} + \bar{x}_3$$

and suppose we compute Shannon's first expansion with respect to the variable x_1. We have

$$f(x_3, x_2, 1) = (1 + x_2) \cdot \overline{(1 \cdot x_2 + 0 \cdot x_3)} + \bar{x}_3$$
$$= (1 + x_2) \cdot (\bar{x}_2) + \bar{x}_3 = \bar{x}_2 + \bar{x}_3$$
$$f(x_3, x_2, 0) = (0 + x_2) \cdot \overline{(0 \cdot x_2 + 1 \cdot x_3)} + \bar{x}_3$$
$$= x_2(0) + \bar{x}_3 = \bar{x}_3$$

so that we obtain the expansion

$$f(x_3, x_2, x_1) = (x_2 + \bar{x}_3) \cdot x_1 + (\bar{x}_3) \cdot \bar{x}_1$$

EXAMPLE 1.26

Consider the same function $f(x_3, x_2, x_1)$ as in Example 1.25. If, instead, we want the *second* Shannon expansion with respect to the variable x_2, we write

$$f(x_3, 0, x_1) = (x_1 + 0) \cdot (\overline{x_1 \cdot 0 + \bar{x}_1 \cdot x_3}) + \bar{x}_3$$
$$= x_1 \cdot (0) + \bar{x}_3 = \bar{x}_3$$
$$f(x_3, 1, x_1) = (x_1 + 1) \cdot (\overline{x_1 \cdot 1 + \bar{x}_1 \cdot x_3}) + \bar{x}_3$$
$$= (1)(\overline{\bar{x}_1 + \bar{x}_1 x_3}) + \bar{x}_3$$
$$= (1)(x_1) + \bar{x}_3 = x_1 + \bar{x}_3$$

and then, according to Eq. 1.24,

$$f(x_3, x_2, x_1) = [(\bar{x}_3) + x_2] \cdot [(x_1 + \bar{x}_3) + \bar{x}_2]$$

Beginning with Shannon's expansion theorem, we are aiming toward standard or canonical forms for expressing Boolean polynomials. (The situation is somewhat analogous to the desire for standard forms—Fourier series, Taylor series, etc.—for expressing functions of real variables.) Meanwhile, we must introduce the "minterms" and "maxterms," which serve as the fundamental constituents in the canonical expansions.

1.11 MINTERMS AND MAXTERMS

Suppose that in the interest of notational convenience, we agree to use parenthetical exponents 0, 1 (elements of B) on Boolean variables in the following sense:

$$x_i^{(0)} \equiv \bar{x}_i \qquad x_i^{(1)} \equiv x_i$$

Then, a product of the form

$$x_n^{(b_n)} x_{n-1}^{(b_{n-1})} \cdots x_1^{(b_1)} \qquad (b_i \in B)$$

is called a *minterm* of the n Boolean variables $x_n, x_{n-1}, \cdots, x_1$, while a sum

$$x_n^{(b_n)} + x_{n-1}^{(b_{n-1})} + \cdots + x_1^{(b_1)} \qquad (b_i \in B)$$

is called a *maxterm* of these n variables.

EXAMPLE 1.27

If $n = 4$,

$$\bar{x}_4 x_3 x_2 \bar{x}_1 = x_4^{(0)} x_3^{(1)} x_2^{(1)} x_1^{(0)}$$

is a minterm of the four Boolean variables x_4, x_3, x_2, x_1, whereas the product $\bar{x}_4 x_2 \bar{x}_1$ is not a minterm of these variables. Similarly

$$\bar{x}_4 + x_3 + \bar{x}_2 + \bar{x}_1 = x_4^{(0)} + x_3^{(1)} + x_2^{(0)} + x_1^{(0)}$$

is a maxterm of these four variables.

We mentioned in Example 1.21 that for every integer $n \geq 1$, B^n has 2^n elements. On account of the notation we have chosen for representing minterms and maxterms, it follows immediately that *there are exactly 2^n minterms and 2^n maxterms of n Boolean variables.* Furthermore, using the result of Prob. 0.13, we find that these minterms and maxterms are related by the following theorem.

Theorem 1.12 The complement of any minterm is a maxterm, and conversely. Moreover, when they are labeled with subscripts (cf. Eq. 0.66)

$$x_n^{(b_n)} x_{n-1}^{(b_{n-1})} \cdots x_1^{(b_1)} \equiv m_i \longleftrightarrow \partial(b_n, b_{n-1}, \cdots, b_1) = i \qquad (1.25)$$

$$x_n^{(b_n)} + x_{n-1}^{(b_{n-1})} + \cdots + x_1^{(b_1)} \equiv M_j \longleftrightarrow \partial(b_n, \cdots, b_1) = j \qquad (1.26)$$

then

$$\bar{m}_i = M_{2^n-1-i} \qquad (1.27)$$

$$\bar{M}_j = m_{2^n-1-j} \qquad (1.28)$$

PROOF. Suppose $m_i = x_n^{(b_n)} x_{n-1}^{(b_{n-1})} \cdots x_1^{(b_1)}$, where

$$\partial(b_n, b_{n-1}, \cdots, b_1) = i$$

Then, by De Morgan's theorem,

$$\bar{m}_i = x_n^{(\bar{b}_{n-1})} + x_{n-1}^{(\bar{b}_{n-1})} + \cdots + x_1^{(\bar{b}_1)} = M_k$$

where, according to Eq. 1.26,

$$\partial(\bar{b}_n, \bar{b}_{n-1}, \cdots, \bar{b}_1) = k$$

By Prob. 0.13 and Eq. 0.66,

$$i + k = \sum_{i=1}^{n} b_i 2^{i-1} + \sum_{i=1}^{n} \bar{b}_i 2^{i-1}$$

$$= \sum_{i=1}^{n} (b_i + \bar{b}_i) 2^{i-1}$$

$$= \sum_{i=1}^{n} 2^{i-1} = 2^n - 1$$

which is the result we need to conclude $\bar{m}_i = M_{2^n-1-i}$. Similarly, one shows $\bar{M}_j = m_{2^n-1-j}$. ∎

EXAMPLE 1.28

Consider the minterm of Example 1.27:

$$m_6 = \bar{x}_4 x_3 x_2 \bar{x}_1 = x_4^{(0)} x_3^{(1)} x_2^{(1)} x_1^{(0)} \qquad (\partial(0, 1, 1, 0) = 6)$$

We have, since $n = 4$,

$$\bar{m}_6 = M_{2^4-1-6} = M_9 = x_4^{(1)} + x_3^{(0)} + x_2^{(0)} + x_1^{(1)}$$
$$= x_4 + \bar{x}_3 + \bar{x}_2 + x_1$$

In addition to Theorem 1.11, minterms and maxterms satisfy the properties expressed in the following theorem.

Theorem 1.13   The Boolean sum of all 2^n minterms of n Boolean variables is the identity

$$\sum_{i=0}^{2^n-1} m_i = 1 \tag{1.29}$$

and the pairwise product of two distinct minterms is zero:

$$m_i \cdot m_k = 0 \qquad (i \neq k) \tag{1.30}$$

Dually, the Boolean product of all 2^n maxterms is zero:

$$\prod_{j=0}^{2^n-1} M_j = 0 \tag{1.31}$$

whereas the sum of two distinct maxterms is the identity:

$$M_j + M_k = 1 \qquad (j \neq k) \tag{1.32}$$

PROOF.   For the first assertion about minterms, we use an inductive argument. If $n = 1$,

$$\sum_{i=0}^{2^n-1} m_i = \sum_{i=0}^{1} m_i = x_1^{(0)} + x_1^{(1)} = \bar{x}_1 + x_1 = 1$$

If we suppose that for some $n \geq 1$,

$$\sum_{i=0}^{2^n-1} m_i = 1$$

we use the Shannon expansion theorem with respect to the variable x_{n+1}, to imply that the sum of all minterms of $n + 1$ variables is necessarily 1:

$$\sum_{i=0}^{2^{n+1}-1} m_i = \sum_{b \in B^{n+1}} x_{n+1}^{(b_{n+1})} x_n^{(b_n)} x_{n-1}^{(b_{n-1})} \cdots x_1^{(b_1)}$$

$$= \left(\sum_{b \in B^n} x_n^{(b_n)} x_{n-1}^{(b_{n-1})} \cdots x_1^{(b_1)}\right) \cdot x_{n+1}$$

$$+ \left(\sum_{b \in B^n} x_n^{(b_n)} x_{n-1}^{(b_{n-1})} \cdots x_1^{(b_1)}\right) \cdot \bar{x}_{n+1}$$

$$= \left(\sum_{i=0}^{2^n-1} m_i\right) \cdot x_{n+1} + \left(\sum_{i=0}^{2^n-1} m_i\right) \cdot \bar{x}_{n+1}$$

$$= 1 \cdot x_{n+1} + 1 \cdot \bar{x}_{n+1} = x_{n+1} + \bar{x}_{n+1} = 1$$

Now consider two distinct minterms, m_i and m_j:

$$m_i = x_n^{(b_n)} x_{n-1}^{(b_{n-1})} \cdots x_1^{(b_1)}$$

$$m_j = x_n^{(b'_n)} x_{n-1}^{(b'_{n-1})} \cdots x_1^{(b'_1)}$$

If they are distinct, then for some index k, $1 \leq k \leq n$, we must have

$$b_k \neq b'_k$$

Without loss of generality, suppose $b_k = 0$, $b'_k = 1$. Then

$$m_i \cdot m_j = 0$$

because $x_k^{(b_k)} \cdot x_k^{(b'_k)} = \bar{x}_k \cdot x_k = 0$. ∎

As usual, we omit the proof of the dual statements regarding maxterms.

1.12 CANONICAL FORMS

We return now to the study of arbitrary Boolean polynomials $f(x_n, x_{n-1}, \cdots, x_1)$ in n Boolean variables. If Shannon's first expansion is performed on such a polynomial with respect to the first variable x_1, we obtain

$$f(x_n, x_{n-1}, \cdots, x_1) = f(x_n, x_{n-1}, \cdots, x_2, 1) \cdot x_1$$
$$+ f(x_n, x_{n-1}, \cdots, x_2, 0) \cdot \bar{x}_1$$

We notice that the factors $f(x_n, x_{n-1}, \cdots, x_2, 1)$ and $f(x_n, x_{n-1}, \cdots, x_2, 0)$ in this expansion are themselves Boolean polynomials in $n - 1$ variables: $x_n, x_{n-1}, \cdots, x_2$ (cf. Sec. 1.9); therefore, we can perform similar expansions with respect to the variable x_2 on these two polynomials, and we obtain

$$f(x_n, x_{n-1}, \cdots, x_1) = f(x_n, x_{n-1}, \cdots, x_3, 1, 1) \cdot x_2 x_1$$
$$+ f(x_n, x_{n-1}, \cdots, x_3, 1, 0) \cdot x_2 \bar{x}_1$$
$$+ f(x_n, x_{n-1}, \cdots, x_3, 0, 1) \cdot \bar{x}_2 x_1$$
$$+ f(x_n, x_{n-1}, \cdots, x_3, 0, 0) \cdot \bar{x}_2 \bar{x}_1$$

Repeating this process a total of n times yields the representation

$$f(x_n, x_{n-1}, \cdots, x_1) = f(1, 1, \cdots, 1. 1, 1)x_n x_{n-1} \cdots x_3 x_2 x_1$$
$$+ f(1, 1, \cdots, 1, 1, 0)x_n x_{n-1} \cdots x_3 x_2 \bar{x}_1$$
$$+ f(1, 1, \cdots, 1, 0, 1)x_n x_{n-1} \cdots x_3 \bar{x}_2 x_1$$
$$+ \cdots + f(0, 0, \cdots, 0, 0, 0)\bar{x}_n \bar{x}_{n-1} \cdots \bar{x}_3 \bar{x}_2 \bar{x}_1$$
$$= \sum_{b \in B^n} f(b_n, b_{n-1}, \cdots, b_1)x_n^{(b_n)}x_{n-1}^{(b_{n-1})} \cdots x_1^{(b_1)} \quad \textbf{(1.33)}$$

which is called the *minterm canonical form* of the Boolean function f. (This is one of the generalizations of Theorem 1.4 we were seeking.) Since its coefficients $f(b_n, b_{n-1}, \cdots, b_1)$ are elements of $B = \{0, 1\}$, the minterm canonical form is simply a sum of products in which each product is a minterm. A minterm $x_n^{(b_n)} \cdot x_{n-1}^{(b_{n-1})} \cdots x_1^{(b_1)}$ appears as a term in the minterm canonical form of f if and only if $f(b_n, b_{n-1}, \cdots, b_1) = 1$.

Alternatively, we could have applied Shannon's second expansion to $f(x_n, x_{n-1}, \cdots, x_1)$ a total of n times, with the dual result

$$f(x_n, x_{n-1}, \cdots, x_1) = \prod_{b \in B^n} [f(\bar{b}_n, \bar{b}_{n-1}, \cdots, \bar{b}_1)$$

$$+ x_n^{(b_n)} + x_{n-1}^{(b_{n-1})} + \cdots + x_1^{(b_1)})] \tag{1.34}$$

This dual representation is called the *maxterm canonical form* of f. Again the coefficients are elements of B, so that the maxterm canonical form is a product of sums in which each sum is a maxterm. A particular maxterm $x_n^{(b_n)} + x_{n-1}^{(b_{n-1})} + \cdots + x_1^{(b_1)}$ appears as a factor in the maxterm canonical form of f if and only if $f(\bar{b}_n, \bar{b}_{n-1}, \cdots, \bar{b}_1) = 0$.

EXAMPLE 1.29

Suppose we illustrate the derivation of these canonical forms with the polynomial

$$f(x_3, x_2, x_1) = (x_2 + \bar{x}_3) \cdot x_1 + \bar{x}_3 \cdot \bar{x}_1$$

which has been introduced in Example 1.25. We can obtain both canonical forms as soon as we compute the coefficients:

$$f(0, 0, 0) = (0 + \bar{0}) \cdot 0 + \bar{0} \cdot \bar{0}$$
$$= (0 + 1) \cdot 0 + 1 \cdot 1 = 1$$
$$f(0, 0, 1) = 1$$
$$f(0, 1, 0) = 1$$
$$f(0, 1, 1) = 1$$
$$f(1, 0, 0) = 0$$
$$f(1, 0, 1) = 0$$
$$f(1, 1, 0) = 0$$
$$f(1, 1, 1) = 1$$

Substitution of these coefficients in Eqs. 1.33 and 1.34 yields the minterm and maxterm canonical forms

$$f(x_3, x_2, x_1) = \bar{x}_3 \bar{x}_2 \bar{x}_1 + \bar{x}_3 \bar{x}_2 x_1 + \bar{x}_3 x_2 \bar{x}_1 + \bar{x}_3 x_2 x_1 + x_3 x_2 x_1$$

and

$$f(x_3, x_2, x_1) = (\bar{x}_3 + \bar{x}_2 + x_1)(\bar{x}_3 + x_2 + \bar{x}_1)(\bar{x}_3 + x_2 + x_1)$$

respectively. In our alternate (subscripted) notation these become

$$f(x_3, x_2, x_1) = m_0 + m_1 + m_2 + m_3 + m_7$$
$$f(x_3, x_2, x_1) = M_1 M_2 M_3$$

Note that if one or the other of the two canonical forms is given in this subscripted notation, the other can be found from DeMorgan's theorem and Theorems 1.12 and 1.13. Suppose, for example, that we know only

$$f = m_0 + m_1 + m_2 + m_3 + m_7$$

Then, by Eq. 1.29,

$$\bar{f} = m_4 + m_5 + m_6$$

so that

$$f = \bar{m}_4 \cdot \bar{m}_5 \cdot \bar{m}_6 = M_{7-4} M_{7-5} M_{7-6} = M_3 M_2 M_1$$

using DeMorgan's theorem and Eq. 1.27. The process for converting a maxterm canonical form to minterm form is completely dual.

1.13   TRUTH TABLES

With each Boolean polynomial $f(x_n, x_{n-1}, \cdots, x_1) \in \mathrm{FB}(n)$ we associate a *Boolean function*

$$f : B^n \longrightarrow B$$

according to the method of Sec. 1.10, that is,

$$(b_n, b_{n-1}, \cdots, b_1) \overset{f}{\longrightarrow} 1 \qquad \text{if} \quad f(b_n, b_{n-1}, \cdots, b_1) = 1$$
$$(b_n, b_{n-1}, \cdots, b_1) \overset{f}{\longrightarrow} 0 \qquad \text{if} \quad f(b_n, b_{n-1}, \cdots, b_1) = 0$$

When we wish to emphasize the distinction between such functions and the "incompletely specified Boolean functions," to be introduced in Chapter 3, we will call the former *completely specified*.

EXAMPLE 1.30

Again we utilize the polynominal

$$f(x_3, x_2, x_1) = (x_2 + \bar{x}_3) \cdot x_1 + \bar{x}_3 \bar{x}_1$$

From the calculations of Example 1.29 we see that this polynomial determines the Boolean function

$$(0, 0, 0) \overset{f}{\longrightarrow} 1$$
$$(0, 0, 1) \overset{f}{\longrightarrow} 1$$
$$(0, 1, 0) \overset{f}{\longrightarrow} 1$$
$$(0, 1, 1) \overset{f}{\longrightarrow} 1$$
$$(1, 0, 0) \overset{f}{\longrightarrow} 0$$
$$(1, 0, 1) \overset{f}{\longrightarrow} 0$$
$$(1, 1, 0) \overset{f}{\longrightarrow} 0$$
$$(1, 1, 1) \overset{f}{\longrightarrow} 1$$

which is more commomly displayed in the tabular form

x_3 x_2 x_1	f
0 0 0	1
0 0 1	1
0 1 0	1
0 1 1	1
1 0 0	0
1 0 1	0
1 1 0	0
1 1 1	1

and is then known as the *truth table* of the Boolean polynomial (of n variables).

Now consider the element $\rho(f) \in FL(3)$, which corresponds (cf. Example 1.19) to the polynomial

$$f(x_3, x_2, x_1) = (x_2 + \bar{x}_3) \cdot x_1 + \bar{x}_3 \bar{x}_1$$

(See Fig. 1.14.)

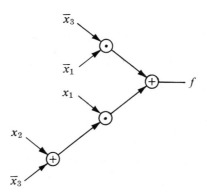

FIGURE 1.14

The preceding truth table gives the output (1 or 0) of the "black box"

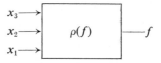

for all $2^3 = 8$ combinations of the input wires as high (1) or low (0) voltages. Thus, if x_3 is high, x_2 is low, and x_1 is high, we find from the sixth row of the truth table that the output will be low. Evidently the truth table completely characterizes the digital behavior of the circuit $\rho(f)$, thus explaining their usefulness in the analysis of digital circuits.

The synthesis techniques for the design of digital circuits necessarily proceeds in the opposite direction from the line of reasoning given in the preceding example. The logical designer is presented (or presents himself) with a truth table of n variables, which describes a desired "black box" digital behavior. The synthesis problem then becomes one of finding an acceptable and economical logic circuit $c \in FL(n)$ that is acceptable in the sense that the truth table of $\rho^{-1}(c)$ is the given truth table, and economical in the sense that the cost of fabricating c is relatively inexpensive when compared (by some cost criterion) with other circuits c' for which $\rho^{-1}(c')$ has the given truth table.

EXAMPLE 1.31

In adding two integers expressed in the base 2 (cf. Sec. 0.13), using pencil and paper,

$$c_{i-1}$$

$$x_p x_{p-1} \cdots x_i x_{i-1} \cdots x_1 x_0. \qquad (x_i \in B)$$

$$+ y_q y_{q-1} \cdots y_i y_{i-1} \cdots y_1 y_0. \qquad (y_i \in B)$$

$$\cdots z_i z_{i-1} \cdots z_1 z_0. \qquad (z_i \in B)$$

one must utilize the addition tables

+	0	1
0	0	1
1	1	^{1}0

in order to determine the sum digit (*bit* is the more commonly used term) z_i, which results from adding x_i, y_i, and the previous "carry" c_{i-1}. If, instead, this operation were to be mechanized, one would seek a logic circuit c having the behavior of the truth table:

c_{i-1}	x_i	y_i	z_i
0	0	0	0
0	0	1	1
0	1	0	1
0	1	1	0
1	0	0	1
1	0	1	0
1	1	0	0
1	1	1	1

which summarizes the desired outcome z_i for all eight possibilities for x_i, y_i, and c_{i-1}. (Evidently one also needs a circuit that will generate the "carry" c_i to be used for the addition of x_{i+1} and y_{i+1}.) We do not yet have criteria for comparing acceptable circuits for relative economy, but we can at least give one acceptable circuit. One has only to ask for the minterm (for example) canonical form of any Boolean polynomial $z_i = f(c_{i-1}, x_i, y_i)$, that has the given truth table. Reflecting on Examples 1.29 and 1.30, we see that

$$f(c_{i-1}, x_i, y_i) = m_1 + m_2 + m_4 + m_7$$

$$= \bar{c}_{i-1} \bar{x}_i y_i + \bar{c}_{i-1} x_i \bar{y}_i + c_{i-1} \bar{x}_i \bar{y}_i + c_{i-1} x_i y_i$$

is the desired canonical form, so that the circuit of Fig. 1.15 is acceptable in that is behaves as specified by the given truth table. As yet, however, we can make no claims as to its relative economy.

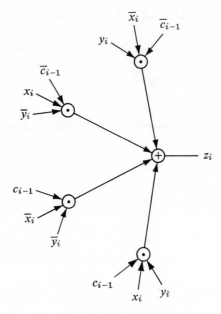

FIGURE 1.15

1.14 COMPLETELY SPECIFIED BOOLEAN FUNCTIONS

In the remarks of Sec. 1.9 and the examples of Sec. 1.13 we have seen the importance of completely specified Boolean functions (c.s.b.f.'s) or truth tables in the design of digital circuits. It is therefore of interest to know *how many* (completely specified) *Boolean functions of n variables exist*, and we find the answer in the following theorem.

Theorem 1.14 There are 2^{2^n} completely specified Boolean functions of n variables.

PROOF. A c.s.b.f. f of n variables is a mapping

$$f : B^n \longrightarrow B$$

We know that B^n has 2^n elements. Thus the one-dimensional array (column) of images of f is an element of B^{2^n} (written vertically rather than horizontally). Since the set B^{2^n} has 2^{2^n} elements and two c.s.b.f.'s f and g are regarded as *equal* iff they are identical as functions, that is, iff

$$f(b_n, b_{n-1}, \cdots, b_1) = g(b_n, b_{n-1}, \cdots, b_1)$$
$$\text{for all } (b_n, b_{n-1}, \cdots, b_1) \in B^n$$

we have reached the desired conclusion. ∎

Corollary 1.15

$$|\text{FB}(n)| = |\text{L}(n)| = 2^{2^n}$$

PROOF. FB(n) would appear to be an infinite set (because of the way it was constructed) except for the observation that to any given Boolean polynomial $f(x_n, x_{n-1}, \cdots, x_1)$, there corresponds an infinite number of polynomials, each equal to the given one in the Boolean algebra FB(n). Their corresponding logic circuits belong to the same equivalence class in FL(n), and their corresponding c.s.b.f.'s (truth tables) are identical. Thus

$$c_1 \sim c_2 \text{ in FL}(n) \Longleftrightarrow \rho^{-1}(c_1) \text{ and } \rho^{-1}(c_2) \text{ have the same truth table.}$$

Hence

$$|\text{FB}(n)| = |\text{L}(n)| = \text{number of equivalence classes}$$
$$\text{in FL}(n)$$
$$= \text{number of c.s.b.f.'s of } n$$
$$\text{variables}$$
$$= 2^{2^n} \ \blacksquare$$

This number 2^{2^n} grows quite rapidly with n, as pointed out in Table 1.1.

n	2^{2^n}
1	4
2	16
3	256
4	65,536
5	$\approx 4 \cdot 10^9$

TABLE 1.1

This fact helps to account for the large number of unsolved problems in switching theory.

Let $B(n)(\cong \text{FB}(n))$ denote the set of all c.s.b.f.'s of n variables; that is,

$$B(n) = \{f; f : B^n \longrightarrow B\} \tag{1.35}$$

When n is small ($n = 1, 2, 3$), some form of enumeration of the elements of $B(n)$ is useful in order that "catalogs" of logic circuits may be constructed. It is no doubt apparent when $n = 1$ that $B(n)$ consists of the

x_1	f_0	f_1	f_2	f_3
0	0	1	0	1
1	0	0	1	1

TABLE 1.2

four c.s.b.f.'s of Table 1.2, usually denoted

$$f_0(x_1) = 0$$
$$f_1(x_1) = \bar{x}_1$$
$$f_2(x_1) = x_1$$
$$f_4(x_1) = 1$$

respectively. Similarly, Table 1.3 is a representation of the 16 c.s.b.f.'s of $B(2)$, several of which are of such importance as to have "names."

$x_2\ x_1$	f_0	f_1	f_2	f_3	f_4	f_5	f_6	f_7	f_8	f_9	f_{10}	f_{11}	f_{12}	f_{13}	f_{14}	f_{15}
0 0	0	1	0	1	0	1	0	1	0	1	0	1	0	1	0	1
0 1	0	0	1	1	0	0	1	1	0	0	1	1	0	0	1	1
1 0	0	0	0	0	1	1	1	1	0	0	0	0	1	1	1	1
1 1	0	0	0	0	0	0	0	0	1	1	1	1	1	1	1	1

TABLE 1.3

The reader will want to compare the truth tables of the "or" function f_{14} and the "and" function f_8 with the behavior of the "or" circuit and the "and" circuit of Example 1.19. The function f_6 is commonly called the "exclusive or" function, since

$$f_6(x_2, x_1) = 1 \iff \begin{cases} x_2 = 1 \\ \text{or} \\ x_1 = 1 \end{cases} \quad \text{(but not both)}$$

The notation

$$f_6(x_2, x_1) = x_2 \oplus x_1$$

is often used in place of the minterm canonical form

$$f_6(x_2, x_1) = m_1 + m_2 = \bar{x}_2 x_1 + x_2 \bar{x}_1$$

of the truth table f_6. If it is necessary to make a distinction, f_{14} is called the *inclusive or* function.

The function $f_1(x_2, x_1) = \bar{x}_2 \bar{x}_1$ is sometimes written $x_2 \downarrow x_1$ and read as "x_2 Pierce x_1," after the American logician C. Pierce. This function has the interesting property that through its exclusive use, one can construct any Boolean function. A proof of this statement could be based on the following program:

(1) Show that the "or" function can be constructed by using the "and" function and complementation. (Cf. P9a). (Note that this statement alone shows that we can construct any Boolean function by using only complementation and the "and" function).

(2) Show that the "and" function can be constructed by using "Pierce" functions alone.

(3) Show that complementation can be acheived by using the "Pierce" function alone.

The construction of such a proof would be an illuminating exercise for the reader.

This property of the "Pierce" function, then, has an obvious practical application, which should be transparent in the light of Examples 1.18 and 1.19.

Note that each function f of Tables 1.2 and 1.3 bears a subscript $\eta(f)$ (the *characteristic number* of f), defined for $f \in B(n)$ by

$$\eta(f) = \sum_{b \in B^n} f(b_n, b_{n-1}, \cdots, b_1) 2^{\partial(b_n, b_{n-1}, \cdots, b_1)} \qquad (1.36)$$

Thus, the characteristic number of the "or" function f is

$$\eta(f) = \sum_{b \in B^2} f(b_2, b_1) 2^{\partial(b_2, b_1)}$$

$$= f(0, 0) 2^{\partial(0, 0)} + f(0, 1) 2^{\partial(0, 1)} + f(1, 0) 2^{\partial(1, 0)}$$
$$+ f(1, 1) 2^{\partial(1, 1)}$$

$$= 0 \cdot 2^0 + 1 \cdot 2^1 + 1 \cdot 2^2 + 1 \cdot 2^3 = 14$$

*1.15 EQUIVALENCE RELATIONS ON $B(n)$

To partially compensate for the large number 2^{2^n} obtained in Theorem 1.14, we define a relation $\cong$ on the set $B(n)$ by writing $f \cong g$ iff there exists a permutation $\pi : n^+ \dashrightarrow n^+$ (cf. Example 0.12) and an element $b \in B^n$ such that

$$f(x_n, x_{n-1}, \cdots, x_1) = g(x_{\pi(n)}^{(b_{\pi(n)})}, x_{\pi(n-1)}^{(b_{\pi(n-1)})}, \cdots, x_{\pi(1)}^{(b_{\pi(1)})}) \qquad (1.37)$$

Concerning this definition, we immediately establish the next theorem.

Theorem 1.16   The relation $\cong$ is an equivalence relation on $B(n)$.

PROOF.   For reflexivity, take

$$\pi = 1 = 1_{n^+} \quad \text{and} \quad b = \overbrace{(1, 1, \cdots, 1)}^{n}$$

for then

$$f(x_n, x_{n-1}, \cdots, x_1) = f(x_{1(n)}^{(1)}, x_{1(n-1)}^{(1)}, \cdots, x_{1(1)}^{(1)})$$

showing $f \cong f$ for any $f \in B(n)$.

If we suppose $f \cong g$, so that there exists a permutation $\pi : n^+ \longrightarrow n^+$ and an element $b \in B^n$ for which

$$f(x_n, x_{n-1}, \cdots, x_1) = g(x_{\pi(n)}^{(b_{\pi(n)})}, x_{\pi(n-1)}^{(b_{\pi(n-1)})}, \cdots, x_{\pi(1)}^{(b_{\pi(1)})})$$

we simply consider the permutation π^{-1} and the element

$$a = (a_n, a_{n-1}, \cdots, a_1) = (b_{\pi(n)}, b_{\pi(n-1)}, \cdots, b_{\pi(1)})$$

in B^n. After a change of variables,

$$x_j = y_{\pi(j)}^{(b_{\pi(j)})} \qquad (j = 1, 2, \cdots, n) \tag{1.38}$$

we can write

$$\begin{aligned}
g(x_n, x_{n-1}, \cdots, x_1) &= g(y_{\pi(n)}^{(b_{\pi(n)})}, y_{\pi(n-1)}^{(b_{\pi(n-1)})}, \cdots, y_{\pi(1)}^{(b_{\pi(1)})}) \\
&= f(y_n, y_{n-1}, \cdots, y_1) \\
&= f(x_{\pi^{-1}(n)}^{(b_n)}, x_{\pi^{-1}(n-1)}^{(b_{n-1})}, \cdots, x_{\pi^{-1}(1)}^{(b_1)}) \\
&= f(x_{\pi^{-1}(n)}^{(a_{\pi^{-1}(n)})}, x_{\pi^{-1}(n)}^{(a_{\pi^{-1}(n-1)})}, \cdots, x_{\pi^{-1}(1)}^{(a_{\pi^{-1}(1)})})
\end{aligned}$$

since

$$y_j = x_{\pi^{-1}(j)}^{(b_j)} \qquad (j = 1, 2. \cdots, n)$$

This shows that $\cong$ is symmetric. We leave the verification of transitivity as an exercise. ∎

According to Theorem 0.3, the relation $\cong$ partitions $B(n)$ into nonoverlapping classes of equivalent functions. From the definition (Eq. 1.37), these classes must consist of functions that are obtained from one another by permutation and complementation of variables.

EXAMPLE 1.32

Suppose

$$f(x_3, x_2, x_1) = \bar{x}_3\bar{x}_2 + x_3x_2\bar{x}_1 = f_{67}$$
$$g(x_3, x_2, x_1) = x_3x_1 + \bar{x}_3\bar{x}_2\bar{x}_1 = f_{161}$$

with truth tables shown in Table 1.4 (note our use of characteristic numbers).

x_3	x_2	x_1	f_{67}	f_{161}
0	0	0	1	1
0	0	1	1	0
0	1	0	0	0
0	1	1	0	0
1	0	0	0	0
1	0	1	0	1
1	1	0	1	0
1	1	1	0	1

TABLE 1.4

Then $f \cong g$ because

$$f(x_3, x_2, x_1) = g(\bar{x}_3, x_1, \bar{x}_2) = g(x_{\pi(3)}^{(b_{\pi(3)})}, x_{\pi(2)}^{(b_{\pi(2)})}, x_{\pi(1)}^{(b_{\pi(1)})})$$

for the permutation $\pi = (12)$ (cf. Example 0.12) and $b = (0,0,1)$.

Note that the two functions of Example 1.32 are not equal in the Boolean algebra $B(n)$ (see Prob. 1.25), since they do not have identical truth tables. Nevertheless, their equivalence is noteworthy, for the study of switching theory is vastly facilitated in several areas of investigation when the decomposition of $B(n)$ into its equivalence classes is employed. This technique can be used to partially compensate for the fact that $|B(n)| = 2^{2^n}$, for it often happens that equivalent Boolean functions have similar behavior with regard to some property under investigation (see Corollary 1.18). One can then achieve considerable economy in the investigation by taking account of this fact.

In such circumstances, it becomes of interest to know the number (N_t) of equivalence classes and the number of elements (or functions, together with their characteristic numbers) in each class—that is, the complete details of the class decomposition. We have tabulated the answer to this first question in Table 1.5, which the reader should compare with Table

n	No. (N_t) of $\cong$ Classes	No. of $\sim$ Classes	No. (N) of $\simeq$ Classes
1	3	3	2
2	6	5	4
3	22	9	14
4	402	17	222
5	1,228,158	33	616,126
6	$\approx 4 \times 10^{14}$	65	

TABLE 1.5   NUMBER OF EQUIVALENCE CLASSES IN $B(n)$

1.1. These figures have been obtained experimentally[†] since there is no general formula known that will give the number of classes. A comparison of Tables 1.1 and 1.5 indicates that the details of the class decomposition for $\cong$ may be useful for discussing problems in which $n = 3$ or 4.[‡]

It should be clear that a necessary (but, by no means sufficient) condition for equivalence of f and g is that they have the same number of "ones" in their truth table. This condition alone, however, would give rise to another equivalence relation (call it $\sim$) on $B(n)$. Clearly, the number of classes for this relation is one larger than the number of rows (2^n) in a truth table for n variables. For completeness sake, we tabulate these values also in Table 1.5. The assertions of this paragraph are summarized in the statement that

†D. Slepian, "On the Number of Symmetry Types of Boolean Functions," *Canadian Jour. Math.*, 5, 2 (1953).

‡A procedure will be described in Chapter 2 for obtaining the complete class decomposition when $n = 3$.

$$f \cong g \Longrightarrow f \sim g \qquad \text{for } f, g \in B(n)$$

but the converse is not true.

As another equivalence relation on $B(n)$, suppose we agree to write $f \simeq g$ if f can be obtained from g by permuting and or complementing variables *and or* complementing the function, that is, if there exists a permutation $\pi : n^+ \longrightarrow n^+$, an element $b \in B^n$, *and* an element $a \in B$ such that

$$f(x_n, x_{n-1}, \cdots, x_1) = [g(x_{\pi(n)}^{(b_{\pi(n)})}, x_{\pi(n-1)}^{(b_{\pi(n-1)})}, \cdots, x_{\pi(1)}^{(b_{\pi(1)})})]^{(a)}$$

Now comparing with the definition for $\cong$, we see that

$$f \cong g \Longrightarrow f \simeq g$$

since we may take $a = 1$ when π and b are given which cause $f \cong g$.

Now suppose $f \in B(n)$ is a Boolean function whose truth table is "less than half-ones." The function $\bar{f}$ is equivalent ($\bar{f} \simeq f$) to f, since

$$\bar{f}(x_n, x_{n-1}, \cdots, x_1) = [f(x_{1(n)}^{(1)}, x_{1(n-1)}^{(1)}, \cdots, x_{1(1)}^{(1)})]^{(0)}$$

and yet $\bar{f} \not\cong f$ because $\bar{f}$ has "more than half-ones." Thus, $f \simeq g \not\Longrightarrow f \cong g$, and it would then appear at a glance that there are exactly half as many equivalence classes for $\simeq$ as there are for $\cong$, and that the $\simeq$ classes contain exactly twice as many functions as do the $\cong$ classes. This casual observation fails to be true (if $n \geq 4$) for the following reason: Some functions f having exactly "half-ones, half-zeros" in their truth table have the property that $\bar{f} \cong f$, and therefore one does not obtain a merging of the classes of f and of $\bar{f}$ for such functions by introducing the more general equivalence relation $\simeq$ because the functions f and $\bar{f}$ were already equivalent with the relation $\cong$. Such functions f for which $\bar{f} \cong f$ are called *self-complementary*. If we agree to call a function $f \in B(n)$ *neutral* if half of its truth table consists of ones and half-zeros, then we have the necessary condition

$$f \text{ is self-complementary} \Longrightarrow f \text{ is neutral}$$

But the reader can easily construct an example to show that the condition of neutrality is not sufficient to guarantee that the function be self-complementary. Furthermore, if f and g are neutral and $g \cong f$, the reader can verify that

$$f \text{ is self-complementary} \Longleftrightarrow g \text{ is self-complementary}$$

so that either an entire class of equivalent (with respect to $\cong$) functions are self-complementary or no member of that class is self-complementary. Elspas[†] has computed the number N_{sc} of self-complementary classes

---

[†]B. Elspas, "Self-Complementary Symmetry Types of Boolean Functions," *I.R.E. Trans. on Electronic Computers*, EC-9, 2 (June 1960).

among the neutral classes of the partition due to $\cong$, and we have tabulated his results for $n \leq 5$ in Table 1.6.

n	No. (N_t) of Neutral Classes	No. (N_{se}) of Self-Complementary Classes
1	1	1
2	2	2
3	6	6
4	74	42
5	169,112	4094

TABLE 1.6

Because of the self-complementary classes in the partition due to $\cong$, the number (N) of classes in the partition due to $\simeq$ is greater (cf. Table 1.5) than half the number N_t. Precisely,

$$N = \frac{N_t - N_n}{2} + \frac{N_n - N_{se}}{2} + N_{se}$$

$$= \frac{N_t - N_{se}}{2} + N_{se} = \frac{N_t + N_{se}}{2} \qquad (1.39)$$

Nevertheless, when a property of Boolean functions is invariant among functions that are equivalent in the sense of $\simeq$, one nearly achieves a 50 percent reduction in effort by considering the classes due to $\simeq$ rather than $\cong$. The reader may have occassion to make use of this savings in his future studies.

*1.16 EQUIVALENCE CLASSES IN $B(2)$

In order to illustrate the material of the preceding section and provide information for subsequent developments, we now discuss several useful partitions of $B(2)$ into nonoverlapping classes. $B(2)$ itself consists of the 16 functions shown in Table 1.3.

First we consider the equivalence relation $\cong$, defined (as in Sec. 1.15) by

$$f \cong g \longleftrightarrow \begin{cases} \text{there exists a permutation } \pi : 2^+ \longrightarrow 2^+ \\ \text{and an element } b = (b_2, b_1) \in B^2 \text{ such that} \\ f(x_2, x_1) = g(x_{\pi(2)}^{(b_{\pi(2)})}, x_{\pi(1)}^{(b_{\pi(1)})}) \end{cases}$$

We already know that

$$f \cong g \Longrightarrow f \sim g$$

so that the functions f_0 and f_{15} must form classes by themselves. The results of Prob. 1.35 then yield the partition

$$\lambda_1 = \{\bar{f}_0; \bar{f}_{15}; \bar{f}_1, \bar{f}_2, \bar{f}_4, \bar{f}_8; \bar{f}_3, \bar{f}_5, \bar{f}_{10}, \bar{f}_{12}; \bar{f}_7, \bar{f}_{11}, \bar{f}_{13}, \bar{f}_{14}; \bar{f}_6, \bar{f}_9\}$$

showing the six classes referred to in Table 1.5 (for $n = 2$).

Each of the neutral classes ($\{f_3, f_5, f_{10}, f_{12}\}$ and $\{f_6, f_9\}$) are self-complementary, so that the less restrictive equivalence relation $\simeq$ (cf. Sec. 1.15) gives rise to the partition

$$\lambda_2 = \{\overline{f_0, f_{15}}; \overline{f_1, f_2, f_4, f_8, f_7, f_{11}, f_{13}, f_{14}}; \overline{f_3, f_5, f_{10}, f_{12}}; \overline{f_6, f_9}\}$$

exhibiting the four classes claimed in Table 1.5 for the relation $\simeq$.

Since $\sim$ simply "merges" functions that have an equivalent number of "ones" in their truth table, we obtain the partition

$$\lambda_3 = \{\bar{f}_0; \bar{f}_{15}; \overline{f_1, f_2, f_4, f_8}; \overline{f_3, f_5, f_{10}, f_{12}, f_6, f_9}; \overline{f_7, f_{11}, f_{13}, f_{14}}\}$$

for this relation.

For certain applications (see Sec. 1.18) yet another equivalence relation on $B(2)$ is useful. We assume the availability of wires 0, x_1, x_2 and their complements, and let

$$F = \{f_0, f_3, f_5, f_{10}, f_{12}, f_{15}\} = \{f_0, f_3, f_5, \bar{f}_0, \bar{f}_3, \bar{f}_5\}$$

denote the collection of "trivial" functions—trivial in the sense that no logical circuitry is needed to implement them. The symbol "F" can best be remembered as standing for "free." Then let

$$A = \{f_1, f_{14}\} = \{f_1, \bar{f}_1\}$$

$$B = \{f_1, f_{13}\} = \{f_2, \bar{f}_2\}$$

$$C = \{f_4, f_{11}\} = \{f_4, \bar{f}_4\}$$

$$D = \{f_8, f_7\} = \{f_8, \bar{f}_8\}$$

denote the sets of functions that can be implemented from the circuits (gates) of Figs. 1.16(a), (b), (c), and (d), respectively.

(To denote complementation, we now use a small circle rather than the symbolic inverter circuit of Example 1.19. This deemphasis of the inverter circuit reflects the fact that many electronic realizations of the symbolic circuits of Fig. 1.12 will automatically implement (as a second output wire) the complementary output as well). We are left with the set of functions

$$E = \{f_6, f_9\} = \{f_6, \bar{f}_6\}$$

where each can be implemented from either of the two circuits of Fig. 1.16(e). (The fact that the first circuit simultaneously implements the

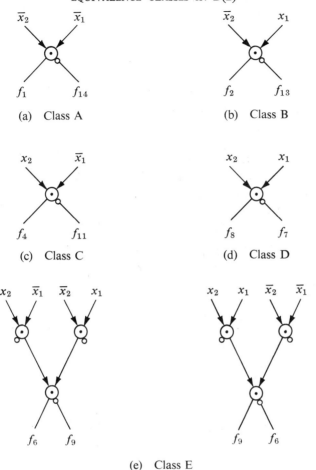

(a) Class A

(b) Class B

(c) Class C

(d) Class D

(e) Class E

FIGURE 1.16

classes B, C, and the second the classes A, D, will be of interest in sub-sequent developments.) For mnemonic purposes, one can think of E as standing for "exclusive or," while the meanings of A, B, C, D are best remembered from lettering the four locations on a two-variable truth table:

$x_2\ x_1$	
0 0	A
0 1	B
1 0	C
1 1	D

Thus, $B = \{f_2, f_{13}\}$ contains the two functions with truth tables

x_2	x_1	f_2	f_{13}	
0	0	0	1	
0	1	1	0	B
1	0	0	1	
1	1	0	1	

From Theorem 0.3, the partition

$$\lambda_4 = \{A, B, C, D, E, F\}$$
$$= \{\overline{f_1, f_{14}}; \overline{f_2, f_{13}}; \overline{f_4, f_{11}}; \overline{f_8, f_7}; \overline{f_6, f_9}; \overline{f_0, f_3, f_5, f_{10}, f_{12}, f_{15}}\}$$

defines an equivalence relation (call it $\equiv$) on $B(2)$. This relation (which will occupy a central position in subsequent investigations) has the important property

$$f \equiv g \Leftrightarrow \begin{cases} \text{every logic circuit that implements} \\ f \text{ also implements } g \text{ "free of charge"} \\ \text{and conversely} \end{cases} \quad \textbf{(1.40)}$$

Note the assumption that complementation is available free of charge—consistent with the parenthetical remark above.

We shall make an early application (Sec. 1.18) of these equivalence relations to the two-variable minimization problem. The more general n-variable problem (whose existence has already been suggested) will be precisely defined immediately.

*1.17 COMPLETELY SPECIFIED MINIMIZATION PROBLEMS

For any logic circuit N, we define a *cost* $c(N)$, which simply counts (excluding inverter circuits) the number of inputs (arrows) to gates in the circuit. Ordinarily, this figure will be a realistic measure of the relative expense of fabricating the circuit, counting as it does the number of transistors (for example) required for the implementation.

EXAMPLE 1.33

The circuit N of Fig. 1.17 has the cost

$$c(N) = 11$$

Although we will rarely be able to compute its value, it is useful to have a symbol $m(f)$ to denote the smallest cost among the infinitely many circuit implementations of a given Boolean function $f : B^n \rightarrow B$. Symbolically, the *cost* $m(f)$ of f is written (cf. Prob. 0.30)

$$m(f) = \min_{f = \rho^{-1}(N)} c(N) \quad \textbf{(1.41)}$$

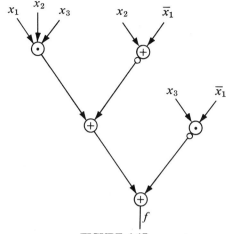

FIGURE 1.17

The difficulty in computing $m(f)$ is apparent here, for one must consider all circuits N whose corresponding polynomial $\rho^{-1}(N)$ is equal to f in the Boolean algebra $FB(n)$ and take as $m(f)$ the minimum among the costs $c(N)$ of such circuits. Using this figure, however, it is possible to phrase the (completely specified,[†] single output) *minimization problem of switching theory*: Given $f : B^n \longrightarrow B$, find a (single output) logic circuit N (interconnecting only the component circuits of Fig. 1.12, except that each gate is allowed to have a complementary output as well as its indicated output) for which

$$\rho^{-1}(N) = f \qquad (1.42)$$

$$c(N) = m(f) \qquad (1.43)$$

Such a circuit is said to be a *minimal circuit* for f. The first condition insists that N have the input-output characteristics specified in the truth table of f; the second (minimality) condition insists that N be a "most economical" (in terms of the cost function c) circuit among those that satisfy condition 1.42. Since $m(f)$ is generally not known in advance, we might prefer to replace Eq. 1.43 by the equivalent condition

$$\rho^{-1}(N') = f \Longrightarrow c(N) \leq c(N') \qquad (1.43a)$$

Except for a few isolated cases (one of which we treat in the next section), the solution to this minimization problem is not known. Further restrictions must be placed on the problem (usually restrictions on the form of the logic circuits to be considered) if it is to be manageable. This will be done in two ways (see Chapters 3 and 6) in this text.

†See Chapter 3 for the meaning of "incompletely specified."

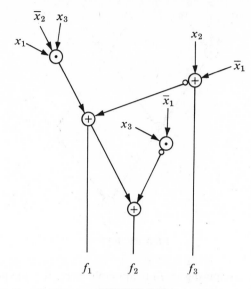

FIGURE 1.18

A still more general problem can be stated if we consider logic circuits of the type depicted in Fig. 1.18, that is, *multiple output* logic circuits. (From the Boolean functional point of view, one considers a family or collection of functions

$$F = \{f_1, f_2, \cdots, f_k\}$$

where

$$f_j : B^n \longrightarrow B \qquad (j = 1, 2, \cdots, k)$$

it being assumed that each f_j is a Boolean function of the *same* Boolean variables $x_n, x_{n-1}, \cdots, x_1$.) Now any logic circuit N having k outputs will determine k single-output logic circuits $N_1, N_2, \cdots, N_k$ obtained in the following manner for output j:

(1) Output j is obtained from a gate having inputs (arrows) $x^{(1)}, x^{(2)}, \cdots, x^{(m)}$.

(2) Each arrow $x^{(i)}$ is traced "upstream" to its source:
    (a) the output of another gate of N or
    (b) an input wire x_α of N.

(3) Repeat steps 1 and 2 for all arrows of type 2(a) until[†] only input wires x_α are obtained in step 2.

(4) The resulting logic circuit is denoted N_j.

---

†The process terminates if (as we must certainly do) we permit only "loop free" circuits, that is, circuits without circulatory paths.

EXAMPLE 1.34

The multiple-output logic circuit N of Fig. 1.18 determines the three single-output logic circuits N_1, N_2, N_3 of Fig. 1.19.

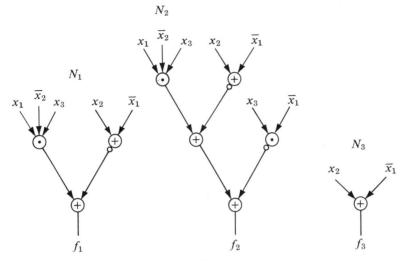

FIGURE 1.19

By analogy with the preceding discussion, we define the (completely specified) *multiple-output minimization problem of switching theory:* Given a family

$$F = \{f_j; f_j: B^n \longrightarrow B\} \qquad (j = 1, 2 \cdots, k)$$

of csbf's; find a logic network N having k outputs such that

$$\rho^{-1}(N_j) = f_j \qquad (j = 1, 2, \cdots, k) \tag{1.44}$$

$$\left. \begin{array}{l} \rho^{-1}(N_j') = f_j \qquad (j = 1, 2, \cdots, k) \\ \quad \text{for a logic circuit } N' \end{array} \right\} \Longrightarrow c(N) \leq c(N') \tag{1.45}$$

Note that we have chosen to generalize Eq. 1.43a rather than Eq. 1.43. The other alternative would necessitate the definition of the *cost* (cf. Prob. 0.30);

$$m(F) = \min_{\substack{\rho^{-1}(N_j) = f_j \\ (j = 1, 2, \cdots, k)}} c(N) \tag{1.46}$$

of a family of functions.

If the single-output problem is unsolved, the same is all the more true regarding the multiple-output problem. Nevertheless, we will arrive (in Chapters 3 and 6) at several solutions to more restrictive, and hence more manageable, problems that are of immense practical value. Moreover, we will obtain in the next section an exact solution to the completely specified multiple-output problem for an important special case—where each f_i is a function of the same two variables.

Meanwhile, the principal application of the equivalence relation $\cong$ on $B(n)$ can be described in terms of the transformations

$$\tau_\pi^b : \mathrm{FL}(n) \longrightarrow \mathrm{FL}(n)$$

for $\pi : n^+ \longrightarrow n^+$, $b \in B^n$, which simply rename the inputs x_i for $N \in \mathrm{FL}(n)$ according to the rule

$$x_i \longrightarrow x_{\pi(i)}^{(b\pi(i))} \qquad (i = 1, 2, \cdots, n)$$

The resulting relabeled circuit is taken as $\tau_\pi^b(N)$.

EXAMPLE 1.35

Let N be the logic circuit of Fig. 1.20.

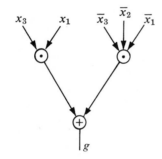 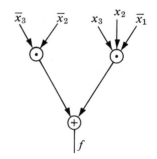

| **FIGURE 1.20** | **FIGURE 1.21** |

Suppose $\pi = (12)$ and $b = (0, 0, 1)$. Then

$$x_1 \longrightarrow \bar{x}_2$$
$$x_2 \longrightarrow x_1$$
$$x_3 \longrightarrow \bar{x}_3$$

so that $\tau_\pi^b (N)$ is the circuit of Fig. 1.21.

In the light of the preceding discussion about $\cong$, the reader should be in a position to accept the following, theorem.

Theorem 1.17   Let $f, g \in B(n)$ and $f \cong g$ via $\pi : n^+ \to n^+$, $b \in B^n$ and Eq. 1.37. Then if $N \in \mathrm{FL}(n)$ is any circuit with $\rho^{-1}(N) = g$, we have

$$\rho^{-1}(\tau_\pi^b(N)) = f$$

If this is not the case, the following example will surely alleviate the need for a rigorous proof.

EXAMPLE 1.36

Let $f, g : B^3 \to B$ be the functions of Example 1.32. The circuit N of Example 1.35 (Fig. 1.20) has the property $\rho^{-1}(N) = g$. Furthermore, the circuit

$\tau_\pi^b(N)$ of Fig. 1.21 is seen to possess the property $\rho^{-1}(\tau_\pi^b(n)) = f$, illustrating Theorem 1.17.

When it is realized that $c(N) = c(\tau_\pi^b(N))$ for any π and b, the theorem has the obvious consequence:

Corollary 1.18   Let $f, g \in B(n)$ and $f \cong g$. Then

$$m(f) = m(g)$$

Furthermore, N is a minimal cost circuit for g iff $\tau_\pi^b(N)$ is a minimal cost circuit for f.

Thus the problem of finding minimum cost circuits for all Boolean functions $f \in B(n)$ is reduced to finding a minimum cost circuit for a representative function chosen from each ($\cong$) equivalence class. If complementary-output gates are employed, it is evident that we can replace the ($\cong$) classes by the ($\simeq$) classes with a further reduction in effort. (Cf. Table 1.5.)

*1.18   MINIMAL TWO-VARIABLE CIRCUITS

Because of Corollary 1.18 and Eq. 1.40, the circuits of Fig. 1.16 are shown to be minimal circuits unless there are cheaper (in terms of the cost function c) implementations of f_1 (say) and f_6. That f_1 could not be implemented at cost less than 2 (for it would then cost zero) is obvious, and by exhaustive methods one could prove that no logic circuit exists with cost less than 6 and having the truth table of f_6. Thus the circuits of Fig. 1.16 *are* minimal, explaining the figures in Table 1.7.

	Class:	F	A	B	C	D	E
Representative		f_0	f_1	f_2	f_4	f_8	f_6
x_2	x_1						
0	0	0	1	0	0	0	0
0	1	0	0	1	0	0	1
1	0	0	0	0	1	0	1
1	1	0	0	0	0	1	0
$m(f_i)$		0	2	2	2	2	6

TABLE 1.7

The multiple-output minimization problem is only slightly more difficult to discuss. In so doing, we will again be aided by the class decomposition

$$\lambda_4 = \{A, B, C, D, E, F\}$$

of Sec. 1.16. Let[†]

$$\mathscr{F} = \{F_1, F_2, \cdots, F_k\}$$

be a given family of functions $F_j \in B(2)$.

We begin by "casting out" all occurrences of "free functions in $\mathscr{F}$; that is, we delete F_j from $\mathscr{F}$ if $F_j \in F$. Stated another way, we could assume without loss of generality that the F_j are each belonging to one of the classes A, B, C, D, E, but with repetitions allowed in the sense that (particularly for large k) more than one F_j may belong to the same class. If $\mathscr{F} \neq \varnothing$ (after our deletion) and we consider only those classes that occur (or more precisely, a representative of which occurs) among the F_i, we have $2^5 - 1 = 31$ possible *outcomes*, which we identify as "products" of the classes A, B, C, D, and E as depicted in Table 1.8.

Category	Outcome	$m(\mathscr{F})$	Category	Outcome	$m(\mathscr{F})$
Y_0	F	0	Y_5	E	
Y_1	A			AE	
	B	2		BE	
	C			CE	6
	D			DE	
				ADE	
Y_2	AB			BCE	
	AC				
	AD	4	Y_6	ABE	
	BC			ACE	
	BD			BDE	
	CD			CDE	8
Y_3	ABC			ABCE	
	ABD			ABDE	
	ACD	6		ACDE	
	BCD			BCDE	
Y_4	ABCD	8	Y_7	ABCDE	10

TABLE 1.8

These products P are to be read as if the omitted multiplication signs were pronounced "and"; thus, the product $P = ACE$ might identify or represent the family $\mathscr{F} = \{f_6, f_9, f_4, f_1, f_{11}, f_5\}$, since $f_6, f_9 \in E, f_4, f_{11} \in C, f_1 \in A$, $f_5 \in F$; the notation ACE indicates that circuits must be constructed to

[†]We are prevented here from using the notation $F = \{f_1, f_2 \cdots f_k\}$ because of the likelihood of confusing this F with the class F and the f_j with the notation of Table 1.3.

implement functions of class A *and* of class C *and* of class E. For completeness sake, we denote the outcome $\mathscr{F} = \varnothing$ by the product F.

Including the possibility of obtaining the product F, the 32 possible outcomes (= products of classes) so obtained may be considered as forming a partially ordered set (call it Y) that is isomorphic (by an obvious mapping) to $\mathscr{P}(S_5)$, but we prefer to invert the partial order induced by this natural isomorphism so that $(Y, \geq)$ has the Hasse diagram partially sketched in Fig. 1.22(a). We do this because it will later (see Sec. 3.16) seem natural to think of $(Y, \geq)$ as being isomorphically imbedded[†] in the lattice FD(5) (cf. Example 1.11) whose elements are renamed as $x_1 = A$, $x_2 = B$, $x_3 = C$, $x_4 = D$, $x_5 = E$, $1 = F$, etc., and whose (renamed) Hasse diagram has 7581 elements, as partially sketched in Fig. 1.22(b). (See Prob. 1.24.)

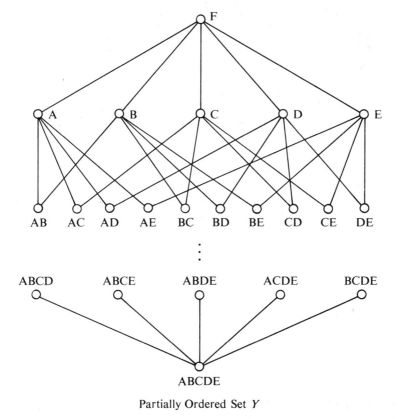

Partially Ordered Set Y

FIGURE 1.22a

†By this we mean that Y is isomorphic (as a partially ordered set) to a subset of FD(5).

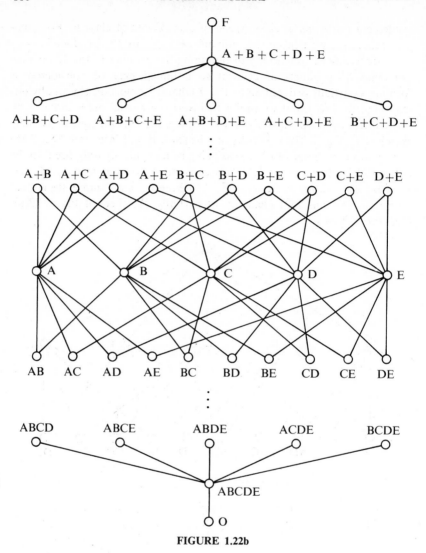

FIGURE 1.22b

We partition the set Y into eight disjoint *categories*, Y_i,

$$Y = \bigcup_{i=0}^{7} Y_i$$

as indicated in Table 1.8, where the categories Y_i ($0 \leq i \leq 4$) contain all elements of Y (products of classes) in which the class E does not appear, whereas the categories Y_i ($5 \leq i \leq 7$) contain products in which E occurs. The entire procedure for finding a minimal circuit for $\mathscr{F}$ may now be described.

(1) Determine the product of classes P corresponding to the family $\mathscr{F}$.

(2a) If $P \in Y_i$ ($0 \leq i \leq 4$), one simply constructs i gates, forming a representative of each class appearing in P.

(2b) If $P \in Y_i$ ($5 \leq i \leq 7$), the class E is required. One chooses that E circuit of Fig. 1.16 that simultaneously implements the greatest number (0, 1, or 2) of otherwise required classes. Those not implemented by the E circuit must be formed separately.

(3) The resulting logic circuit should have cost as listed in Table 1.8.

EXAMPLE 1.37

$$\mathscr{F} = \{F_1, F_2, F_3, F_4, F_5, F_6, F_7, F_8, F_9\}$$

where the F_i have the truth tables

$x_2\ x_1$	F_1	F_2	F_3	F_4	F_5	F_6	F_7	F_8	F_9	F_1	F_3	F_4	F_5	F_7	F_9
0 0	0	1	0	1	1	1	1	0	1	0	0	1	1	1	1
0 1	1	1	1	0	1	0	0	0	1	1	1	0	1	0	1
1 0	1	0	0	1	0	1	0	0	0	1	0	1	0	0	0
1 1	0	0	0	1	1	0	0	0	1	0	0	1	1	0	1

We follow the Procedure given above.

(1) We immediately discard F_2, F_6, and F_8, since they belong to F. We have

$$F_1 \in E$$
$$F_3, F_4 \in B$$
$$F_5, F_9 \in C$$
$$F_7 \in A$$

so that $P = ABCE$.

(2b) Since $P \in Y_6$, the class E is required. Now the first E circuit of Fig. 1.16 simultaneously implements classes B and C, whereas the second uses A and D. Our otherwise required classes are A, B, and C, so that we choose the first E circuit.

(3) The resulting logic circuit is shown in Fig. 1.23 and has cost 8 (in agreement with Table 1.8).

Our exhaustive treatment of the two-variable minimization problem has yielded the following useful estimates.

Theorem 1.19   Let $f \in B(2)$. Then $m(f) \leq 6$. For a family

$$F = \{f_1, f_2, \cdots, f_k\}$$

with $f_j \in B(2)$, ($j = 1, 2, \cdots, k$), we have $m(F) \leq 10$.

Because of the fact that $|B(n)| = 2^{2^n}$, an exhaustive treatment of the minimization problem is not practical for large n, and thus we must seek other methods. A considerable body of the literature on switching theory

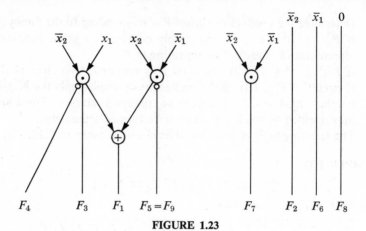

FIGURE 1.23

has arisen from this search. Representative of this literature is the material of the succeeding two chapters.

PROBLEMS

1.1 Show that the lattice $(\mathscr{P}(S), \cup, \cap)$ is a Boolean algebra for any set S.

1.2 Let $L = \{n \in Z^+; n \mid 30\} = \{1,2,3,4,5,6,10,15,30\}$. For n, $m \in L$, define the relation

$$n \geq m \Longleftrightarrow m \mid n$$

(m "divides" n in the sense that there exists an integer q such that $n = qm$).
(a) Show that $(L, \geq)$ is a partially ordered set.
(b) Draw its Hasse diagram.
(c) Show that $(L, \geq)$ is a lattice with l.u.b.'s and g.l.b.'s corresponding to least common multiples and greatest common divisors, respectively.
(d) Show that $(L, +, \cdot)$ is a Boolean algebra.
(e) Show that the Boolean algebra $(L, +, \cdot)$ is isomorphic to that of Prob. 1.1 for $S = \{a, b, c\}$.

1.3 Consider the accompanying diagrams.

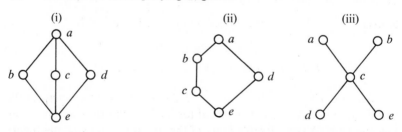

(a) Determine the ($\geq$) relation matrices for the partially ordered sets having Hasse diagrams (i), (ii), and (iii).

(b) Which of the partially ordered sets in (a) are lattices?

(c) Of those that are lattices, which are distributive?

*1.4 Let X be the set of all continuous real-valued functions f defined on the interval $0 \leq x \leq 1$. Define $f \geq g$ to mean $f(x) \geq g(x)$ for all x with $0 \leq x \leq 1$.

(a) Show that $(X, \geq)$ is a partially ordered set.

(b) Define $f + g$ and $f \cdot g$ appropriately and prove that $(X, +, \cdot)$ forms a lattice.

1.5 Let $X = R^2 = R \times R$, the Cartesian plane. For points (a, b) and (a', b') in X, which of the following relations will make X into a partially ordered set?

$(a', b') \geq (a, b)$ means:

(a) $a' \geq a$ and $b' \geq b$.

(b) Either $(a' > a)$ or $(a' = a$ and $b' > b)$.

(c) $a' \geq a + b$ and $b' \geq b$.

In (a), (b), and (c), the usual sense of $\geq$ is intended.

Note: The order relation (b) is called the *lexicographical order* (dictionary order). In this text we will try to reserve the symbol $\gtrdot$ (writing $(a', b') \gtrdot (a, b)$) for the order relation (b).

1.6 Let X be a set of elements with a relation $>$, which is transitive and *irreflexive* ($x > x$ is false for every $x \in X$). Define $x \geq y$ to mean that either $x > y$ or $x = y$. Show that $(X, \geq)$ is a partially ordered set.

1.7 Show that every finite lattice has a zero and an identity.

*1.8 Show that if X is a finite partially ordered set with a zero and an identity that has the property: If for any four elements (not necessarily distinct), x_1, x_2, y_1, y_2 in X with $x_i \geq y_i$ $(i = 1, 2)$, there exists an element z such that

$$x_i \geq z \geq y_i \qquad (i = 1, 2)$$

then X is a lattice.

1.9 Show that in any lattice $(L, \geq) = (L, +, \cdot)$,

$$x \geq y \Longrightarrow x \cdot (y + z) \geq y + (x \cdot z)$$

1.10 A lattice is called *modular* if

$$x \geq y \Longrightarrow x \cdot (y + z) = y + (x \cdot z)$$

(See Prob. 1.9.) Show that the lattice of Prob. 1.3(ii) is not modular.

1.11 Show that every distributive lattice is modular (see Prob. 1.10) and hence every Boolean algebra is modular.

1.12 Show that if $(L, \geq) = (L, +, \cdot)$ is a modular lattice (see Prob. 1.10)

$$x \leq y \Longrightarrow x + (y \cdot z) = y \cdot (x + z)$$

1.13 Show that in any lattice, the absorption laws hold:

$$\textbf{(P4a)} \quad x + x \cdot y = x \qquad \textbf{P4b} \quad x \cdot (x + y) = x$$

1.14   Obtain the complements of
   (a) $(a + \bar{b}\bar{c}d)(\bar{a}\bar{d} + f(b\bar{c} + e))$.
   (b) $a\bar{b}c + (\bar{a} + b + e)(ab\bar{e} + \bar{d})$.

1.15   Prove the following identities:
   (a) $(a + b)(\bar{a} + b) = b$.
   (b) $a\bar{b} + c(\bar{a} + b + d) = c + a\bar{b}$.
   (c) $a\bar{b}d + \bar{a}bc = (ad + bc)(\bar{a} + \bar{b})$.
   (d) $ab + \bar{a}c + bc = ab + \bar{a}c$.

1.16   Suppose we are given the Boolean polynomial

$$f(x_3, x_2, x_1) = \overline{[(x_1 + \bar{x}_2) \cdot \bar{x}_3 + x_1]} + \bar{x}_2 \cdot x_3$$

   (a) Obtain the two Shannon expansions of f with respect to x_1.
   (b) Obtain the two Shannon expansions of f with respect to x_2.
   (c) Write f in minterm canonical form.
   (d) Write f in maxterm canonical form.
   (e) Obtain the truth table of f.
   (f) Compute $\eta(f)$, the characteristic number of f.

1.17   Obtain the minterm and maxterm canonical forms of the following Boolean polynomials:
   (a) $f_1 = \bar{b}\bar{c} + ab + bc + \bar{a}\bar{c}$.
   (b) $f_2 = \bar{c}\bar{d}\bar{e} + cde + \bar{a}\bar{b}d + abcd + bce + a\bar{b}\bar{c}e$.
   (c) $f_3 = (a\bar{b} + \bar{c}d)(b + d)(a + \bar{c}\bar{d})$.

1.18   Obtain the truth tables of the Boolean polynomials of Prob. 1.17.

1.19   Given that $ab = ac$ and $a + b = a + c$, show that $b = c$. (In a Boolean algebra, division and subtraction have no meaning, so that the conclusion $b = c$ would not follow from one or the other of the two given equations.)
   Give an example of a Boolean algebra and three elements a, b, and c that satisfy $b \neq c$ but $ab = ac$.

1.20   Write truth tables for the following polynomials:
   (a) $f_1 = ab + b\bar{c}$.
   (b) $f_2 = (a + b)(b + c)$.
   (c) $f_3 = \bar{a}b + c\bar{d} + a\bar{c}d$.

1.21   Convert the three variable minterm forms: (a) $m_1 + m_2 + m_6$ and (b) $m_1 + m_2 + m_5 + m_6$ to maxterm cononical form.
   Convert the three variable maxterm forms: (c) $M_1 M_2 M_3$ and (d) $M_0 M_3 M_6 M_7$ to minterm canonical form.

1.22   (a) Work the exercise suggested in Sec. 1.14 concerning the Pierce function.
   (b) Write $a\bar{b} + \bar{a}bc$, using only the Pierce function.

1.23   Complete the proof of Lemma 1.2 by showing that

$$x \cdot y = y \Longrightarrow x \geq y$$

$$x \geq y \Longrightarrow x + y = x$$

for elements x and y in a lattice.

1.24 Draw the Hasse diagram of the lattice FD(3).

1.25 If $f, g \in B(n)$, define $f \geq g$ to mean

$$g(b_n, b_{n-1}, \cdots, b_1) = 1 \Longrightarrow f(b_n, b_{n-1}, \cdots, b_1) = 1$$

for all $(b_n, b_{n-1}, \cdots, b_1) \in B_n$.
(a) Show that $(B(n), \geq)$ is a partially ordered set; a lattice; a Boolean algebra having 2^{2^n} elements.
(b) Show that $B^{2^n} \cong B(n)$.
(c) Is $B(n)$ isomorphic to FB(n)?

1.26 Show that every irredundant covering of a set S is a grouping of S, but that the converse is not necessarily true. Establish a similar result for groupings and set systems.

*1.27 Show that the relation $\cong$ is transitive on $B(n)$, thereby completing the proof of Theorem 1.16.

*1.28 Prove that the definition of Eq. 1.21 meets the requirements
(a) $\lambda + \gamma$ is a partition of S.
(b) $\lambda + \gamma$ is the l.u.b. of λ and γ in the partially ordered set $(\Lambda(S), \geq)$.

1.29 Let $S = 8^+$ and

$$\lambda = \{\overline{1,3}; \ \overline{2,4}; \ \overline{5}; \ \overline{6}; \ \overline{7,8}\}$$

$$\gamma = \{\overline{1,8}; \ \overline{2,4,6,7}; \ \overline{3}; \ \overline{5}\}$$

$$\mu = \{\overline{1,2}; \ \overline{3,4}; \ \overline{5,6,7}; \ \overline{8}\}$$

elements of $\Lambda(S)$. Compute

(a) $\lambda + \gamma$ (d) $\lambda \cdot \gamma$
(b) $\lambda + \mu$ (e) $\lambda \cdot \mu$
(c) $\gamma + \mu$ (f) $\gamma \cdot \mu$

1.30 Draw the logic circuit $\rho(f)$, where f is the Boolean polynomial of Prob. 1.16. Draw five circuits that are equivalent to $\rho(f)$, each having less cost. Estimate $m(f)$.

1.31 Let $g \in B(3)$ be the function having characteristic number $\eta(g) = 22$. If $\pi = (123)$ and $b = (0, 1, 0)$, compute $\eta(f)$ for the function $f \in B(3)$ for which

$$f(x_3, x_2, x_1) = g(x_{\pi(3)}^{(b_{\pi(3)})}, x_{\pi(2)}^{(b_{\pi(2)})}, x_{\pi(1)}^{(b_{\pi(1)})})$$

1.32 Derive a minimal circuit for the family

$$\mathscr{F} = \{F_1, F_2, F_3, F_4, F_5, F_6, F_7, F_8\}$$

if the F_i have truth tables:

x_2	x_1	F_1	F_2	F_3	F_4	F_5	F_6	F_7	F_8
0	0	1	1	0	0	1	0	0	1
0	1	0	1	0	1	0	0	0	0
1	0	1	1	1	0	1	0	1	0
1	1	1	0	1	0	1	1	0	1

1.33   For the function $f : B^3 \longrightarrow B$ of Prob. 1.16(e), find a function $g \in B(3)$ for which $g \cong f$ but $g \neq f$. Illustrate Theorem 1.17 with circuits N_f and N_g, for which $\rho^{-1}(N_f) = f$, $\rho^{-1}(N_g) = g$.

*1.34   Show that the set of all set systems of a finite set forms a lattice.

1.35   Obtain the class decomposition of $B(2)$ relative to the relation $\cong$.

SUGGESTED REFERENCES

1-1   BIRKHOFF, GARRETT, *Lattice Theory* (New York: American Mathematical Society Colloquium Publications), Vol. XXV, 1948.

1-2   JACOBSON, N. *Lectures in Abstract Algebra* (Princeton, N.J.: D. Van Nostrand Co.) Vol. I, 1951.

1-3   HOHN, F. E., *Applied Boolean Algebra* (New York: The Macillan Co.), 1960.

CHAPTER 2 | THE CELLULAR
n-CUBE

2.1 INTRODUCTION

In the preceding chapter, the minimization problem of switching theory was defined. We mentioned that it is necessary to place restrictions on the class of logic circuits and Boolean polynomials to be considered if this problem is to be manageable. Among the classes of representations that we might consider, the "Boolean sums of Boolean products" are the best understood. Indeed, we will give a complete solution to the minimization problem as restricted to this important class in the next chapter. We should point out that the dual class—"Boolean products of Boolean sums"—is handled in a dual fashion; we will be able to transform all our results, through the duality of Boolean algebra, into results for this alternate class.

In Sec. 2.5, we exhibit a 1–1 correspondence between all Boolean products of n variables and the "cells" of the cellular "n-dimensional cube." This highly geometrical model, together with an alternate decimal characterization (Sec. 2.8) will then serve as intuitive and computational aids for the minimization theory and miscellaneous applications. Typical of these applications is the determination of the complete ($\cong$) class decomposition of $B(3)$, with which the chapter concludes.

2.2 THE N-CUBE

The unit interval

$$I = \{x \in R; \ 0 \le x \le 1\} \tag{2.1}$$

may be studied from various points of view in mathematics. In the subjects of point-set topology and real variables, one ordinarily studies the structure of I relative to its collection $\mathcal{U}$ of "open" subsets.† ($\mathcal{U}$, $\supseteq$), with $\supseteq$ taken as the inclusion relation, is an infinite (in fact, uncountable) partially ordered set whose structure is by no means simple to describe. All the more complex is the topological description of the *n-cube*

$$I^n = \{(x_n, x_{n-1}, \cdots, x_1); \ x_i \in I \quad \text{for } i = 1, 2, \cdots, n\} \tag{2.2}$$

when a suitable generalization of the one-dimensional open sets has been given.

In contrast, the replacement of $\mathcal{U}$ by the finite (partially ordered) set

$$C = \{\{0\}, \{1\}, I\} \tag{2.3}$$

with the order relation $\ge$ of Fig. 2.1 effects a discretization that emphasizes the "cellular" structure of I, that is, its composition as a line seg-

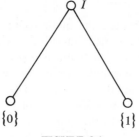

FIGURE 2.1

†A subset $\mathcal{O}$ of I is said to be *open* if for each $x \in \mathcal{O}$ there exists an open interval $J_{x,r} = \{y \in I; |y - x| < r\}$ for some $r > 0$ such that $J_{x,r} \subseteq \mathcal{O}$.

ment I with two included vertices $\{0\}$ and $\{1\}$. The partially ordered (cf. Sec. 1.8) set

$$C^n = \{(c_n, c_{n-1}, \cdots, c_1); c_i \in C\} \qquad (1 \leq n < \infty) \qquad (2.4)$$

with the order relation

$$(c_n, c_{n-1}, \cdots, c_1) \supseteq (c'_n, c'_{n-1}, \cdots, c'_1)$$
$$\Longleftrightarrow c_i \geq c'_i \text{ in } C \qquad (i = 1, 2, \cdots, n) \qquad (2.5)$$

is called the *cellular n cube* (C^n, $\supseteq$). Its elements (cells) $c = (c_n, c_{n-1}, \cdots, c_1)$ are called k *cells*, where $\theta(c) = k$(the *order* of c) is simply the number of components c_i for which $c_i = I$. A cell $c \in C^n$ is called a *vertex* if it is a 0 cell, that is, if $c_i \in B$ for all $i = 1, 2, \cdots, n$. Evidently, $B^n \subseteq C^n$ represents the set of vertices in C^n, so that C^n has 2^n vertices.

EXAMPLE 2.1

In Fig. 2.2, various k cells ($k = 0,1,2$) of C^3 have been labeled. The 3-cell (I, I, I) evidently contains every cell of C^3. Note, as implied above, that for convenience we suppress the braces $\{\ \}$ that might otherwise occur in the coordinates, c_i.

Clearly, (C^n, $\supseteq$) has the natural identity element $1 = (I, I, \cdots, I)$, and if it becomes necessary to do so, we can postulate the existence of

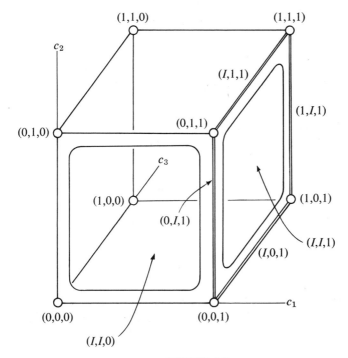

FIGURE 2.2

a *zero* element 0 by merely annexing an element to the bottom of the Hasse diagram for C^n. It would then seem reasonable to say that *the cell 0 has order* -1.

2.3   HAMMING† DISTANCE

Consider the subset $B^n \subseteq C^n$ of vertices

$$B^n = \{v = (v_n, v_{n-1}, \cdots, v_1); v_i \in B\}$$

It is possible to introduce several "distance functions" (or *metrics*, as they are often called) on B^n. By a *distance function d* on B^n, we mean a real-valued function

$$d : B^n \times B^n \longrightarrow R$$

with the properties:

(1) $d(v, v') \geq 0$ for all $v, v' \in B^n$ and $d(v, v') = 0 \Longrightarrow v = v'$,
(2) $d(v, v') = d(v', v)$ for all $v, v' \in B^n$,
(3) $d(v, v'') \leq d(v, v') + d(v', v'')$ for all $v, v', v'' \in B^n$.

Rather than use the ordinary *Euclidean distance*

$$\delta(v, v') = \sqrt{\sum_{i=1}^{n} (v_i - v_i')^2} = \sqrt{\sum_{i=1}^{n} |v_i - v_i'|} \tag{2.6}$$

we will find it convenient to employ the *Hamming distance*

$$\Delta(v, v') = \sum_{i=1}^{n} |v_i - v_i'| = (\delta(v, v'))^2 \tag{2.7}$$

which simply counts the number of coordinates in which $v = (v_n, v_{n-1}, \cdots, v_1)$ and $v' = (v_n', v_{n-1}', \cdots, v_1')$ differ.

EXAMPLE 2.2

In Fig. 2.2 we have $\Delta(v, v') = 2$ if $v = (1,1,0)$ and $v' = (1,0,1)$, since

$$\sum_{i=1}^{3} |v_i - v_i'| = |v_3 - v_3'| + |v_2 - v_2'| + |v_1 - v_1'|$$

$$= 0 + 1 + 1 = 2$$

Note that $\delta(v, v') = \sqrt{2}$.

Several geometric notions concerning vertices and cells can be conveniently described in terms of the Hamming distance. The first of

†R. W. Hamming, "Error Detecting and Correcting Codes," *Bell System Tech. Jour.*, 26 (1950).

these is the notion of "adjacency." Two vertices v, v' in C^n are said to be *adjacent* if $\Delta(v, v') = 1$.

Now suppose that $c = (c_n, c_{n-1}, \cdots, c_1) \in C^n$. The vertices

$$\min(c) = (v_n, v_{n-1}, \cdots, v_1)$$
$$\max(c) = (v'_n, v'_{n-1}, \cdots, v'_1)$$

defined according to the rules

$$c_i \in B \Longrightarrow v_i = v'_i = c_i \tag{2.8a}$$

$$c_i = I \Longrightarrow v_i = 0, \quad v'_i = 1 \tag{2.8b}$$

are called the *minimum* and *maximum* vertices of c, respectively. The reasons for this terminology are revealed when we realize that among all vertices $v \subseteq c$, the vertices $\min(c)$ and $\max(c)$ have the minimum and maximum Hamming distances from the "origin" $(0,0, \cdots, 0)$, respectively.

EXAMPLE 2.3

Suppose $v = (0,1,0,1,1)$ and $v' = (0,1,0,0,1)$ in C^5. Since

$$\Delta(v, v') = 1$$

we say that v and v' are adjacent. Note that the Hamming distance serves to extend algebraically the geometric notion of adjacency to cubes whose dimension prohibits a pictorial interpretation.

EXAMPLE 2.4

Let $c = (I,I,1,I,0)$ be a 3-cell in C^5. According to Eq. 2.5,

$$c = (I,I,1,I,0) \supseteq (v_5,v_4,v_3,v_2,v_1) = v$$

for vertices $v \in C^5$ if and only if

$$I \geq v_5, \quad I \geq v_4, \quad 1 \geq v_3, \quad I \geq v_2, \quad 0 \geq v_1$$

in the Hasse diagram of Fig. 2.1. Evidently we must have $v_3 = 1$, $v_1 = 0$, while v_5, v_4, and v_2 may be arbitrarily chosen elements of B. Thus, c contains the eight vertices: $(0,0,1,0,0)$, $(0,0,1,1,0)$, $(0,1,1,0,0)$, $(0,1,1,1,0)$, $(1,0,1,0,0)$, $(1,0,1,1,0)$, $(1,1,1,0,0)$, $(1,1,1,1,0)$. Note that among these, the first is nearest and the last is farthest from the origin in terms of the Hamming distance.

Had we computed $\min(c)$ and $\max(c)$ from Eqs. 2.8 we would have obtained

(i) $v_3 = v'_3 = c_3 = 1$; $v_1 = v'_1 = 0$,

(ii) $v_5 = v_4 = v_2 = 0$; $v'_5 = v'_4 = v'_2 = 1$,

so that

$$\min(c) = (v_5, v_4, v_3, v_2, v_1) = (0,0,1,0,0)$$
$$\max(c) = (v'_5, v'_4, v'_3, v'_2, v'_1) = (1,1,1,1,0)$$

in agreement with the two vertices that are respectively nearest and farthest (in c) from $(0,0,0,0,0)$.

Two vertices v and v' are said to be *diagonally opposite* vertices of a k cell c if $v \subseteq c$, $v' \subseteq c$, and $\Delta(v, v') = k$. It is clear that diagonally opposite vertices are as far away from each other, in the sense of the Hamming distance, as two vertices of the cell c may be. (See Prob. 2.3.) Furthermore, if c is a k cell, we learn from Eqs. 2.8 and 2.7 that

$$\Delta(\min(c), \max(c)) = \sum_{c_i = I} 1 = k$$

so that $\min(c)$ and $\max(c)$ are diagonally opposite. The reader will be able to find diagonally opposite pairs of vertices other than $\min(c)$ and $\max(c)$ in Example 2.4, thereby convincing himself that diagonally opposite vertices are not necessarily minimum and maximum vertices. (See Example 2.5.)

The idea that two cells may have no vertices in common is also capable of expression in terms of the Hamming distance. We say that cells c and c' are *disjoint* if

$$\Delta(v, v') > 0 \qquad \text{for all } v \subseteq c, \quad v' \subseteq c'$$

Note that this definition is consistent with that for "disjointness" of sets (cf. Sec 0.3) if the cells c, $c' \in C^n$ are considered as subsets of I^n as introduced in Eq. 2.2.

In Probs. 2.4 through 2.8 the reader is asked to certify a series of straightforward characterizations of the geometric notions of this section in terms of relations among the coordinates of the vertices and cells under consideration. The problem statements (if not their proofs) warrant attention for an appreciation of the computational procedures to be presented in this and the next chapter.

EXAMPLES 2.5

In the cell $c = (I,I,1,I,0)$ of Example 2.4, the vertices $v = (0,0,1,1,0)$ and $v' = (1,1,1,0,0)$ are diagonally opposite, since

$$\Delta(v, v') = 3 = k \qquad (c \text{ is a 3-cell})$$

Generally speaking, if v is a vertex with $v \subseteq c$, there is always a unique vertex $v' \subseteq c$ that is diagonally opposite to v in c. It is obtained by complementing those coordinates of v that correspond to indices j for which $c_j = I$. Thus, if $v = (1,0,1,1,0) = (v_5,v_4,v_3,v_2,v_1)$ in our present example, cell $c = (I,I,1,I,0)$, we obtain the diagonally opposite vertex v' in c by complementing the second, fourth, and fifth coordinates of v; that is, $v' = (0,1,1,0,0)$.

As yet another geometric concept related to the notion of "distance," let us say that two cells $c = (c_n, c_{n-1}, \cdots, c_1)$ and $c' = (c'_n, c'_{n-1}, \cdots, c'_n)$ of C^n are *parallel* (written $c \,|\, c'$) if $c_i = I \Longleftrightarrow c'_i = I$; that is, if both c and c' have I in the same coordinates. With this definition, we have $c \,|\, c$ for any cell c ($|$ is a reflexive relation on C^n), and if we want to emphasize that $c \,|\, c'$, but $c \neq c'$, we will write $c \,\|\, c'$. Note that every pair of vertices v, $v' \in C^n$ is parallel, by definition. Moreover, we can extend the notion of "distance" to all pairs of parallel cells in an obvious way: If $c|c'$ we define

$$\Delta(c, c') = \sum_{c_i \neq I} |c_i - c_i'|,$$

for the coordinates $c_i' \neq I$ are the same ones as those for which $c_i \neq I$. Thus $c' = (I,I,0,I,1)$ is parallel to the cell c of Example 2.5 and $\Delta(c,c') = 2$.

2.4 BASIS

Let $c \in C^n$ be a k cell. The collection

$$X = \{v^{(1)}, v^{(2)}, \cdots, v^{(k)}\}$$

of k vertices is said to be a *basis*† for c if
(1) $v^{(i)} \subseteq c$ $(i = 1, 2, \cdots, k)$.
(2) There exists a vertex $v \subseteq c$ such that $v^{(i)}$ is adjacent to v for each $i = 1, 2, \cdots, k$.

The existence of bases and the number of bases for a cell c are learned from the following theorem.

Theorem 2.1.   Let $c \in C^n$ be a k cell and $v \subseteq c$. Then the collection

$$X_{v,c} = \{v^{(i)}; v^{(i)} \text{ is adjacent to } v \text{ and } v^{(i)} \subseteq c\}$$

is a basis for c (see Prob. 2.5), and if $k \neq 2$, the mapping

$$v \longrightarrow X_{v,c}$$

is a 1–1 mapping of all vertices of c onto the family of all bases for c. Thus, a k cell has 2^k bases ($k \neq 2$).

PROOF.   If c is a k cell in C^n, $X_{v,c}$ will have k elements and is therefore immediately seen to be a basis for c. Suppose $X_{v,c} = X_{u,c}$ and $k \neq 2$. Then, according to property (3), Sec. 2.3, of a distance function,

$$\Delta(u, v) \leq \Delta(u, v^{(i)}) + \Delta(v^{(i)}, v) = 1 + 1 + 2 \qquad (2.9)$$

Now if $\Delta(u,v) = 1$, we have $u \in X_{v,c}$ and $v \in X_{u,c}$. Furthermore, since $\Delta(u,v) = 1$ implies that $v = (u_n, u_{n-1}, \cdots, u_{i+1}, \bar{u}_i, u_{i-1}, \cdots, u_1)$ for some i, we must have that

$$\left.\begin{array}{c} w \in X_{u,c} \\ w \neq v \end{array}\right\} \Longrightarrow \Delta(w, v) = 2 \Longrightarrow w \notin X_{v,c} = X_{u,c}$$

†The reader who has some familiarity with linear algebra will wonder about this terminology until Theorem 2.8 exhibits an algebraic analogy to the concept of a basis for a vector space.

and, similarly,

$$\left.\begin{array}{l} w \in X_{v,c} \\ w \neq u \end{array}\right\} \Longrightarrow w \notin X_{u,c} = X_{v,c}$$

Together these imply

$$\{v\} = X_{u,c} = X_{v,c} = \{u\}$$

so that $u = v$ and $\Delta(u,v) = \Delta(u,u) = 0$, a contradiction.

If $\Delta(u, v) = 2$, $v = (u_n, u_{n-1}, \cdots, \bar{u}_i, \cdots, \bar{u}_j, \cdots, u_1)$ for some pair of indices i, j $(1 \leq j \leq i \leq n)$. An analysis similar to the preceding one will show that

$$\{u^{(i)}, u^{(j)}\} = X_{u,c} = X_{v,c}$$

where

$$u^{(i)} = (u_n, u_{n-1}, \cdots, u_i, \cdots, \bar{u}_j, \cdots, u_1)$$

$$u^{(j)} = (u_n, u_{n-1}, \cdots, \bar{u}_i, \cdots, u_j, \cdots, u_1)$$

so that, necessarily, $k = 2$ (c is a cell whose vertices have exactly two adjacent vertices in c). But we were assuming that $k \neq 2$, so that the situation $\Delta(u, v) = 2$ cannot arise.

Thus, Eq. 2.9 and the above analyses give

$$X_{u,c} = X_{v,c} \Longrightarrow \Delta(u, v) = 0 \Longrightarrow u = v$$

because of property (1) Sec. 2.3, of a distance function, showing that the mapping $v \to X_{v,c}$ is 1–1 if $k \neq 2$. The mapping is onto the entire collection of bases, for if $X = \{v^{(1)}, v^{(2)}, \cdots, v^{(k)}\}$ is any basis for c, there exists a vertex $v \subseteq c$ such that $v^{(i)}$ is adjacent to v for each $i = 1, 2, \cdots, k$, and clearly $v \to X_{v,c} = X$. This completes the proof, since B^n is known to have 2^n elements. ∎

The reader will certainly see that in the exceptional case where c is a 2-cell, c will have 2 (rather than $2^2 = 4$) bases corresponding to its two pairs of diagonally opposite vertices. It will not be necessary to treat this case specially in the following theorem.

Theorem 2.2. Let $v \in B^n \subseteq C^n$ and suppose $X = \{v^{(1)}, v^{(2)}, \cdots, {}^{(k)}\}$ is a collection of vertices of C^n with $v^{(i)}$ adjacent to v for each $i = 1, 2, \cdots, k$, $(k \leq n)$. Then there is a unique cell $c \in C^n$ for which X is a basis for c. Furthermore, c is a k cell and $X = X_{v,c}$.

PROOF. By the definition of adjacency, we must have $\Delta(v^{(i)}, v) = 1$ for each $i = 1, 2, \cdots, k$ so that

$$v^{(i)} = (v_n, v_{n-1}, \cdots, \bar{v}_{j_i}, \cdots, v_1) \qquad (i = 1, 2, \cdots, k)$$

for a collection of distinct indices $J = \{j_1, j_2, \cdots, j_k\} \subseteq n^+$. Now consider the k cell $c = (c_n, c_{n-1}, \cdots, c_1)$ defined by the rules:

(a) $c_j = I$ if $j \in J$.
(b) $c_j = v_j$ otherwise.

We then have $v \subseteq c$ and $v^{(i)} \subseteq c$ $(i = 1, 2, \cdots, k)$ according to Eq. 2.5. Hence, X is a basis for c and $X = X_{v,c}$. We leave the proof of uniqueness as an exercise. ∎

EXAMPLE 2.6

Consider the 3-cell $c = (I,I,1,I,0)$ of C^5 and the vertex $v = (1,0,1,1,0) \subseteq c$. (Cf. Example 2.4.) Then

$$X_{v,c} = \{(1,0,1,0,0), (1,1,1,1,0), (0,0,1,1,0)\}$$

is obtained by complementing coordinates of v one at a time for each index j for which $c_j = I$. (See Fig. 2.3.)

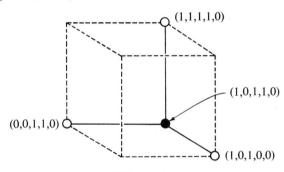

FIGURE 2.3

EXAMPLE 2.7

Suppose $v = (1,0,1,0,1,1) \in C^6$. Vertices that are adjacent to v are obtained by complementing coordinates of v one at a time. Thus

$$v^{(1)} = (1,1,1,0,1,1) = (v_6, \bar{v}_5, v_4, v_3, v_2, v_1)$$
$$v^{(2)} = (1,0,0,0,1,1) = (v_6, v_5, \bar{v}_4, v_3, v_2, v_1)$$
$$v^{(3)} = (1,0,1,0,0,1) = (v_6, v_5, v_4, v_3, \bar{v}_2, v_1)$$
$$v^{(4)} = (1,0,1,0,1,0) = (v_6, v_5, v_4, v_3, v_2, \bar{v}_1)$$

are four of the six vertices adjacent to v in C^6. If

$$X = \{v^{(1)}, v^{(2)}, v^{(3)}, v^{(4)}\}$$

there is (as asserted in Theorem 2.2) exactly one cell $c \in C^6$ having X as a basis. Since $J = \{5, 4, 2, 1\} \subseteq 6^+$ is the set of indices referred to in that theorem, we must have
(i) $c_j = I$ for $j = 1, 2, 4, 5$.
(ii) $c_j = v_j$ otherwise.
Hence, $c = (1,I,I,0,I,I)$ is the required 4-cell. Clearly, $X = X_{v,c}$.

Finally, when X is a basis for a cell c and Y is a subset of X, we say that Y is a *subbasis* of X. On account of Theorem 2.2 a subbasis will automatically be a basis for some cell c', and it is clear that $c' \subseteq c$ in the partially ordered set C^n and that $c' = c$ iff $Y = X$.

2.5 BOOLEAN PRODUCTS AND CELLS

Before the theory of the cellular n cube C^n is completely developed, it is well that we illustrate the connection between C^n and the minimization problems defined in Sec. 1.17. In the introduction to this chapter, we implied that a reasonably satisfactory solution to such problems can be obtained by concentrating on representations of Boolean functions as "Boolean sums of Boolean products." It will be convenient, in introducing Boolean products, to augment our use of parenthetical exponents on variables (cf. Sec. 1.11):

$$x_i^{(0)} \equiv \bar{x}_i$$
$$x_i^{(1)} \equiv x_i$$

to include also

$$x_i^{(I)} = 1 \qquad \text{(or the absence of } x_i \text{ in a product)}$$

Then we say that a *Boolean product* p in the variables $x_n, x_{n-1}, \cdots, x_1$ is a product:

$$p = x_n^{(c_n)} \cdot x_{n-1}^{(c_{n-1})} \cdots x_1^{(c_1)}; \quad c_i \in C = \{0, 1, I\} \qquad (i = 1, 2, \cdots, n)$$

$$(2.10)$$

and we denote the set of all such products by

$$P^n = \{ p; p \text{ is a Boolean product in } x_n, x_{n-1}, \cdots, x_1 \}$$

EXAMPLE 2.8

$$p = x_5^{(0)} \cdot x_4^{(I)} \cdot x_3^{(1)} \cdot x_2^{(1)} \cdot x_1^{(0)} = \bar{x}_5 x_3 x_2 \bar{x}_1$$

is a Boolean product in the variables x_5, x_4, x_3, x_2, x_1. Note that it is not a minterm in these variables, however. But it is true that every minterm is a Boolean product. Note that in Eq. 2.10,

$$p \text{ is a minterm} \Longleftrightarrow c_i \in B = \{0, 1\} \qquad (i = 1, 2, \ldots, n) \qquad (2.11)$$

Now it is no doubt intuitively clear that when a product p is used to define a Boolean polynomial (and hence a function $f: B^n \longrightarrow B$),

$$f(x_n, x_{n-1}, \cdots, x_1) = p; \quad p \in P^n$$

this function has as its minimal circuit (cf. Sec. 1.17) the "and" gate N_p, whose inputs are precisely those variables $x_j^{(c_j)}$ for which $c_j \neq I$ in Eq. 2.10. For this reason, we define for $p \in P^n$:

$$m(p) = \sum_{i=1}^{n} m_i(p) = c(N_p) \tag{2.12}$$

where

$$m_i(p) = 1 \quad \text{if } c_i \in B$$
$$m_i(p) = 0 \quad \text{otherwise}$$

EXAMPLE 2.9

For $p = \bar{x}_5 x_3 x_2 \bar{x}_1$ as in the previous example, we have

$$m(p) = \sum_{i=1}^{5} m_i(p) = 1 + 1 + 1 + 0 + 1 = 4 = c(N_p)$$

where N_p is the "and" gate with inputs $\bar{x}_1$, x_2, x_3, and $\bar{x}_5$.

Motivated by an attempt to use C^n as a mathematical model for studying P^n and thence the "sum of products" minimization problem, we impose a partial order $\supseteq$ on P^n by defining for

$$p = x_n^{(c_n)} x_{n-1}^{(c_{n-1})} \cdots x_1^{(c_1)} \qquad (c_i \in C)$$
$$q = x_n^{(d_n)} x_{n-1}^{(d_{n-1})} \cdots x_1^{(d_1)} \qquad (d_i \in C)$$

the relation (see Prob. 2.9)

$$p \supseteq q \Longleftrightarrow c_i \geq d_i \quad \text{in } C \qquad (i = 1, 2, \cdots, n) \tag{2.13}$$

EXAMPLE 2.10

If p is the product of Example 2.8 and

$$q = x_5^{(0)} x_4^{(0)} x_3^{(1)} x_2^{(1)} x_1^{(0)} = \bar{x}_5 \bar{x}_4 x_3 x_2 \bar{x}_1$$

$p \supseteq q$, since $0 \geq 0$, $I \geq 0$, $1 \geq 1$, $1 \geq 1$, and $0 \geq 0$ in C. On the other hand, if $r = \bar{x}_5 x_2$, $r \supseteq p$ while p is not comparable (we neither have $s \supseteq p$ nor $p \supseteq s$) with $s = x_5 x_3 x_1$.

While the order relation (Eq. 2.13) in P^n may seem unnatural, and the reader may have preferred that it be inverted, our reason for defining it in this way can be explained by the following consequence (and by Prob. 2.9).

Theorem 2.3. $P^n \cong C^n$.

PROOF. Define the mapping

$$\tau : P^n \longrightarrow C^n$$

so that

$$p = x_n^{(c_n)} x_{n-1}^{(c_{n-1})} \cdots x_1^{(c_1)} \xrightarrow{\ \tau\ } (c_n, c_{n-1}, \cdots, c_1)$$

Evidently τ is 1–1 and onto C^n while preserving the relation $\supseteq$. Hence, P^n is isomorphic to C^n. ∎

Corollary 2.4. If $p \in P^n$,

$$m(p) + \theta(\tau(p)) = n \tag{2.14}$$

PROOF. Suppose $p = x_n^{(c_n)} x_{n-1}^{(c_{n-1})} \cdots x_1^{(c_1)}$ is a Boolean product with $c_j = I$ for k of the indices $j = 1, 2, \cdots, n$. Then

$$\tau(p) = (c_n, c_{n-1}, \cdots, c_1)$$

is a k cell; that is,

$$\theta(\tau(p)) = k$$

while

$$m(p) = \sum_{i=1}^{n} m_i(p) = n - k$$

so that Eq. 2.14 holds. ∎

Now suppose that p is a minterm. Then, from Eqs. 2.11 and 2.12, we have $m(p) = n$ so that $\theta(\tau(p)) = 0$, from Eq. 2.14. Thus we have concluded half of the following corollary.

Corollary 2.5. p is a minterm $\Longleftrightarrow$ $\tau(p)$ is a vertex

And the other half is equally transparent. Because of this last result, we are able to represent each Boolean function $f:B^n \longrightarrow B$ in its minterm canonical form as a collection $K^0(f)$ of vertices of the n cube C^n.

EXAMPLE 2.11

Consider the Boolean function $f = f(x_3, x_2, x_1)$ given by the minterm canonical form

$$f(x_3, x_2, x_1) = \bar{x}_3 \bar{x}_2 \bar{x}_1 + \bar{x}_3 x_2 \bar{x}_1 + x_3 \bar{x}_2 \bar{x}_1 + x_3 x_2 \bar{x}_1 + x_3 x_2 x_1$$

or equivalently by the truth table

x_3	x_2	x_1	f
0	0	0	1
0	0	1	0
0	1	0	1
0	1	1	0
1	0	0	1
1	0	1	0
1	1	0	1
1	1	1	1

The correspondence τ yields the set of (black) vertices of Fig. 2.4 so that

$$K^0(f) = \{(0,0,0), (0,1,0), (1,0,0), (1,1,0), (1,1,1)\}$$

The equality

$$f(x_3, x_2, x_1) = \bar{x}_1 + x_3 x_2$$

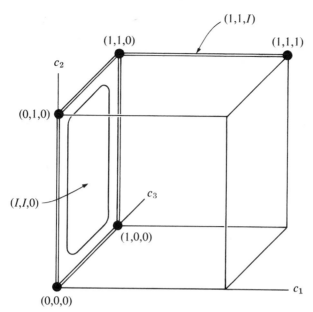

FIGURE 2.4

(which could be obtained

$$f(x_3, x_2, x_1) = \bar{x}_3\bar{x}_2\bar{x}_1 + \bar{x}_3x_2\bar{x}_1 + x_3\bar{x}_2\bar{x}_1 + x_3x_2\bar{x}_1 + x_3x_2x_1$$
$$= (\bar{x}_3\bar{x}_2\bar{x}_1 + \bar{x}_3x_2\bar{x}_1) + (x_3\bar{x}_2\bar{x}_1 + x_3x_2\bar{x}_1)$$
$$+ (x_3x_2\bar{x}_1 + x_3x_2x_1)$$
$$= (\bar{x}_3\bar{x}_1 + x_3\bar{x}_1) + x_3x_2 = \bar{x}_1 + x_3x_2$$

by applying the theorems of Boolean algebra) is revealed in Fig. 2.4 when we observe that the vertices of $K^0(f)$ are "covered" by the cells $(I,I,0)$ and $(1,1,I)$. The inverse mapping τ^{-1} (which exists because τ is an isomorphism) then yields

$$(I, I, 0) \xrightarrow{\tau^{-1}} \bar{x}_1$$
$$(1, 1, I) \xrightarrow{\tau^{-1}} x_3x_2$$

the two products of Eq. 2.15. While we will eventually replace such geometric observations by computational procedures, the usefulness of the cellular n cube C_n as a mathematical model for the sum of products minimization theory becomes evident.

Note in Fig. 2.4 that the collection of cells

$$K(f) = K^0(f) \cup \{(I,0,0), (1,I,0), (I,1,0), (0,I,0), (I,I,0), (1,1,I)\}$$

has the "complex" property

$$c \in K(f), \quad c' \subseteq c \Longrightarrow c' \in K(f) \tag{2.16}$$

and the "Boolean complex"[†] property

———

[†]A term suggested by J.P. Roth, "Combinatorial Topological Methods in the Synthesis of Switching Circuits," *I.B.M. Research Report RC-11*, 1957.

$$v \in K(f) \text{ for every vertex } v \subseteq c \Longrightarrow c \in K(f) \qquad (2.17)$$

These observations will be important when we formalize and generalize the techniques illustrated in the preceding example; furthermore, they serve as motivation for the material of the next section.

2.6 CELL COMPLEXES AND SKELETONS

Guided by Eqs. 2.16 and 2.17 as applied to Example 2.11, we make the following definitions:

A *cell complex K* in C^n is a subset of C^n having the property that

$$c \in K, \quad c' \subseteq c \Longrightarrow c' \in K \qquad (2.18)$$

Such a cell complex is said to be *Boolean* if

$$v \in K \text{ for every vertex } v \subseteq c \Longrightarrow c \in K \qquad (2.19)$$

Comparing Eqs. 2.16 and 2.17 with Eqs. 2.18 and 2.19 the reader can anticipate that there is a natural Boolean cell complex to associate with a Boolean function $f:B^n \to B$. By reviewing Example 2.11, he will appreciate the way in which this association comes about.

Suppose $f \in B(n)$, that is, $f:B^n \to B$. We consider the set[†]

$$K(f) = \{c \in C^n; f(v) = 1 \text{ for all vertices } v \subseteq c\} \qquad (2.20)$$

It is then a simple matter to establish the result:

Theorem 2.6 $\quad K(f)$ is a Boolean cell complex.

PROOF. Suppose $c \in K(f)$ and $c' \subseteq c$. We have $f(v) = 1$ for all vertices $v \subseteq c$, so that also $f(v) = 1$ for all $v \subseteq c'$ because $v \subseteq c'$ implies $v \subseteq c$, showing that $c' \in K(f)$; that is, $K(f)$ is a complex. That $K(f)$ is Boolean is also easily shown, for suppose $v \in K(f)$ for every vertex $v \subseteq c$. This means that $f(v) = 1$ for all vertices $v \subseteq c$, so that $c \in K(f)$. ∎

For an example, the reader is invited to reexamine Example 2.11. Incidentally, we should point out that

$$\bar{K}(f) = \{c \in C^n; f(v) = 0 \quad \text{for all vertices } v \subseteq c\} \qquad (2.21)$$

is also a Boolean complex, and in reexamining Example 2.11, the reader should try to list the cells of $\bar{K}(f)$. Note that

$$\bar{K}(f) = K(\bar{f}) \qquad (2.22)$$

---

†If $v = (v_n, v_{n-1}, \cdots, v_1) \in B^n \subseteq C^n$, we mean by $f(v)$ the "value" $f(v_n, v_{n-1}, \cdots, v_1)$ of the function f when $x_i = v_i$ $(i = 1, 2, \cdots, n)$.

for any Boolean function f. Here $\bar{f}$ is the function obtained from f by complementing every element in the truth table of f. (Cf. Prob. 1.25.)

A *subcomplex* L of a complex K is a subset of K, which is itself a cell complex. The reader should see that a subset of a complex is not necessarily a subcomplex and that a subcomplex L of a Boolean complex K is not necessarily Boolean. Important (particularly when $q = 0$) among the subcomplexes of a given complex K are the *q-dimensional skeletons* $K^q (q \geq 0)$, which consist of all cells of K having order $\leq q$. Thus

$$K^q = \{c \in K; \ \theta(c) \leq q\} \qquad (2.23)$$

When $K = K(f)$ is the Boolean complex corresponding (cf. Eq. 2.20) to a function $f \in B(n)$, its 0-dimensional skeleton

$$K^0(f) = \{v \in B^n; \ f(v) = 1\} \qquad (2.24)$$

is seen to consist precisely of those vertices v for which the function has the value 1 in its truth table. (Cf. Example 2.11.)

Except for the description of certain decimal computations in C^n and the exposition of the lattice structure of the n cube, we have already developed enough mathematical machinery to state precisely and to solve conveniently the completely specified minimization problem as restricted to "sum of products" (or dually, "product of sums") representations. These two omissions will be treated in the succeeding two sections. Then, rather than state and solve the problem (which is no easy task—even with our machinery), we will delay doing so until the following chapter. Instead we will make an application of our cellular theory to the determination of the complete class decomposition of $B(3)$.

2.7 LATTICE STRUCTURE OF C^n

We have described the partially ordered set $(C^n, \supseteq)$ and have discussed several of its geometric properties with respect to the Hamming distance. However, the n cube has a natural structure as a lattice, the knowledge of which adds considerably to our geometric insight and computational facility.

For each cell $c = (c_n, c_{n-1}, \cdots, c_1)$ in C^n, there is a natural associated subset (call it S_c) of I^n (cf., Eq. 2.2), namely,

$$S_c = \{(x_n, x_{n-1}, \cdots, x_1); \ x_i = c_i \text{ if } c_i \in B,$$
$$0 \leq x_i \leq 1 \text{ otherwise}\} \qquad (2.25)$$

This set is simply the set of all points $x = (x_n, x_{n-1}, \cdots, x_1)$ of I^n, which one would think of as being contained in the cell c. Thus $(\frac{1}{2}, \frac{1}{4}, 0) \in S_c$, but $(\frac{1}{2}, \frac{1}{4}, \frac{1}{8}) \notin S_c$ if $c = (I, I, 0)$. If $c = (c_n, c_{n-1}, \cdots, c_1)$ and $d = (d_n, d_{n-1}, \cdots, d_1)$ are arbitrary cells in C^n, we would like to define $c \cdot d$ to be that cell whose associated subset is $S_c \cap S_d$; that is, we want

$$S_{c \cdot d} = S_c \cap S_d \qquad (2.26)$$

Here we have to be prepared for the possibility that S_c and S_d are disjoint. But we remarked at the conclusion of Sec. 2.2 that we could postulate the existence of a zero element 0 in C^n. Thus, if S_c and S_d are disjoint sets (which happens iff c and d are disjoint cells in the sense of Sec. 2.3), we could take as their product this 0 element. It can be seen that the cell $c \cdot d$ we are defining will correspond to the g.l.b. of c and d in terms of the order relation $\supseteq$ on C^n.

Now the set union $S_c \cup S_d$ does not correspond to a cell of C^n, so that in defining $c + d$, we could only resort to a description based on a l.u.b. operation in $(C^n, \supseteq)$. There exist cells—$1 = (I, I, \cdots, I)$ is an example—which contain both c and d in $(C^n, \supseteq)$, and we must take as $c + d$ the "smallest" such cell.

These remarks are not intended as a definition of addition and multiplication in C^n, but are instead designed to motivate the coordinate-wise definitions that follow. We return first to the partially ordered set C in Fig. 2.1. There we adjoin the empty set $\varnothing$ as zero element, denoting the resulting lattice by C'. Clearly, C' has the addition and multiplication tables (with braces omitted from $\{0\}$ and $\{1\}$):

+	$\varnothing$	0	1	I
$\varnothing$	$\varnothing$	0	1	I
0	0	0	I	I
1	1	I	1	I
I	I	I	I	I

$\cdot$	$\varnothing$	0	1	I
$\varnothing$	$\varnothing$	$\varnothing$	$\varnothing$	$\varnothing$
0	$\varnothing$	0	$\varnothing$	0
1	$\varnothing$	$\varnothing$	1	1
I	$\varnothing$	0	1	I

Using only the dotted portion of these tables (since the coordinates of cells are 0,1, or I) as coordinate-wise definitions for addition and multiplication in C^n,

$$c + d = (c_n + d_n, c_{n-1} + d_{n-1}, \cdots, c_1 + d_1) \qquad (2.27)$$

$$c \cdot d = (c_n \cdot d_n, c_{n-1} \cdot d_{n-1}, \cdots, c_1 \cdot d_1) \qquad (2.28)$$

we obtain the sum and product that we originally had in mind. Of course we must put $c \cdot d = 0$ if $c_i \cdot d_i = \varnothing$ for some i because (see Prob. 2.8)

$$S_c \cap S_d = \varnothing \longleftrightarrow d_i = \bar{c}_i \qquad \text{for some } i$$

We leave to the reader the task of verifying that $(C^n, +, \cdot)$ is a lattice when $(+)$ and $(\cdot)$ are defined by Eqs. 2.27 and 2.28.

EXAMPLE 2.12

In Fig. 2.1 consider the cells $c = (1,I,0)$ and $d = (1,0,I)$. From Eq. 2.27,

$$c + d = (1 + 1, I + 0, 0 + I) = (1,I,I)$$

which is recognized as the "smallest" cell containing each of the line segments c and d. Now suppose instead that $c = (1,I,I)$ and $d = (I,I,0)$. Then, according to Eq. 2.28, we have

$$c \cdot d = (1 \cdot I, I \cdot I, I \cdot 0) = (1,I,0)$$

This cell is seen to be the line segment that is the intersection of the cells c and d considered as sets, that is,

$$S_{(1, I, 0)} = S_{(1, I, I)} \cap S_{(I, I, 0)}$$

As an example in the use of the addition operation in C^n, we now illustrate the *Quine-McClusky algorithm* (see the appropriate reference in Chapter 3) for generating all cells of a Boolean complex

$$K = K^0 \cup \left(\bigcup_{q=0}^{n-1} (K^{q+1} - K^q) \right)$$

when given only its 0-skeleton K^0. The algorithm depends upon the identities

(1) $\quad K^1 - K^0 = \{v + v'; \; v, v' \in K^0, \Delta(v, v') = 1\}$, $\qquad$ **(2.29a)**
(2) $\quad$ and for all $q \geq 1$,

$$K^{q+1} - K^q = \{c + c'; \; c, c', \in K^q - K^{q-1}, c \,\|\, c', \Delta(c, c') = 1\} \quad \textbf{(2.29b)}$$

which the reader should not find difficult to verify. (See Prob. 2.31.) One simply uses Eq. 2.29 successively to derive $K^1 - K^0$ from K^0, $K^2 - K^1$ from $K^1 - K^0$, etc., terminating the process when the difference set $K^q - K^{q-1}$ has no pair of cells (c and c') satisfying $c \,\|\, c'$ and $\Delta(c, c') = 1$.

EXAMPLE 2.13

Suppose K is the Boolean cell complex in C^5 whose 0-skeleton is the set of vertices in the list at the left of the following array (with parentheses and commas removed for the sake of simplicity).

The vertices in the list K^0 (as well as the cells in the successive lists $K^q - K^{q-1}$) are partitioned into "blocks" of vertices having the same number of "1" coordinates. This is done for ease in applying Eq. 2.29; one can use the fact that $c \,\|\, c'$ and $\Delta(c, c') = 1$ imply that c and c' occupy neighboring "blocks" of the partition, thereby narrowing the search for pairs of cells that qualify in Eq. 2.29.

Thus, $v = (0,0,0,0,0)$ need be compared only with the vertices $u = (0,0,1,0,0)$ and $w = (0,1,0,0,0)$ of the neighboring block. Similarly, u needs only to be compared with $x = (0,0,0,1,1)$, $y = (1,0,1,0,0)$, and $z = (1,1,0,0,0)$

K^0	$K^1 - K^0$	$K^2 - K^1$
0 0 0 0 0 ✓	0 0 I 0 0	0 I I 1 1
0 0 1 0 0 ✓	0 I 0 0 0	I 0 I 1 1
0 1 0 0 0 ✓	I 0 1 0 0	I I 1 1 1
0 0 0 1 1 ✓	I 1 0 0 0	
1 0 1 0 0 ✓	0 0 I 1 1 ✓	
1 1 0 0 0 ✓	0 I 0 1 1 ✓	
0 0 1 1 1 ✓	I 0 0 1 1 ✓	
0 1 0 1 1 ✓	1 I 1 0 0	
1 0 0 1 1 ✓	1 1 I 0 0	
1 1 1 0 0 ✓	0 I 1 1 1 ✓	
0 1 1 1 1 ✓	0 1 I 1 1 ✓	
1 0 1 1 1 ✓	I 0 1 1 1 ✓	
1 1 1 1 0 ✓	1 0 I 1 1 ✓	
1 1 1 1 1 ✓	1 1 1 I 0	
	I 1 1 1 1 ✓	
	1 I 1 1 1 ✓	
	1 1 1 1 I	

in testing for adjacency (every pair of vertices is parallel, so that the condition $v\|v'$ would have been redundant in Eq. 2.29a). On the basis of the comparisons cited here, we put

$$v + u = (0,0,I,0,0)$$
$$v + w = (0,I,0,0,0)$$
$$u + y = (I,0,1,0,0)$$

in the list $K^1 - K^0$. After completing the list $K^1 - K^0$, its members are rearranged or partitioned according to the same scheme used for K^0, whence the comparison process is repeated, using Eq. 2.29b in order to derive $K^2 - K^1$, etc. Thus, $c = (0,0,I,1,1)$ and $c' = (0,1,I,1,1)$ satisfy $c\|c'$, $\Delta(c,c') = 1$, so we put $c + c' = (0,I,I,1,1)$ in the list $K^2 - K^1$. (Note that $d = (0,I,0,1,1)$ and $d' = (0,I,1,1,1)$ also meet the conditions of Eq. 2.29b, but we obtain the same sum $d + d' = (0,I,I,1,1)$.)

We have put check marks ($\checkmark$) beside cells that could be added in an application of Eq. 2.29. Those that remain unchecked are necessarily "maximal" cells of the complex K. These occupy a position of central importance in the minimization theory. (See Theorem 3.6.) The reader may have anticipated as much from his consideration of Example 2.11.

For our purposes, an important result concerning the lattice structure of C^n is the following

Theorem 2.7. Let c be any cell of C^n. Then

$$c = \min(c) + \max(c)$$

PROOF. The proof is obvious from the preliminary definition of addition in C^n; that is, one can easily see that c is the smallest cell that contains the vertices $\min(c)$ and $\max(c)$. Thus, it is necessary only to be convinced that the coordinate-wise definition of Eq. 2.27 agrees with the preliminary one. ∎

This result will be useful in computing the coordinates of c from those of two vertices v and v', which are known to be its minimum and maximum vertices. Of course the argument that establishes Theorem 2.7 would also deliver the more general result

$$c = v + v' \tag{2.30}$$

for *any* pair of diagonally opposite vertices v and v' of c; but by virtue of their uniqueness, we prefer to concentrate, when possible or practical, on the minimum and maximum vertices. An added reason for preferring them is contained in the following observation: When the strings of coordinates for the vertices of a cell are interpreted as integers in the base 2, and the resulting integers are converted to the base 10 (as we will soon have occasion to do), the minimum and maximum vertices will have minimum and maximum magnitudes, respectively, among the collection of decimal integers so obtained; thus, they are more easily recognized than are an arbitrary pair of diagonally opposite vertices.

EXAMPLE 2.14

In Example 2.4 we computed

$$\min(c) = (0,0,1,0,0)$$
$$\max(c) = (1,1,1,1,0)$$

for a cell $c \in C^5$. Note that

$$\min(c) + \max(c) = (0 + 1,\ 0 + 1,\ 1 + 1,\ 0 + 1,\ 0 + 0)$$
$$= (I,I,1,I,0) = c$$

as predicted by Theorem 2.7. Similarly, for the diagonally opposite vertices $v = (0,0,1,1,0)$ and $v' = (1,1,1,0,0)$ of Example 2.5, we again obtain

$$v + v' = (0 + 1,\ 0 + 1,\ 1 + 1,\ 1 + 0,\ 0 + 0)$$
$$= (I,I,1,I,0) = c$$

in agreement with Eq. 2.30.

Note that $\partial(\min(c)) = 4$ and $\partial(\max(c)) = 30$, and these are the smallest and largest among the eight decimal integers 4, 6, 12, 14, 20, 22, 28, 30 obtained by computing $\partial(v_5, v_4, v_3, v_2, v_1)$ for all eight vertices $(v_5, v_4, v_3, v_2, v_1)$ of the cell $c = (I,I,1,I,0)$, as tabulated in Example 2.4.

2.8   THE DECIMAL TRANSFORM

While the cellular n cube C^n has obvious geometric and intuitive value in representing Boolean products, we would be severely hampered in the applications if we attempted to use its notation exclusively. For computational purposes, it would be convenient to have a natural way of representing each cell as a decimal integer. A natural representation of this sort is already available for the vertices. We can simply use the function $\partial : B^n \longrightarrow Z_{2^n}$ of Eq. 0.66. But if we do this, we exhaust the set of decimal integers in Z_{2^n} with the vertices alone, and there seems to be no way of representing also the higher-order cells within such a framework.

A solution to this dilemma is at hand, however, if we allow pairs (X, Y) of decimal integers in our representations. We have learned from Theorem 2.7 that a cell $c \in C^n$ is uniquely determined by its minimum and maximum vertices and that c and be computed quite effectively from $\min(c)$ and $\max(c)$. We therefore define the *decimal transform*

$$D : C^n \longrightarrow Z_{2^n} \times Z_{2^n}$$

according to the rule

$$D(c) = (\partial(\min(c)), \partial(\max(c))) \tag{2.31}$$

EXAMPLE 2.15

The effect of the transform D on C^4 is illustrated in Fig. 2.5. The cell $c = (I,0,1,I)$ has the transform

$$\begin{aligned} D(c) &= (\partial(\min(c)), \partial(\max(c))) \\ &= (\partial(0,0,1,0), \partial(1,0,1,1)) \\ &= (2, 11) \end{aligned}$$

and has been labeled as a transformed 2-cell in Fig. 2.5. There we notice that D is not onto $Z_{2^4} \times Z_{2^4} = Z_{16} \times Z_{16}$. Evidently the "grid points" of $Z_{2^n} \times Z_{2^n}$, which do not occur as images under D, have coordinates $(X, Y) = (\partial(v), \partial(v'))$ for vertices v and v', which are diagonally opposite, but are not minimum and maximum vertices of some cell c. In our example, with $n = 4$, the point $(X, Y) = (3, 10)$ does not occur as an image under D. Note that the vertices $v = (0,0,1,1)$ and $v' = (1,0,1,0)$ are diagonally opposite in $c = (I,0,1,I)$, but are not minimum and maximum vertices of c.

In our computational applications of the decimal transform, we will be most interested in a related mapping

$$D' : Z_{2^n} \times Z_{2^n} \longrightarrow C^n$$

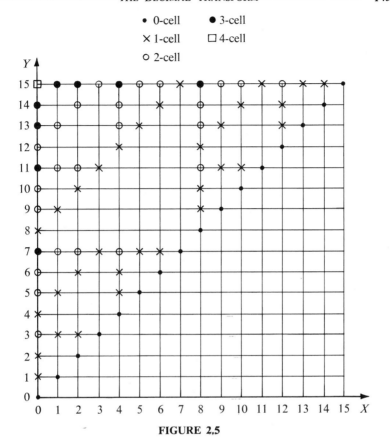

FIGURE 2.5

which transforms pairs (X, Y) into cells. It is clear that this cannot be a true inverse mapping because D is not onto (although it is 1–1). But the mapping $\partial : B^n \longrightarrow Z_{2^n}$ is 1–1 and onto, so that ∂^{-1} exists. (Cf. Sec. 0.4.) Evidently ∂^{-1} is essentially a decimal to binary base conversion. We then define

$$D'(X, Y) = \partial^{-1}(X) + \partial^{-1}(Y) \qquad (2.32)$$

and by Eq. 2.30, this gives the cell $c = D'(X, Y)$, which has $\partial^{-1}(X)$ and $\partial^{-1}(Y)$ as diagonally opposite vertices. Now the computation

$$(D' \cdot D)(c) = D'(\partial(\min(c)), \partial(\max(c)))$$
$$= \partial^{-1}(\partial(\min(c))) + \partial^{-1}(\partial(\max(c)))$$
$$= \min(c) + \max(c) = c$$

shows that $D' \cdot D = 1_{C^n}$. We have to expect that the equation $D \cdot D' = 1_{Z_{2^n} \times Z_{2^n}}$ is not true, since D could not possibly have an inverse. This will be illustrated in the following example.

EXAMPLE 2.16

Consider the cell $c = (I,1,0,1,I,I,0) \in C^7$. Using Eq. 2.31, we obtain

$$D(c) = (\partial(\min(I,1,0,1,I,I,0)), \partial(\max(I,1,0,1,I,I,0)))$$
$$= (\partial(0,1,0,1,0,0,0), \partial(1,1,0,1,1,1,0)) = (40, 110)$$

and in the other direction we use Eq. 2.32:

$$D'(40, 110) = \partial^{-1}(40) + \partial^{-1}(110)$$
$$= (0,1,0,1,0,0,0) + (1,1,0,1,1,1,0)$$
$$= (I,1,0,1,I,I,0) = c$$

Now, if we apply D' to the pair (44, 106), we have

$$D'(44, 104) = \partial^{-1}(44) + \partial^{-1}(106)$$
$$= (0,1,0,1,1,0,0) + (1,1,0,1,0,1,0)$$
$$= (I,1,0,1,I,I,0) = c$$

so that

$$D(D'(44, 106)) = D(c) = (40, 110) \neq (44, 106)$$

which shows that $D \cdot D' \neq 1_{Z_{2^n} \times Z_{2^n}}$.

We wish to remark in passing that if v is a vertex, we have

$$D(v) = (\partial(v), \partial(v))$$

since $\min(v) = \max(v) = v$. Accordingly, we will occasionally say that

$$D(v) = \partial(v) = V \tag{2.33}$$

If it is understood that v is a vertex, this practice will not lead to confusion.

2.9 COMPUTATIONS WITH TRANSFORMED CELLS

If the transformed cells $D(c) = (X, Y) = Z$ for $c \in C^n$ are to be useful, we should be able to perform most of the required computations of Chapter 3 in decimal, referring to their cellular equivalents $D'(Z) = c$ as little as possible. In this section, we will describe these required computations, calling attention to instances where the conversion to cellular notation is necessary or convenient. When using the decimal notation, much of the geometric flavor is lost, even though we use the same cellular terminology (vertex, cell adjacent, etc.) in discussing the transforms of these notions. The best we can do in keeping the distinction between vertices and transformed vertices at a minimum is to use the symbol V for $D(v)$ as in Eq. 2.33. (We are prevented from using the desirable notation

$$D(c) = (X, Y) = C$$

because of the extreme likelihood of confusion with $C = \{0,1,I\}$.) Replacement of the notation for a basis

$$X = \{v^{(1)}, v^{(2)}, \cdots, v^{(k)}\}$$

by the "transformed" notation

$$\mathscr{X} = \{V^{(1)}, V^{(2)}, \cdots, V^{(k)}\}$$

will again serve to reinforce the connection to the cellular geometry.

Among the calculations one is often required to perform in Chapter 3 is that of *computing the n vertices* $V^{(1)}, V^{(2)}, \cdots, V^{(n)}$ *adjacent to a given vertex* V *in* Z_{2^n}. Now if $\partial^{-1}(V) = v$, where $v = (v_n, v_{n-1}, \cdots, v_1)$, we have n adjacent vertices to v,

$$v^{(i)} = (v_n, v_{n-1}, \cdots, \bar{v}_i \cdots, v_1) \qquad (i = 1, 2, \cdots, n) \qquad \textbf{(2.34)}$$

so that we may take

$$V^{(i)} = V \pm 2^{i-1} \qquad (i = 1, 2, \cdots, n) \qquad \textbf{(2.35)}$$

choosing $(+)$ if $v_i = 0$ and $(-)$ if $v_i = 1$.

EXAMPLE 2.17

If $V = 22$ and $n = 5$, we compute

$$v = \partial^{-1}(V) = (1,0,1,1,0)$$

Thus

$$V^{(1)} = V + 2^0 = V + 1 = 23$$

$$V^{(2)} = V - 2^1 = V - 2 = 20$$

$$V^{(3)} = V - 2^2 = V - 4 = 18$$

$$V^{(4)} = V + 2^3 = V + 8 = 30$$

$$V^{(5)} = V - 2^4 = V - 16 = 6$$

The most often used computation in Chapter 3 requires that *all of the 2^k vertices of the* k *cell* $Z = (X, Y)$ *be calculated from a given basis* $\mathscr{X} = \{V^{(1)}, V^{(2)}, \cdots, V^{(k)}\}$ *for* Z. If $\mathscr{X}$ is a basis, there exists a (unique if $k \neq 2$) vertex V such that $V \subseteq Z$ and $V^{(i)}$ is adjacent to V for each $i = 1, 2, \ldots, k$. Hence, we may suppose that V as well as $\mathscr{X}$ is given. Much as in Eq. 2.35, we must have

$$\Delta_i \equiv V^{(i)} - V = \pm 2^{j_i - 1} \qquad (i = 1, 2, \cdots, k) \qquad \textbf{(2.36)}$$

for distinct integers $j_1, j_2, \cdots, j_k$ with $1 \leq j_i \leq n$ $(i = 1, 2, \cdots, k)$, n being the order of the cellular cube in which the vertices $V^{(i)}$ are found. For each $i = 1, 2, \cdots, k$, we have

$$\partial^{-1}(V^{(i)}) = v^{(i)} = (v_n^{(i)}, v_{n-1}^{(i)}, \cdots, v_1^{(i)})$$

$$= (v_n, v_{n-1}, \cdots, \bar{v}_{j_i}, \cdots, v_1)$$

where $\partial^{-1}(V) = v = (v_n, v_{n-1}, \cdots, v_1)$, and it is here we see that the particular index j_i, in which the coordinate of $v^{(i)}$ is complementary to that of v is responsible for the difference Δ_i of Eq. 2.36. We have the $(+)$ sign there if $v_{j_i} = 0$ and the $(-)$ sign otherwise.

While we have used the inverse transformation ∂^{-1} to illuminate the source of Eq. 2.36, the following important theorem will pave the way for the *complete decimal* solution to the above computational problem.

Theorem 2.8. Let $\mathscr{X} = \{V^{(1)}, V^{(2)}, \cdots, V^{(k)}\}$ be a basis for a k cell $Z = (X, Y)$ and suppose that $V^{(i)}$ is adjacent to $V(i = 1, 2, \cdots, k)$; then every vertex W of Z can be written in the form

$$W = V + \sum_{i=1}^{k} b_i(V^{(i)} - V) = V + \sum_{i=1}^{k} b_i \Delta_i \qquad (2.37)$$

for suitable elements $b_i \in B$. Conversely, every integer W of the form of Eq. 2.37 is a vertex of Z.

PROOF. Suppose W is a vertex of Z. Then

$$\partial^{-1}(w) = w = (w_n, w_{n-1}, \cdots, w_1)$$

can disagree with v only in coordinates indexed by $j_1, j_2, \cdots, j_k$. Choose

$$b_i = 0 \quad \text{if } w_{j_i} = v_{j_i}$$
$$b_i = 1 \quad \text{otherwise (that is, if } w_{j_i} \text{ and } v_{j_i} \text{ are complementary)}$$

Then

$$W - V = \partial(w) - \partial(v)$$
$$= \sum_{j=1}^{n} w_j 2^{j-1} - \sum_{j=1}^{n} v_j 2^{j-1}$$
$$= \sum_{j=1}^{n} (w_j - v_j) 2^{j-1} = \sum_{i=1}^{k} (w_{j_i} - v_{j_i}) 2^{j_i - 1}$$
$$= \sum_{i=1}^{k} b_i \Delta_i$$

by the definition of ∂ and Eq. 2.36, thereby establishing the representation of Eq. 2.37. We leave the converse as an exercise. ∎

While Theorem 2.8 does give a means for computing all 2^k vertices W, we will find that these vertices can be obtained more systematically according to the following program† based on double subscripted sets M_{ij} $(1 \leq i \leq k, 1 \leq j \leq k - i + 1)$, on their unions

---

†The impatient reader will want to turn almost immediately to the last part of Example 2.18, where a convenient format for deriving these vertices is presented. He would then require only a brief examination of the detailed set-theoretic presentation we are about to give.

$$N_{ij} = \bigcup_{\rho=1}^{j} M_{i\rho} \qquad (2.38)$$

and finally on sets

$$N_0 = \{V\}$$

$$N_i = N_{i,k-i+1} = \bigcup_{j=1}^{k-i+1} M_{ij} \qquad (1 \leq i \leq k) \qquad (2.39)$$

for which $\bigcup_{\sigma=0}^{k} N_\sigma$ is the required set of 2^k vertices.

It is only necessary to take

$$\begin{aligned}
M_{1j} &= \{V^{(j)}\} && (j = 1, 2, \cdots, k) \\
M_{2j} &= \{W + \Delta_j; \; W \in N_1 - N_{1j}\} && (j = 1, 2, \cdots, k-1) \\
M_{3j} &= \{W + \Delta_j; \; W \in N_2 - N_{2j}\} && (j = 1, 2, \cdots, k-2) \\
&\;\cdot \\
&\;\cdot \\
&\;\cdot \\
M_{k1} &= \{W + \Delta_1; \; W \in N_{k-1} - N_{k-1,1}\}
\end{aligned} \qquad (2.40)$$

EXAMPLE 2.18

The collection of vertices $\{3,5,15,39\} = \{V^{(1)}, V^{(2)}, V^{(3)}, V^{(4)}\}$ are seen to be a basis $\mathcal{X}$ for some 4-cell $Z = (X, Y)$ of the cellular 6-cube, since each $V^{(i)}$ is adjacent to $V = 7$. (The reader should compute each $\partial^{-1}(V^{(i)})$ and also $\partial^{-1}(V)$ in order to be fully convinced of this.) Using the differences of Eq. 2.36,

$$\begin{aligned}
\Delta_1 &= -4 && (j_1 = 3) \\
\Delta_2 &= -2 && (j_2 = 2) \\
\Delta_3 &= 8 && (j_3 = 4) \\
\Delta_4 &= 32 && (j_4 = 6)
\end{aligned}$$

we learn from Theorem 2.8 that every vertex W of Z is of the form

$$W = 7 - 4b_1 - 2b_2 + 8b_3 + 32b_4 \qquad (2.41)$$

for $(b_4, b_3, b_2, b_1) \in B^4$. Thus, a random substitution of the 16 elements of B^4 in Eq. 2.41 would deliver the required 16 vertices W of Z.

Alternatively, we can take

$$N_0 = \{V\} = \{7\}$$

$$M_{11} = \{V^{(1)}\} = \{3\} \qquad N_{11} = \bigcup_{\rho=1}^{1} M_{1\rho} = \{3\}$$

$$M_{12} = \{V^{(2)}\} = \{5\} \qquad N_{12} = \bigcup_{\rho=1}^{2} M_{1\rho} = \{3, 5\}$$

$$M_{13} = \{V^{(3)}\} = \{15\} \qquad N_{13} = \bigcup_{\rho=1}^{3} M_{1\rho} = \{3, 5, 15\}$$

$$M_{14} = \{V^{(4)}\} = \{39\} \qquad N_{14} = \bigcup_{\rho=1}^{4} M_{1\rho} = \{3, 5, 15, 39\}$$

$$N_1 = N_{14} = \{3, 5, 15, 39\}$$

$$M_{21} = \{W + \Delta_1; \; W \in N_1 - N_{11}\} \qquad N_{21} = \{1, 11, 35\}$$
$$= \{W + \Delta_1; \; W \in \{5, 15, 39\}\}$$
$$= \{1, 11, 35\}$$

$$M_{22} = \{W + \Delta_2; \; W \in N_1 - N_{12}\} \qquad N_{22} = \{1, 11, 35, 13, 37\}$$
$$= \{W + \Delta_2; \; W \in \{15, 39\}\}$$
$$= \{13, 37\}$$

$$M_{23} = \{W + \Delta_3; \; W \in N_1 - N_{13}\} \qquad N_{23} = \{1, 11, 35, 13, 37, 47\}$$
$$= \{W + \Delta_3; \; W \in \{39\}\}$$
$$= \{47\}$$

$$N_2 = N_{23} = \{1, 11, 35, 13, 37, 47\}$$

$$M_{31} = \{W + \Delta_1; \; W \in N_2 - N_{21}\} \qquad N_{31} = \{9, 33, 43\}$$
$$= \{W + \Delta_1; \; W \in \{13, 37, 47\}\}$$
$$= \{9, 33, 43\}$$

$$M_{32} = \{W + \Delta_2; \; W \in N_2 - N_{22}\} \qquad N_{32} = \{9, 33, 43, 45\}$$
$$= \{W + \Delta_2; \; W \in \{47\}\}$$
$$= \{45\}$$

$$N_3 = N_{32} = \{9, 33, 43, 45\}$$

$$M_{41} = \{W + \Delta_1; \; W \in N_3 - N_{31}\}$$
$$= \{W + \Delta_1; \; W \in \{45\}\}$$
$$= \{41\}$$
$$N_4 = \{41\}$$

and then

$$\bigcup_{\sigma=0}^{4} N_\sigma = \{7,3,5,15,39,1,11,35,13,37,47,9,33,43,45,41\}$$

is the required set of 16 vertices.

The reader will perhaps fail to see the advantage of the alternate computation until he arranges the data in the convenient format[†]:

$\Delta_j =$	-4	-2	8	32			
	M_{11}	M_{12}	M_{13}	M_{14}	M_{21}	M_{22}	M_{23}
$7\,/3$	5	15	$39/$	1			
N_0					11	13	
		N_1			35	37	$47\;/9$
					N_2	33	
					43	45	$/41$
						N_3	N_4

(table approximate — see note)

$\Delta_j = \quad -4 \quad -2 \quad 8 \quad 32$

$\qquad M_{11} \quad M_{12} \quad M_{13} \quad M_{14} \quad M_{21} \quad M_{22} \quad M_{23}$

$\underbrace{7\,/3 \quad 5 \quad\; 15 \quad\; 39/}\;\; 1$

N_0

$\qquad\qquad\qquad\qquad 11 \qquad 13 \qquad\qquad M_{31} \quad M_{32}$

$\qquad\qquad N_1 \qquad\; \underbrace{35 \qquad 37 \qquad 47}\,/9$

$\qquad\qquad\qquad\qquad\qquad N_2 \qquad 33 \qquad\qquad\qquad M_{41}$

$\qquad\qquad\qquad\qquad\qquad \underbrace{43 \qquad 45} \;/\underbrace{41}$

$\qquad\qquad\qquad\qquad\qquad\qquad N_3 \qquad\quad N_4$

[†]As a check on the computations when arranged in this format, one should always have $|N_\sigma| = \binom{k}{\sigma}$, the binomial coefficients in row k of Pascal's triangle (cf. Table 0.1).

with columns labeled M_{ij} and ($/$) separating the sets N_σ for $\sigma = 0, 1, 2, 3, \ldots, k$. After he studies the patterns that show the additions required in forming the new columns,

```
  -4                  -4                      -4
×/×5 15 39/ 1     ×/× × × × ×/×         ×/× × × × ×/×
         11              ×13                  × ×
         35              ×37 47/ 9            × × ×/×
                              33                    ×
                              43                  ×45/41


   -2                    -2
×/× × 15 39/ 1     ×/× × × × ×/×
        11 13            × ×
        35 37            × ×  47/ 9
                              33
                              43 45


    8
×/× × × 39/ 1
       11 13
       35 37 47
```

the reader will be able to perform the entire computation in this format, without formally determining the sets M_{ij}.

If it is desired to know the cell $c \in C^6$ for which $D(c) = Z$, we can compute

$$D'(1,47) = \partial^{-1}(1) + \partial^{-1}(47)$$
$$= (0,0,0,0,0,1) + (1,0,1,1,1,1) = (I,0,I,I,I,1)$$

or

$$D'(7,41) = \partial^{-1}(7) + \partial^{-1}(41)$$
$$= (0,0,0,1,1,1) + (1,0,1,0,0,1) = (I,0,I,I,I,1)$$

whichever is more convenient. In the first case, 1 and 47 are minimum and maximum vertices of Z, whereas 7 and 41 are merely diagonally opposite.

Another often used computation in Chapter 3 is that of *determining a decimal representation* $Z = (X, Y)$ *for the cell* c *whose basis* $\mathscr{X} = \{V^{(1)}, V^{(2)}, \cdots, V^{(k)}\}$ *is given.* Again we may suppose that V (for which $V^{(i)}$ is adjacent to V ($i = 1, 2, \cdots, k$)) as well as $\mathscr{X}$ is given. We have asked for "a" representation $Z = (X, Y)$ rather than "the" representation, since we have seen that there is no special reason for preferring X and Y for which $\partial^{-1}(X) = \min(c)$, $\partial^{-1}(Y) = \max(c)$. This is because $D'(X, Y) = c$ for every pair of diagonally opposite vertices X and Y of Z (see Eq. 2.30). According to Eq. 2.37 we see that

$$Y = V + \sum_{i=1}^{k} \Delta_i$$

is diagonally opposite V, so that we may take

$$X = V, \quad Y = V + \sum_{i=1}^{k} \Delta_i.$$

EXAMPLE 2.19

Suppose $\mathscr{X} = \{3,5,15,39\}$ as in the preceding example. Then $V = 7$ as before, and we may take

$$X = V = 7, \quad Y = V + \sum_{i=1}^{k} \Delta_i = 7 - 4 - 2 + 8 + 32 = 41$$

Thus, $Z = (X, Y) = (7,41)$ is a decimal representation of c.

While the last two types of computations are performed almost entirely in the decimal notation, our final computation can be most conveniently performed with the aid of decimal to binary conversion. *Given a basis* $\mathscr{X} = \{V^{(1)}, V^{(2)}, \cdots, V^{(k)}\}$ *for a k cell*

$$Z = \left(V, V + \sum_{i=1}^{k} \Delta_i \right)$$

and a vertex W in Z, find the subbasis $\mathscr{Y}$ of $\mathscr{X}$ for the cell $(V, W) \subseteq Z$. According to Eq. 2.37, there exists an element $(b_k, b_{k-1}, \cdots, b_1) \in B^k$ such that

$$W = V + \sum_{i=1}^{k} b_i \, \Delta_i \tag{2.42}$$

Evidently the subbasis $\mathscr{Y}$ is known as soon as the elements b_i are found, for we have then only to take

$$\mathscr{Y} = \{V^{(i)} \in \mathscr{X}; \ b_i = 1\} \tag{2.43}$$

These elements b_i are most easily determined by first converting

$$\partial^{-1}(W) = (w_n, w_{n-1} \cdots, w_1)$$
$$\partial^{-1}(V) = (v_n, v_{n-1}, \cdots, v_1)$$

and then noting that (cf. Eq. 2.36)

$$b_i = 1 \Longleftrightarrow w_{j_i} = \bar{v}_{j_i} \tag{2.44}$$

EXAMPLE 2.20

Suppose $\mathscr{X} = \{3,5,15,39\} = \{V^{(1)}, V^{(2)}, V^{(3)}, V^{(4)}\}$, as in Example 2.18, and that $W = 33$. We wish to determine the elements $b_i \in B$ in Eq. 2.42; that is,

$$33 = 7 - 4b_1 - 2b_2 + 8b_3 + 32b_4 \tag{2.45}$$

These are easily found by writing

$$\partial^{-1}(33) = (1,0,0,0,0,1) = (w_6, w_5, w_4, w_3, w_2, w_1)$$
$$\partial^{-1}(7) \ = (0,0,0,1,1,1) = (v_6, v_5, v_4, v_3, v_2, v_1)$$

Now consulting Example 2.18, we have

$$j_1 = 3 \quad \text{and} \quad w_3 = \bar{v}_3 \qquad \text{so that } b_1 = 1$$
$$j_2 = 2 \quad \text{and} \quad w_2 = \bar{v}_2 \qquad \text{so that } b_2 = 1$$

$$j_3 = 4 \quad \text{and} \quad w_4 = v_4 \quad \text{so that } b_3 = 0$$

$$j_4 = 6 \quad \text{and} \quad w_6 = \bar{v}_6 \quad \text{so that } b_4 = 1$$

giving a solution to Eq. 2.45, that is, $33 = 7 - 4 - 2 + 32$. Thus, according to Eq. 2.43, we have $\mathscr{U} = \{V^{(1)}, V^{(2)}, V^{(4)}\} = \{3,5,39\}$.

*2.10   VERTEX MAPS AND CELLULAR TRANSFORMATIONS

The application of the cellular n cube C^n to the study of the complete class decomposition of $B(n)$ relative to the equivalence relation of Eq. 1.37 is aided by the decimal transform theory. Thus, when we define for a permutation $\pi: n^+ \longrightarrow n^+$ and $b = (b_n, b_{n-1}, \cdots, b_1) \in B^n$, the *vertex map*

$$t_\pi^b : B^n \longrightarrow B^n$$

according to the rule

$$t_\pi^b(v_n, \cdots, v_1) = (v_{\pi(n)}^{(b_{\pi(n)})}, \cdots, v^{(b_{\pi(1)})}) \tag{2.46}$$

we simultaneously introduce a corresponding *decimal vertex map*

$$T_\pi^b : Z_{2^n} \longrightarrow Z_{2^n}$$

according to a naturally suggested procedure, that is, we put

$$T_\pi^b = \partial \cdot t_\pi^b \cdot \partial^{-1} \tag{2.47}$$

Clearly, the diagram of 1–1 and onto mappings so obtained,

$$
\begin{array}{ccc}
B^n & \xrightarrow{\ t_\pi^b\ } & B^n \\
\partial \Big\uparrow\Big\downarrow \partial^{-1} & & \partial \Big\uparrow\Big\downarrow \partial^{-1} \\
Z_{2^n} & \xrightarrow[\ T_\pi^b\ ]{} & Z_{2^n}
\end{array}
$$

is commutative in the sense of Sec. 0.4.

EXAMPLE 2.21

If $n = 3$, $\pi = (12)$, $b = (0,0,1)$, then t_π^b is the mapping

$$(0,0,0) \xrightarrow{\ t_\pi^b\ } (1,0,1) \qquad 0 \xrightarrow{\ T_\pi^b\ } 5$$

$$(0,0,1) \xrightarrow{\ t_\pi^b\ } (1,1,1) \qquad 1 \xrightarrow{\ T_\pi^b\ } 7$$

$$(0,1,0) \xrightarrow{\ t_\pi^b\ } (1,0,0) \qquad 2 \xrightarrow{\ T_\pi^b\ } 4$$

$$(0,1,1) \xrightarrow{\ t_\pi^b\ } (1,1,0) \qquad 3 \xrightarrow{\ T_\pi^b\ } 6$$

$$(1,0,0) \xrightarrow{t^b_\pi} (0,0,1) \qquad 4 \xrightarrow{T^b_\pi} 1$$

$$(1,0,1) \xrightarrow{t^b_\pi} (0,1,1) \qquad 5 \xrightarrow{T^b_\pi} 3$$

$$(1,1,0) \xrightarrow{t^b_\pi} (0,0,0) \qquad 6 \xrightarrow{T^b_\pi} 0$$

$$(1,1,1) \xrightarrow{t^b_\pi} (0,1,0) \qquad 7 \xrightarrow{T^b_\pi} 2$$

where we have shown the corresponding decimal map alongside.

Suppose we associate with each $f \in B(n)$ the 0 skeleton $K^0(f)$ defined in Sec. 2.6, Eq. 2.24. Then the usefulness of the vertex maps is described by the following theorem.

Theorem 2.9. Let f, $g \in B(n)$. Then $f \cong g$ if and only if there exists a permutation $\pi: n^+ \longrightarrow n^+$ and an element $b \in B^n$ such that

$$K^0(g) = \{t^b_\pi(v); \ v \in K^0(f)\} \equiv t^b_\pi(K^0(f))$$

PROOF. First suppose $f \cong g$. Then there exists $\pi: n^+ \longrightarrow n^+$ and $b \in B^n$ for which

$$f(x_n, x_{n-1}, \cdots, x_1) = g(x^{(b_{\pi(n)})}_{\pi(n)}, x^{(b_{\pi(n-1)})}_{\pi(n-1)}, \cdots, x^{(b_{\pi(1)})}_{\pi(1)})$$

Now consider any vertex $v \in K^0(f)$. This means that

$$v = (v_n, v_{n-1}, \cdots, v_1) \in B^n$$

has the property

$$f(v_n, v_{n-1}, \cdots, v_1) = 1$$

If we now look at the mapped vertex $t^b_\pi(v) = (v^{(b_{\pi(n)})}_{\pi(n)}, \cdots, v^{(b_{\pi(1)})}_{\pi(1)})$ we have

$$g(v^{(b_{\pi(n)})}_{\pi(n)}, v^{(b_{\pi(n-1)})}_{\pi(n-1)}, \cdots, v^{(b_{\pi(1)})}_{\pi(1)})$$
$$= f(v_n, v_{n-1}, \cdots, v_1) = 1$$

so that $t^b_\pi(v) \in K^0(g)$. This much shows that $t^b_\pi(K^0(f)) \subseteq K^0(g)$.

Using the fact that $\cong$ is symmetric, one obtains also $t^b_\pi(K^0(f)) \supseteq K^0(g)$, so we have $K^0(g) = t^b_\pi(K^0(f))$. Thus we have shown that

$$f \cong g \Longrightarrow K^0(g) = t^b_\pi(K^0(f))$$

for some permutation π and $b \in B^n$.

Conversely, if there is some permutation $\pi: n^+ \longrightarrow n^+$ and an element $b \in B^n$ for which

$$K^0(g) = t^b_\pi(K^0(f))$$

then for every vertex $v = (v_n, v_{n-1}, \cdots, v_1) \in B^n$ we have

$$f(v) = 1 \Longleftrightarrow v \in K^0(f) \Longleftrightarrow t^b_\pi(v) \in K^0(g)$$
$$\Longleftrightarrow g(t^b_\pi(v)) = 1$$

so that

$$f(v_n, v_{n-1}, \cdots, v_1)$$
$$= g(v_{\pi(n)}^{(b_{\pi(n)})}, v_{\pi(n-1)}^{(b_{\pi(n-1)})}, \cdots, v_{\pi(1)}^{(b_{\pi(1)})})$$

and $f \cong g$. ∎

This theorem is most easily applied in its decimal form.

Corollary 2.10. $f \cong g \longleftrightarrow \mathcal{K}^0(g) = T_\pi^b(\mathcal{K}^0(f))$ for some permutation $\pi : n^+ \longrightarrow n^+$ and $b \in B^n$ where

$$\mathcal{K}^0(f) = \{\partial(v); \, v \in K^0(f)\} \equiv \partial(K^0(f)) \tag{2.48}$$

is the decimal transform of the 0 skeleton $K^0(f)$ for any $f \in B(n)$.

EXAMPLE 2.22

Let $f = f_{67} \in B(3)$ be the function of Example 1.32, and suppose that $\pi = (12)$ and $b = (0,0,1)$. Then, using the results of Example 2.21 and the definition of Eq. 2.48,

$$T_\pi^b(\mathcal{K}^0(f)) = T_\pi^b(\partial(\{(0, 0, 0), (0, 0, 1), (1, 1, 0)\}))$$
$$= T_\pi^b(\{0, 1, 6\}) = \{T_\pi^b(0), T_\pi^b(1), T_\pi^b(6)\}$$
$$= \{5, 7, 0\} = \mathcal{K}^0(g)$$

where $g = f_{161}$ has the truth table of Table 1.4. By Corollary 2.10 we have shown that $f_{67} \cong f_{161}$ in $B(3)$. The same result was already known in Example 1.32, but the advantages of our decimal verification will soon become clear.

Concerning the preceding example, we notice from Fig. 2.6 that the equivalent functions f and g have "similar geometric structure." This is no accident, for the vertex maps can be factored or decomposed (cf. Sec. 0.4) into products

$$t_\pi^b = t_\pi \cdot t^b \tag{2.49}$$

where

$$t^b(v_n, v_{n-1}, \cdots, v_1) = (v_n^{(b_n)}, v_{n-1}^{(b_{n-1})}, \cdots, v_1^{(b_1)})$$
$$t_\pi(v_n, v_{n-1}, \cdots, v_1) = (v_{\pi(n)}, v_{\pi(n-1)}, \cdots, v_{\pi(1)})$$
$$\text{for all} \quad (v_n, v_{n-1}, \cdots, v_1) \in B^n$$

and each of these vertex maps t^b and t_π have the property of "preserving the cellular structure" of C^n, so that the same is true of their composite t_π^b. By "preserving the cellular structure" of C^n, we mean that they are 1–1 and onto mappings for which

(1) $\{v^{(i)}\}$ form a k cell iff $t^b(v^{(i)})$ form a k cell, so that it would be clear what is meant by the cell $t^b(c)$ if $c \in C^n$,

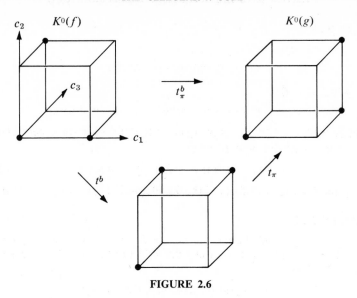

FIGURE 2.6

(2) $c \subseteq c' \longleftrightarrow t^b(c) \subseteq t^b(c')$,

and similarly for t_π for any permutation π. Intuitively, this is to be expected, since the vertex maps t_π simply relabel the coordinate axes, and the maps t^b are merely reflections of C^n through "planes" perpendicular to the various coordinate axes.

Because of property (1) above, we can extend the vertex maps t^b, t_π (and hence t^b_π) to *cellular transformations* (there is no need to rename them)

$$t^b : C^n \longrightarrow C^n \qquad t_\pi : C^n \longrightarrow C^n$$

(and hence also $t^b_\pi : C^n \rightarrow C^n$), which have cells as arguments and whose values are also cells of C^n. As expected, one defines for $c \in C^n$ having vertices $\{v^{(i)}\}$:

$$t^b(c) = \text{the cell with vertices } \{t^b(v^{(i)})\} \qquad \textbf{(2.50)}$$

and similarly for t_π, t^b_π. Then property (2) asserts (since our vertex maps were 1–1 and onto) that these cellular transformations are isomorphisms of C^n onto itself, so that the geometric structure of C^n is preserved by its cellular transformations. Now the statement that "equivalent ($\cong$) functions have similar geometric structure" can be precisely phrased as a generalization of Theorem 2.9.

Theorem 2.11

$$f \cong g \longleftrightarrow K(g) = t^b_\pi(K(f)) \qquad \text{for some permutation}$$
$$\pi : n^+ \longrightarrow n^+ \text{ and } b \in B^n$$

Thus the complexes $K(f)$ and $K(g)$ of equivalent functions are geometrically congruent or similar, and conversely, congruent complexes define equivalent functions.

Consequently, when attempting in the next section to determine the complete class decomposition of $B(3)$, we have merely to enumerate the 22 noncongruent geometric structures (Fig. 2.7) that can serve to specify

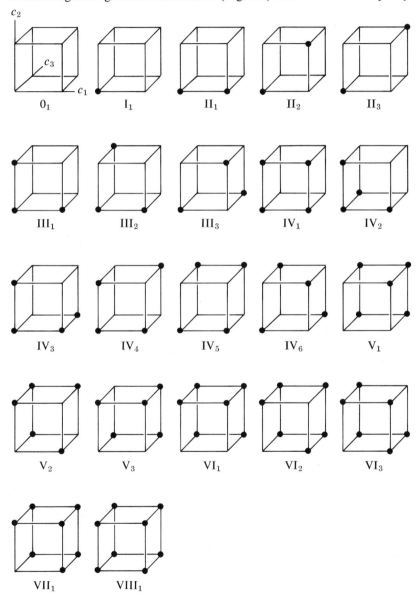

FIGURE 2.7

$K^0(f)$ for $f \in B(3)$. We then use Theorem 2.9 or its corollary to determine for these 22 functions (f) the classes†

$$[f] = \{g;\ g \cong f\} \tag{2.51}$$

by using all 6 permutations $\pi : 3^+ \longrightarrow 3^+$ and all 8 elements $b \in B^3$.

*2.11   EQUIVALENCE CLASSES IN $B(3)$

As an aid in using Corollary 2.10, we first develop tables that show how the set $Z_{2^3} = Z_8$ is transformed by the decimal vertex maps T^b and T_π. Here T^b and T_π are defined in a manner analogous to Eq. 2.47; that is,

$$T^b = \partial \cdot t^b \cdot \partial^{-1} \tag{2.52}$$

$$T_\pi = \partial \cdot t_\pi \cdot \partial^{-1} \tag{2.53}$$

The results appear in Tables 2.1 and 2.2 respectively.

EXAMPLE 2.23

By way of illustration, suppose $b = (1,0,1)$ and $V = 6 \in Z_8$. Then $\partial^{-1}(V) = \partial^{-1}(6) = (1,1,0)$ and

$$t^b(1,1,0) = (1^{(1)},\ 1^{(0)},\ 0^{(1)}) = (1,0,0)$$

Since $\partial(1,0,0) = 4$, we have

$$T^b(6) = \partial(t^b(\partial^{-1}(6))) = 4$$

as shown in the third row of Table 2.1.

EXAMPLE 2.24

To illustrate the derivation of Table 2.2, take $\pi = (123)$ and $V = 4$. Then

$$\begin{aligned} T_\pi(4) &= \partial(t_\pi(\partial^{-1}(4))) \\ &= \partial(t_\pi(1,0,0)) \\ &= \partial(0,1,0) = 2 \end{aligned}$$

as seen in the fourth row of Table 2.2.

These two arrays also serve to tabulate the values $T_\pi^b(V)$, for T_π^b is the composite mapping

$$\begin{aligned} T_\pi^b &= \partial \cdot t_\pi^b \cdot \partial^{-1} = \partial \cdot t_\pi \cdot t^b \cdot \partial^{-1} \\ &= \partial \cdot t_\pi \cdot \partial^{-1} \cdot \partial \cdot t^b \cdot \partial^{-1} \\ &= T_\pi \cdot T^b \end{aligned} \tag{2.54}$$

†There is a danger that the notation $\bar{f}$ (as in Eq. 0.47) would be confused with the complement of f in $B(n)$.

TABLE 2.1 $T^b(V)$

V / b	0	1	2	3	4	5	6	7
111	0	1	2	3	4	5	6	7
110	1	0	3	2	5	4	7	6
101	2	3	0	1	6	7	4	5
100	3	2	1	0	7	6	5	4
011	4	5	6	7	0	1	2	3
010	5	4	7	6	1	0	3	2
001	6	7	4	5	2	3	0	1
000	7	6	5	4	3	2	1	0

TABLE 2.2 $T_\pi(V)$

V / π	0	1	2	3	4	5	6	7
1	0	1	2	3	4	5	6	7
(21)	0	2	1	3	4	6	5	7
(32)	0	1	4	5	2	3	6	7
(123)	0	4	1	5	2	6	3	7
(132)	0	2	4	6	1	3	5	7
(31)	0	4	2	6	1	5	3	7

To illustrate, we have for b and π, as in Examples 2.23 and 2.24,

$$T^b_\pi(6) = T_\pi(T^b(6)) = T_\pi(4) = 2$$

which could be learned from using the arrays of Tables 2.1 and 2.2 in succession.

The information of Tables 2.1 and 2.2 is useful in connection with the characteristic number (cf. Eq. 1.36) of a function $f \in B(3)$. In the abbreviated notation

$$\eta(f) = \sum_{v \in b^n} f(v)2^{\partial(v)} \tag{2.55}$$

we have

$$f(v) = 1 \Longleftrightarrow v \in K^0(f)$$

so that it is equally correct to write

$$\eta(f) = \sum_{v \in K^0(f)} 2^{\partial(v)} = \sum_{V \in \mathcal{K}^0(f)} 2^V \tag{2.56}$$

EXAMPLE 2.25

Let $f \in B(3)$ have the truth table

x_3	x_2	x_1	f
0	0	0	1
0	0	1	1
0	1	0	0
0	1	1	0
1	0	0	0
1	0	1	0
1	1	0	1
1	1	1	0

Then $\mathscr{K}^0(f) = \{0,1,6\}$ and

$$\eta(f) = 2^0 + 2^1 + 2^6 = 1 + 2 + 64 = 67$$

It is often convenient to denote the function with characteristic number $\eta(f)$ as $f_{\eta(f)}$. Thus we write $f = f_{67}$ in our present example.

Suppose $f \in B(3)$ is given (or equivalently $\eta(f)$ is given) as well as a permutation $\pi : 3^+ \longrightarrow 3^+$ and an element $b = (b_3, b_2, b_1) \in B^3$. Then

$$\partial^{-1}(\eta(f)) = (w_7, w_6, w_5, w_4, w_3, w_2, w_1, w_0) \in B^8$$

where

$$w_V = 1 \Longleftrightarrow V \in \mathscr{K}^0(f) \tag{2.57}$$

From Corollary 2.10 we learn that $f \cong g$ if

$$\mathscr{K}^0(g) = T_\pi^b(\mathscr{K}^0(f)) \tag{2.58}$$

Thus we can use Tables 2.1 and 2.2 in Eq. 2.58 after having computed $\mathscr{K}^0(f)$ in Eq. 2.57. Taking the cue from Eq. 2.56, we then write

$$\eta(g) = \sum_{V \in \mathscr{K}^0(g)} 2^V$$

and this will give the characteristic number of a function $g \cong f$.

EXAMPLE 2.26

Take $f = f_{67}$ as in Example 2.25, with $b = (0,0,1)$ and $\pi = (12)$. Now

$$\partial^{-1}(\eta(f)) = \partial^{-1}(67) = (0,1,0,0,0,0,1,1)$$
$$= (w_7, w_6, w_5, w_4, w_3, w_2, w_1, w_0)$$

so that, according to Eq. 2.57,

$$\mathscr{K}^0(f) = \{0,1,6\}$$

Using Tables 2.1 and 2.2, the function g that is equivalent to f via b and π has the decimal 0 skeleton

$$\mathscr{K}^0(g) = \{T_\pi^b(0), T_\pi^b(1), T_\pi^b(6)\}$$
$$= \{T_\pi(6), T_\pi(7), T_\pi(0)\} = \{5,7,0\}$$

so that
$$\eta(g) = 2^0 + 2^5 + 2^7 = 1 + 32 + 128 = 161$$
(See Table III_2 of the Appendix.)

If we were to tabulate the resulting characteristic numbers $\eta(g)$ for all functions $g \cong f = f_{67}$ by applying the above procedure to the 48 combinations of b and π available, we would obtain Table III_2 of the Appendix. There we learn that $[f_{67}] \equiv III_2$ is a class of 24 functions.

Choosing (as we have done for III_2) the representative functions indicated in Fig. 2.7 for the classes 0_1 through IV_6, we find (as above) the composition of these classes as depicted in Tables 0_1 through IV_6 of the Appendix.[†] At the same time, we learn the number of members in each class; we have tabulated these figures in Table 2.3.

We do not show tables in the Appendix for the classes V_1 through VIII_1, since the complementation rules[‡]:

$$V_1 = \overline{III}_1 \qquad VI_1 = \overline{II}_1 \qquad VII_1 = \overline{I}_1$$
$$V_2 = \overline{III}_3 \qquad VI_2 = \overline{II}_2 \qquad VIII_1 = \overline{0}_1$$
$$V_3 = \overline{III}_2 \qquad VI_3 = \overline{II}_3$$

allow us to conclude that these tables would simply contain entries y, which are the differences $y = 255 - x$ of the corresponding entries x in the complementary tables.

For easy reference, the class name for each characteristic number $\eta(f)$, $0 \le \eta(f) \le 255$ is shown in a separate listing (Table I of the Appendix). These entries are simply a rearrangement of a part of the information of the previously discussed Appendix tables. The information is used in conjunction with the Tables 0_1 through IV_6 when one has a catalog of economical circuits for the 22 representative functions of Table 2.3. (Cf. Theorem 1.16 and Corollary 1.17.)

If we were to investigate the decomposition due to the equivalence relation $\simeq$ (cf. Sec. 1.15), we would find (when $n = 3$) that every neutral class is self-complementary, so that (cf. Eq. 1.39)

$$N = \frac{N_t + N_{sc}}{2} = \frac{22 + 6}{2} = 14$$

with the larger classes:

$$0_1' = 0_1 \cup VIII_1 \qquad I_1' = I_1 \cup VII_1$$
$$II_1' = II_1 \cup VI_1 \qquad II_2' = II_2 \cup VI_2 \qquad II_3' = II_3 \cup VI_3$$
$$III_1' = III_1 \cup V_1 \qquad III_2' = III_2 \cup V_3 \qquad III_3' = III_3 \cup V_2$$
$$IV_i' = IV_i \qquad (i = 1, 2, 3, 4, 5, 6)$$

[†]It is clear that class 0_1 contains only the function with characteristic number 0.

[‡]That $V_2 = \overline{III}_3$ rather than $\overline{III}_2$ is simply a peculiarity of the Roman enumerated "Harvard class names" (see Ref. 2-2).

TABLE 2.3

CLASS NAME	REPRESENTATIVE	NUMBER OF MEMBERS
0_1	f_0	1
I_1	f_1	8
II_1	f_3	12
II_2	f_9	12
II_3	f_{129}	4
III_1	f_7	24
III_2	f_{67}	24
III_3	f_{41}	8
IV_1	f_{15}	6
IV_2	f_{23}	8
IV_3	f_{39}	24
IV_4	f_{135}	24
IV_5	f_{195}	6
IV_6	f_{105}	2
V_1	f_{248}	24
V_2	f_{214}	8
V_3	f_{188}	24
VI_1	f_{252}	12
VI_2	f_{246}	12
VI_3	f_{126}	4
VII_1	f_{254}	8
VIII_1	f_{255}	1

PROBLEMS

2.1   Prove (by induction) that C^n has 3^n elements.

2.2   Obtain a formula for the number of k cells in C^n.

2.3   Prove that if v and v' are two vertices of the k cell c in C^n,

$$0 \leq \Delta(v, v') \leq k$$

2.4   Let $v, v' \in B^n \subseteq C^n$. Show that v is adjacent to v' iff for some index j, $1 \leq j \leq n$, we have

$$v'_j = \bar{v}_j, \quad v'_i = v_i \qquad (i \neq j)$$

2.5 Show that if $v = (v_n, v_{n-1}, \ldots, v_1) \in B^n \subseteq C^n$, the vertices

$$v^{(n)} = (\bar{v}_n, v_{n-1}, \ldots, v_1)$$
$$v^{(n-1)} = (v_n, \bar{v}_{n-1}, \ldots, v_1)$$
$$\cdot$$
$$\cdot$$
$$\cdot$$
$$v^{(1)} = (v_n, v_{n-1}, \ldots, \bar{v}_1)$$

and only these are adjacent to v.

2.6 Show that a k cell c has 2^{k-1} pairs of diagonally opposite vertices and that if

$$v = (v_n, v_{n-1}, \ldots, v_1) \subseteq (c_n, c_{n-i}, \ldots, c_1) = c$$

the vertex

$$v' = (v'_n, v'_{n-1}, \ldots, v'_1)$$

defined by

(a) $c_i \in B \Longrightarrow v'_i = v_i$ and
(b) $c_i = I \Longrightarrow v'_i = \bar{v}_i$

is diagonally opposite to v in c.

2.7 Show that if $v, v' \in B^n \subseteq C^n$ are two vertices, the cell $c = (c_n, c_{n-1}, \ldots, c_1)$ defined by
(a) $v'_i = v_i \Longrightarrow c_i = v_i$ and
(b) $v'_i = \bar{v}_i \Longrightarrow c_i = I$
is such that $v \subseteq c$, $v' \subseteq c$ and v and v' are diagonally opposite in c.

2.8 Show that two cells $c = (c_n, c_{n-1}, \ldots, c_1)$ and $c' = (c'_n, c'_{n-1}, \ldots, c'_1)$ are disjoint if and only if $c'_i = \bar{c}_i$ for some i, $1 \leq i \leq n$.

2.9 Let $p, q \in P^n$ (cf. Sec. 2.5). Then there are natural functions $f, g \in B(n)$ to associate with these products, that is, those for the polynomials

$$f(x_n, x_{n-1}, \ldots, x_1) = p$$
$$g(x_n, x_{n-1}, \ldots, x_1) = q$$

Show that

$$p \supseteq q \Longleftrightarrow f \geq g$$

where the first-order relation is that of Eq. 2.13 and the latter is that of Prob. 1.25.

2.10 Which pairs of cells chosen from the following list:

$$a = (I,0,1,I,I) \qquad e = (I,0,1,1,1)$$
$$b = (0,I,1,I,0) \qquad f = (I,1,I,I,I)$$
$$d = (1,I,0,I,I) \qquad g = (0,1,I,I,I)$$

are disjoint in C^5?

2.11 (a) Find all pairs of diagonally opposite vertices for the cells of Prob. 2.10.

     (b) Find the minimum and maximum vertices for each cell in Prob. 2.10.

     (c) For each cell c in Prob. 2.10, find the basis $X_{\min(c),\,c}$.

2.12 Given the vertex $v = (1,0,0,1,0)$ and the 3-cell $c = (1,I,0,I,I)$:

     (a) Show that $v \subseteq c$.

     (b) Compute the five vertices of C^5 that are adjacent to v.

     (c) Compute the three vertices of c that are adjacent to v.

     (d) Compute the vertex $v' \subseteq c$ that is diagonally opposite v in c.

     (e) Compute $\min(c)$, $\max(c)$.

     (f) Compute the basis $X_{\min(c),\,c}$ for the cell c.

2.13 Draw the Hasse diagram of C^2.

2.14 Compute the cell $c \in C^6$ for which

$$\min(c) = (0,1,1,0,0,0)$$
$$\max(c) = (1,1,1,0,1,1)$$

If $v = (1,1,1,0,1,0)$ and $v' = (0,1,1,0,0,1)$, compute the cell c that has v and v' as diagonally opposite vertices.

2.15 Compute the cell $c \in C^5$ that has

$$X = \{(1,1,1,1,0),\ (0,0,1,1,0),\ (0,1,1,0,0)\}$$

as a basis.

2.16 Repeat Prob. 2.15 for

     (a) $X = \{(1,0,1,1,0,1),\ (0,0,0,1,0,1),\ (0,0,1,1,1,1),\ (0,0,1,1,0,0)\}$,

     (b) $X = \{(0,1,1,0,1,0,0),\ (1,1,1,0,1,0,1),\ (0,0,1,0,1,0,1),\ (0,1,1,1,1,0,0)\}$,

     where $n = 6,7$, respectively.

*2.17 Prove the uniqueness of the cell c in Theorem 2.2.

2.18 (a) Draw a figure similar to that of Fig. 2.4 for $f \in B(3)$ with $\eta(f) = 217$.

     (b) Determine $K(f)$ and $K^0(f)$.

*2.19 (a) Show that $(C^n,\ +,\ \cdot)$ is a lattice.

     (b) Show that it is not a distributive lattice.

2.20 For the cells of Prob. 2.10, compute (a) $a + b$; (b) $a \cdot b$; (c) $a \cdot g$; (d) $e + f$; (e) $g + a \cdot b$; and (f) $d \cdot (a + f)$.

2.12 Compute $D(c)$ for each cell c of Prob. 2.10.

2.22 (a) For v and c, as in Prob. 2.12, compute $\partial(v)$ and $D(c)$.

     (b) Find the basis $\mathscr{X} = (V^{(1)}, V^{(2)}, V^{(3)})$ for $Z = (X, Y) = D(c)$ for which $V^{(i)}$ is adjacent to $V(i = 1,2,3)$.

     (c) Compute the $2^3 = 8$ vertices of Z in the format of the alternate computation of Example 2.18.

2.23   Transform the bases of Prob. 2.16 to decimal and compute all vertices of the cells $Z = (X, Y)$ that have these bases, using the format of the alternate computation of Example 2.18.

2.24   (a)   Illustrate the derivation of the third row of Table 2.1.
       (b)   Illustrate the derivation of the third row of Table 2.2.

2.25   (a)   Illustrate the derivation of two entries other than 161 in the Appendix Table III_2.
       (b)   Illustrate Theorem 1.16 with the functions g whose characteristic numbers $\eta(g)$ were found in (a).

2.26   Show that when $c, c' \in C^n$, $c \subseteq c'$ if and only if every vertex of c is also a vertex of c'.

2.27   Show that if $b \in B$, $c \in C$, and $b \leq c$, $b^{(c)} = 1$.

2.28   Show that parallelism is an equivalence relation on C^n.

2.29   Show that $c \| c' \Longrightarrow c$ and c' are disjoint.

2.30   Show that $c \cdot c' = 0 \Longleftrightarrow c$ and c' are disjoint.

2.31   Prove Eqs. 2.29.

SUGGESTED REFERENCES

2–1   ALEXANDROFF, P. S. *Combinatorial Topology* (Rochester, N.Y.: Graylock Press) Vol. 1, 1956.

2–2   GREA R., and R. HIGONNET, *The Logical Design of Electrical Circuits* (New York: McGraw-Hill Book Co.), 1958.

2–3   HOCKING, J. G., and G. S. YOUNG, *Topology* (Reading, Mass. Addison-Wesley Publishing Co.), 1961.

2–4   HARRISON, M. A., *Introduction to Switching and Automata Theory* (New York: McGraw-Hill Book Co.), 1965.

CHAPTER 3 | MINIMIZATION THEORY

3.1 INTRODUCTION

Our main objective here is to formulate and solve the minimization problems of switching theory (cf. Sec. 1.17) as restricted to the class of representations of functions as Boolean sums of Boolean products. The solution will rely heavily on the geometric theory of Chapter 2 because of its inherent intuitive advantages. Before we state the problem in Sec. 3.3, it is advisable to introduce a more general type of Boolean function of immense practical importance—the incompletely specified Boolean function. Since the c.s.b.f.'s studied heretofore are particularizations of these more general functions, and since the minimization problem for the latter is only slightly more difficult to discuss than that for the c.s.b.f.'s, it is desirable to introduce these "i.s.b.f.'s" at an early stage of the discussion, giving a pronounced economy of presentation.

Toward the end of the chapter, certain related problems discussed are a direct outgrowth of the recognition of incompletely specified functions. Representative of these is the need for a generalization of the material of Sec. 1.18 to the case where incompletely specified functions of two variables are admitted.

3.2   INCOMPLETELY SPECIFIED BOOLEAN FUNCTIONS

In accordance with the situation most commonly encountered in the design of digital computer logic circuits, we wish to allow functions $f: B^n \longrightarrow B$, whose values are perhaps not specified (that is, they are undefined) for some of its arguments. Such a situation occurs in practice when the designer of a logical "black box"

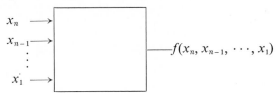

does not care whether the output $f(x_n, x_{n-1}, \cdots, x_1)$ is 0 or 1 for particular input configurations

$$(x_n, x_{n-1}, \cdots, x_1) = (b_n, b_{n-1}, \cdots, b_1) = b \in B^n$$

This might be the case if the wires $x_n, x_{n-1}, \cdots, x_1$ are themselves outputs of logical circuits of such a character that these particular configurations cannot occur.

EXAMPLE 3.1

Consider the case where we have two input wires x_2 and x_1, and suppose the designer wishes to construct a "box" whose output $f(x_2, x_1)$ is "1" if and only if both x_2 and x_1 are "1." The truth table

x_2	x_1	f
0	0	0
0	1	0
1	0	0
1	1	1

would ordinarily suggest the logic circuit

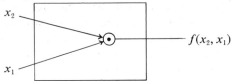

But suppose that x_2 and x_1 are themselves outputs of the circuits

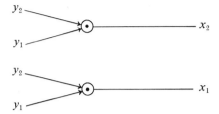

From their truth tables

y_2	y_1	x_2	x_1
0	0	0	0
0	1	0	1
1	0	0	1
1	1	1	1

we see that the configuration $(x_2, x_1) = (1, 0)$ cannot occur. In this situation, the designer of the original "box" does not care which output (0 or 1) *would occur if it were possible* for x_2 and x_1 to assume respectively the values 1 and 0. Hence, his wishes are better reflected by the partial truth table

x_2	x_1	f
0	0	0
0	1	0
1	0	
1	1	1

than by the truth table we originally gave. Correspondingly, he would be satisfied with the truth table

x_2	x_1	f
0	0	0
0	1	0
1	0	1
1	1	1

(knowing that the third entry will never occur) and the logic circuit

$$x_2 \longrightarrow \boxed{} \longrightarrow f(x_2, x_1)$$
$$x_1 \longrightarrow$$

which has zero cost and is therefore preferable to the original circuit.

All of the foregoing example motivates the definition: A mapping $f : B^n \longrightarrow C = \{0,1,I\}$ is called an *incompletely specified Boolean function* (i.s.b.f.). We put

$$(b_n, b_{n-1}, \cdots, b_1) \overset{f}{\longrightarrow} I$$

for precisely those arguments $(b_n, b_{n-1}, \cdots, b_1)$ for which the designer is unconcerned. The example above then has the *incomplete truth table*

x_2	x_1	f
0	0	0
0	1	0
1	0	I
1	1	1

The use of the symbol I (aside from the mnemonic aids: $I = In$-complete $= I$ don't care) is prompted by the following observations:

To generalize the notation $B(n)$, let

$$C(n) = \{f; f : B^n \longrightarrow C\} \qquad (3.1)$$

denote the set of all i.s.b.f.'s of n variables. Then consider the diagram of sets and mappings:

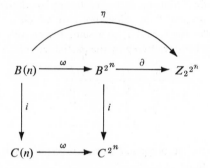

in which the characteristic number mapping η (cf. Eq. 1.36) has been factored (in the sense of Sec. 0.4) into the product

$$\eta = \partial \cdot \omega \qquad (3.2)$$

where

$$\omega(g) = (g(1,1, \cdots, 1,1), g(1,1, \cdots, 1,0), \cdots, g(0,0, \cdots, 0,0)) \qquad (3.3)$$

for $g \in B(n)$ and i is the inclusion map (cf. Eq. 0.11) of B^{2^n} into C^{2^n}. This point of view allows us to consider

$$v_g = \omega(g) \qquad (3.4)$$

as a vertex of the 2^n cube. In a similar way, an i.s.b.f., f, gives rise to a cell

$$c_f = \omega(f)$$

(one can again use Eq. 3.3 to describe ω) of C^{2^n}, and it is easily seen that

$$\left.\begin{array}{l}\text{The truth table of } g \\ \text{agrees with that of } f \\ \text{whenever } f \text{ is specified}\end{array}\right\} \Longleftrightarrow v_g \subseteq c_f \text{ in } C^{2^n} \qquad (3.5)$$

Since the statement on the left of Eq. 3.5 verbalizes the design requirements of the incompletely specified synthesis problem (given $f \in C(n)$,
find $g \in B(n)$ such that $\cdots$) of finding *some* circuit that behaves as specified by a given i.s.b.f., our decision to write I for the unspecified entries
allows us to phrase the synthesis problem in cellular notation.

EXAMPLE 3.2

Suppose that the incompletely specified function f is given with (incomplete) truth table

x_3	x_2	x_1	f
0	0	0	1
0	0	1	I
0	1	0	I
0	1	1	1
1	0	0	0
1	0	1	1
1	1	0	0
1	1	1	1

Then

$$c_f = \omega(f) = (1,0,1,0,1,I,I,1)$$

is a 2-cell in $C^{2^3} = C^8$ having four vertices $(1,0,1,0,1,0,0,1)$, $(1,0,1,0,1,0,1,1)$,
$(1,0,1,0,1,1,0,1)$, $(1,0,1,0,1,1,1,1)$. Each of these vertices v arises $(v = v_g)$ when
considering c.s.b.f.'s g that agree in the six specified entries of f. Thus the last
vertex comes from considering the c.s.b.f. g with truth table

x_3	x_2	x_1	g
0	0	0	1
0	0	1	1
0	1	0	1
0	1	1	1
1	0	0	0
1	0	1	1
1	1	0	0
1	1	1	1

since $v_g = (1,0,1,0,1,1,1,1)$. Evidently, this last truth table shows that the
circuit of Fig. 3.1 will meet the requirements of the given i.s.b.f. f.

FIGURE 3.1

3.3 INCOMPLETELY SPECIFIED MINIMIZATION PROBLEMS

Using Eq. 3.5, it is possible to generalize the (single output) minimization problem of switching theory (cf. Sec. 1.17) as follows: Given $f : B^n \to C$, find a Boolean polynomial g in the variables $x_1, x_2, \cdots, x_n$ such that[†]

$$v_g \subseteq c_f \qquad (3.6)$$

$$\left.\begin{array}{c} v_h \subseteq c_f \\ h \in \mathrm{FB}(n) \end{array}\right\} \Longrightarrow c(\rho(g)) \leq c(\rho(h)) \qquad (3.7)$$

This is the formulation of the *incompletely specified single-output minimization problem.* Note that we have preferred to state the problem in polynomial language rather than the circuit language used in the more restricted formulation of Sec. 1.17. Therefore, in Eq. 3.7 it was necessary to consider $\rho(g)$, $\rho(h)$ and the costs of these logic circuits. We have left the statement of the corresponding multiple-output minimization problem as an exercise (see Prob. 3.12) for the reader, where he will probably find it more convenient to use a "circuit language" formulation (cf. Sec. 1.17).

As expected, we immediately add a further restriction to Eqs. 3.6 and 3.7 in order that the problem be solvable. In the "classical" minimization theory we are about to develop, attention is limited to polynomials g of the form

$$g = \sum_{j=1}^{r} p_j; \quad p_j \in P^n \qquad (j = 1, 2, \cdots, r) \qquad (3.8)$$

that is, to sums of Boolean products (cf. Eq. 2.10) or to products of Boolean sums (as we consider in Sec. 3.11). With such polynomials, the reference to their logic circuits (as in Eq. 3.7) can be circumvented if we decide on a cost $\mu(g)$ when g has the form of Eq. 3.8. There are several standard cost criteria in use; one of these, the so-called *diode cost*[§] (cf. Eq. 2.12),

$$\mu_0(g) = r + \sum_{j=1}^{r} m(p_j) \qquad (3.9)$$

[†]Here g refers also to the truth table (c.s.b.f.) of the given polynomial g.

[‡]M. Karnaugh, "The Map Method for Synthesis of Combinatorial Logic Circuits," *Trans. AIEE*, 72, Part I (1953).

[§]J. T. Chu, "Some Methods for Simplifying Switching Circuits Using 'Don't Care' Conditions," J. of ACM, 8, 4 (October 1961).

counts (unless $r = 1$ or $m(p_j) = 1$ for some j) the number of diodes used in the obvious "two-level" diode circuit realization of g. A closely related criterion, the *literal cost*,

$$\mu_1(g) = \sum_{j=1}^{r} m(p_j) \tag{3.10}$$

counts the number of "literals" (x_i or $\bar{x}_i$) occurring in the products of g. This cost differs from that of Eq. 3.9 only in that it fails to take account of the number of inputs to the "or" gate used in implementing g. There are several types of transistor circuitry for which this criterion is more realistic than that of Eq. 3.9. Furthermore, it is important to observe that much of the pioneering work[†] on the minimization problem was done with this measure of economy.

If only the number of gates are of interest in establishing a relative cost, the *gate cost*

$$\mu_2(g) = r \tag{3.11}$$

(or $\mu_2(g) = r + 1$; there is little difference, relatively speaking) can be used. We will commonly employ a hybrid criterion

$$\mu(g) = \left(r, \sum_{j=1}^{r} m(p_j) \right) \tag{3.12}$$

which has found wide acceptance.[‡] Here, the cost is a pair of integers, and relative economy is dictated by the lexicographical order (cf. Prob. 1.5) in $Z \times Z$; that is,

$$\mu(g) \leqslant \mu(g') \Longleftrightarrow \begin{cases} r < r' \\ \text{or} \\ r = r' \text{ and } \sum_{j=1}^{r} m(p_j) \leq \sum_{j=1}^{r'} m(p'_j) \end{cases} \tag{3.13}$$

for

$$g = \sum_{j=1}^{r} p_j \text{ and } g' = \sum_{j=1}^{r'} p'_j$$

Thus, the gate-cost criterion is used unless there is a "tie," in which case the literal cost criterion is invoked to break the tie. This hybrid criterion has several theoretical advantages that cannot be immediately appreciated. But the justification for our concentrating on one criterion (Eqs. 3.12 and 3.13) is revealed in Prob. 3.10, which assures that the minimization theory we are about to develop would, for the most part, be unchanged if one of the other three criteria were adopted instead.

[†]W. V. Quine, "The Problem of Simplifying Truth Functions," *Amer. Math. Monthly*, 59 (1952); "A Way to Simplify Truth Functions," *Amer. Math. Monthly*, 62 (1955).

[‡]E. J. McClusky Jr., "Minimization of Boolean Functions," *Bell System Tech. J.*, XXXV, 6 (November 1956).

EXAMPLE 3.3

Consider the sums of products

$$g_1 = \bar{x}_4 x_3 + x_2 \bar{x}_1 + x_3 \bar{x}_2 + x_1$$

$$g_2 = \bar{x}_4 x_3 x_2 + x_4 x_2 \bar{x}_1 + x_3 \bar{x}_2 x_1$$

$$g_3 = \bar{x}_4 x_2 + x_4 \bar{x}_3 x_2 x_1 + \bar{x}_4 x_3 x_2 \bar{x}_1$$

The tabulated costs for the four different criteria are as follows:

Eq. NO:	3.9	3.10	3.11	3.12
g_1	11	7	4	(4,7)
g_2	12	9	3	(3,9)
g_3	13	10	3	(3,10)

In this table, g_1 has least cost according to criteria (3.9) and (3.10), but g_2 has least cost according to criterion (3.12). Note in Fig. 3.2 (as mentioned in the parenthetical remark following Eq. 3.9) that the logic circuit $N_1 = \rho(g_1)$ has cost $c(N_1) = 10$ rather than 11.

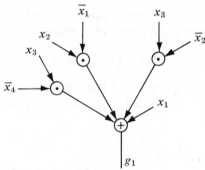

FIGURE 3.2

After a suitable cost criterion $\mu(g)$ has been selected, we say that g is a *minimal* (sum of products) *form* of $f \in C(n)$ if

(1) g has the form of Eq. 3.8,
(2) $v_g \subseteq c_f$,
(3) $\left. \begin{array}{l} v_h \subseteq c_f \\ h \text{ having form of Eq. 3.8} \end{array} \right\} \Longrightarrow \mu(g) \leqslant \mu(h)$

Ordinarily, μ will be taken to have the meaning of Eq. 3.12 with relative economy ($\leqslant$) measured by Eq. 3.13. We have chosen to write "a" minimal form rather than "the" minimal form because the corresponding minimization problem does not generally have a unique solution. Nevertheless, we can be sure that two such minimal forms will agree in their gate cost and their literal cost. Hence, the *sum of products cost*

$$M(f) = \mu_2(g) + \mu_1(g) = \mu_0(g) \tag{3.14}$$

is a well-defined integer for g any minimal form of f. (Similarly we could unambiguously define

$$\mu_1(f) = \mu_1(g) \tag{3.15}$$

for g any minimal form of f.) Note that we are not claiming that

$$M(f) = \min\{\mu_0(g); v_g \subseteq c_f\}$$

(See Prob. 3.9.) But our hope for a minimal form is that $M(f)$ for an i.s.b.f. $f \in C(n)$ is a reasonably good approximation to

$$m(f) = \min_{\substack{v_h \subseteq c_f \\ h \in B(n)}} m(h) \tag{3.16}$$

where $m(h)$ is defined by Eq. 1.41. Since $m(f)$ is generally unknown, we are rarely sure of the degree to which this hope is fulfilled. Nevertheless, the "classical" minimization theory is of great importance in the face of the relative lack of success when more general forms of polynomials are admitted into consideration. Illustrative of the theoretical importance of Eq. 3.14 and the concept of a minimal form are Probs. 3.3 through 3.8, whose proofs may be phrased in such a way that the lemma we are about to state may be employed. First it must be understood that the notation $p(b_n, b_{n-1}, \cdots, b_1)$ for $p \in P^n$ and $(b_n, b_{n-1}, \cdots, b_1) \in B^n$ is intended to denote that element of B that results from the substitutions $x_n = b_n$, $x_{n-1} = b_{n-1}$, $\cdots$, $x_1 = b_1$ in the product $p = x_n^{(c_n)} x_{n-1}^{(c_{n-1})} \cdots x_1^{(c_1)}$. Thus, if $p = \bar{x}_5 x_4 \bar{x}_2 x_1$ and $(b_5, b_4, b_3, b_2, b_1) = (0,1,1,1,1)$, we have

$$p(0,1,1,1,1) = 0^{(0)} 1^{(1)} 1^{(I)} 1^{(0)} 1^{(1)} = \bar{0} \cdot 1 \cdot 1 \cdot \bar{1} \cdot 1 = 0$$

Lemma 3.1. Let

$$g = \sum_{j=1}^{r} p_j$$

be a sum of Boolean products

$$p_j = x_n^{(c_n^j)} x_{n-1}^{(c_{n-1}^j)} \cdots x_1^{(c_1^j)} \qquad (j = 1, 2, \cdots, r)$$

Then

$$g(b_n, b_{n-1}, \cdots, b_1) = 1 \Longleftrightarrow p_k(b_n, b_{n-1}, \cdots, b_1) = 1$$
$$\text{for some } k(1 \le k \le r) \tag{3.17}$$

PROOF. If $p_k(b_n, b_{n-1}, \cdots, b_1) = 1$ for some k, then

$$g(b_n, b_{n-1} \cdots, b_1) = \left(\sum_{j=1}^{r} p_j\right)(b_n, b_{n-1}, \cdots, b_1)$$

$$= \sum_{j=1}^{r} p_j(b_n, b_{n-1}, \cdots, b_1)$$

$$= p_k(b_n, b_{n-1}, \cdots, b_1) + \sum_{j \neq k} p_j(b_n, b_{n-1}, \cdots, b_1)$$

$$= 1 + \sum_{j \neq k} = 1$$

Conversely, if $p_k(b_n, b_{n-1}, \cdots, b_1) = 0$ for every k, we see that $g(b_n, b_{n-1}, \cdots, b_1) = 0$. ∎

Corollary 3.2. If $m = x_n^{(b_n)} x_{n-1}^{(b_{n-1})} \cdots x_1^{(b_1)}$ is a minterm and g is as in Lemma 3.1,

$$g(b_n, b_{n-1}, \cdots, b_1) = 1 \Longleftrightarrow m \subseteq p_k \quad \text{for some } k(1 \le k \le r) \qquad \textbf{(3.18)}$$

EXAMPLE 3.4

The lemma (or its corollary) provides an improved method (over that outlined in Examples 1.29 and 1.30) for constructing the truth table of a sum of products

$$g = \sum_{j=1}^{r} p_j$$

Suppose

$$g = \bar{x}_3 x_1 + \bar{x}_2 + \bar{x}_4 x_3 x_1 = \sum_{j=1}^{3} p_j$$

where

$$p_1 = \bar{x}_3 x_1 = x_4^{(I)} x_3^{(0)} x_2^{(I)} x_1^{(1)}$$
$$p_2 = \bar{x}_2 = x_4^{(I)} x_3^{(I)} x_2^{(0)} x_1^{(I)}$$
$$p_3 = \bar{x}_4 x_3 x_1 = x_4^{(0)} x_3^{(1)} x_2^{(I)} x_1^{(1)}$$

Now the lemma and its corollary provide necessary and sufficient conditions in order that $g(b_n, b_{n-1}, \cdots, b_1) = 1$; that is, in order that there be a "1" in a particular row of the truth table of g. Computing the cells $c_j = \tau(p_j)$ for each product p_j,

$$c_1 = \tau(p_1) = (I,0,I,1)$$
$$c_2 = \tau(p_2) = (I,I,0,I)$$
$$c_3 = \tau(p_3) = (0,1,I,1)$$

we use Theorem 2.3 and Corollary 3.2 to conclude that

$$g(0,0,0,1) = g(0,0,1,1) = g(1,0,0,1) = g(1,0,1,1) = 1$$

because the vertices $(0,0,0,1)$, $(0,0,1,1)$, $(1,0,0,1)$, $(1,0,1,1)$ are contained in c_1. Continuing in this way, we obtain the truth table

x_4	x_3	x_2	x_1	g
0–0	0	0	0	1
1–0	0	0	1	1
2–0	0	1	0	0
3–0	0	1	1	1
4–0	1	0	0	1
5–0	1	0	1	1
6–0	1	1	0	0
7–0	1	1	1	1
8–1	0	0	0	1
9–1	0	0	1	1
10–1	0	1	0	0
11–1	0	1	1	1
12–1	1	0	0	1
13–1	1	0	1	1
14–1	1	1	0	0
15–1	1	1	1	0

If we were interested in an economy of presentation, the equivalent information (in the form of $\mathcal{K}^0(g)$ rather than in the form of a truth table) could be found from the decimal computations introduced in Example 2.18:

$$C_1 = D(c_1) = (1,11)$$
$$C_2 = D(c_2) = (0,13)$$
$$C_3 = D(c_3) = (5,7)$$

C_1: 1 / 3 9 / 11
C_2: 0 / 1 4 8 / 5
                    9 12 / 13
C_3: 5 / 7

from which we learn that

$$\mathcal{K}^0(g) = \{0, 1, 3, 4, 5, 7, 8, 9, 11, 12, 13\}$$

in agreement with the above truth table.

EXAMPLE 3.5

Denote by h the function of Example 2.11. The reader should suspect (it is true!) that

$$H = \bar{x}_1 + x_3 x_2 = \sum_{j=1}^{r} p_j \qquad (r = 2) \tag{3.19}$$

is a minimal form for $h : B^3 \longrightarrow B$. Now consider the function $f : B^4 \longrightarrow B$ defined by

$$f(x_4, x_3, x_2, x_1) = x_4 \cdot h(x_3, x_2, x_1) \tag{3.20}$$

(See Table 3.1.) It is reasonable to suppose that f has a minimal form F whose

x_4	x_3	x_2	x_1	f
0	0	0	0	0
0	0	0	1	0
0	0	1	0	0
0	0	1	1	0
0	1	0	0	0
0	1	0	1	0
0	1	1	0	0
0	1	1	1	0
1	0	0	0	1
1	0	0	1	0
1	0	1	0	1
1	0	1	1	0
1	1	0	0	1
1	1	0	1	0
1	1	1	0	1
1	1	1	1	1

TABLE 3.1

products are obtained by multiplying those of Eq. 3.19 by x_4; that is,

$$F = x_4 \bar{x}_1 + x_4 x_3 x_2$$

That this is true is exactly the claim of Prob. 2.3. Note that

$$M(f) = \mu_0(F) = 2 + (2 + 3) = 7$$

and

$$M(h) = \mu_0(H) = 2 + (1 + 2) = 5$$

so that

$$M(f) = r + M(h)$$

as claimed in Prob. 3.3. The reader should try his hand at the construction of examples for Probs. 3.4 through 3.8.

3.4   MINIMAL COVERINGS[†]

Let L be a subcomplex of a cell complex K(cf. Sec. 2.6) and let $M = \{c_1, c_2, \cdots, c_r\}$ be a subset of C^n. Then M is said to be a *covering of L^0 by cells of K* if

(1) $M \subseteq K$,
(2) $v \in L^0 \Longrightarrow$ there exists $c_k \in M$ such that $v \subseteq c_k$

If, in addition,

(3) M' a covering of L^0 by cells of $K \Longrightarrow w(M) \leqslant w(M')$ where the *weight $w(M)$* of any subset $M = \{c_1, c_2, \cdots, c_r\} \subseteq K$ is defined by

$$w(M) = \left(r, \sum_{j=1}^{r} (n - \theta(c_j)) \right) \tag{3.21}$$

then M is said to be a *minimal covering* of L^0 by cells of K. (Here, the lexicographical order $\leqslant$ is again to be used in $Z \times Z$.) The reader will undoubtedly appreciate our defining the *weight $w(c)$* of a cell $c \in C^n$ to be $n - \theta(c)$.

Suppose $f : B^n \to C$ is an i.s.b.f. We associate two cell complexes $L \subseteq K$ with f as follows (see Probs. 3.1 and 3.11)

$$L = K(f_{\min}) = K(\omega^{-1}(\min(\omega(f)))) \tag{3.22}$$
$$K = K(f_{\max}) = K(\omega^{-1}(\max(\omega(f)))) \tag{3.23}$$

where

$$f_{\min} = \omega^{-1}(\min(\omega(f))) = \omega^{-1}(\min c_f) \tag{3.24}$$

[†]The terminology of the following sections is close to that of J. P. Roth "Algebraic Topological Methods for the Synthesis of Switching Systems," *Trans. Amer. Math. Soc.*, 88, 2 (July 1958), and to that of R. H. Urbano and R. K. Mueller, "A Topological Method for the Determination of the Minimal Forms of a Boolean Function," *IRE Trans. on Electronic Computers*, EC-5 (September 1956).

$$f_{\max} = \omega^{-1}(\max(\omega(f))) = \omega^{-1}(\max c_f) \qquad (3.25)$$

are c.s.b.f.'s so that $K(f_{\min})$ and $K(f_{\max})$ have the meanings intended in Eq. 2.20. According to Theorem 2.6, these will be Boolean cell complexes. When L and K have this interpretation, a minimal covering M of L^0 by cells of K is termed a *minimal covering of the i.s.b.f.* f. (Similarly, M is termed a *covering* of f if only conditions (1) and (2) are satisfied.)

The reader should be anticipating (when Example 2.11 is reexamined) here our attempt to phrase the minimization problem in cellular language. Thus, Eq. 3.21 is the analog of Eq. 3.12 (see Corollary 2.4). And we should point out (cf. the note at the conclusion of Prob. 3.10) that three other "weights" might have been chosen had we a different cost criterion than that of Eqs. 3.12 and 3.13 in mind. The culmination of our complete rephrasing of the minimization problem is expressed in the following theorem.

Theorem 3.3. Let $f : B^n \to C$ be an i.s.b.f. and let

$$g = \sum_{j=1}^{r} p_j$$

be a sum of Boolean products with $p_j \in P^n$. Put

$$c_j = \tau(p_j) \qquad (j = 1, 2, \cdots, r)$$

and let $M = \{c_1, c_2, \cdots, c_r\}$ be the corresponding collection of cells of C^n. Then g is a minimal form of f if and only if M is a minimal covering of f.

PROOF. First suppose that g is a minimal form of f so that g satisfies, in addition to the hypothesis, properties (2) and (3) of Sec. 3.3:

(2) $v_g \subseteq c_f,$

(3) $\left. \begin{array}{l} v_h \subseteq c_f, \\ h \text{ of form of Eq. 3.8} \end{array} \right\} \Longrightarrow \mu(g) \leqslant \mu(h)$

Let L and K have the meanings of Eqs. 3.22 and 3.23, respectively. Now consider any cell $c_j \in M$ to which corresponds a product $p_j = \tau^{-1}(c_j)$ of the sum g. For each vertex $(v_n, \cdots, v_1) = v \subseteq c_j$ there corresponds similarly a minterm $m = \tau^{-1}(v)$ and each such $m \subseteq p_j$ because τ is an isomorphism (Theorem 2.3). By Corollary 3.2, $g(v_n, v_{n-1}, \cdots, v_1) = 1$, so that property (2) implies that $f(v_n, v_{n-1}, \cdots, v_1) \neq 0$ and $f_{\max}(v_n, v_{n-1}, \cdots, v_1) = 1$. By Eqs. 2.20 and 3.23, we have $v \in K$. Since K is a Boolean complex, we have shown that $c_j \in K$. But c_j was an arbitrary member of M, so we have verified property (1) in the definition of "minimal covering", namely,

$$M \subseteq K$$

Now let $v = (v_n, v_{n-1}, \cdots, v_1) \in L^0$. Then $f_{\min}(v) = 1$ and also $f(v) = 1$, so that $g(v) = 1$ by property (2). Again using Corollary 3.2, there must exist a product p_k for some k ($1 \leq k \leq r$) such that $m \subseteq p_k$; here we denote $x_n^{(v_n)} x_{n-1}^{(v_{n-1})} \cdots x_1^{(v_1)} = m$. But since τ is an isomorphism,

$$m \subseteq p_k \Longrightarrow v = \tau(m) \subseteq \tau(p_k) = c_k$$

so that M is a covering of f.

As for the minimality of M, suppose

$$M' = \{c_1', c_2', \cdots, c_s'\}$$

is a covering, that is,

(1') $M' \subseteq K$,
(2') $v \in L^0 \Longrightarrow$ there exists $c_j' \in M'$ such that $v \subseteq c_j'$.

We have to show that $w(M) \leqslant w(M')$. Consider the products $p_j' = \tau^{-1}(c_j')$ and the sum of products

$$g' = \sum_{j=1}^{s} p_j'$$

It is apparent already that g' satisfies (1') in the definition of minimal form, and we will show also that $v_{g'} \subseteq c_f$. To do this, let $v = (v_n, v_{n-1}, \cdots, v_1)$ be a vertex for which f is specified; that is, $f(v) \neq I$. Let $m = x_n^{(v_n)} x_{n-1}^{(v_{n-1})} \cdots x_1^{(v_1)} = \tau^{-1}(v)$ be the corresponding minterm. If $f(v) = 1$, $v \in L^0$, and by (2') there exists $c_j' \in M'$ such that $v \subseteq c_j'$. Since τ is an isomorphism, we have

$$m \subseteq \tau^{-1}(c_j') = p_j'$$

By Corollary 3.2 we must have $g'(v) = 1$. Alternatively, if $f(v) = 0$, we cannot have $g'(v) = 1$ because this would imply that $m \subseteq p_k'$ for some k and hence $v \subseteq c_k' \in M' \subseteq K$, contradicting the fact that $f(v) = 0$. Thus we have (2') $v_{g'} \subseteq c_f$ and since g is a minimal form, we must have the cost inequality

$$\left(r, \sum_{j=1}^{r} m(p_j)\right) = \mu(g) \leqslant \mu(g') = \left(s, \sum_{j=1}^{s} m(p_j')\right)$$

But according to Corollary 2.4,

$$m(p_j) = n - \theta(c_j)$$
$$m(p_j') = n - \theta(c_j')$$

so that

$$w(M) = \left(r, \sum_{j=1}^{r} (n - \theta(c_j))\right)$$
$$= \left(r, \sum_{j=1}^{r} m(p_j)\right) \leqslant \left(s, \sum_{j=1}^{s} m(p_j')\right) = w(M')$$

showing that M is a minimal covering of f. The converse amounts to a simple inversion of the preceding arguments, so we leave its proof to the interested reader. ∎

Thus we have succeeded in rephrasing the minimization problem (to find a minimal form of an i.s.b.f.) as a covering problem in the cellular n cube. The rephrased problem has the advantage of a geometrical language and its accompanying intuitive aids. The computational procedures of Chapter 2 (in particular, the decimal computations of Sec. 2.9) are also at our disposal, and the mappings D' (cf. Eq. 2.32) and τ^{-1} allow us to transform our answer (a minimal covering) into a minimal form of the given i.s.b.f. f.

EXAMPLE 3.6

Take $f : B^3 \longrightarrow C$ to be the i.s.b.f. with incomplete truth table

x_3	x_2	x_1	f
0	0	0	1
0	0	1	0
0	1	0	I
0	1	1	0
1	0	0	0
1	0	1	0
1	1	0	1
1	1	1	I

(See Fig. 3.3 with solid circles at vertices $v \in L^0$ and open circles at vertices $v \in (K^0 - L^0)$.)[†] By an inspection of Fig. 3.3, or through the use of the Quine-McClusky algorithm (cf. Example 2.13), which is the most suitable alternative when $n > 3$, we learn that

$$K = \{(0,0,0), (0,1,0), (1,1,0), (1,1,1), (0,I,0), (I,1,0,), (1,1,I)\}$$

$$L = \{(0,0,0), (1,1,0)\}$$

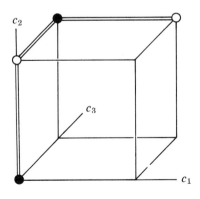

FIGURE 3.3

[†]Often the elements of $K^0 - L^0$ are called "don't care" vertices.

To obtain coverings of f we have only to cover the vertices of $L^0 = L$ with cells of K. This can be done in at least six ways:

$$M_1 = \{(0,0,0), (1,1,0)\} \quad w(M_1) = (2, 3 + 3) = (2,6)$$
$$M_2 = \{(0,0,0), (I,1,0)\} \quad w(M_2) = (2, 3 + 2) = (2,5)$$
$$M_3 = \{(0,0,0), (1,1,I)\} \quad w(M_3) = (2,5)$$
$$M_4 = \{(0,I,0,), (1,1,0)\} \quad w(M_4) = (2, 5)$$
$$M_5 = \{(0,I,0), (I,1,0)\} \quad w(M_5) = (2,2 + 2) = (2,4)$$
$$M_6 = \{(0,I,0), (1,1,I)\} \quad w(M_6) = (2,4)$$

The last two are minimal coverings so, that, according to Theorem 3.3, $\bar{x}_3\bar{x}_1 + x_2\bar{x}_1$ and $\bar{x}_3\bar{x}_1 + x_3x_2$ are minimal forms of f.

3.5 BASIC CELLS AND ESSENTIAL CELLS[†]

With Eqs. 3.22 and 3.23, we have shown how to associate two cell complexes $L \subseteq K$ with each $f \in C(n)$. Two complexes arising in this way are said to constitute a *pair* (K, L). Now let $f : B^n \longrightarrow C$ be an i.s.b.f. and let (K, L) be the associated pair of complexes. A cell $c = (c_n, c_{n-1}, \cdots, c_1) \in K$ is called a *basic cell* of f with respect to the vertex $v = (v_n, v_{n-1}, \cdots, v_1) \in L^0$ if

(A) $v \subseteq c$,
(B) c is maximal in K; that is, $c' \supseteq c, c' \in K \Rightarrow c' = c$.

Theorem 3.4. Every vertex $v \in L^0$ has a basic cell. (No claim of uniqueness is made, however.)

PROOF. If v itself is not a basic cell with respect to v, then $v \subset c_1$ for some $c_1 \in K$, where we have proper inclusion ($v \subseteq c_1$ but $v \neq c_1$). Then either c_1 is basic with respect to v or $c_1 \subset c_2$ for some $c_2 \in K$. Continuing this reasoning we obtain an increasing sequence

$$v \subset c_1 \subset c_2 \cdots \subset c_q \subset \cdots$$

which must (since $0 = \theta(v) < \theta(c_1) < \theta(c_2) < \cdots < \theta(c_q) < \cdots$ and C^n is a finite-dimensional cube) eventually terminate,

$$v \subset c_1 \subset c_2 \subset \cdots \subset c_p$$

in a basic cell c_p. ∎

[†]This terminology is that of Urbano and Mueller (cf. footnote on page 178). In the language of W. V. Quine, these are called *prime implicants* and *core prime implicants*, respectively, whereas J. P. Roth would refer to them as "cocycles" and "extremals," respectively.

A quite similar proof will yield the following theorem

Theorem 3.5. If $c \in K$, $v \in L^0$ and $v \subseteq c$, then c is contained in a basic cell b with respect to vertex v.

If a vertex $v \in L^0$ has but one basic cell e, e is called an *essential cell* with respect to v, in which case v is termed a *distinguished* vertex of e. The concepts of basic and essential cells play an important role in the minimization theory, as the following theorems demonstrate.

Theorem 3.6. Let $f : B^n \to C$ be an i.s.b.f. If $M = \{c_1, c_2, \cdots, c_r\}$ is a minimal covering of f, then each c_j ($j = 1, 2, \cdots, r$) is a basic cell (of f).

PROOF. Let (K, L) be the associated pair of complexes. If, contrary to the desired conclusion, we had "c_s is not a basic cell of f" for some $c_s \in M$ that is, if "c_s is basic to v" is false for every $v \in L^0$), either

(A') $v \notin c_s$ for every $v \in L^0$, or
(B') c_s is not maximal in K.

In case (A') the set

$$M' = \{c_1\, c_2, \cdots, c_{s-1}, c_{s+1}, \cdots, c_r\} = M - \{c_s\}$$

satisfies

(1) $M' \subseteq M \subseteq K$
(2) $v \in L^0 \Longrightarrow$ there exists $c_j \in M$ such that $v \subseteq c_j$
$\Longrightarrow$ there exists $c_j \in M'$ such that $v \subseteq c_j$
because of (A').

Furthermore,

$$w(M) = \left(r, \sum_{j=1}^{r} (n - \theta(c_j)) \right) \succ \left((r - 1), \sum_{j \neq s} (n - \theta(c_j)) \right) = w(M')$$

contradicting the minimality of M.

In case (B') there exists a cell $c_t \subset c_s$ with proper inclusion for which $c_t \in K$, and in this case we consider the set

$$M' = \{c_1, c_2, \cdots, c_{s-1}, c_t, c_{s+1}, \cdots, c_r\}$$

Then

(1') $M' \subseteq K$ because $c_t \in K$, $M \subseteq K$.
(2') $v \in L^0 \Longrightarrow$ there exists $c_j \in M$ such that $v \subseteq c_j$
$\Longrightarrow$ there exists $c_j \in M'$ such that $v \subseteq c_j$
because $c_s \subset c_t$,

and again we get a contradiction to the minimality of M because $c_s \subset c_t$ implies $\theta(c_s) < \theta(c_t)$ so that

$$w(M) = \left(r, \sum_{j=1}^{r} (n - \theta(c_j))\right)$$

$$= \left(r, (n - \theta(c_s)) + \sum_{j \neq s} (n - \theta(c_j))\right)$$

$$\succ \left(r, (n - \theta(c_t)) + \sum_{j \neq s} (n - \theta(c_j))\right)$$

$$= w(M')$$

Hence we conclude that M must consist entirely of basic cells. ∎

EXAMPLE 3.7

In Example 3.6, the cells $(0,I,0)$, $(I,1,0)$, $(1,1,I)$ and only these are basic. Note that each of the two minimal coverings M_5 and M_6 consists of basic cells. Generally speaking, we learn from Theorem 3.6 the importance of the maximal (unchecked) cells arising in the Quine-McClusky algorithm (cf. Example 2.13); no other cells are to be considered in the formation of a minimal covering. But maximal cells of K are not necessarily basic (they may not contain any vertices of L^0), so that among these "unchecked" cells, only those that contain some vertex of L^0 should be retained for consideration.

Returning to Example 3.6, we notice that the cell $e = (0,I,0)$ is essential to the distinguished vertex $u = (0,0,0) \in L^0$. It is no accident that $e \in M_5$ and $e \in M_6$, for this is the content of our next important result—Theorem 3.7.

Theorem 3.7. Let $f : B^n \rightarrow C$ be an i.s.b.f. If e is an essential cell of f and M is any minimal covering of f, then $e \in M$.

PROOF. Let (K, L) have the usual meaning and suppose, contrary to the desired conclusion, that e is an essential cell of f with distinguished vertex $v \in L^0$, but $e \notin M$. By (2) in the definition of minimal covering, there exists some cell $c \in M$ such that $v \subseteq c \neq e$. By Theorem 3.6, c is a basic cell; this contradicts the definition of e; that is, e should be the *only* basic cell with respect to v. ∎

Thus, essential cells (when they exist) are members of every minimal covering. The discovery of an essential cell e has a simplifying effect on the minimization problem, which we describe in terms of the *complex* $|e|$:

$$|e| = \{c \in C^n; c \subseteq e\} \tag{3.26}$$

generated by e.

Theorem 3.8. Let f, (K, L) be as in the preceding theorems and let $e \in K$ be an essential cell for the distinguished vertex $u \in L^0$. Then $M \cup \{e\}$ is a minimal covering of f if and only if M is a minimal covering of $L^0 - (|e|^0 \cap L^0)$ by cells of K.

PROOF. Suppose $M = \{c_1, c_2, \cdots, c_r\}$ is a minimal covering of $L^0 - (|e|^0 \cap L^0)$ by cells of K. This means that

(1) $M \subseteq K$.

(2) $v \in L^0 - (|e|^0 \cap L^0) \Rightarrow \begin{cases} \text{there exists } c_j \in M \\ \text{such that } v \subseteq c_j \end{cases}$.

(3) If M' is any other covering of $L^0 - (|e|^0 \cap L^0)$ by cells of K, then $w(M) \leqslant w(M')$.

Now consider the set $N = M \cup \{e\} = \{e, c_1, c_2, \cdots, c_r\}$. We have $e \in K$, so that

(1') $N \subseteq K$.

Next suppose $v \in L^0$. Then either $v \subseteq e$ or $v \nsubseteq e$. In the first caset here exists the cell $e \in N$ for which $v \subseteq e$, while in the second case, $v \in L^0 - (|e|^0 \cap L^0)$ so that by (2) there exists $c_j \in M$ such that $v \subseteq c_j$. Since $M \subseteq N = M \cup \{e\}$ we can state that in either case

(2') $v \in L^0 \Rightarrow$ there exists a cell $c \in N$ such that $v \subseteq c$, so that N is a covering of f.

For the minimality, suppose N' is any other subset of C^n satisfying (1') and (2'). In particular, since $u \in L^0$, (2') implies the existence of a cell $c \in N'$ such that $u \subseteq c$. Thus, we denote

$$N' = \{c, c_1', c_2', \cdots, c_s'\}$$

By Theorem 3.5 there exists a basic cell b for which $u \subseteq c \subseteq b$, and since e is essential to vertex u by hypothesis, we must have $b = e$. Now put $M' = N' - c = \{c_1', c_2', \cdots, c_s'\}$. Clearly, M' satisfies (1) and (2) so that $w(M) \leqslant w(M')$ by the minimality of M. Now either

(a) $r < s$ so that $r + 1 < s + 1$ and $w(N) \leqslant w(N')$, or

(b) $r = s$, in which case $w(M) \leqslant w(M')$ implies that

$$\sum_{j=1}^{r} (n - \theta(c_j)) \leq \sum_{j=1}^{s} (n - \theta(c_j'))$$

and hence, because $c \subseteq e$ implies $\theta(c) \leq \theta(e)$, we obtain

$$(n - \theta(e)) + \sum_{j=1}^{r} (n - \theta(c_j)) \leq (n - \theta(c)) + \sum_{j=1}^{s} (n - \theta(c_j'))$$

so that $w(N) \leqslant w(N')$ in this case as well.

Thus $N = M \cup \{e\}$ is a minimal covering of f. Again we leave the proof of the converse as an exercise. ∎

EXAMPLE 3.8

In Examples 3.6 and 3.7 we found that $e = (0,I,0)$ was an essential cell to vertex $u = (0,0,0)$. Then, since

$$|e| = \{(0,I,0), (0,0,0), (0,1,0)\}$$
$$L^0 - (|e|^0 \cap L^0) = \{(1,1,0)\}$$

we learn from Theorem 3.9 that $M \cup \{e\}$ is a minimal covering of f if and only if M is a minimal covering of $\{(1,1,0)\}$ by cells of K. The cell $(0,I,0)$ is no longer basic, since it covers no vertices of the new $L^0 = L^0 - (|e|^0 \cap L^0) = \{(1,1,0)\}$. Hence, only $(I,1,0)$ and $(1,1,I)$ are basic. We may choose to cover $\{(1,1,0)\}$ with either of these to obtain the minimal coverings M_5 and M_6 of Example 3.6. Note that when the essential cell e is found, it is as if we were beginning anew with the incomplete truth table

x_3	x_2	x_1	f
0	0	0	I
0	0	1	0
0	1	0	I
0	1	1	0
1	0	0	0
1	0	1	0
1	1	0	1
1	1	1	I

since the vertex $(0,0,0)$ is already covered by e, which is going to be (by Theorem 3.7) a member of every minimal covering.

This theorem reduces the minimization problem (to find the minimal coverings of L^0 by cells of K) to a smaller problem (that of finding the minimal coverings of $L^0 - (|e|^0 \cap L^0)$ by cells of K) whenever an essential cell e is found. We say "smaller" because L^0 contains at least one vertex $u \subseteq e$ so that we have a proper inclusion

$$L^0 - (|e|^0 \cap L^0) \subset L^0$$

Of course we would be extremely fortunate if the essential cells of f should cover L^0, for then the collection

$$M = E \equiv \{e \in K; \ e \text{ is an essential cell of } f\} \qquad (3.27)$$

would (by Theorem 3.7) represent a unique solution. In general, however, this is not the case. We often find instead that

$$R \equiv L^0 - \bigcup_{e \in E} (|e|^0 \cap L^0) \qquad (3.28)$$

is not empty. This set, R, is called the *residue* of f and represents the vertices of L^0 that are not covered by the essential cells. We can concisely phrase the conclusions of this paragraph in the following.

Corollary 3.9. The minimization problem has the unique solution $M = E$ if $R = \varnothing$.

3.6   IRREDUNDANT COVERINGS

We have learned from Theorem 3.6 that every minimal covering consists of basic cells. So, let $f : B^n \longrightarrow C$ be an i.s.b.f. with the associated pair of complexes (K, L). Suppose $M = \{b_1, b_2, \cdots, b_r\}$ is a covering (not necessarily minimal) of L^0 by basic cells b_1, b_2, $\cdots$, b_r of K. (Recall that a covering satisfies properties (1) and (2), but not necessarily (3) in the definition of minimal covering.) Then M is called an *irredundant* covering if it satisfies the condition

(4) $M - \{b_j\}$ is not a covering for $j = 1, 2, \cdots, r$,

rather than (3). That is, the removal of a basic cell from an irredundant covering M causes the set M to be no longer a covering.

EXAMPLE 3.9

Consider the i.s.b.f. f with incomplete truth table

x_3	x_2	x_1	f
0	0	0	1
0	0	1	1
0	1	0	0
0	1	1	1
1	0	0	1
1	0	1	0
1	1	0	I
1	1	1	I

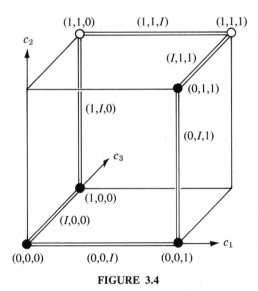

FIGURE 3.4

From Fig. 3.4, or the Quine-McClusky algorithm, we learn that

$L^0 = \{(0,0,0), (0,0,1), (0,1,1), (1,0,0)\}$

$K = \{(0,0,0), (0,0,1), (0,1,1), (1,0,0),$

$(0,0,I), (I,0,0,), (0,I,1), (1,I,0)\ (I,1,1), (1,1,I)\}$

Here, every 1-cell of K is basic except $(1,1,I)$. (Why this exception?) There are no essential cells, since every $v \in L^0$ is covered by two basic cells; f has the irredundant coverings

$$M_1 = \{(I,0,0), (0,I,1)\}$$
$$M_2 = \{(I,0,0), (0,0,I), (I,1,1)\}$$
$$M_3 = \{(0,0,I), (I,1,1), (1,I,0)\}$$
$$M_4 = \{(0,0,I), (0,I,1), (1,I,0)\}$$
$$M_5 = \{(0,0,I), (I,1,1), (I,0,0)\}$$

The usefulness of the concept of irredundancy is revealed in the following theorem.

Theorem 3.10. Let $f : B^n \to C$ be an i.s.b.f. and let M be a minimal covering of f. Then M is irredundant.

PROOF. Assume that M is minimal but not irredundant. Then, by Theorem 3.6, M consists of basic cells

$$M = \{b_1, b_2, \cdots, b_r\}$$

and if M is not irredundant, then for some index s, $1 \le s \le r$,

$$M - \{b_s\} = \{b_1, b_2, \cdots, b_{s-1}, b_{s+1}, \cdots, b_r\}$$

is a covering. But the inequality,

$$w(M) = \left(r, \sum_{j=1}^{r} (n - \theta(b_j))\right) \succ \left((r-1), \sum_{j \ne s} (n - \theta(b_j))\right)$$
$$= w(M - \{b_s\})$$

contradicts the minimality of M. ∎

Hence, every minimal covering is irredundant. That the converse is not always true is revealed by Example 3.9, where M_2 (for instance) is irredundant but not minimal, since

$$w(M_2) = (3,6) \succ (2,6) = w(M_1)$$

Theorem 3.10 is applied to the minimization problem after the *core E* (cf. Eq. 3.27) has been determined. We state the application in the following corollary.

Corollary 3.11. Let $f : B^n \to C$ be an i.s.b.f. with core E and residue R. Then each minimal covering M of f is a union

$$M = E \cup M_i$$

where M_i is an irredundant covering of the residue R. Conversely, such a union is a minimal covering of f if M_i is minimal among the irredundant coverings $\{M_i\}$ of R.

3.7 STARS AND ESSENTIAL VERTICES

Corollary 3.11 shows that the minimization problem can effectively be split into two parts:

Problem A   The determination of the core E.

Problem B   The determination of the irredundant coverings $\{M_i\}$ of the residue R.

It is toward Problem B that the material of this section is directed.

The *basic star*, bst(v), of a vertex $v \in R$ is the set

$$\text{bst}(v) = \{b \in K; \; b \text{ is a basic cell with respect to } v\}$$

A basic star is called an *essential star* if it does not properly contain (cf. Sec. 0.3) another basic star. The vertex v associated with an essential star bst(v) is called an *essential vertex*. The following lemma is somewhat analogous (at least in its proof) to Theorem 3.4.

Lemma 3.12.   Every basic star contains an essential star.

PROOF.   Let bst(v) be the basic star for a vertex $v \in R$. If bst(v) is not itself essential, then it properly contains another basic star bst(v_1). Either bst(v_1) is essential or it properly contains a basic star bst(v_2). Continuing in this way, we obtain a decreasing sequence:

$$\text{bst}(v) \supset \text{bst}(v_1) \supset \text{bst}(v_2) \supset \cdots \supset \text{bst}(v_q) \supset \cdots$$

and since the inclusions are proper and C^n is finite-dimensional, the sequence must terminate,

$$\text{bst}(v) \supset \text{bst}(v_1) \supset \text{bst}(v_2) \supset \cdots \supset \text{bst}(v_p)$$

in an essential star bst(v_p). ∎

The usefulness of the set R' of essential vertices of the residue R is revealed by the following theorem and its application to Problem B.

Theorem 3.13.   Let $f : B^n \longrightarrow C$ be an i.s.b.f. with residue R. Let $R' \subseteq R$ be the subset of R that consists of its essential vertices. If $C(R)$ and $C(R')$ denote the set of all irredundant coverings of R and R', respectively, then

$$C(R) = C(R')$$

PROOF.   First we show that $C(R') \subseteq C(R)$. Let $M' \in C(R')$. To show that M' is a covering of R, suppose that it is not; that is, suppose there exists a vertex $v \in R$ (evidently $v \notin R'$) which is not covered by the cells of M'. By Lemma 3.12,

$$\text{bst}(v) \supset \text{bst}(v')$$

where $\text{bst}(v')$ is an essential star with essential vertex $v' \in R'$. The basic cells of $\text{bst}(v')$ each contain the vertex v, and one of these basic cells is in M' because M' is a covering of R'; this is contrary to the assumption that v is not covered by the cells of M'. Hence, M' is a covering of R. We have to show that M' covers R irredundantly. To do this, suppose $b' \in M'$. Then $M' - \{b'\}$ fails to cover some vertex $u' \in R'$ because M' is an irredundant covering of R'. But $u' \in R' \subseteq R$, so that $u' \in R$, showing that R is irredundantly covered by M'.

Conversely, suppose $M \in C(R)$. Clearly, M is a covering of R' because $R' \subseteq R$. To see that M covers R' irredundantly, suppose it does not. Then, for some basic cell $b_1 \in M$, the set

$$M_1 = M - \{b_1\}$$

also covers R'. Either M_1 is an irredundant covering of R' or we can remove still another basic cell $b_2 \in M$, and

$$M_2 = M_1 - \{b_2\} = M - \{b_1, b_2\}$$

also covers R'. After finitely many such removals, we arrive at an irredundant covering

$$M_k = M - \{b_1, b_2, \cdots, b_k\}$$

of R'. But according to the half $(C(R') \subseteq C(R))$ of the theorem already proved, M_k is an irredundant covering of R. Since M was an irredundant covering of R to begin with, we have a contradiction, which completes the proof. ∎

In order to indicate the application of this theorem to Problem B, we rephrase Corollary 3.11 (in the light of our new information) as a new corollary.

Corollary 3.14. Let $f : B^n \longrightarrow C$ be an i.s.b.f. with core E, residue R, and let R' denote the essential vertices of R. Then each minimal covering M of f is a union

$$M = E \cup M'_i$$

where M'_i is an irredundant covering of R'. Conversely, such a union is a minimal covering of f if M'_i is minimal among the irredundant coverings $\{M'_i\}$ of R'.

The material of Chapter 2. has been designed to provide two quite different methods for the determination of the minimal coverings—a binary computation based on the Quine-McClusky algorithm (cf. Example 2.13) and a decimal procedure having the computations of Sec. 2.9 as its basis. The reader who is primarily interested in the former may want to proceed directly to Sec. 3.10 for its presentation.

The decimal computation[†] of the minimal coverings will be presented in three stages. In order that its total discussion be digestable, we will devote a single section to each stage of the process. Corresponding to Problems A and B defined at the outset of this section, we will discuss

CALCULATION A: The decimal computation of the essential cells.
CALCULATION B: The decimal computation of the basic stars of the residue.

This leaves

PROBLEM B′:   The determination of the set of essential vertices of the residue and its irredundant coverings.

Naturally, the discussion will rely heavily on the theorems of this chapter and the computations of Sec. 2.9. Hopefully, the theory has been described in such depth that the reader will be able to generalize from a discussion of what we think to be well-chosen examples.

3.8   DECIMAL COMPUTATION OF ESSENTIAL CELLS

As our first example, we take an incompletely specified Boolean function $f: B^6 \rightarrow C = \{0,1,I\}$ whose residue $\mathscr{R} = \varnothing$. For if this is the case, Corollary 3.9 states that the minimization problem has the unique solution[‡]

$$\mathscr{M} = \mathscr{E} = \{E \in \mathscr{K} \,;\, E \text{ is an essential cell of } f\}$$

and the entire solution to the problem rests upon the computation of the essential cells E.

EXAMPLE 3.10

The function we have in mind has Table 3.2 as its incomplete truth table. In abbreviated form,

†R. E. Prather, "Computational Aids for Determining the Minimal Form of a Truth Function," J. ACM, 7, 4 (October 1960).

‡Note that we are following the convention of Sec. 2.9, namely, replacing small letters by capital letters and capital letters by script letters when we speak of the decimal transformation of a concept defined in C^n.

x_6	x_5	x_4	x_3	x_2	x_1	f
0	0	0	0	0	0	0
0	0	0	0	0	1	*I*
0	0	0	0	1	0	*I*
0	0	0	0	1	1	*I*
0	0	0	1	0	0	0
0	0	0	1	0	1	1
0	0	0	1	1	0	0
0	0	0	1	1	1	1
0	0	1	0	0	0	*I*
0	0	1	0	0	1	*I*
			.			.
			.			.
			.			.
0	1	1	1	1	1	*I*
1	0	0	0	0	0	0
1	0	0	0	0	1	*I*
1	0	0	0	1	0	*I*
1	0	0	0	1	1	*I*
1	0	0	1	0	0	0
1	0	0	1	0	1	1
1	0	0	1	1	0	1
1	0	0	1	1	1	0
1	0	1	0	0	0	1
1	0	1	0	0	1	*I*
1	0	1	0	1	0	*I*
1	0	1	0	1	1	*I*
1	0	1	1	0	0	1
1	0	1	1	0	1	0
1	0	1	1	1	0	0
1	0	1	1	1	1	0
1	1	0	0	0	0	0
1	1	0	0	0	1	*I*
1	1	0	0	1	0	*I*
1	1	0	0	1	1	*I*
1	1	0	1	0	0	1
1	1	0	1	0	1	0
1	1	0	1	1	0	1
1	1	0	1	1	1	0
1	1	1	0	0	0	1
1	1	1	0	0	1	*I*
1	1	1	0	1	0	*I*
1	1	1	0	1	1	*I*
1	1	1	1	0	0	0
1	1	1	1	0	1	0
1	1	1	1	1	0	0
1	1	1	1	1	1	1

TABLE 3.2

$$\mathcal{L}^0 = \{5, 7, 37, 38, 40, 44, 52, 54, 56, 63\}$$

while $\mathcal{K}$ consists of all cells $Z \in D(C^6)$ whose vertices V are in $\mathcal{L}^0$ or among the list $\mathcal{K}^0 - \mathcal{L}^0$:

1–3	(1 through 3)
8–31	(8 through 31)
33–35	(33 through 35)
41–43	(41 through 43)
49–51	(49 through 51)
57–59	(57 through 59)

of unspecified (don't care) vertices.

The calculation of essential cells can begin with any vertex, $V \in \mathcal{L}^0$. (In the absence of a reason for doing otherwise, we will begin at the first vertex, 5.) Using a computation of Sec. 2.9 (cf. Example 2.17), one can determine the six adjacent vertices 4, 1, 7, 13, 21, 37 to 5 in C^6. Of these, all but the first is in $\mathcal{L}^0$ or on the list of unspecified vertices. Hence, it is possible that there is an essential 5-cell to vertex 5, namely, the cell C with the basis $\mathcal{X} = \{1, 7, 13, 21, 37\}$. In order that this may indeed be the case, it is necessary to show that each vertex of C is either in $\mathcal{L}^0$ or on the "unspecified list" $\mathcal{K}^0 - \mathcal{L}^0$. One uses another computation of Sec. 2.9 (cf. Example 2.18) to determine these vertices, halting the procedure if a vertex encountered is not in $\mathcal{L}^0$ and not on the unspecified list. Such a vertex is then encircled:

$$
\begin{array}{ccccc}
& -4 & +2 & +8 & +16 \\
5 \,/ & 1 & 7 \;\; 13 & 21 \;\; 37 \,/ & 3 \\
& & & & 9 \;\; 15 \\
& & & & 17 \;\; 23 \\
& & & & 33 \;\; \circled{39}
\end{array}
$$

Here we halt and circle 39 because it is not in $\mathcal{L}^0$ and not an unspecified vertex. Evidently this means that there does not exist an essential cell E with respect to vertex 5 (although 5 may be included in a cell that is essential to some other vertex), for such a cell E must have order $k \leq 4$ and a basis $\mathcal{Y}$ which is a subbasis of $\mathcal{X}$. There would then exist at least one vertex $V \in \mathcal{X} - \mathcal{Y}$ and the 1-cell $(5, V)$ is, by Theorem 3.5, contained in a basic cell B with respect to vertex 5. Clearly, $B \neq E$ because $V \not\subseteq E$. Hence, E could not be essential to 5 because it is not the *only* basic cell covering 5.

Proceeding to the next vertex 7 in $\mathcal{L}^0$, we find four adjacent vertices in $\mathcal{L}^0$ or in the list of unspecified vertices, namely, 3, 5, 15, 23. But in this case, the cell C_1 with the basis $\mathcal{X} = \{3, 5, 15, 23\}$ is found to be a member of $\mathcal{K}$ because the computation

$$-4 \ -2 \ +8 \ +16$$
$$7 \, / \quad 3 \quad 5 \quad 15 \quad 23 \, / \quad 1$$
$$11 \quad 13$$
$$19 \quad 21 \quad 31 \, / \quad 9$$
$$17$$
$$27 \quad 29 \, / \, 25$$

produces only vertices of $\mathscr{K}^0$. Hence, C_1 is an essential cell with respect to 7, since it is the only basic cell that covers 7:

$$C_1 = (1, 31) = (\min(C_1), \max(C_1))$$

According to Theorem 3.8, the discovery of C_1 reduces the problem of finding the minimal coverings of $\mathscr{L}^0$ by cell of $\mathscr{K}$ to that of finding the minimal coverings of

$$\mathscr{L}^0 - (|\,C_1\,|^0 \cap \mathscr{L}^0) = \mathscr{L}^0 - \{5,7\}$$
$$= \{37, 38, 40, 44, 52, 54, 56, 63\}$$

by cells of $\mathscr{K}$. (Rather than rewriting the "new" $\mathscr{L}^0$ each time that an essential cell E is found, it is simpler to underline the vertices of $|\,E\,|^0 \cap \mathscr{L}^0$:

$$\mathscr{L}^0 = \{\underline{5}, \underline{7}, 37, 38, 40, 44, 52, 54, 56, 63\}$$

and *treat the underlined vertices as members of the unspecified list thereafter*.) Those vertices of $\mathscr{L}^0$ that remain "un-underlined" throughout the entire computation of essential cells then constitute the residue $\mathscr{R}$.

The remaining calculations are as shown below:

$$37 \, / \quad 5 \quad 33 \, / \quad 1 \qquad\qquad\qquad\qquad C_2 = (1, 37)$$
$$38 \, / \, 34 \quad 54 \, / \, 50 \qquad\qquad\qquad\qquad C_3 = (34,54)$$
$$40 \, / \quad 8 \quad 41 \quad 42 \quad 44 \quad 56 \, / \quad 9$$
$$10 \quad 43$$
$$12 \;\textcircled{45}$$
$$24$$

$$44 \, / \, 12 \quad 40 \, / \quad 8 \qquad\qquad\qquad\qquad C_4 = (8, 44)$$
$$52 \, / \, 20 \quad 54 \, / \, 22 \qquad\qquad\qquad\qquad C_5 = (20,54)$$
$$56 \, / \, 24 \quad 40 \quad 57 \quad 58 \, / \quad 8$$
$$25 \quad 41$$
$$26 \quad 42 \quad 59 \, / \quad 9 \qquad\qquad C_6 = (8, 59)$$
$$10$$
$$27 \quad 43 \, / \, 11$$
$$63 \, / \, 31 \quad 59 \, / \, 27 \qquad\qquad\qquad\qquad C_7 = (31,59)$$

and since every vertex of $\mathscr{L}^0$ is underlined at the conclusion, $\mathscr{R} = \varnothing$ and $\mathscr{L}^0$ has the unique minimal covering

$$\mathscr{M} = \{C_1, C_2, C_3, C_4, C_5, C_6, C_7\}$$

and f has the unique minimal form

$$f(x_6, x_5, x_4, x_3, x_2, x_1) = \sum_{j=1}^{7} \tau^{-1}(D'(C_j))$$

Computing these inverses,

$$(1, 31) \xrightarrow{D'} (0,0,0,0,0,1) + (0,1,1,1,1,1) = (0,I,I,I,I,1) \xrightarrow{\tau^{-1}} \bar{x}_6 x_1$$

$$(1, 37) \xrightarrow{D'} (0,0,0,0,0,1) + (1,0,0,1,0,1) = (I,0,0,I,0,1) \xrightarrow{\tau^{-1}} \bar{x}_5 \bar{x}_4 \bar{x}_2 x_1$$

$$(34, 54) \xrightarrow{D'} (1,0,0,0,1,0) + (1,1,0,1,1,0) = (1,I,0,I,1,0) \xrightarrow{\tau^{-1}} x_6 \bar{x}_4 x_2 \bar{x}_1$$

$$(8, 44) \xrightarrow{D'} (0,0,1,0,0,0) + (1,0,1,1,0,0) = (I,0,1,I,0,0) \xrightarrow{\tau^{-1}} \bar{x}_5 x_4 \bar{x}_2 \bar{x}_1$$

$$(20, 54) \xrightarrow{D'} (0,1,0,1,0,0) + (1,1,0,1,1,0) = (I,1,0,1,I,0) \xrightarrow{\tau^{-1}} x_5 \bar{x}_4 x_3 \bar{x}_1$$

$$(8, 59) \xrightarrow{D'} (0,0,1,0,0,0) + (1,1,1,0,1,1) = (I,I,1,0,I,I) \xrightarrow{\tau^{-1}} x_4 \bar{x}_3$$

$$(31, 59) \xrightarrow{D'} (0,1,1,1,1,1) + (1,1,1,0,1,1) = (I,1,1,I,1,1) \xrightarrow{\tau^{-1}} x_5 x_4 x_2 x_1$$

so that

$$f(x_6, x_5, x_4, x_3, x_2, x_1) = \bar{x}_6 x_1 + \bar{x}_5 \bar{x}_4 \bar{x}_2 x_1 + x_6 \bar{x}_4 x_2 \bar{x}_1 + \bar{x}_5 x_4 \bar{x}_2 \bar{x}_1$$
$$+ x_5 \bar{x}_4 x_3 \bar{x}_1 + x_4 \bar{x}_3 + x_5 x_4 x_2 x_1$$

is the unique minimal form of the Boolean function f.

It is important to note that we need not have written the cells C_1, C_2, $\cdots$, C_7 in terms of their minimum and maximum vertices. Any diagonally opposite pair of vertices would serve equally well. In particular, we could have chosen to write:

$$C_1 = (7,25) \xrightarrow{D'} (0,0,0,1,1,1) + (0,1,1,0,0,1) = (0,I,I,I,I,1) \xrightarrow{\tau^{-1}} \bar{x}_6 x_1$$

$$C_2 = (37,1) \xrightarrow{D'} (1,0,0,1,0,1) + (0,0,0,0,0,1) = (I,0,0,I,0,1) \xrightarrow{\tau^{-1}} \bar{x}_5 \bar{x}_4 \bar{x}_2 x_1$$

$$C_3 = (38,50) \xrightarrow{D'} (1,0,0,1,1,0) + (1,1,0,0,1,0) = (1,I,0,I,1,0) \xrightarrow{\tau^{-1}} x_6 \bar{x}_4 x_2 \bar{x}_1$$

etc., since these "first and last" vertices are diagonally opposite and more easily spotted than are the minimum and maximum vertices.

3.9 DECIMAL COMPUTATION OF STARS

In direct contrast to that of the preceding section, we chose here an example in which the residue is nearly as large as the 0 skeleton $\mathscr{L}^0$. (One can actually construct examples for which $E = \varnothing$ and $R = L^0$.)

EXAMPLE 3.11

Let $n = 5$ and suppose that

$$\mathscr{L}^0 = \{0, 1, 3, 5, 8, 13, 20, 22, 23, 28\}$$

and that the vertices

$$\mathcal{X}^0 - \mathcal{L}^0 = \{2, 7, 9, 10, 11, 12, 14, 15, 17, 21, 30, 31\}$$

are unspecified for a Boolean function $f : B^5 \longrightarrow C$. As in the preceding example, we first determine whether or not there are any essential cells. After the essential cell $E = (0,11)$,

$$0 \,/\, 1 \quad 2 \quad 8 \,/\, 3$$
$$9 \quad 10 \,/\, 11$$

is found, the remaining calculations,

$$5 \,/\, 1 \quad 7 \quad 13 \quad 21 \,/\, \quad 3$$
$$9 \quad 15$$
$$17 \quad 23 \,\, \circled{29}$$

$$13 \,/\, 5 \quad 9 \quad 12 \quad 15 \,/\, \quad 1$$
$$\circled{4}$$

$$20 \,/\, 21 \quad 22 \quad 28 \,/\, \quad 23$$
$$\circled{29}$$

$$22 \,/\, 20 \quad 23 \quad 30 \,/\, \quad 21$$
$$28 \qquad 31 \,/\, 29$$

$$23 \,/\, 7 \quad 21 \quad 22 \quad 31 \,/\, \quad 5$$
$$\circled{6}$$

$$28 \,/\, 12 \quad 20 \quad 30 \,/\, \circled{4}$$

fail to result in essential cells. We have a residue

$$\mathcal{R} = \{5, 13, 20, 22, 23, 28\}$$

whose vertices are yet to be covered. It is then necessary to compute the basic stars BST(5), BST(13), BST(20), BST(22), BST(23), BST(28). The order in which these vertices are considered is unimportant, so we begin with vertex. 5.

The 4-cell C with basis $\mathcal{X} = \{V^{(1)}, V^{(2)}, V^{(3)}, V^{(4)}\} = \{1, 7, 13, 21\}$ contains every cell that is basic with respect to $V = 5$. We are therefore interested to know which subbases of $\mathcal{X}$ will result in basic cells. Our previous calculation,

$$5 \,/\, 1 \quad 7 \quad 13 \quad 21 \,/\, \quad 3$$
$$9 \quad 15$$
$$\underline{17 \quad 23 \,\, \circled{29}}$$
$$N_2$$

completed the determination of all vertices in N_2. (Cf. Eq. 2.39) These vertices of N_2 might be replaced by the compatibility matrix (cf. Eq. 0.54)

7	1		
13	1	1	
21	1	1	0
	1	7	13

for the compatibility (cf. Eqs. 0.52 and 0.53) relation $\approx$ on $\mathcal{X}$, defined as

$$V^{(i)} \approx V^{(j)} \longleftrightarrow (V + \Delta_i + \Delta_j) \in \mathscr{K}^0 \qquad (3.29)$$

As such, the relation has the maximal compatibles (cf. Example 0.30) $\{1,7,13\}$ and $\{1,7,21\}$, while

$$\gamma^2(5) = \{\overline{1,7,13}; \overline{1,7,21}\} \qquad (3.30)$$

is the corresponding grouping (cf. Sec. 0.9 and Theorem 0.6) of $\mathscr{X}$ Every basic cell with respect to vertex $V = 5$ must now have a basis that is a subbasis of one of the blocks of $\gamma^2(5)$.

An alternate point of view is provided by the calculation of the subbasis $\mathscr{Y}(29)$ of $\mathscr{X}$, which has V and $W = 29$ as diagonally opposite vertices. (Cf. Example 2.20.) Since we find that the equation

$$29 = 5 - 4b_1 + 2b_2 + 8b_3 + 16b_4$$

has the solution $b_1 = b_2 = 0$, $b_3 = b_4 = 1$, we have $\mathscr{Y}(29) = \{13,21\}$. It follows that any subbasis of $\mathscr{X}$ that contains $\mathscr{Y}(29)$ will *not* correspond to a basic cell with respect to the vertex $V = 5$. Using this information, we replace $\mathscr{X}$ by a covering (cf. Sec. 0.3) of $\mathscr{X}$ by subsets (subbases) that are maximal with respect to the property of not containing $\mathscr{Y}(29)$. Thus, we replace

$$\gamma^1(5) = \{\mathscr{X}\} = \{\overline{1,7,13,21}\}$$

by the covering (here a grouping)

$$\gamma^2(5) = \{\overline{1,7,13}; \overline{1,7,21}\}$$

the result being the same as in Eq. 3.30.

The advantage of the second point of view is seen in the extension to higher dimensions. (Eq. 3.29 cannot be extended beyond N_2 if it is to be a *binary* relation; but see Sec. 3.14). In N_3,

$$5 \,/\, 1 \quad 7 \quad 13 \quad 21 \,/\, 3$$
$$9 \quad 15$$
$$17 \quad 23 \quad 29 \,/\, 11$$
$$19$$
$$\underbrace{25 \quad 31}_{N_3} \,/$$

we have

$$\mathscr{Y}(19) = \{1,7,21\}$$
$$\mathscr{Y}(25) = \{1,13,21\}$$

so that it is necessary to replace the block $\{1,7,21\}$ of $\gamma^2(5)$ by subsets $\{1,7\}$, $\{1,21\}$, $\{7,21\}$, which are maximal with respect to the property of not containing $\mathscr{Y}(19)$, while $\mathscr{Y}(25)$ does not necessitate any replacements in $\gamma^2(5)$. (Why?)

Keeping in mind that we are looking for subbases of $\mathscr{X}$ that correspond to *basic* cells containing $V = 5$, we do not write the subset $\{1,7\}$ in $\gamma^3(5)$ because $\{1,7\} \subset \{1,7,13\}$. Thus, we put

$$\gamma^3(5) = \{\overline{1,7,13}; \overline{1,21}; \overline{7,21}\}$$

This operation is to be continued $\gamma^1(V)$, $\gamma^2(V)$, $\cdots$, $\gamma^k(V)$ until

$$\langle \gamma^k(V) \rangle \leq k \qquad (3.31)$$

(the notation $\langle \ \ \rangle$ for coverings being quite analogous to that for partitions; cf. Eq. 0.42), for an examination of N_{k+1} would then be futile. (Why?) For the least value of k satisfying Eq. 3.31, $\gamma(V) = \gamma^k(V)$ is a covering of $\mathscr{X}$ by blocks, which as subsets of $\mathscr{X}$ represent all the bases for basic cells with respect to V. Then the elements of BST(V) may be computed by the procedure of Example 2.19.

In our example, we have already reached the condition of Eq. 3.31 for $V = 5$, since $\langle \gamma^3(5) \rangle = 3$. Thus

$$\gamma(5) = \{\overline{(1,7,13};\ \overline{1,21};\ \overline{7,21}\}$$
$$\text{BST}(5) = \{(5, 5 - 4 + 2 + 8),\ (5, 5 - 4 + 16),\ (5, 5 + 2 + 16)\}$$
$$= \{(5,11),\ (5,17),\ (5,23)\}$$
$$= \{(1,15),\ (1,21),\ (5,23)\} = \{B_1,\ B_2,\ B_3\}$$

where we have chosen in the last line to write the basic cells in terms of their minimum and maximum vertices, that is,

$$DD'(5,11) = D((0,0,1,0,1) + (0,1,0,1,1)) = D(0,I,I,I,1)$$
$$= (\partial(0,0,0,0,1),\ \partial(0,1,1,1,1)) = (1,15)$$
$$DD'(5,17) = (1,21)$$
$$DD'(5,23) = (5,23)$$

Alternatively, one might prefer to compute all vertices of the basic cells, writing

$$5 / 1 \quad 7 \quad 13 \ / \ 3$$
$$9 \quad 15 \ / \ 11$$
$$5 / 1 \quad 21 \quad / \quad 17$$
$$5 / 7 \quad 21 \quad / \quad 23$$

to see that BST(5) = $\{(1,15),\ (1,21),\ (5,23)\} = \{B_1, B_2, B_3\}$.

For the remaining vertices of $\mathscr{R}$, we have similar computations; we find

$$\gamma(13) = \{\overline{5,9,15};\ \overline{9,12,15}\}$$
$$\gamma(20) = \{\overline{21,22};\ \overline{22,28}\}$$
$$\gamma(22) = \{\overline{20,23};\ \overline{20,30};\ \overline{23,30}\}$$
$$\gamma(23) = \{\overline{7,21};\ \overline{7,31};\ \overline{21,22};\ \overline{22,31}\}$$
$$\gamma(28) = \{\overline{12,30};\ \overline{20,30}\}$$

so that the basic cells

$$13 / 5 \quad 9 \quad 15 / \quad 1$$
$$7 \quad 1 / \ 3 \qquad B_1 = (1,15)$$
$$13 / 9 \quad 12 \quad 15 / \ 8$$
$$11 \quad 14 / \ 10 \qquad B_4 = (8,15)$$

$$20 / 21 \quad 22 / 23 \qquad B_5 = (20,23)$$
$$20 / 22 \quad 28 / 30 \qquad B_6 = (20,30)$$
$$22 / 20 \quad 23 / 21 \qquad B_5 = (20,23)$$

$$
\begin{array}{llll}
22 \ / \ 20 & 30 \ / \ 28 & B_6 = (20,30) \\
22 \ / \ 23 & 30 \ / \ 31 & B_7 = (22,31) \\
23 \ / \ \ 7 & 21 \ / \ \ 5 & B_3 = (5, \ 23) \\
23 \ / \ \ 7 & 31 \ / \ 15 & B_8 = (7, \ 31) \\
23 \ / \ 21 & 22 \ / \ 20 & B_5 = (20,23) \\
23 \ / \ 22 & 31 \ / \ 30 & B_7 = (22,31) \\
28 \ / \ 12 & 30 \ / \ 14 & B_9 = (12,30) \\
28 \ / \ 20 & 30 \ / \ 22 & B_6 = (20,30)
\end{array}
$$

comprise the basic stars

$$
\begin{aligned}
\text{BST}(\ 5) &= \{B_1, B_2, B_3\} \\
\text{BST}(13) &= \{B_1, B_4\} \\
\text{BST}(20) &= \{B_5, B_6\} \\
\text{BST}(22) &= \{B_5, B_6, B_7\} \\
\text{BST}(23) &= \{B_3, B_5, B_7, B_8\} \\
\text{BST}(28) &= \{B_6, B_9\}
\end{aligned}
$$

3.10 BASIC CELL MATRICES[†]

We have not yet described a procedure for finding all irredundant coverings (from which the minimal coverings may be extracted) of the set $\mathscr{R}'$ of essential vertices of the residue $\mathscr{R}$. This will be done in Sec. 3.12 through the use of a vehicle known as the *basic cell matrix* of f; when the Quine-McClusky algorithm (cf. Example 2.13) has been used to determine all basic cells of f, it is a rectangular array whose column headings are the vertices v_j of L^0 and whose row headings are the basic cells b_i of f; when the decimal computations of the two preceding sections have been used instead, it has as column headings the vertices V_j of $\mathscr{R}'$ and as row headings those basic cells B_i that are elements of $\text{BST}(V_j)$ for some $V_j \in \mathscr{R}'$. In either event, the rule for constructing the matrix $A = (a_{ij})$ is the same:

$$
a_{ij} = 1 \iff b_i \in \text{bst}(v_j) \qquad (B_i \in \text{BST}(V_j))
$$

A *solution* (irredundant covering) *of the basic cell matrix* corresponds to a selection of rows (basic cells) of the matrix having the properties:

(1) There is a "1" in each column of some selected row (the *covering* property).

(2) The deletion of a selected row will destroy property (1) (the *irredundant* property).

†In the terminology of Quine or McClusky, such matrices would be called *prime implicant tables*.

Among the irredundant coverings (solutions of the basic cell matrix), we have to expect in general that some will be minimal and others will not. In this connection, a distinction should be drawn between the two problems: that of finding *all* minimal coverings and that of finding *some* minimal covering. If we are interested only in the latter, Roth's "less than" operation may be applied, often reducing the number of rows of A while still retaining some minimal covering. The row (basic cell) B_r is said to (strongly) *dominate* row B_s if

(a) $a_{sj} = 1 \Longrightarrow a_{rj} = 1$.
(b) $w(B_r) \leq w(B_s)$.

(If only (a) is satisfied, B_r dominates B_s *weakly*.) In deleting the strongly dominated row B_s from A, we will have retained a row B_r, which certainly covers every column (vertex) of A that B_s did; moreover, the weight of B_r is no greater than that of B_s. Hence the reduced matrix retains a minimal covering.

EXAMPLE 3.12

If the basic stars of Example 3.11 are examined, one finds an inclusion BST(20 $\subset$ BST(22). According to the definition of Sec. 3.7, this indicates that vertex 22 is not essential. All other vertices of $\mathcal{R} = \{5,13,20,22,23,28\}$ are essential since their stars do not properly contain other basic stars. Hence, $\mathcal{R}' = \{5,13,20,23,28\}$ and we obtain the basic cell matrix of Table 3.3. It is from this matrix that the irredundant coverings of $\mathcal{R}'$ are selected. The selection

$w(B_i)$	BASIC CELLS	ESSENTIAL VERTICES				
		5	13	20	23	28
2	B_1	1	1			
3	B_2	1				
3	B_3	1			1	
2	B_4		1			
3	B_5			1	1	
3	B_6			1		1
3	B_7				1	
3	B_8				1	
3	B_9					1

TABLE 3.3

$\{B_1,B_5,B_6\}$ enjoys both properties (1) and (2) and is therefore an irredundant covering of $\mathcal{R}'$. Now it can be seen that every covering must correspond to a selection of three or more basic cells, and a covering that includes both 3-cells, B_1 and B_4, is not irredundant (and hence, by Theorem 3.10, not minimal). Thus

$$\mathcal{M}'_1 = \{B_1, B_5, B_6\}$$

is a minimal covering of $\mathcal{R}'$, so that (by Corollary 3.14)

$$\mathcal{M} = \{E, B_1, B_5, B_6\}$$

is a minimal covering of f. Computing the products

$$E = (0,11) \xrightarrow{\;D'\;} (0,0,0,0,0) + (0,1,0,1,1) = (0,I,0,I,I) \xrightarrow{\;\tau^{-1}\;} \bar{x}_5\bar{x}_3$$

$$B_1 = (1,15) \xrightarrow{\;D'\;} (0,0,0,0,1) + (0,1,1,1,1,) = (0,I,I,I,1) \xrightarrow{\;\tau^{-1}\;} \bar{x}_5 x_1$$

$$B_5 = (20,23) \xrightarrow{\;D'\;} (1,0,1,0,0) + (1,0,1,1,1) = (1,0,1,I,I) \xrightarrow{\;\tau^{-1}\;} x_5 \bar{x}_4 x_3$$

$$B_6 = (20,30) \xrightarrow{\;D'\;} (1,0,1,0,0) + (1,1,1,1,0) = (1,I,1,I,0) \xrightarrow{\;\tau^{-1}\;} x_5 x_3 \bar{x}_1$$

in the usual way, we obtain a minimal form

$$f(x_5,x_4,x_3,x_2,x_1) = \bar{x}_5\bar{x}_3 + \bar{x}_5 x_1 + x_5 \bar{x}_4 x_3 + x_5 x_3 \bar{x}_1$$

of the original i.s.b.f. f appearing in Example 3.11.

Here it is clear that $\mathcal{M}'_1$ was not a unique minimal covering of $\mathcal{R}'$. The reader should try to list five other ones.

EXAMPLE 3.13

In Example 2.13, every "unchecked" cell of K is basic (this is not quite true when f is incompletely specified, as has already been pointed out). Writing the decimal transforms of the vertices of $L^0 = K^0$ for the sake of simplicity, we obtain the basic cell matrix

	0	3	4	7	8	11	15	19	20	23	24	28	30	31
$(0,I,I,1,1)$		1		1		1	1							
$(I,0,I,1,1)$		1		1				1		1				
$(I,I,1,1,1)$				1			1			1				1
$(0,0,I,0,0)$	1		1											
$(0,I,0,0,0)$	1				1									
$(I,0,1,0,0)$			1						1					
$(I,1,0,0,0)$					1						1			
$(1,I,1,0,0)$									1			1		
$(1,1,I,0,0)$											1	1		
$(1,1,1,I,0)$												1	1	
$(1,1,1,1,I)$													1	1

Now a distinction between our two minimization methods can be made clear. In the decimal method of the two preceding sections, the theory of Secs. 3.5 and 3.7 is applied *prior* to the construction of a basic cell matrix; the essential cells E are extracted and vertices

$$V \in \bigcup_{E \in \mathcal{E}} (|E|^0 \cap \mathcal{L}^0)$$

do not appear as column headings in the resulting matrix and neither do inessential vertices of the residue. At the same time, the row headings are restricted to those basic cells $B \in \mathrm{BST}(V)$ for some $V \in \mathscr{R}'$. With the Quine-McClusky method, however, this theory is applied only *after* the complete basic cell matrix has been formed. Then a distinguished vertex v for an essential cell e will correspond to a column (v) of the basic cell matrix having but a single "1," the associated row heading (e) being an essential cell. Theorem 3.8 is applied by deleting from the matrix row e and all columns in which row e has "1." An inessential vertex u of the residue will then correspond to a column (u) that has "1" in every row as does some other column (w). We say that column u *dominates* column w if this is the case. Theorem 3.13 is applied by deleting the *dominating* column (u) from the matrix. Having applied Theorem 3.8 or 3.13, or both, there may result rows having no "1"—these are, of course, to be deleted as well.

In our present example, $(0,I,I,1,1)$ and $(I,0,I,1,1)$ are essential cells with distinguished vertices 11 and 19, respectively. After applying Theorem 3.8 we have the matrix

	0	4	8	20	24	28	30	31
$(I,I,1,1,1)$								1
$(0,0,I,0,0)$	1	1						
$(0,I,0,0,0)$	1		1					
$(I,0,1,0,0)$		1		1				
$(I,1,0,0,0)$		1			1			
$(1,I,1,0,0)$				1		1		
$(1,1,I,0,0)$					1	1		
$(1,1,1,I,0)$						1	1	
$(1,1,1,1,I)$							1	1

Since no column dominance exists in the resulting matrix, Theorem 3.13 cannot be applied, and $\mathscr{R} = \mathscr{R}' = \{0,4,8,20,24,28,30,31\}$. This matrix is then identical to that which would result from the decimal method of the two preceding sections. (What are its minimal coverings?)

In the problems that conclude this chapter, one is given the opportunity to show (see Prob. 3.10) that the minimization theory depends little on the choice made from among the four common cost criteria introduced in Sec. 3.3. All discrepancies or distinctions between the sets of minimal forms obtained from two different criteria will be due *solely* to the selection of an irredundant covering of $\mathscr{R}'$. Assuming once more that we are interested only in finding *some* minimal covering, but that the gate cost (cf. Eq. 3.11) is our criterion for minimality, we are allowed to delete weakly dominated rows (as well as those that are strongly dominated) from the basic cell matrix.

EXAMPLE 3.14

In the reduced matrix of Example 3.13, the cell $(I,I,1,1,1)$ is weakly dominated by $(1,1,1,1,I)$. Hence, if the gate cost criterion were being employed, we could delete the first row from this matrix. Since $w(I,I,1,1,1) = 3 < 4 = w(1,1, 1,1,I)$, the cell $(I,I,1,1,1)$ is not strongly dominated by $(1,1,1,1,I)$, so that this deletion would not be permissible with the cost criteria of Eqs. 3.12 and 3.31.

In the basic cell matrix of Table 3.3, we observe that B_1 strongly dominates B_2. Thus, with either cost criterion, B_2 may be deleted. Repeated application of (strong) row dominance arguments reduces Table 2.3 to the following matrix:

	5	13	20	23	28
B_1	1	1			
B_3	1			1	
B_5			1	1	
B_6			1		1

The original matrix (Table 3.3) could not exhibit "column dominance" because of the fact that we first deleted inessential vertices. But now we see that column 5 dominates column 13 and column 20 dominates column 28. Here the *dominating* (note this important distinction) columns may be removed, and we obtain the matrix:

	13	23	28
B_1	1		
B_3		1	
B_5		1	
B_6			1

Now, since B_3 and B_5 dominate each other, we may remove either row (say, B_3) and we obtain

	13	23	28
B_1	1		
B_5		1	
B_6			1

Having used strong row dominance everywhere, $\{B_1, B_5, B_6\}$ is a minimal covering by either cost criterion. This is the covering cited in Example 3.12. But observe that we have lost other minimal coverings in making the matrix reductions.

The indiscriminate use of row dominance (strong and weak) and column dominance arguments for reducing A to a *cyclic matrix* (one having no dominance) generally brings us closer to a "near minimal" (with respect to our hybrid criteria) covering of $\mathscr{R}'$ than we were to a minimal covering of $\mathscr{R}'$ before reduction. We say "near minimal" because the weak row-dominance reduction could delete a basic cell that is large (and hence of small weight) in favor of a relatively small one that just happens to cover more of the required vertices. (Cf. Example 3.14.) But one must not be led to think that cyclic basic-cell matrices necessarily enjoy any of the simplicities observed in the three-rowed matrix which concluded Example 3.14.

EXAMPLE 3.15

The basic cell matrix

	V_1	V_2	V_3	V_4	V_5
B_1	1	1	1		
B_2		1			1
B_3		1		1	
B_4	1			1	
B_5			1	1	1

is cyclic, and yet the complete collection of its irredundant coverings is not nearly so apparent as one would like. We will return to this example in Sec. 3.12.

*3.11 THE DUAL MINIMIZATION PROBLEM

We have mentioned throughout this chapter that the theory (Sec. 3.4 through 3.7) and computational techniques (Sec. 3.8 through 3.10) of this chapter apply equally well to the "dual minimization problem" of finding the simplest product of sum representation of an i.s.b.f. To gain insight as to how this dual problem is attacked, we first recall the way in which the truth table of a function $f : B^n \rightarrow B$ is related to its minterm and maxterm canonical forms. (Cf. Eqs. 1.33 and 1.34, respectively.)

Suppose $f : B^n \rightarrow B$ is given in truth table form. (For the time being, we assume that f is completely specified.) Then if $f = \sum m_i$ is the minterm canonical form of f, we know that the minterm $m_i = x_n^{(b_n)} x_{n-1}^{(b_{n-1})} \cdots x_1^{(b_1)}$ appears in the canonical form of f if and only if $f(b_n, b_{n-1}, \cdots, b_1) = 1$. Hence we can write, for definiteness,

$$f = \sum_{V \in \mathscr{K}^0(f)} m_V \tag{3.32}$$

Dually, if $f = \Pi M_j$ is the maxterm canonical form of f, we have that the maxterm $M_j = x_n^{(b_n)} + x_{n-1}^{(b_{n-1})} + \cdots + x_1^{(b_1)}$ appears in the canonical form of f if and only if $f(\bar{b}_n, \bar{b}_{n-1}, \cdots, \bar{b}_1) = 0$, so that

$$f = \prod_{V \in Z_{2^n} - \mathscr{K}^0(f)} M_{2^n - 1 - V} = \prod_{V \in \tilde{\mathscr{K}}^0(f)} M_V \tag{3.33}$$

where $Z_{2^n} - \mathscr{K}^0(f)$ is the set of decimal numbers $V \in Z_{2^n}$ for which $f(\partial^{-1}(V)) = 0$. Hence $\tilde{\mathscr{K}}^0(f)$ must be defined as

$$\tilde{\mathscr{K}}^0(f) = \{2^n - 1 - V; V \in Z_{2^n} - \mathscr{K}^0(f)\}$$
$$= \{\partial(v); v \in \tilde{K}^0(f)\} \tag{3.34}$$

the decimal transform of

$$\tilde{K}^0(f) = \{\bar{v}; v = (v_n, v_{n-1}, \cdots, v_1) \in B^n - K^0(f)\} \tag{3.35}$$

EXAMPLE 3.16

Suppose $f: B^3 \longrightarrow B$ has the truth table

x_3	x_2	x_1	f
0	0	0	0
0	0	1	1
0	1	0	1
0	1	1	0
1	0	0	0
1	0	1	1
1	1	0	0
1	1	1	0

Then $f = m_1 + m_2 + m_5$ and $\mathscr{K}^0(f) = \{1,2,5\}$. Hence,

$$\tilde{\mathscr{K}}^0(f) = \{7 - V; V \in \{0,3,4,6,7\}\} = \{0,1,3,4,7\}$$

and $f = M_0 M_1 M_3 M_4 M_7$.

In Chapter 2 we represented Boolean products $x_n^{(c_n)} x_{n-1}^{(c_{n-1})} \cdots x_1^{(c_1)}$ as cells $(c_n, c_{n-1}, \cdots, c_1)$, and the theory of Secs. 3.4 through 3.7 was almost entirely based on the property P8a: $a + \bar{a} = 1$ for a Boolean algebra. Whenever P8a could be applied to a sum of products, it was reflected geometrically in that two vertices of $K^0(f)$ could form a line segment of $K(f)$, in that two line segments could form a face, etc. In the dual problem, we make a slight change in the meaning of parenthetical exponents on variables (cf. Sec. 2.5),

$$x_i^{(0)} = \bar{x}_i$$

$$x_i^{(1)} = x_i$$

$$x_i^{(I)} = 0 \qquad \text{(rather than 1)}$$

and represent Boolean sums $x_n^{(c_n)} + x_{n-1}^{(c_{n-1})} + \cdots + x_1^{(c_1)}$ as cells $(c_n, c_{n-1}, \cdots, c_1)$ of C^n; the theory that is dual to that of Secs. 3.4 through 3.7 will, in essence, be making use of the property P8b: $a \cdot \bar{a} = 0$, to simplify product of sums polynomials.

If the i.s.b.f.'s are to be treated, one has only to remember to transform the "don't care" vertices by subtraction from $2^n - 1$ in exactly the way that the vertices of $Z_{2^n} - \mathscr{K}^0(f)$ are to be transformed into $\tilde{\mathscr{K}}^0(f)$. In this way, a *dual pair* of cell complexes $(\tilde{K}, \tilde{L})$ is constructed. The entire computational solution to the dual minimization problem proceeds as before, with $(\tilde{\mathscr{K}}, \tilde{\mathscr{L}})$ replacing $(\mathscr{K}, \mathscr{L})$. One has only to remember that cells $(c_n, c_{n-1}, \cdots, c_1)$, which occur in minimal coverings, must be transformed into sums $x_n^{(c_n)} + x_{n-1}^{(c_{n-1})} + \cdots + x_1^{(c_1)}$ rather than products. Due to the complete duality, an example should suffice to demonstrate the "product of sums" minimization theory.

EXAMPLE 3.17

Let $f(x_4, x_3, x_2, x_1)$ have the incomplete truth table shown in Table 3.4.

x_4	x_3	x_2	x_1	f
0	0	0	0	0
0	0	0	1	1
0	0	1	0	0
0	0	1	1	I
0	1	0	0	1
0	1	0	1	0
0	1	1	0	1
0	1	1	1	I
1	0	0	0	I
1	0	0	1	0
1	0	1	0	1
1	0	1	1	1
1	1	0	0	1
1	1	0	1	0
1	1	1	0	0
1	1	1	1	1

TABLE 3.4

Then

$$\mathscr{X}^0 = \{1,3,4,6,7,8,10,11,12,15\}$$

$$\mathscr{L}^0 = \{1,4,6,10,11,12,15\}$$

$$\tilde{\mathscr{X}}^0 = \{15 - 0, 15 - 2, 15 - 3, 15 - 5, 15 - 7, 15 - 8$$
$$15 - 9, 15 - 13, 15 - 14\}$$

$$= \{1,2,6,7,8,10,12,13,15\}$$

$$\tilde{\mathscr{L}}^0 = \{15 - 0, 15 - 2, 15 - 5, 15 - 9, 15 - 13, 15 - 14\}$$

$$= \{1,2,6,10,13,15\}$$

Now applying the usual computational techniques of Secs. 3.8 through 3.10, we have

$$
\begin{array}{lll}
1\,/ & & E = (1,1) \\
2\,/ & 6 \quad 10\,/\,\circled{14} \\
6\,/ & 2 \quad 7\,/\,\circled{3} \\
10\,/ & 2 \quad 8\,/\,\circled{0} \\
13\,/ & 12 \quad 15\,/\,\circled{14} \\
15\,/ & 7 \quad 13\,/\,\circled{5}
\end{array}
$$

giving only the essential cell

$$E = (1,1) \xrightarrow{\ D'\ } (0,0,0,1) \xrightarrow{\ \tilde{\tau}^{-1}\ } \bar{x}_4 + \bar{x}_3 + \bar{x}_2 + x_1$$

and the basic cell matrix

	2	6	10	13	15
(2,6)	1	1			
(2,10)	1		1		
(6,7)		1			
(8,10)			1		
(12,13)				1	
(13,15)				1	1
(7,15)					1

From this, the irredundant covering $M = \{(2,6), (2,10), (13,15)\}$ might be selected. Since

$$(2,6) \xrightarrow{D'} (0,0,1,0) + (0,1,1,0) = (0,I,1,0) \xrightarrow{\tilde{\tau}^{-1}} \bar{x}_4 + x_2 + \bar{x}_1$$

$$(2,10) \xrightarrow{D'} (0,0,1,0) + (1,0,1,0) = (I,0,1,0) \xrightarrow{\tilde{\tau}^{-1}} \bar{x}_3 + x_2 + \bar{x}_1$$

$$(13,15) \xrightarrow{D'} (1,1,0,1) + (1,1,1,1) = (1,1,I,1) \xrightarrow{\tilde{\tau}^{-1}} x_4 + x_3 + x_1$$

we have a minimal product of sums representation:

$$f = (\bar{x}_4 + \bar{x}_3 + \bar{x}_2 + x_1)(\bar{x}_4 + x_2 + \bar{x})_1(\bar{x}_3 + x_2 + \bar{x}_1)(x_4 + x_3 + x_1)$$

In conclusion, we should emphasize that if one is looking for the most economical two-level logic circuit for a given i.s.b.f. f, one should compare the minimal form as a sum of products with the simplest product of sums representation, choosing that formula with lowest cost.

*3.12 SOLUTION OF BASIC CELL MATRICES[†]

In this section we show how the general problem of finding all irredundant coverings of a basic cell matrix can be reduced to the problem of transforming a Boolean product of sums into a sum of products. Our discussion of the dual minimization problem will be essential to the reduction.

EXAMPLE 3.18

Consider the basic cell matrix of Example 3.14. The fact that the matrix is cyclic will *not* be of importance in our discussion. We define a lattice polynomial (a product of sums)

†See I. B. Pyne and E. J. McClusky, Jr., "The Reduction of Redundancy in Solving Prime Implicant Tables," IRE *Trans. on Electronic Computers*, EC-11, 4 (August 1962); or S. R. Petrick, "A Direct Determination of the Irredundant Forms of a Boolean Function from the Set of Prime Implicants," A. F. Cambridge Res. Ctr., Tech. Rept. No. AFCRC-TR-56-10, 1956.

$$f(B_5,B_4,B_3,B_2,B_1) = (B_4 + B_1)(B_3 + B_2 + B_1)(B_5 + B_1)$$
$$(B_5 + B_4 + B_3)(B_5 + B_2) \qquad (3.36)$$

from the free distributive lattice (cf. Example 1.11) FD(5) with five generators, which is intended to signify that we may choose B_4 or B_1 to cover V_1; and B_3 or B_2 or B_1 to cover V_2; and so on; and that all five choices must be made. Now $FD(n) \subseteq FB(n)$—as seen by the remarks concluding Example 1.18—so that f may be treated as a c.s.b.f. in $B(n)$ with variables B_i rather than x_i. As such, the minimal form of f will be a sum of products that exhibits all irredundant coverings of the vertices V_1, V_2, V_3, V_4, V_5. (Why?)

To obtain it, we simply work the computations of Sec. 3.11 in reverse; that is,

$$B_4 + B_1 \xrightarrow{\tilde{\tau}} (I,1,I,I,1) \xrightarrow{D} (9,31)$$
$$B_3 + B_2 + B_1 \xrightarrow{\tilde{\tau}} (I,I,1,1,1) \xrightarrow{D} (7,31)$$
$$B_5 + B_1 \xrightarrow{\tilde{\tau}} (1,I,I,I,1) \xrightarrow{D} (17,31)$$
$$B_5 + B_4 + B_3 \xrightarrow{\tilde{\tau}} (1,1,1,I,I) \xrightarrow{D} (28,31)$$
$$B_5 + B_2 \xrightarrow{\tilde{\tau}} (1,I,I,1,I) \xrightarrow{D} (18,31)$$

Computing all the vertices of these cells,

$$9 \,/\, 11 \quad 13 \quad 25 \,/\, 15$$
$$27 \quad 29 \,/\, 31$$
$$7 \,/\, 15 \quad 23 \,/\, 31$$
$$17 \,/\, 19 \quad 21 \quad 25 \,/\, 23$$
$$27 \quad 29 \,/\, 31$$
$$28 \,/\, 29 \quad 30 \,/\, 31$$
$$18 \,/\, 19 \quad 22 \quad 26 \,/\, 23$$
$$27 \quad 30 \,/\, 31$$

we find (after canceling duplications)

$$\tilde{\mathscr{K}}^0(f) = \{7,9,11,13,15,17,18,19,21,22,23,25,26,27,28,29,30,31\}$$
$$Z_{32} - \mathscr{K}^0(f) = \{0,1,2,3,4,5,6,8,9,10,12,13,14,16,18,20,22,24\}$$
$$\mathscr{K}^0(f) = \{7,11,15,17,19,21,23,25,26,27,28,29,30,31\}$$

Now computing essential cells,

$$7 \,/\, 15 \quad 23 \quad \,/\, 31 \qquad\qquad (7, 31)$$
$$11 \,/\, 15 \quad 27 \quad \,/\, 31 \qquad\qquad (11,31)$$
$$17 \,/\, 19 \quad 21 \quad 25 \,/\, 23$$
$$27 \quad 29 \,/\, 31 \qquad (17,31)$$
$$26 \,/\, 27 \quad 30 \quad \,/\, 31 \qquad\qquad (26,31)$$
$$28 \,/\, 29 \quad 30 \quad \,/\, 31 \qquad\qquad (28,31)$$

and transforming to products,

$$(7,31) \xrightarrow{D'} (I,I,1,1,1) \xrightarrow{\tau^{-1}} B_3 B_2 B_1$$

$$(11,31) \xrightarrow{D'} (I,1,I,1,1) \xrightarrow{\tau^{-1}} B_4 B_2 B_1$$

$$(17,31) \xrightarrow{D} (1,I,I,1,1) \xrightarrow{\tau^{-1}} B_5 B_1$$

$$(26,31) \xrightarrow{D'} (1,1,I,1,I) \xrightarrow{\tau^{-1}} B_5 B_4 B_2$$

$$(28,31) \xrightarrow{D'} (1,1,1,I,I) \xrightarrow{\tau^{-1}} B_5 B_4 B_3$$

we obtain the minimal form

$$f = B_3 B_2 B_1 + B_4 B_2 B_1 + B_5 B_1 + B_5 B_4 B_2 + B_5 B_4 B_3 \qquad (3.37)$$

which would have resulted had we "multiplied out" Eq. 3.36 and used the absorption law in FD(5). Equation 3.37 signifies that we may choose to cover our five vertices with B_3 *and* B_2 *and* B_1; *or* B_4 *and* B_2 *and* B_1; *or* so on; *and* any one of these five choices may be made. As a result, the given basic cell matrix has five irredundant coverings: $\{B_3, B_2, B_1\}$, $\{B_4, B_2, B_1\}$, $\{B_5, B_1\}$, $\{B_5, B_4, B_2\}$, and $\{B_5, B_4, B_3\}$.

We wish to emphasize that the technique of Example 3.18 does not in any way depend on the fact that we began with a cyclic matrix. It can be used whenever all irredundant coverings of a basic cell matrix are desired. The importance of the technique will grow as additional examples of basic cell matrices arise.

The reader might expect that with certain basic cell matrices arising from the residue of a Boolean function, one could obtain yet another residue from the application of the above procedure. However, the Boolean functions $f(B_n, B_{n-1}, \cdots, B_1)$ that one forms from a basic cell matrix are *unate*[†] (no variable appears in both the complemented and uncomplemented forms), since they are elements of FD(n), and the following theorem applies.

Theorem 3.15.   Unate functions have an empty residue.

This is well known (we omit the proof) and shows that the function $f(B_n, B_{n-1}, \cdots, B_1)$ has a unique minimal form (because of Corollary 3.9).

*3.13   THE MULTIPLE-OUTPUT PROBLEM

Suppose we are given three Boolean functions

†R. McNaughton, "Unate Truth Functions, "*IRE Trans. on Electronic Computers*, EC-10 (March 1956).

x_3	x_2	x_1	f_3	f_2	f_1
0	0	0	1	0	1
0	0	1	0	0	0
0	1	0	0	0	1
0	1	1	1	1	1
1	0	0	0	1	1
1	0	1	0	0	0
1	1	0	0	0	0
1	1	1	1	1	0

of the same Boolean variables x_3, x_2, x_1. (It is not essential to our discussion that they be completely specified.) By the techniques already developed, one can compute the minimal forms:

$$g_3 = \bar{x}_3\bar{x}_2\bar{x}_1 + x_2x_1$$

$$g_2 = x_2x_1 + x_3\bar{x}_2\bar{x}_1$$

$$g_1 = \bar{x}_3x_2 + \bar{x}_2\bar{x}_1$$

suggesting the logic circuit of Fig. 3.5. In Fig. 3.6(a) the product x_2x_1 is formed only once, with an obvious saving in cost. By almost any criteria for minimality, Fig. 3.6(b) would be considered as being even more economical than Fig. 3.6(a). Note in this circuit that the expression for g_1 *does not* consist of prime implicants (alias basic cells).

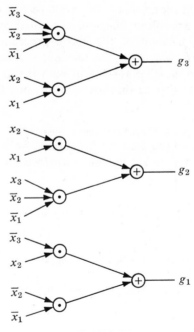

FIGURE 3.5

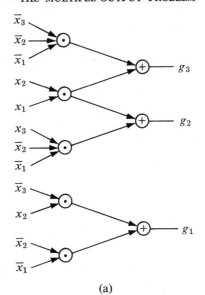

(a)

FIGURE 3.6a

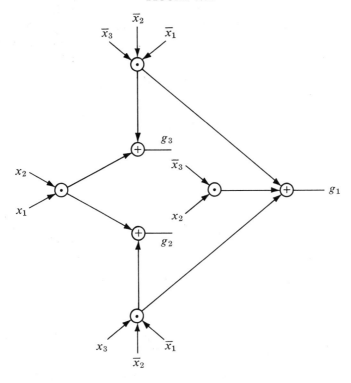

(b)

FIGURE 3.6b

(We are attempting to illustrate that the multiple-output minimization cannot generally be effected by minimization of the separate functions and by observing common terms in the various sums.)

The topological aspects of a circuit like Fig. 3.6 can be presented by a sum of products expression, for Fig. 3.6(a), say,

$$g = \bar{f}_2\bar{f}_1\bar{x}_3\bar{x}_2\bar{x}_1 + \bar{f}_1 x_2 x_1 + \bar{f}_3\bar{f}_1 x_3\bar{x}_2\bar{x}_1 + \bar{f}_3\bar{f}_2\bar{x}_3 x_2 + \bar{f}_3\bar{f}_2\bar{x}_2\bar{x}_1$$

where the interpretation of the first term is that $\bar{x}_3\bar{x}_2\bar{x}_1$ is sent only to f_3; the interpretation of the second term is that $x_2 x_1$ is sent to both f_3 and f_2; etc. Note that

$$g_3(x_3,x_2,x_1) = g(1,0,0,x_3,x_2,x)$$
$$g_2(x_3,x_2,x_1) = g(0,1,0,x_3,x_2,x_1)$$
$$g_1(x_3,x_2,x_1) = g(0,0,1,x_3,x_2,x_1)$$

so that the expression g contains the algebraic as well as the topological information regarding the logic circuit. A procedure[†] has been developed for obtaining economical multiple-output networks of the type considered here (that is, several sums of products in which products may be shared by various outputs), and the material of this section is a deliberate adaptation of this procedure to the framework of our single-output theory.[‡]

Let $F = \{f_m, f_{m-1}, \cdots, f_1\}$ be m incompletely specified Boolean functions of the n Boolean variables x_n, x_{n-1}, $\cdots$, x_1; that is,

$$f_j : B^n \longrightarrow C \qquad (j = 1, 2, \cdots, m)$$

so that the family F gives rise to a mapping (also called F)

$$F : B^n \longrightarrow C^m$$

according to the convention

$$F(b_n, b_{n-1}, \cdots, b_1)$$
$$= (f_m(b_n, b_{n-1}, \cdots, b_1), f_{m-1}(b_n, b_{n-1}, \cdots, b_1) \cdots,$$
$$f_1(b_n, b_{n-1}, \cdots, b_1)) \tag{3.38}$$

A sum of products $g(f_m, f_{m-1}, \cdots, f_1, x_n, x_{n-1}, \cdots, x_1)$ is called a *presentation* of F if

(1) The appearance of any f_j in g is complemented
(2) $v_{gj} \subseteq c_{fj} \qquad (j = 1, 2, \cdots, m)$
     where g_j is the sum of products $g_j(x_n, x_{n-1}, \cdots, x_1)$ defined by

---

†An alternate procedure is that of D. E. Muller, "Application of Boolean Algebra to Switching Circuit Design and Error Detection," *IRE Trans. on Electronic Computers* (September 1954).

‡T. C. Bartee, "Computer Design of Multiple Output Logical Networks," *IRE Trans. on Electronic Computers*, EC-10, 1 (March 1961).

$$g_j(x_n, x_{n-1}, \cdots, x_1) = g(0,0, \cdots, 0, \overset{j}{1}, 0, \cdots, 0, x_n, x_{n-1}, \cdots, x_1) \quad (3.39)$$

for $j = 1, 2, \cdots, m$.

For the products

$$p = f_m^{(d_m)} f_{m-1}^{(d_{m-1})} \cdots f_1^{(d_1)} x_n^{(c_n)} x_{n-1}^{(c_{n-1})} \cdots x_1^{(c_1)}$$

in a presentation g, we have by (1) that each $d_j \in \{0, I\}$, while $c_j \in C = \{0, 1, I\}$ according to our customary use of exponents on variables. For each such product p, we associate a product $p' \in P^n$ by writing

$$p' = x_n^{(c_n)} x_{n-1}^{(c_{n-1})} \cdots x_1^{(c_1)}$$

Then if g is a presentation with products $p_1, p_2, \cdots, p_r$, we define the *multiple-output cost*

$$\mu(g) = \left(r, \sum_{j=1}^{r} m(p_j') \right) \quad (3.40)$$

Note that Eq. 3.40 is a generalization of Eq. 3.12.

Now, if $F : B^n \longrightarrow C^m$ is a collection of m incompletely specified Boolean functions, a presentation g of F is said to be *minimal* if

$$\mu(g) \leqslant \mu(h)$$

for every presentation h of F. (Here the lexicographical order $\leqslant$ is used.)

EXAMPLE 3.19

For the presentation

$$g = \bar{f}_2 \bar{f}_1 \bar{x}_3 \bar{x}_2 \bar{x}_1 + \bar{f}_1 x_2 x_1 + \bar{f}_3 \bar{f}_1 x_3 \bar{x}_2 \bar{x}_1 + \bar{f}_3 \bar{f}_2 \bar{x}_3 x_2 + \bar{f}_3 \bar{f}_2 \bar{x}_2 \bar{x}_1$$

considered earlier, we have

$$g = \sum_{j=1}^{5} p_j$$

with associated products

$$p_1' = \bar{x}_3 \bar{x}_2 \bar{x}_1, \quad p_2' = x_2 x_1, \quad p_3' = x_3 \bar{x}_2 \bar{x}_1, \quad p_4' = \bar{x}_3 x_2, \quad p_5' = \bar{x}_2 \bar{x}_1$$

in P^3. Hence, according to Eq. 3.40,

$$\mu(g) = (5, 3 + 2 + 3 + 2 + 2) = (5, 12)$$

Let $F : B^n \longrightarrow C^m$ be as before. We will describe a transformation T,

$$T : F \longrightarrow f = T(F)$$

of F into a (single-output) incompletely specified Boolean function

$$f : B^{n+m} \longrightarrow C$$

whose minimal forms g correspond to minimal presentations of F. Each vertex $v = (v_n, v_{n-1}, \cdots, v_1)$ of C^n corresponds to an m cell $c_v = T(v)$, namely,

$$v = (v_n, v_{n-1}, \cdots, v_1) \overset{T}{\longrightarrow} (\overbrace{I, I, \cdots, I}^{m}, v_n, v_{n-1}, \cdots, v_1) = c_v$$

of the cellular $n + m$ cube C^{n+m}. Now let $j_1, j_2, \cdots, j_{r_v}$ be the distinct indices j $(m \geq j_{r_v} > j_{r_v-1} > \cdots > j_1 \geq 1)$ for which $f_j(v_n, v_{n-1}, \cdots, v_1) \neq 0$. That is,

$F(v_n, v_{n-1}, \cdots, v_1)$

$$= (0,0, \cdots, 0, f_{j_{r_v}}(v_n, v_{n-1}, \cdots, v_1), 0,0, \cdots, 0, f_{j_{r_v-1}}(v_n, v_{n-1},$$

$$\cdots, v_1), \cdots, f_{j_1}(v_n, v_{n-1}, \cdots, v_1), 0,0, \cdots, 0) \qquad (3.41)$$

These indices determine an r_v cell $c_v' \subseteq c_v$, namely,

$$c_v = (0,0, \cdots, \underbrace{0, \overset{n+j_{r_v}}{\underset{\downarrow}{I}}, 0, 0, \cdots, 0, \overset{n+j_{r_v}-1}{\underset{\downarrow}{I}}, \cdots, \overset{n+j_1}{\underset{\downarrow}{I}}, 0, 0, \cdots, 0}_{m}, v_n, v_{n-1}, \cdots, v_1)$$

Furthermore, if

$$V = \partial(v) = \sum_{i=1}^{n} v_i 2^{i-1} = \partial(\tilde{v})$$

where

$$\tilde{v} = (\overbrace{0,0, \cdots, 0}^{m}, v_n, v_{n-1}, \cdots v_1)$$

then the 2^{r_v} decimal vertices of c_v' are found by the usual computation,

$$V / V + 2^{n+j_1-1}, V + 2^{n+j_2-1}, \cdots, V + 2^{n+j_{r_v}-1} / \cdots$$

$$\cdots / V + \sum_{\rho=1}^{r_v} 2^{n+j_\rho-1}$$

while the 2^m decimal vertices of c_v are similarly found from a computation

$$V / V + 2^n, V + 2^{n+1}, \cdots, V + 2^{n+m-1} / \cdots$$

$$\cdots / V + \sum_{j=1}^{m} 2^{n+j-1}$$

Now let $v_1, v_2, \cdots, v_{r_v}$ denote the r_v adjacent vertices to v in c_v'. In terms of the decimal transforms, we have

$$V_1 = V + 2^{n+j_1-1}$$

$$V_2 = V + 2^{n+j_2-1}$$

$$\vdots$$

$$V_{r_v} = V + 2^{n+j_{r_v}-1}$$

We define $f = T(F)$ on c_v as follows:

(a) $f(v_i) = f_{j_i}(v)$ $(i = 1,2, \cdots, r_v)$.
(b) $f(u) = I$ for vertices $u \subseteq c_v'$; $\Delta(u, \tilde{v}) > 1$.
(c) $f(\tilde{v}) = I$.
(d) $f(u) = 0$ for vertices $u \subseteq c_v$, $u \nsubseteq c_v'$.

Then, since

$$c_v \cap c_w = \varnothing$$

for $v \neq w \in C^n$, this definition of f on its m cells c_v does not lead to a conflict. And, moreover, we define f everywhere on the vertices of C^{n+m} in this way because

$$\bigcup_{\substack{v \in C^n \\ v \text{ a vertex}}} \{u \in C^{n+m}; u \text{ a vertex}, u \subseteq c_v\}$$

gives all vertices of C^{n+m}.

The proof of the following theorem would be quite lengthy (in spite of its concise statement) and somewhat repetitious when taken with the earlier proofs of this chapter, so we omit it.

Theorem 3.16. Let $F : B^n \longrightarrow C^m$ be m incompletely specified Boolean functions with the transform $T(F) = f : B^{n+m} \longrightarrow C$. Then g is a minimal presentation of F if and only if g is a minimal form of f.

EXAMPLE 3.20

Consider Bartee's example (Table 3.5). Since we are interested only in the minimal form g of the transformed i.s.b.f. $f = T(F)$, we will be content to know $\mathscr{L}^0$ together with the list $\mathscr{K}^0 - \mathscr{L}^0$ of unspecified vertices for f. These can be obtained without developing the truth table of f. For consider the typical vertex $v = (0,1,0,1) \in C^4$ with $\tilde{v} = (0,0,0,0,1,0,1) \in C^7$ for which

$$V = \partial(v) = 5 = \partial(v)$$

We have $r_v = 2$ and

$$c_v = (I,I,I,0,1,0,1)$$
$$c_v' = (0,I,I,0,1,0,1)$$

since $F(v) = (0,1,1)$. Thus

$$V_1 = 5 + 2^{4+1-1} = 5 + 16 = 21$$
$$V_2 = 5 + 2^{4+2-1} = 5 + 32 = 37$$

and

x_4	x_3	x_2	x_1	f_3	f_2	f_1
0	0	0	0	0	0	0
0	0	0	1	1	0	1
0	0	1	0	0	0	0
0	0	1	1	0	0	0
0	1	0	0	0	1	1
0	1	0	1	0	1	1
0	1	1	0	1	1	0
0	1	1	1	1	1	0
1	0	0	0	0	0	0
1	0	0	1	1	0	1
1	0	1	0	0	1	1
1	0	1	1	1	0	1
1	1	0	0	0	1	1
1	1	0	1	0	1	1
1	1	1	0	1	1	1
1	1	1	1	1	1	1

TABLE 3.5

(a) $f(v_1) = f_1(v) = 1$,
   $f(v_2) = f_2(v) = 1$,
   so that 21,37 $\in \mathscr{L}^0$.

(b) $f(u) = I$ for all vertices $u \subseteq (0,I,I,0,1,0,1) = c'_v$ for which $\Delta(u, \tilde{v}) > 1$. The decimal vertices in c'_v are 5 / 21, 37 / 53, so that 53 is on the unspecified list $\mathscr{K}^0-\mathscr{L}^0$, and also

(c) 5 is on the unspecified list.

(d) The other decimal vertices in C_v,

$$5 / 21 \quad 37 \quad 69 / 53$$
$$85 \quad 101 / 117$$

are neither in $\mathscr{L}^0$ nor on the list of unspecified vertices.

In this way, we can determine for each vertex $v \in C^n$ those vertices of c_v that are in $\mathscr{L}^0$ or unspecified for f. (The reader should check a few other entries in the Table 3.6.)

V	$\mathscr{L}^0$	$\mathscr{K}^0 - \mathscr{L}^0$
0		
1	17, 65	1, 81
2		
3		
4	20, 36	4, 52
5	21, 37	5, 53
6	38, 70	6, 102
7	39, 71	7, 103
8		
9	25, 73	9, 89
10	26, 42	10, 58
11	27, 75	11, 91
12	28, 44	12, 60
13	29, 45	13, 61
14	30, 46, 78	14, 62, 94, 110, 126
15	31, 47, 79	15, 63, 95, 111, 127

TABLE 3.6

Computing the minimal form of f by the methods presented earlier, one finds four essential cells:

$$C_1 = (1,89) \xrightarrow{D'} (I,0,I,I,0,0,1) \xrightarrow{\tau^{-1}} \bar{f}_2 \bar{x}_3 \bar{x}_2 x_1$$
$$C_2 = (4,61) \xrightarrow{D'} (0,I,I,I,1,0,I) \xrightarrow{\tau^{-1}} \bar{f}_3 x_3 \bar{x}_2$$
$$C_3 = (6,111) \xrightarrow{D'} (I,I,0,I,1,1,I) \xrightarrow{\tau^{-1}} \bar{f}_1 x_3 x_2$$
$$C_4 = (10,62) \xrightarrow{D} (0,I,I,1,I,1,0) \xrightarrow{\tau^{-1}} \bar{f}_3 x_4 x_2 \bar{x}_1$$

and the basic cell

$$B = (11,95) \xrightarrow{D'} (I,0,I,1,I,1,1) \xrightarrow{\tau^{-1}} \bar{f}_2 x_4 x_2 x_1$$

is the obvious choice from the basic cell matrix of the residue, since it covers all three vertices 75, 27, 31 of the residue.

Hence

$$g = \bar{f}_2 \bar{x}_3 \bar{x}_2 x_1 + \bar{f}_3 x_3 \bar{x}_2 + \bar{f}_1 x_3 x_2 + \bar{f}_3 x_4 x_2 \bar{x}_1 + \bar{f}_2 x_4 x_2 x_1$$

is the minimal form of f. By Theorem 3.16, g is also the minimal presentation of F, so that the logic circuit of Fig. 3.7 is optimum with respect to the cost criterion of Eq. 3.40.

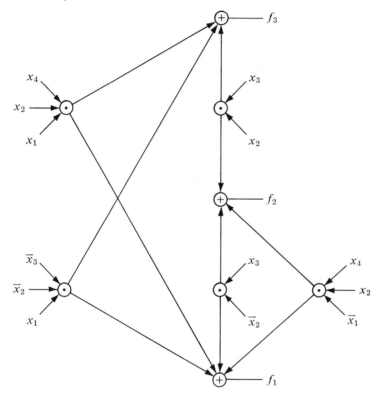

FIGURE 3.7

While it did not occur in Example 3.20, the reader should be warned that minimal presentations $g(f_m, f_{m-1}, \cdots, f_1, x_n, x_{n-1}, \cdots, x_1)$ are likely to contain *superfluous* or redundant products p' for certain g_j. The detection and removal of these can reduce the number of inputs to the corresponding jth "or" gate over that involved in the implementation of the minimal presentation. It is not surprising that this can happen, for the cost criterion of Eq. 3.40 does not take the number of inputs to "or" gates (outputs from "and" gates) into account. Even the simplest of examples,

x_2	x_1	f_2	f_1
0	0	1	1
0	1	0	1
1	0	0	1
1	1	1	0

will serve to illustrate this curious behavior. One finds the unique minimal presentation

$$g = \bar{f}_2\bar{x}_2 + \bar{f}_2\bar{x}_1 + \bar{x}_2\bar{x}_1 + \bar{f}_1 x_2 x_1$$

so that

$$g_2 = \bar{x}_2\bar{x}_1 + x_2 x_1$$

$$g_1 = \bar{x}_2 + \bar{x}_1 + \bar{x}_2\bar{x}_1$$

Clearly, the product $p' = \bar{x}_2\bar{x}_1$ is superfluous in g_1, and we could just as well take $g_1 = \bar{x}_2 + \bar{x}_1$. It is because $\mu(g) = \mu(h)$, if

$$h = \bar{f}_2\bar{x}_2 + \bar{f}_2\bar{x}_1 + \bar{f}_1\bar{x}_2\bar{x}_1 + \bar{f}_1 x_2 x_1$$

that the cost criterion of Eq. 3.40 fails to take this redundancy into account. Generally speaking, one could draw "basic cell matrices" for each g_j having the vertices of $\mathcal{K}^0(f_j)$ as column headings and the cells $b_j = \tau(p'_j)$ as row headings—one for each p'_j occurring in the sum g_j. (Note that the b_j need not be basic cells of f_j—as with $p' = \bar{x}_2\bar{x}_1$ above—so that the name "basic cell matrices" is somewhat of a misnomer here) Choosing minimal (with respect to gate cost) coverings of each matrix so obtained, one can minimize the number of inputs to "or" gates after having selected a minimal presentation.

*3.14   SIMPLICIAL COMPLEXES

In Sec. 3.9 the reader has already encountered examples of certain geometric structures that have come to be known as "simplicial complexes."[†] Since such structures will occur with some frequency as we proceed, it is well that we formalize the concept at this time, thereby ensuring that any geometric or intuitive advantages will be at our disposal when these occurrences arise. A close analogy between the cellular or cubical complexes of Chapter 2 and the simplicial complexes will be noted; this will be especially true if one mentally replaces the geometric images (vertex, line segment, face or square, cube, etc.) by their simplicial equivalents (point, line, triangle, tetrahedron, etc.). The material of Sec.

†See Ref. 2–3.

3.9 will provide ample illustration of the new concept and will motivate the discussion of the connection between certain simplicial complexes and their assiciated compatibility relations.

A *simplicial complex* $K = (S_n, \Gamma_{S_n})$ is a pair consisting of a set

$$S_n = \{x_1, x_2, \cdots, x_n\}$$

whose elements x_i are called *points* (to call them "vertices" would invite confusion) and a collection $\Gamma = \Gamma_{S_n}$ of (*simplexes*) subsets of $S_n(\Gamma \subseteq \mathscr{P}(S_n))$ for which

$$\sigma \in \Gamma, \sigma' \subseteq \sigma \Longrightarrow \sigma' \in \Gamma \qquad (3.42)$$

(Note the similarity to Eq. 2.18.) By analogy with the definition of the order of a cell $c \in C^n$, we define the *dimension* $d(\sigma) = |\sigma| - 1$ of a simplex σ to be one less than the number of elements in the subset σ. We impose this normalization in order that a single-element subset be called a "0-dimensional" simplex (point), a two-element subset be represented by a "1-dimensional" simplex (line) joining its two points, etc. We say that σ is a *k simplex* if $d(\sigma) = k$.

Now suppose that $K = (S_n, \Gamma_{S_n})$ is a simplicial complex and $\sigma \in \Gamma = \Gamma_{S_n}$ is a simplex of K. By analogy with the notion of a basic cell, we say that σ is a *basic simplex* of K if

$$\sigma' \supseteq \sigma, \quad \sigma' \in \Gamma \Longrightarrow \sigma' = \sigma$$

that is, if σ is maximal in Γ. Similarly, if there is a point $x_i \in S_n$ for which σ is the only basic simplex with $x_i \in \sigma$, we say that σ is an *essential simplex* of K. Denoting (cf. Eq. 2.23)

$$\Gamma^q = \{\sigma \in \Gamma; d(\sigma) \leq q\}$$

as the *q-dimensional skeleton* of K, it is clear that the collection

$$\gamma = \{\sigma \in \Gamma; \sigma \text{ is a basic simplex of } K\} \qquad (3.43)$$

will be a set system (cf. Example 1.6) of Γ^0; and since

$$\Gamma = \{\sigma'; \sigma' \subseteq \sigma \text{ for some simplex } \sigma \in \gamma\} \qquad (3.44)$$

can be recovered from γ, the representation of Γ in the abbreviated form (Eq. 3.43) will have obvious notational advantages.

EXAMPLE 3.21

In the minimization theory, let

$$S_n = \{x_1, x_2, \cdots, x_n\} = \{V^{(1)}, V^{(2)}, \cdots, V^{(n)}\} = \mathscr{X}$$

be a basis for a cell $Z = (X, Y)$ with $V^{(i)}$ adjacent to V ($i = 1, 2, \cdots, n$). We suppose that $V, V^{(1)}, V^{(2)}, \cdots, V^{(n)} \in \mathscr{X}^0$ and define $\Gamma \subseteq \mathscr{P}(\mathscr{X})$ as follows: For $\sigma \in \mathscr{P}(\mathscr{X})$, say

$$\sigma = \{V^{(i_1)}, V^{(i_2)}, \cdots, V^{(i_k)}\}$$

with $\{i_1, i_2, \cdots, i_k\} \subseteq n^+$, put

$$\sigma = \Gamma \longleftrightarrow V + \sum_{j=1}^{k} b_j \Delta_{i_j} \in \mathscr{K}^0 \qquad \text{for all } (b_k, b_{k-1}, \cdots, b_1) \in B^k \qquad \textbf{(3.45)}$$

Then it is easily seen that $K = (S_n, \Gamma_{S_n}) = (\mathscr{X}, \Gamma_{\mathscr{X}})$ is a simplicial complex.
In Example 3.11, take

$$S_n = \{x_1, x_2, x_3, x_4\} = \{1, 7, 13, 21\} = \mathscr{X}$$

and $V = 5$. Then the 2-simplex $\sigma = \{1, 7, 13\} \in \Gamma$, as shown by the computation

$$5 \,/\, 1 \;\; 7 \;\; 13 \,/\, 3$$
$$9 \;\; 15 \,/\, 11$$

Other computations in that example imply that

$$\Gamma = \{\{1,7,13\}, \{1,7\}, \{1,13\}, \{7,13\}, \{1,21\},$$
$$\{7,21\}, \{1\}, \{7\}, \{13\}, \{21\}\}$$

or, using the abbreviated form of Eq. 3.43,

$$\gamma = \{\{1,7,13\}, \{1,21\}, \{7,21\}\}$$
$$= \{\overline{1,7,13};\; \overline{1,21};\; \overline{7,21}\}$$

where only the basic simplexes are listed. This is the covering of $\mathscr{X}$, which was originally denoted $\gamma(5)$. The simplicial complex $K = (\mathscr{X}, \Gamma_{\mathscr{X}})$ is presumed to have the geometric significance depicted in Fig. 3.8.

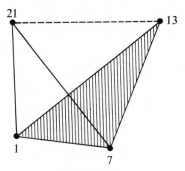

FIGURE 3.8

Now let $K = (S_n, \Gamma_{S_n})$ be any simplicial complex. The definition

$$x_i \underset{r}{\approx} x_j \longleftrightarrow \{x_i, x_j\} \in \Gamma = \Gamma_{S_n} \qquad \textbf{(3.46)}$$

is a compatibility relation $\underset{r}{\approx}$ on Γ^0 (if we understand that $\{x_i, x_i\} = \{x_i\}$). Now, for each r $(1 \leq r \leq n)$, define an "auxiliary" simplicial complex $(\Gamma^0, \Gamma^{(r)})$ by

$$\Gamma^{(r)} = \{\sigma \in \mathscr{P}(\Gamma^0);\; \sigma' \in \Gamma \text{ for all } \sigma' \subseteq \sigma \text{ with } |\sigma'| \leq r\}$$

Then take γ^r to be the corresponding collection of basic simplexes. We have a sequence of set systems:

$$\{\Gamma^0\} = \gamma^1 \supseteq \gamma^2 \supseteq \cdots \supseteq \gamma^n = \gamma$$

of Γ^0, in which

$$\gamma^1 = \{\text{basic simplexes of } \Gamma^{(1)}\}$$
$$= \{\Gamma^0\}$$
$$\gamma^2 = \{\text{basic simplexes of } \Gamma^{(2)}\}$$
$$= \{\text{maximal compatibles of } \underset{\Gamma}{\approx}\}$$
$$\vdots$$
$$\gamma^n = \gamma$$

Of course it may happen (when $\langle \gamma^k \rangle \leq k$) that $\gamma^k = \gamma$ for some $k < n$. In particular, if K is an *inductive* complex, that is, if

$$x_i \underset{\Gamma}{\approx} x_j \quad \text{for all } x_i, x_j \in \sigma \Longrightarrow \sigma \in \Gamma \qquad (3.47)$$

(note the analogy to *Boolean* cell complexes) we have the following advantage:

Theorem 3.17. Let $K = (S_n, \Gamma_{S_n})$ be an inductive simplicial complex, and let γ have the meaning of Eq. 3.43. Suppose further that $\underset{\Gamma}{\approx}$ is the associated compatibility relation having the set of maximal compatibles γ^2. Then $\gamma = \gamma^2$; that is, every basic simplex is a maximal compatible, and conversely.

We omit the proof inasmuch as it can be seen to follow immediately from the definition of "inductive". The theorem is usually employed in computing the basic simplexes of an inductive complex; one may compute the maximal compatibles (by the procedure of Sec. 0.10) instead.

EXAMPLE 3.22

If $K = (S_n, \Gamma_{S_n})$ is a complex of the type arising in minimization theory (see Example 3.21) and x_i, x_j are two points of S_n, we have, according to Eqs. 3.45 and 3.46,

$$x_i \underset{\Gamma}{\approx} x_j \Longleftrightarrow \{x_i, x_j\} = \{V^{(i)}, V^{(j)}\} \in \Gamma = \Gamma_{S_n}$$
$$\Longleftrightarrow V + b_i \Delta_i + b_j \Delta_j \in \mathscr{K}^0 \quad \text{for all } (b_i, b_j) \in B^2$$
$$\Longleftrightarrow V + \Delta_i + \Delta_j \in \mathscr{K}^0$$

and this is exactly the sense of the compatibility relation $\approx$ defined by Eq. 3.29.

For the basis $\mathscr{X} = \{1,7,13,21\}$ and $\gamma^1(5) = \{\mathscr{X}\} = \{\overline{1,7,13,21}\}$ in Example 3.11, the relation $\approx$ of Eq. 3.29 gave the maximal compatibles

$$\gamma^2 = \gamma^2(5) = \{\overline{1,7,13}; \ \overline{1,7,21}\}$$

Evidently the simplicial complexes $K = (\mathscr{X}, \Gamma_{\mathscr{X}})$ that arise in minimization theory are *not* inductive complexes, for we have

$$\gamma = \gamma(5) = \{\overline{1,7,13}; \ \overline{1,21}; \ \overline{7,21}\} \neq \gamma^2$$

Thus, when we sought the collection of basic simplexes in K, it was necessary to look beyond compatibility; we had to consider elements of $\mathscr{X}$ taken three at a time, four at a time, etc., in Eq. 3.45.

*3.15 COMPATIBILITY RELATIONS IN $C(n)$

We should have supposed that the functions f_j appearing in the families $F = \{f_1, f_2, \cdots, f_m\}$ of Sec. 3.13 were mutually incompatible (not compatible) in the following sense: f_1, f_2 $B^n \longrightarrow C$ are said to be *compatible* ($f_1 \approx f_2$) if there exists a c.s.b.f. $g : B^n \longrightarrow B$ such that

$$v_g \subseteq c_{f_i} \quad \text{or} \quad v_{\bar{g}} \subseteq c_{f_i} \quad (i = 1, 2) \tag{3.48}$$

Thus, when $f_1 \approx f_2$, there exist i.s.b.f.'s (g is one) that have the property that they are either in complete agreement or in complete disagreement (always complementary) with both f_1 and f_2 for every specified entry in their truth tables. For this reason, a single i.s.b.f. could be implemented in place of the pair f_1, f_2 (provided we are allowing gates with complementary outputs). If the family F should admit of a pair of compatible functions, we could reduce the synthesis problem immediately by "merging" these compatible functions into one whose complementary outputs would serve equally well as implementation of the two compatible functions. The new, smaller family F' should admit a more economical circuit, generally speaking, while presenting a much simplified synthesis problem.

EXAMPLE 3.23

Consider the two i.s.b.f.'s f_1 and f_2 with incomplete truth tables:

x_3	x_2	x_1	f_1	f_2	g	h
0	0	0	0	1	0	0
0	0	1	1	0	1	1
0	1	0	I	0	1	1
0	1	1	0	I	0	0
1	0	0	1	0	1	1
1	0	1	0	I	0	0
1	1	0	I	I	0	I
1	1	1	1	0	1	1

The c.s.b.f. g has the property $v_g \subseteq c_{f_1}$, while $v_{\bar{g}} \subseteq c_{f_2}$. Thus $f_1 \approx f_2$. The i.s.b.f. h (implemented with complementary outputs) would serve equally well as implementation for f_1 and for f_2.

The question arises: When a given family $F = \{f_1, f_2, \cdots, f_m\}$ contains compatible functions, how can "merging" be accomplished in a suitably optimum fashion? The answer is quickly suggested after we define a simplicial complex $K = (S_m, \Gamma_{S_m}) = (F, \Gamma_F) = (F, \Gamma)$ where

$$S_m = F = \{f_1, f_2, \cdots, f_m\}; \quad f_j : B^n \longrightarrow C$$

and for $\sigma \in \mathscr{P}(F)$, say, $\sigma = \{f_{i_1}, f_{i_2}, \cdots, f_{i_k}\}$, we put

$$\sigma \in \Gamma \Longleftrightarrow \begin{cases} \text{there exists a c.s.b.f. } g : B^n \longrightarrow B \\ \text{such that} \\ v_g \subseteq c_{f_{i_j}} \quad \text{or} \quad v_{\bar{g}} \subseteq c_{f_{i_j}} \quad (j = 1, 2, \cdots, k) \end{cases} \tag{3.49}$$

Comparing Eqs. 3.48 and 3.49, we see that $\underset{r}{\approx}$ (defined by Eq. 3.46) is the original compatibility relation. Hence we should seek the covering of $S_m = F$ by its collection γ of basic simplexes of K, for these represent the largest "mergible" classes of functions. But is K an inductive complex so that we can proceed as suggested by Theorem 3.17? The following example gives the answer—no.

EXAMPLE 3.24

Let $F = \{f_1, f_2, f_3\} = S_3$, where the f_j have incomplete truth tables:

x_2	x_1	f_1	f_2	f_3	g_{12}	g_{13}	g_{23}
0	0	0	1	I	0	0	1
0	1	1	0	I	1	1	0
1	0	I	0	1	1	0	0
1	1	0	I	1	0	0	0

Then the 1-simplexes

$$\{f_1, f_2\}, \quad \{f_1, f_3\}, \quad \{f_2, f_3\}$$

are elements of Γ because

$$v_{g_{12}} \subseteq c_{f_1}, \quad v_{\bar{g}_{12}} \subseteq c_{f_2}$$

$$v_{g_{13}} \subseteq c_{f_1}, \quad v_{\bar{g}_{13}} \subseteq c_{f_3}$$

$$v_{g_{23}} \subseteq c_{f_2}, \quad v_{\bar{g}_{23}} \subseteq c_{f_3}$$

But none of the 16 c.s.b.f.'s g of two variables has the property

$$v_g \subseteq c_{f_i} \quad \text{or} \quad v_{\bar{g}} \subseteq c_{f_i} \quad (i = 1, 2, 3)$$

so that $\{f_1, f_2, f_3\} \notin \Gamma$. Hence, $K = (F, \Gamma_F)$ is not inductive, and Theorem 3.17 does not apply to complexes arising as in Eq. 3.49.

In spite of the discouraging answer learned from the preceding example, the maximal compatibles are of considerable aid in determining the basic simplexes. As with the simplicial complexes arising in the minimization theory, the maximal compatibles provide the second in a sequence:

$$\{F\} = \gamma^1 \supseteq \gamma^2 \supseteq \cdots \supseteq \gamma^k = \gamma \quad (\langle \gamma^k \rangle \le k)$$

of coverings of F, which lead to the collection γ of basic simplexes of K.

Ordinarily, one does not expect large subsets of $S_m = F$ to exhibit mutual compatibility, so that k is generally quite small. The tests for compatibility and for membership in Γ are provided by Probs. 3.25(c) and 3.26(c), respectively.

In Probs. 3.25 and 3.26, a complementation for the i.s.b.f.'s and a "star" product of certain i.s.b.f.'s is introduced. For $f \in C(n)$, let $\bar{f} = f^{(0)}$ denote the i.s.b.f. $\bar{f} : B^n \longrightarrow C$, given by

$$\bar{f}(v) = \begin{cases} \overline{f(v)} & \text{if } f(v) \in B \\ f(v) & \text{if } f(v) = I \end{cases}$$

And if $g, f : B^n \longrightarrow C$ have the property $\omega(g) \cdot \omega(f) \neq 0$, we define $g*f : B^n \longrightarrow C$ by

$$g*f = \omega^{-1}(\omega(g) \cdot \omega(f))$$

but if $\omega(g) \cdot \omega(f) = 0$, then the *star product* $g*f$ is undefined. Thus, if $g, f : B^2 \longrightarrow C$ are as shown:

x_2	x_1		g	f	$g*f$	$\bar{f}$
0	0		I	1	1	0
0	1		1	1	1	0
1	0		0	I	0	I
1	1		I	I	I	I

then

$$g*f = \omega^{-1}((I,0,1,I) \cdot (I,I,1,1)) = \omega^{-1}(I,0,1,1)$$

as depicted above, whereas $g*\bar{f}$ is undefined because

$$\omega(g) \cdot \omega(\bar{f}) = (I,0,1,I) \cdot (I,I,0,0) = 0$$

(Under what conditions are both $g*f$ and $g*\bar{f}$ defined?) More generally, for a family $F = \{f_1, f_2, \cdots, f_m\}$ of i.s.b.f.'s $f_i : B^n \longrightarrow C$, we define

$$\prod_{i=1}^{m} *f_i = \omega^{-1}\left(\prod_{i=1}^{m} \omega(f_i)\right)$$

provided

$$\prod_{i=1}^{m} \omega(f_i) \neq 0$$

Now how are the tests of Prob. 3.25(c) and Prob. 3.26(c) to be applied to the problem of determining γ? The first step is clear. Using the test of Prob. 3.25(c)—in words, it states that $f \approx g$ iff there does not exist both a pair of equal specified entries and a pair of complementary specified entries in corresponding rows of their truth tables—one can construct a compatibility matrix

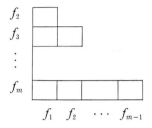

for the given family $F = \{f_1, f_2, \cdots, f_m\}$. Here the maximal compatibles represent the maximal subsets σ of F with respect to the property that every 2-element subset σ' of σ is in Γ. (Note that such subsets σ need not themselves be in Γ.) Thus the collection of maximal compatibles is indeed γ^2, as previously defined.

But given $\gamma^1 = \{F\}$ and γ^2, how do we use the test of Prob. 3.26(c) to obtain the successive refinements $\gamma^3, \gamma^4, \cdots$, and finally γ? Note that by analogy with the computational format of Example 2.18, we can think of the above compatibility matrix N_2 as being embedded in a larger (multidimensional) array:

$$
\begin{array}{l}
f_1 f_2 \quad\ f_m \\
1\ 1\ \cdots\ 1\ /\ r_{21} \\
\qquad r_{31}\ r_{32} \\
\qquad \vdots\quad \vdots \\
\underbrace{r_{m1}\ r_{m2}\ \cdots\ r_m, r_{m-1}}_{N_2}\ /\ r_{321} \\
\qquad\qquad\qquad\qquad\quad r_{421} \\
\qquad\qquad\qquad\qquad\quad \vdots \\
\qquad r_{m21}\ \cdots\ r_{m,\ m-1,\ m-2}\ / \\
\qquad\qquad\qquad\qquad\qquad /\ r_{m,\ m-1,\ \cdots,\ 1}
\end{array}
$$

where for each subset $\sigma = \{f_{i_1}, f_{i_2}, \cdots, f_{i_k}\}$ of F, there is a definite location for indicating (with a 1 or a 0, say) whether or not $\sigma \in \Gamma$. And the decisions could be made with the test of Prob. 3.26(c)—in words, it states that $\sigma \in \Gamma$ iff a star product of all the f_{i_j} (or their complements) exists. But we will not ordinarily require all this information, for suppose γ^s has been determined and we seek γ^{s+1}. It is of no use to know that a subset $\sigma' = \{f_{i_1}, f_{i_2}, \cdots, f_{i_{s+1}}\} \notin \Gamma$ unless $\sigma' \subseteq \sigma$ for some σ in the current γ^s. For if not, we could not (since $\gamma^s \supseteq \gamma^{s+1} \supseteq \cdots \supseteq \gamma$) have $\sigma' \in \Gamma$ in any case. Thus it is computationally expedient when computing γ^{s+1} to examine (in N_{s+1}) only those $(s+1)$-element subsets $\sigma' \in \Gamma^{(s)}$ that are subsets of some σ in the current γ^s. Then, when a negative decision $(\sigma' \notin \Gamma)$ results from the "star product" test, we replace σ by its maximal subsets with respect to the property of not containing σ'. Again, one or more of these may have to be deleted by virtue of being a subset of some other block of the current γ^s. Here we say the "current" γ^s because it is continually being revised (refined) as new negative decisions are discovered, finally resulting in the prime covering γ^{s+1} of F. The method is illustrated in the following example and in the problems that conclude the chapter.

The reader should have sensed throughout this discussion that an alternate computational procedure (for finding γ) might be possible, in which we begin with $\Gamma^0 = F = \{\bar{f}_1; \bar{f}_2; \cdots; \bar{f}_m\}$ and approach Γ "from below," by an iteration that resembles the Quine-McClusky algorithm of minimization theory. A chance to exploit this approach is given in Prob. 3.43.

EXAMPLE 3.25

Applying the criteria of Problem 3.25 to the family $F = \{f_1, f_2, f_3, f_4, f_5, f_6\}$ ($\gamma^1 = \{\bar{f}_1, \bar{f}_2, \bar{f}_3, \bar{f}_4, \bar{f}_5, \bar{f}_6\}$) as shown:

x_3	x_2	x_1	f_1	f_2	f_3	f_4	f_5	f_6
0	0	0	I	1	0	0	I	1
0	0	1	0	0	1	I	0	1
0	1	0	0	1	I	1	1	I
0	1	1	I	0	I	I	I	0
1	0	0	0	1	1	1	1	I
1	0	1	1	1	I	0	I	I
1	1	0	I	0	0	0	0	1
1	1	1	0	0	1	I	0	1

we obtain the compatibility matrix

f_2	0				
f_3	1	0			
f_4	1	0	1		
f_5	0	1	0	1	
f_6	1	0	0	1	1
	f_1	f_2	f_3	f_4	f_5

and maximal compatibles

$$\gamma_2 = \{\overline{f_1, f_3, f_4}; \ \overline{f_1, f_4, f_6}; \ \overline{f_2, f_5}; \ \overline{f_4, f_5, f_6}\}$$

Applying the criteria of Prob. 3.26(c) to 3-element subsets of $\Gamma(2)$, we find that $f_1 * \bar{f}_3 * \bar{f}_4$ and $f_4 * f_5 * \bar{f}_6$ exist but that $f_1^{(b_3)} * f_4^{(b_2)} * f_6^{(b_1)}$ does not, regardless of the element $(b_3, b_2, b_1) \in B^3$ taken. Thus we obtain

$$\gamma^3 = \{\overline{f_1, f_3, f_4}; \ \overline{f_1, f_6}; \ \overline{f_2, f_5}; \ \overline{f_4, f_5, f_6}\} = \gamma$$

the collection (since $\langle \gamma^3 \rangle = 3$) of basic simplexes. (See Fig. 3.9.)

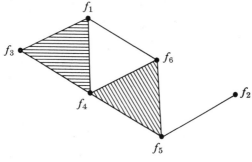

FIGURE 3.9

Let $K = (S, \Gamma)$ be a simplicial complex. The collection γ of basic simplexes will contain as a subset a "minimal" covering $\mu \subseteq \gamma$ of the set Γ^0. Here μ is meant to be *minimal* with regard to the number of blocks (simplexes); that is,

$$\mu' \text{ a covering of } S \underset{\mu' \subseteq \gamma}{\Longrightarrow} |\mu| \le |\mu'| \qquad (3.50)$$

In searching for a minimal covering μ, the essential simplexes play the same role as do the essential cells of the minimization theory (cf. Theorem 3.7); and the residue

$$R = \Gamma^0 - \{x_i \in \Gamma^0; \, x_i \in \sigma \text{ for some essential simplex } \sigma\}$$

should be treated as before; that is, a "basic simplex matrix" is constructed whose columns are labeled with the elements of R. One then obtains all irredundant coverings of R (cf. Sec. 3.12) and selects a minimal irredundant covering μ' of R; it follows (cf. Corollary 3.11) that $\mu = E \cup \mu'$ is a minimal covering of Γ^0, E being the collection:

$$E = \{\sigma \in \gamma; \, \sigma \text{ is an essential simplex}\}$$

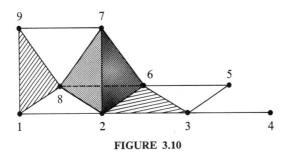

FIGURE 3.10

EXAMPLE 3.26

Consider the simplicial complex of Fig. 3.10, where $S = \{1,2,3,4,5,6,7, 8,9\} = \Gamma^0$. We have

$$E = \overline{\{3,4\}}$$

$$R = \{1,2,5,6,7,8,9\}$$

and the basic simplex matrix of Table 3.7.

	1	2	5	6	7	8	9
{3,5}			1				
{5,6}			1	1			
{2,3,6}		1		1			
{2,6,7,8}		1		1	1	1	
{1,2}	1	1					
{7,9}					1		1
{1,8,9}	1					1	1

TABLE 3.7

Using dominance arguments (since our criterion for minimality is simply the number of simplexes in the covering), Table 3.7 is reduced to the following one:

	1	2	5	7	8	9
{5,6}			1			
{2,6,7,8}		1		1	1	
{1,2}	1	1				
{7,9}				1		1
{1,8,9}	1				1	1

from which the minimal covering

$$\mu' = \{\overline{5,6};\ \overline{2,6,7,8};\ \overline{1,8,9}\}$$

of R is obtained. Hence

$$\mu = E \cup \mu' = \{\overline{3,4};\ \overline{5,6};\ \overline{2,6,7,8};\ \overline{1,8,9}\}$$

is a minimal covering of Γ^0.

When μ is a minimal covering of a simplicial complex $K = (F, \Gamma_F)$ arising from a family $F = \{f_1, f_2, \cdots, f_m\} = \Gamma^0$ of i.s.b.f.'s $f_j : B^n \to C$, one should select a partition π of Γ^0 for which

(1) π is a refinement of μ.

(2) $|\pi| = |\mu|$.

(In this event we say that π is a *subminimal covering* of μ; note the analogy to the concept of a subgrouping; cf. Example 1.6). This should be done in order that the multiple-output truth tables retain as many unspecified entries as is *conveniently* possible. (One might even try to optimize π in this respect.)

EXAMPLE 3.27

The preceding discussions show that the complex of Example 3.25 has a minimal covering:

$$\mu = \{\overline{f_1,f_3,f_4};\ \overline{f_2,f_5};\ \overline{f_1,f_6}\}$$

This covering suggests the three truth tables:

x_3 x_2 x_1	h_1 h_2 h_3	
0 0 0	1 1 0	
0 0 1	0 0 0	$c_{h_1} \subseteq c_{f_1},\quad c_{\bar{h}_1} \subseteq c_{f_3},\quad c_{\bar{h}_1} \subseteq c_{f_4}$
0 1 0	0 1 0	
0 1 1	I 0 1	$c_{h_2} \subseteq c_{f_2},\quad c_{h_2} \subseteq c_{f_5}$
1 0 0	0 1 0	
1 0 1	1 1 1	$c_{h_3} \subseteq c_{f_1},\quad c_{\bar{h}_3} \subseteq c_{f_6}$
1 1 0	1 0 0	
1 1 1	0 0 0	

But the partition (a subminimal covering of μ)

$$\pi = \{\overline{f_1,f_3,f_4};\ \overline{f_2,f_5};\ \overline{f_6}\}$$

that refines μ would allow $h_3 = f_6$, so that the three tables would have three additional unspecified entries if π were taken in place of μ.

*3.16 MINIMAL INCOMPLETELY SPECIFIED TWO-VARIABLE CIRCUITS

In this section we will obtain results that, when added to those of Sec. 1.18, will completely solve the two-variable minimization problem. Since $3^4 = 81$, there are 81 i.s.b.f.'s $f : B^2 \to C$. Of these, we need consider only the set of 18 functions of Table 3.8 that are incompatible with every function in the class $F = \{f_0, f_3, f_5, f_{10}, f_{12}, f_{15}\}$ of Sec. 1.16, the reason being that $f \approx f_i$ for $f_i \in F$ implies that f can be implemented at zero cost. Note the labeling of the eight i.s.b.f.'s in Table 3.8, where $f : B^2 \to C$ is denoted $f_{(X, Y)}$ with $X = \partial(\min(c_f))$, $Y = \partial(\max(c_f))$.

x_2 x_1	f_1 f_{14} f_2 f_{13} f_4 f_{11} f_8 f_7	$f_{(1,9)}$ $f_{(6,14)}$ $f_{(2,6)}$ $f_{(9,13)}$ $f_{(4,6)}$ $f_{(9,11)}$ $f_{(8,9)}$ $f_{(6,7)}$	f_6 f_9
0 0	1 0 0 1 0 1 0 1	1 0 0 1 0 1 I I	0 1
0 1	0 1 1 0 0 1 0 1	0 1 1 0 I I 0 1	1 0
1 0	0 1 0 1 1 0 0 1	0 1 I I 1 0 0 1	1 0
1 1	0 1 0 1 0 1 1 0	I I 0 1 0 1 1 0	0 1
	A B C D	A′ B′ C′ D′	E

TABLE 3.8

It is well that we first obtain the set γ of basic simplexes of the simplicial complex $K = (S, \Gamma)$ consisting of the set S of the 18 functions of Table 3.8 with simplexes $\sigma \in \Gamma$ determined by Eq. 3.49. Toward this end we call attention to the results of Prob. 3.27, the resulting collection of maximal compatibles:

$$\gamma^2 = \{\overline{f_1, f_{14}, f_{(1,9)}, f_{(6,14)}} ; \overline{f_2, f_{13}, f_{(2,6)}, f_{(9,13)}} ;$$

$$\overline{f_4, f_{11}, f_{(4,6)}, f_{(9,11)}} ; \overline{f_8, f_7, f_{(8,9)}, f_{(6,7)}} ;$$

$$\overline{f_6, f_9, f_{(1,9)}, f_{(6,14)}, f_{(2,6)}, f_{(9,13)}, f_{(4,6)}, f_{(9,11)}, f_{(8,9)}, f_{(6,7)}}\}$$

$$= \{\sigma_A, \sigma_B, \sigma_C, \sigma_D, \sigma_E\}$$

Even though Example 3.24 shows that the complex $(C(2), \Gamma_{C(2)})$ is not inductive, we do have $\gamma = \gamma^2$ for the subcomplex (S, Γ_S) considered here. This is demonstrated by the fact that the c.s.b.f.'s f_1, f_2, f_4, f_8, f_6 have the properties

$$v_{f_1} \subseteq c_f \quad \text{or} \quad v_{\bar{f}_1} \subseteq c_f \qquad (\text{all } f \in \sigma_A)$$

$$v_{f_2} \subseteq c_f \quad \text{or} \quad v_{\bar{f}_2} \subseteq c_f \qquad (\text{all } f \in \sigma_B)$$

and so on. Thus, $\gamma = \gamma^2$ is the desired collection of basic simplexes of K. The usefulness of this result is illustrated in the following example.

EXAMPLE 3.28

Consider the family

$$\mathscr{F} = \{F_1, F_2, F_3, F_4, F_5, F_6, F_7, F_8\}$$

with truth tables

x_2 x_1	F_1 F_2 F_3 F_4 F_5 F_6 F_7 F_8	F_2 F_3 F_4 F_6 F_7 F_8
0 0	I 0 0 0 1 1 1 0	0 0 0 1 1 0
0 1	I I 1 1 1 1 0 1	I 1 1 1 0 1
1 0	0 1 1 I 1 1 I 1	1 1 I 1 I 1
1 1	0 0 1 0 1 0 I 1	0 1 0 0 1 1

After casting out functions F_1, F_5, which do not appear in Table 3.8, we have the family

$$\{F_2, F_3, F_4, F_6, F_7, F_8\} = \{f_{(4,6)}, f_{14}, f_{(2,6)}, f_7, f_{(9,13)}, f_{14}\}$$

From the basic simplex matrix

	F_2	F_3	F_4	F_6	F_7	F_8
σ_A		1				1
σ_B			1	1		
σ_C	1					
σ_D				1		
σ_E	1		1	1		

we observe the essential simplexes σ_A and σ_D, so that the matrix is reduced to that of the residue

	F_2	F_4	F_7
σ_B		1	1
σ_C	1		
σ_E	1	1	1

which admits the irredundant coverings $\{\sigma_B, \sigma_C\}$ or $\{\sigma_E\}$. Thus the complex $(\mathscr{F}, \Gamma_{\mathscr{F}})$ has irredundant coverings:

$$\{\sigma_A, \sigma_B, \sigma_C, \sigma_D\} \quad \text{or} \quad \{\sigma_A, \sigma_D, \sigma_E\}$$

This implies that the "products" of classes (cf. Sec. 1.18),

$$P = ABCD \quad \text{or} \quad P = ADE$$

may be employed in implementing $\mathscr{F}$. From Table 1.8 we choose $P = ADE$. From this point, the completion of the synthesis of the family $\mathscr{F}$ is as if we were dealing with a family of completely specified functions (see the three-step procedure of Sec. 1.18.) The resulting logic circuit appears in Fig. 3.11.

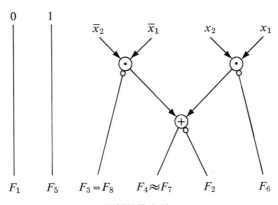

FIGURE 3.11

According to the theory of Sec. 3.12, the original basic cell matrix might have been replaced by the product of sums polynomial

$$(C + E)A \ (B + E)D \ (B + E)A = ABCD + ADE$$

in the lattice FD(5). When converted to sums of products, one again obtains the alternative irredundant coverings, from which the minimal product may be selected, using Table 1.8.

In conclusion, we might wish to update Theorem 1.19 by way of the following corollary.

Corollary 3.18. The estimates of Theorem 1.19 are equally valid if we replace $B(2)$ by $C(2)$.

PROBLEMS

3.1 Let $f : B^n \longrightarrow C$ be an i.s.b.f. and let $c_f = \omega(f) \in C^{2^n}$. Show that there is a "natural" way to associate two c.s.b.f.'s,

$$f_{\min} : B^n \longrightarrow B, \quad f_{\max} : B^n \longrightarrow B$$

with the vertices $\min(c_f)$ and $\max(c_f)$, respectively. Then show that if $g : B^n \longrightarrow B$ is a c.s.b.f. and $\omega(g) = v_g$,

$$v_g \subseteq c_f \Longleftrightarrow f_{\min} \leq g \leq f_{\max}$$

where the latter inequalities are those of the partially ordered set $B(n)$. (Cf. Prob. 1.25.)

3.2   If f_0 and f_1 are two c.s.b.f.'s

$$f_0 : B^n \longrightarrow B, \quad f_1 : B^n \longrightarrow B$$

having the property $f_0 \leq f_1$ in $B(n)$, show that there is a "natural" i.s.b.f.

$$f : B^n \longrightarrow C$$

to associate with them. How is $c_f = \omega(f)$ related to the vertices $v_{f_0} = \omega(f_0)$ and $v_{f_1} = \omega(f_1)$? What would we want to mean by the statement that a sum of products

$$g = \sum_{j=1}^{r} p_j$$

is a minimal form *between* f_0 and f_1?

   For Probs 3.3 through 3.8, a certain familiarity with the material of Secs. 6.3 and 6.4 is helpful, though not essential. The same might be said for the information in Appendix Table II. (In Table II, these problems will be found to correspond to Cases 2(i), 2(v), 2(iv), 3(i), 3(ii), 4, respectively.)

*3.3   Let $f : B^n \longrightarrow B$ have the property
(a) $f(0, x_{n-1}, \cdots, x_1) = 0$.
Show that there exists a c.s.b.f. $h : B^{n-1} \longrightarrow B$ such that
(b) $f(x_n, x_{n-1}, \cdots, x_1) = x_n \cdot h(x_{n-1}, \cdots, x_1)$.
(c) $\mu_1(f) = \mu_1(h)$.
(d) $M(f) = \mu_1(h) + M(h)$
Conversely, if $h : B^{n-1} \longrightarrow B$ and a c.s.b.f. $f : B^n \longrightarrow B$ is defined by (b), show that (a), (c), and (d) hold. (Similar results hold with x_n replaced by $\bar{x}_n$.)
Hint: Define $h : B^{n-1} \longrightarrow B$ by

$$h(x_{n-1}, \cdots, x_1) = f(1, x_{n-1}, \cdots, x_1)$$

and show that for every minimal form

$$H = \sum_{j=1}^{r} p'_j$$

of h having products

$$p'_j = x_{n-1}^{(c_{n-1}^j)} \cdots x_1^{(c_1^j)} \qquad (j = 1, 2, \cdots, r)$$

the corresponding sum

$$F = \sum_{j=1}^{r} p_j \quad \text{with } p_j = x_n \cdot p'_j \qquad (j = 1, 2, \cdots, r)$$

is a minimal form for f. (See Example 3.5.)

*3.4   Let $f : B^n \longrightarrow B$ have the property
      (a) $f(1, x_{n-1}, \cdots, x_1) = 1$.
      Show that there exists a c.s.b.f. $g : B^{n-1} \longrightarrow B$ such that
      (b) $f(x_n, x_{n-1}, \cdots, x_1) = x_n + g(x_{n-1}, \cdots, x_1)$.
      (c) $\mu_1(f) = 1 + \mu_1(g)$.
      (d) $M(f) = 2 + M(g)$.
      Conversely, if $g : B^{n-1} \longrightarrow B$ and a c.s.b.f. $f : B^n \longrightarrow B$ is defined by (b), show that (a), (c), and (d) hold. (Similar results hold with x_n replaced by $\bar{x}_n$.)

*3.5   Let $f : B^n \longrightarrow B$ have the property
      (a) $f(0, x_{n-1}, \cdots, x_1) = \overline{f(1, x_{n-1}, \cdots, x_1)}$.
      Show that there exists a c.s.b.f. $g : B^{n-1} \longrightarrow B$ such that
      (b) $f = g\bar{x}_n + \bar{g}x_n$.
      (c) $\mu_1(f) = \mu_1(g) + \mu_1(\bar{g})$.
      (d) $M(f) = \mu_1(g) + \mu_1(\bar{g}) + M(g) + M(\bar{g})$.
      Conversely, if $g : B^{n-1} \longrightarrow B$ and a c.s.b.f. $f : B^n \longrightarrow B$ is defined by (b), show that (a), (c), and (d) hold.

*3.6   Let $f : B^n \longrightarrow B$ have the property
      (a) $f(0, x_{n-1}, \cdots, x_1) \cdot f(1, x_{n-1}, \cdots, x_1) = 0$.
      Show that there exist c.s.b.f.'s $g, h : B^{n-1} \longrightarrow B$ such that
      (b) $f = g\bar{x}_n + hx_n;\ gh = 0$.
      (c) $\mu_1(f) = \mu_1(g) + \mu_1(h)$.
      (d) $M(f) = \mu_1(g) + \mu_1(h) + M(g) + M(h)$.
      Can you establish a converse?

*3.7   Let $f : B^n \longrightarrow B$ have the property
      (a) $f(0, x_{n-1}, \cdots, x_1) + \overline{f(1, x_{n-1}, \cdots, x_1)} = 1$.
      Show that there exist c.s.b.f.'s $g, h : B^{n-1} \longrightarrow B$ and a third c.s.b.f. $H : B^{n-1} \longrightarrow B$ such that
      (b) $f = g + x_n h = g + x_n H;\ \bar{g}h \leq H \leq h;\ g + \bar{h} = 1$.
      (c) $\mu_1(f) = \mu_1(g) + \mu_1(H)$.
      (d) $M(f) = \mu_1(H) + M(g) + M(H)$.
      Can you establish a converse?
      Hint: Define $g, h : B^{n-1} \longrightarrow B$ by

$$g(x_{n-1}, \cdots, x_1) = f(0, x_{n-1}, \cdots, x_1)$$

$$h(x_{n-1}, \cdots, x_1) = f(1, x_{n-1}, \cdots, x_1)$$

and take

$$H = \sum_{j=1}^{q} p_j' \quad \text{with products } p_j' = x_{n-1}^{(c_{n-1}^j)} \cdots x_1^{(c_1^j)}$$

$$(j = 1, 2, \cdots, q)$$

to be any minimal form between $\bar{g}h$ and h. (Cf. Prob. 3.2.) Then show that for every minimal form

$$G = \sum_{j=q+1}^{r} p_j$$

of g having products

$$p_j = x_{n-1}^{(c_{n-1}^j)} \cdots x_1^{(c_1^j)} \qquad (j = q+1, \cdots, r)$$

the sum

$$F = \sum_{j=1}^{r} p_j \quad \text{with } p_j = x_n \cdot p'_j \qquad (j = 1, 2, \cdots, q)$$

is a minimal form for f.

*3.8   Let $f : B^n \longrightarrow B$. Show that there exist c.s.b.f.'s $g,h : B^{n-1} \longrightarrow B$ and three more c.s.b.f.'s $G,H,K : B^{n-1} \longrightarrow B$ such that
   (a) $f = g\bar{x}_n + hx_n = G\bar{x}_n + Hx_n + K, g\bar{h} \leq G g, \bar{g}h \leq H \leq h,$
       $gh(\bar{G} + \bar{H}) \leq K \leq gh.$
   (b) $\mu_1(f) = \mu_1(G) + \mu_1(H) + \mu_1(K)$
   (c) $M(f) = \mu_1(G) + \mu_1(H) + M(G) + M(H) + M(K).$
   Can you establish a converse?

*3.9   Give an example of an i.s.b.f. $f : B^n \longrightarrow C$ (for some n) whose minimal form with the criteria of Eqs. 3.12 and 3.13 has a greater diode cost $M(f)$ than does that which results from the application of the criterion of Eq. 3.9. Can you find such an example if f is completely specified?

3.10   Show that the validity of Theorems (a) 3.3, (b) 3.6, (c) 3.7, (d) 3.9, and (e) 3.11 are unchanged if the cost criterion of Eq. 3.9 is substituted for that used in the proofs. Does any of these theorems become false if the cost criterion of Eq. 3.10 is used? If the criterion of Eq. 3.11 is used? *Note*: Of course one is expected to alter the "weight" equation accordingly.

3.11   Let $f : B^n \longrightarrow C$ be an i.s.b.f. and let K, L have the meanings of Eqs. 3.22 and 3.23, respectively. Show that (cf. Eq. 2.24)

$$L^0 = K^0(f_{max}) = \{v \in B^n; f(v) = 1\}$$

and

$$K^0 = K^0(f_{max}) = \{v \in B^n; f(v) = 1 \text{ or } f(v) = I\}$$

3.12   Formulate the incompletely specified multiple-output minimization problem of switching theory.

3.13   If $n = 6$, find the weight of the following set of cells: $M = \{C_1, C_2, C_3, C_4, C_5\}$, where $C_1 = (39, 63)$, $C_2 = (0, 11)$, $C_3 = (17, 17)$, $C_4 = (56, 58)$, $C_5 = (7, 47)$. What is the cost (from Eq. 3.12) of the corresponding (via the map D') sum of products?

3.14   Let $f : B^n \longrightarrow C$ be an incompletely specified Boolean function. Verify that the sets K and L (cf. Eqs. 3.22 and 3.23) are cell complexes and that

$$L^0 \subseteq K^0 \subseteq K$$
$$L^0 \subseteq L \subseteq K$$

3.15   Illustrate Lemma 3.1 for the sum of products

$$g = \bar{x}_1 + x_3 x_2$$

3.16 Let f be the incompletely specified Boolean function shown. Draw a figure of the type introduced in Example 3.6; then

(a) Determine K, L, K^0, L^0.

(b) Find a minimal covering of L^0 by cells of K.

(c) Use Theorem 3.3 and the results of (b) to find a minimal form of f.

(d) Which cells of K are basic with respect to some vertex of L^0?

(e) Which cells of K are essential with respect to some vertex of L^0?

(f) Illustrate Theorems 3.4, 3.6, 3.7, and 3.10 with this example.

x_3	x_2	x_1	f
0	0	0	1
0	0	1	0
0	1	0	I
0	1	1	0
1	0	0	I
1	0	1	0
1	1	0	1
1	1	1	1

(g) Using the techniques of Secs. 3.8 through 3.12, find minimal forms of both types (sum of products, product of sums) for f.

3.17 Repeat Prob. 3.16, with the function f having truth table

x_3	x_2	x_1	f
0	0	0	I
0	0	1	1
0	1	0	0
0	1	1	I
1	0	0	0
1	0	1	I
1	1	0	1
1	1	1	1

3.18 Let e be an essential cell with respect to the vertex $v \in L^0$. Show that if d is an essential cell with respect to a vertex $u \in L^0$ and $u \subseteq e$, then $d = e$.

3.19 Prove Corollary 3.2.

3.20 Prove the half of Theorem 3.3 that was not proved in the text.

3.21 Prove Theorem 3.5.

3.22 Prove the half of Theorem 3.8 that was not proved in the text.

3.23 Obtain a minimal form of each type (sum of products, product of sums) for the following c.s.b.f.'s:

(a) $\bar{x}_2\bar{x}_1 + x_3x_2 + x_2x_1 + \bar{x}_3\bar{x}_1$.

(b) $x_3x_2\bar{x}_1 + \bar{x}_2\bar{x}_1 + \bar{x}_3x_1$.

(c) $x_4\bar{x}_2\bar{x}_1 + \bar{x}_4\bar{x}_3\bar{x}_2\bar{x}_1 + \bar{x}_4x_3\bar{x}_2 + x_4\bar{x}_3\bar{x}_2x_1$.

(d) $x_3\bar{x}_2(x_4 + \bar{x}_1) + x_4x_2x_1 + \bar{x}_4\bar{x}_3x_2x_1 + \bar{x}_4\bar{x}_3\bar{x}_1$.

(e) $x_4\bar{x}_3\bar{x}_2 + \bar{x}_5\bar{x}_4x_3x_2 + \bar{x}_4x_3\bar{x}_2 + \bar{x}_3\bar{x}_2\bar{x}_1 + \bar{x}_4\bar{x}_3\bar{x}_2x_1 + \bar{x}_5\bar{x}_4x_3\bar{x}_2x_1$
$+ \bar{x}_4x_3x_2\bar{x}_1$.

(f) $x_5x_2x_1 + \bar{x}_4x_2x_1 + x_6x_5x_3x_1 + \bar{x}_4\bar{x}_3\bar{x}_2x_1 + \bar{x}_5\bar{x}_4x_3x_1$
$+ \bar{x}_5x_4x_3\bar{x}_2x_1 + x_6x_4x_3\bar{x}_2 + \bar{x}_4x_3\bar{x}_2\bar{x}_1$.

(g) $x_5\bar{x}_4\bar{x}_3x_1 + x_3x_2x_1 + \bar{x}_5\bar{x}_3x_2x_1 + \bar{x}_5x_3x_1 + x_5x_4x_1$.

3.24 Recompute both minimal forms for the following (incompletely specified) Boolean functions:

(a) The function in Prob. 3.23(f), if it is known that (x_5,x_3,x_2,x_1) $= (0,0,1,1)$ never occurs.

(b) The function is Prob. 3.23(g), if it is known that $(x_4,x_3) = (1,1,)$ and $(x_4,x_1) = (1,1)$ never occur.

*3.25 Show that the following are equivalent:
(a) $f_1 \approx f_2$ (see Eq. 3.48).
(b) There exists an i.s.b.f. $g : B^n \longrightarrow C$ such that

$$c_g \subseteq c_{f_i} \quad \text{or} \quad c_{\bar{g}} \subseteq c_{f_i} \qquad (i = 1, 2)$$

(c) There do not exist vertices $v,w \in B^n$ with

$$f_1(v) = f_2(v) \neq I \quad \text{and} \quad f_1(w) = \overline{f_2(w)} \neq I$$

*3.26 Show that the following are equivalent:
(a) $\sigma = \{f_{i_1}, f_{i_2}, \cdots, f_{i_k}\}$ is a simplex (see Eq. 3.49).
(b) There exists a c.s.b.f. $f^* : B^n \longrightarrow B$ such that

$$f^* \approx f_{i_\rho} \qquad (\rho = 1, 2, \cdots, k).$$

(c) $\prod_{j=1}^{k} *f_{i_j}^{(b_j)}$ exists for some $(b_k, b_{k-1}, \cdots, b_1) \in B^k$.

3.27 Determine the maximal compatibles (for the compatibility relation of Eq. 3.48) of the collection of functions of Table 3.8.

3.28 Given a c.s.b.f. $f(x_5,x_4,x_3,x_2,x_1)$ with $\mathcal{K}^0(f) = \{0,3,4,7,8,11,15,19,20,24, 28,30,31\}$, determine the minimal form of f. Do the same for $\bar{f}$. Obtain, using De Morgan's theorem, a product of sums representation for f by complementing the minimal form of $\bar{f}$. Does this product of sums necessarily agree with that obtained using the method of Sec. 3.11; that is, is it the minimal (product of sums) form of f? Why or why not?

3.29 Given an i.s.b.f. $f(x_7,x_6,x_5,x_4,x_3,x_2,x_1)$ with $\mathcal{L}^0(f) = \{1,2,3,7,22,30,33, 62,71,78\}$, $\mathcal{K}^0 - \mathcal{L}^0 = \{0,6,14,86\}$, determine the minimal form of f.

3.30 Repeat Prob. 3.28 for $f(x_5,x_4,x_3,x_2,x_1)$ with
(a) $\mathcal{K}^0 = \{0,1,2,3,7,14,15,22,23,29,31\}$.
(b) $\mathcal{K}^0 = \{2,6,7,8,9,12,17,19,21,23,25,27,29,31\}$.

3.31 Repeat Prob. 3.29 for $f(x_6,x_5,x_4,x_3,x_2,x_1)$ with
(a) $\mathcal{L}^0 = \{1,4,7,13,15,20,21,25,31,32,37,42,48,53,55,56,58,63\}$.
$\mathcal{K}^0 - \mathcal{L}^0 = \{0,16,28,35,44,60\}$.
(b) $\mathcal{L}^0 = \{2,6,18,45,50\}$.
$\mathcal{K}^0 - \mathcal{L}^0 = \{0,1,3,5,7,19,20,21,23,24,27,31,32,33,34,38,44,47,52,60, 61,62,63\}$.

3.32 Using Bartee's method, obtain the minimal presentation of the three Boolean functions:

$$f_1 = \bar{x}_4\bar{x}_3 + x_4x_3\bar{x}_2\bar{x}_1$$
$$f_2 = x_4\bar{x}_2\bar{x}_1 + \bar{x}_4\bar{x}_3\bar{x}_2 + \bar{x}_4\bar{x}_3x_1$$
$$f_3 = x_4x_3\bar{x}_1 + x_2\bar{x}_1 + \bar{x}_4\bar{x}_3x_1$$

What saving is achieved over the use of the three separate minimal forms?

3.33 Use Bartee's method to find minimal presentations for the following sets of functions

(a)

x_4	x_3	x_2	x_1	f_2	f_1
0	0	0	0	0	0
0	0	0	1	1	I
0	0	1	0	0	I
0	0	1	1	I	1
0	1	0	0	1	0
0	1	0	1	1	I
0	1	1	0	0	1
0	1	1	1	I	1
1	0	0	0	1	1
1	0	0	1	1	1
1	0	1	0	0	0
1	0	1	1	1	0
1	1	0	0	0	I
1	1	0	1	1	0
1	1	1	0	1	1
1	1	1	1	1	1

(b)

x_3	x_2	x_1	f_3	f_2	f_1
0	0	0	1	0	0
0	0	1	0	0	1
0	1	0	I	1	I
0	1	1	I	0	1
1	0	0	0	0	1
1	0	1	I	1	0
1	1	0	1	I	1
1	1	1	1	I	I

*3.34 Outline a proof of Theorem 3.15.

3.35 Obtain a minimal logic circuit for the family $F = \{f_1, f_2, f_3, f_4, f_5\}$ with truth tables

x_2	x_1	f_1	f_2	f_3	f_4	f_5
0	0	I	0	0	0	1
0	1	0	1	1	1	0
1	0	0	0	1	0	I
1	1	1	0	0	I	1

3.36 Construct the compatibility matrix for the family
$F = \{f_1, f_2, f_3, f_4, f_5, f_6, f_7, f_8\}$,

x_3	x_2	x_1	f_1	f_2	f_3	f_4	f_5	f_6	f_7	f_8
0	0	0	I	I	I	1	0	0	0	1
0	0	1	I	1	0	1	1	1	I	1
0	1	0	1	1	1	0	0	I	I	0
0	1	1	I	0	1	I	1	1	1	I
1	0	0	0	I	1	0	1	I	I	0
1	0	1	1	I	0	1	0	I	I	I
1	1	0	0	0	I	I	I	0	0	1
1	1	1	1	1	I	0	I	I	I	0

and determine the basic simplexes of the simplicial complex (F, Γ_F). From these, select a minimal covering (in the sense of Eq. 3.50) μ of the set F.

3.37 Repeat Prob. 3.36 with the truth tables

x_3	x_2	x_1	f_1	f_2	f_3	f_4	f_5	f_6	f_7	f_8
0	0	0	0	1	I	1	1	I	1	I
0	0	1	1	I	I	I	0	1	1	I
0	1	0	I	0	0	I	0	1	0	0
0	1	1	0	0	I	0	1	0	I	I
1	0	0	1	1	1	I	0	1	I	1
1	0	1	I	0	0	0	0	0	0	1
1	1	0	I	1	I	1	1	0	1	1
1	1	1	0	I	1	0	I	1	I	I

3.38 Compute the costs $\mu(f_i)$ of the following sums of products,

(a) $f_1 = x_4\bar{x}_3x_2 + \bar{x}_4x_3\bar{x}_2 + \bar{x}_5\bar{x}_3x_1$

(b) $f_2 = x_5\bar{x}_4x_3x_2 + \bar{x}_5\bar{x}_4x_3x_2x_1 + x_5x_3$

(c) $f_3 = x_1 + x_3\bar{x}_2 + x_4x_3 + x_5\bar{x}_2$

according to the four cost criteria μ_0, μ_1, μ_2, μ. Which functions are of minimum cost for the various criteria?

3.39 For $n = 3,4$ the Veitch[†] charts

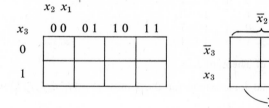

$(n=3)$

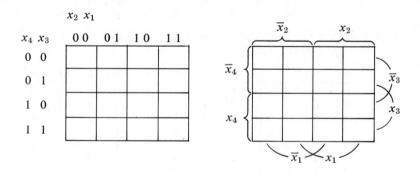

$(n=4)$

or Karnaugh[‡] maps.

[†]E. W. Veitch, "A Chart Method for Simplifying Truth Functions," *Proc. Assn. for Computing Mach.*, Pittsburgh (May 1952).

[‡]See footnote on page 172.

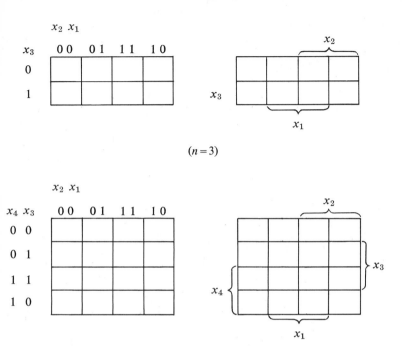

$(n = 3)$

$(n = 4)$

are quite useful in obtaining minimal (sums of products) forms for Boolean functions f. It is clear that the "charts" or "maps" devote one square for each vertex $v = (v_n, v_{n-1}, \cdots, v_1) \in B^n$ ($n = 3$ or 4). Thus, if $f: B^n \longrightarrow C$ ($n = 3$ or 4), we may "plot" f on an appropriate diagram by entering $f(v_n, v_{n-1}, \cdots, v_1)$ in the square devoted to the vertex $v = (v_n, v_{n-1}, \cdots, v_1)$. Assuming one has become familiar with those collections of 2^k squares that correspond to k cells of C^n ($n = 3$ or 4), it is a fairly simple matter to transform our minimization theory to an appropriate theory involving the pattern found on the "plotted" diagram. As illustration we plot the function of Table 3.1 on an appropriate Karnaugh map:

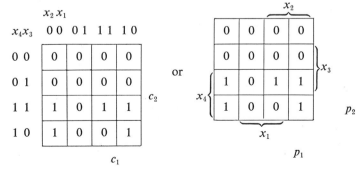

from which the essential cells

$$c_1 = (1,I,I,0) \quad \text{and} \quad c_2 = (1,1,1,I)$$

or the corresponding products

$$p_1 = \tau^{-1}(c_1) = x_4\bar{x}_1 \quad \text{and} \quad p_2 = \tau^{-1}(c_2) = x_4x_3x_2$$

can be detected. Since c_1 and c_2 cover $K^0(f)$, we have

$$f = x_4\bar{x}_1 + x_4x_3x_2$$

as the minimal form.

(a) Determine the collection of squares that correspond to the cells: $(I,0,I,1)$, $(1,1,I,0)$, $(I,I,I,0)$, and $(1,0,I,I)$ on the 4-variable Veitch chart.

(b) Repeat (a) for the 4-variable Karnaugh map.

(c) Establish a preference—on the basis of selected investigations as in (a) and (b)—for one or the other of the two types of diagrams. *Note*: When $n > 4$, either of the two types of diagrams becomes unwieldy (as n increases by 1 the number of squares doubles) If $n = 3$ or $n = 4$ the material of Secs. 1.15 and 1.17 (see Theorem 1.16 and its corollary) shows the feasibility of constructing complete catalogs of minimal circuits. These two statements should explain our treating "minimization by chart methods" as if it were of secondary importance. Nevertheless, the Veitch charts and Karnaugh maps persist in much of the literature, thereby justifying their inclusion here.

3.40 Using Veitch charts or Karnaugh maps, (as determined by the preference established in Prob. 3.39(c)), find minimal forms for the following functions:

(a) Prob. 3.16.   (f) Prob. 3.23(d).
(b) Prob. 3.17.   (g) Prob. 3.2.
(c) Prob. 3.23(a).   (h) f_2 in Prob. 3.33.
(d) Prob. 3.23(b).   (i) f_1 in Prob. 3.33.
(e) Prob. 3.23(c).

3.41 Show that if $F = \{f_1, f_2, \cdots, f_m\}$, where $f_j : B^n \longrightarrow C$ $(j = 1,2, \cdots, m)$, then

$$\underset{\text{for some } i,j}{c_{f_i} \cdot c_{f_j} = 0} \Longleftrightarrow \prod_{j=1}^{n} c_{f_j} = 0$$

and thus conclude that if Eq. 3.49 were replaced by

$$\sigma \in \Gamma \Longleftrightarrow \begin{cases} \text{there exists a c.s.b.f. } g : B^n \longrightarrow B \\ \text{such that } v_g \subseteq c_{f_i}, \ (j = 1,2, \cdots, k) \end{cases}$$

for subsets σ of F, then (F, Γ_F) becomes an inductive simplicial complex.

3.42 Let $\approx$ be the compatibility relation $\underset{\Gamma}{\approx}$ for the simplicial complex of Prob. 3.41. Show that $f \approx g$ if and only if there does not exist a vertex $v = (v_n, v_{n-1}, \cdots, v_1) \in B^n$ such that $f(v) = \overline{g(v)}$.

*3.43 Describe a "Quine-McClusky" method for computing γ, the collection of basic simplexes resulting from a family $F = \{f_1, f_2, \cdots, f_m\}$ of i.s.b.f.'s. Test your method on Prob. 3.36; on Prob. 3.37.

SUGGESTED REFERENCES

3-1 MILLER, R. E., *Switching Theory* (Combinatorial Circuits), (New York: John Wiley and Sons), Vol. I, 1965.

3-2 CHU, Y., *Digital Computer Design Fundamentals* (New York: McGraw-Hill Book Co.), 1962.

3-3 LEDLEY, R. S., *Digital Computer and Control Engineering* (New York: McGraw-Hill Book Co.), 1960.

3-4 CALDWELL, S., *Switching Circuits and Logical Design* (New York: John Wiley and Sons), 1958.

3-5 McCLUSKY, E. J., *Introduction to the Theory of Switching Circuits* (New York: McGraw-Hill Book Co.), 1965.

CHAPTER 4 | MEMORY ELEMENTS

4.1 INTRODUCTION

The logic circuits we have thus far considered are assumed to have the property that their outputs at time t depend only upon their inputs at time t (neglecting "transit time," that is, the time required for a pulse to pass through the circuitry). Such circuits are called *combinational networks*. When analyzing or synthesizing combinational logic, the past history of the inputs is inessential. Boolean functions, or truth tables, provide an adequate mathematical model for the study of these circuits. Furthermore, the preceding chapter provides several reasonably effective means of synthesizing economical realizations of the logic that a truth table dictates.

But the reader who is even remotely familiar with the diversity of tasks (counting, adding, etc.) often required to be performed by digital computer circuitry will immediately recognize that purely combinational networks are generally insufficient. More often than not, the behavior of a digital device must necessarily depend upon the past history of its inputs. For example, suppose a device is required to examine a sequence of five binary digits (or bits, as they are often called) in "serial" form, that is, appearing sequentially in time on a single input wire x; and suppose it is required that the output z should be 1 or 0 (at the conclusion time t of the input sequence) depending upon whether an odd or an even number of 1's appeared in the input string. Evidently a knowledge of the last (time $= t$) input is not sufficient. The device cannot make the correct decision unless it has the capability of remembering the important aspects of its previous inputs. Such devices are called "sequential machines" (as opposed to combinational networks) and we will devote Chapter 5 to their study. Before this can be done, however, we must introduce a new class of "building blocks," the so-called memory elements, which together with the logic circuits of Chapter 1 will constitute a basis for the implementation of the sequential machines.

4.2 A TYPICAL BISTABLE CIRCUIT

In order to motivate the abstract characterization of a memory element presented in Sec. 4.3, it is well that we first discuss a typical example so that the salient features we wish to extract are apparent to the reader.

EXAMPLE 4.1

Consider the transistor circuit of Fig. 4.1. The circuit has two "stable" states:

State 0: T_1 off, T_2 on

State 1: T_1 on, T_2 off

When the circuit is in state 0, output $\bar{q}$ is essentially at ground potential ($\bar{q} = 1$). This near-ground potential is applied through R (approximately 4000 ohms) to the base of T_1, so that T_1 is cut off. Hence, output q is at $-V(q = 0)$, and this voltage is applied in a similar way to the base of T_2, thereby keeping it in saturation. Everything is completely reversed in state 1, owing to symmetry.

Normally, the inputs r and s are at the voltage $-V$ ($r = s = 0$), but an appropriate change in inputs causes the circuit to change its state. (The diodes prevent reverse base current in the nonconducting transistor.) If the circuit is in state 0 ($q = 0$, $\bar{q} = 1$) and the input s rises to ground potential ($s = 1$), T_2 will be turned off, turning T_1 on so that $q = 1$, $\bar{q} = 0$. We say that the circuit

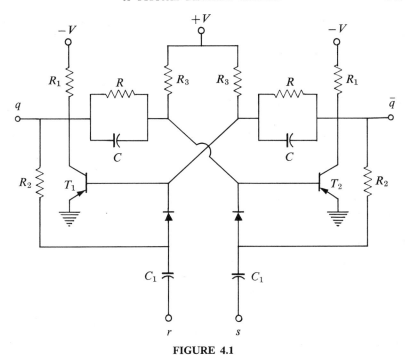

FIGURE 4.1

has been "set" to 1. In state 1, the input $r = 1$ similarly causes a change, "resetting" it to the state $q = 0$.

Note that the nature of the circuit demands that r and s should not simultaneously be 1. We say that the input combination

$$(r, s) = (1, 1)$$

is "unallowed."

The preceding discussion suggests the following *analysis table:*

q	r	s	Q
0	0	0	0
0	0	1	1
0	1	0	0
0	1	1	U
1	0	0	1
1	0	1	1
1	1	0	0
1	1	1	U

In the table, we use Q for the "next state" of q, and the entries U correspond to the unallowed input combinations. It is clear that such a table extracts the observed logical properties of the given circuit, retaining only those features that will play a role in its utilization as a building block for a sequential machine theory.

We are implicitly assuming "synchronous" operation in which the occurrence of inputs r and s are presumed to be synchronized with the appearance of a "clock pulse"—the output of a pulse generator. Such synchronization effects a discretization of time, which is assumed in any of our subsequent discussion of input sequences or state transitions, or of both. While Fig. 4.1 does not explicitly account for this synchronization—and is, in fact, an "asynchronous" circuit—the reader should see that it can easily be accomplished with appropriate "and" gates. Since these add little to the understanding of the logical behavior of sequential circuits, and because we are not primarily concerned with the "hardware" aspects of logical design, we will continue to omit any explicit reference to the synchronizing circuitry. (See Ref. 3-3 or 3-4 for a more complete discussion.)

EXAMPLE 4.2

Suppose that the memory element of Example 4.1 is initially in the state $q = 0$ and that we wish to know the state of the memory element after the sequence (cf. Sec. 0.5) of (allowable) inputs

$$\langle (1,0), (0,1), (0,0), (0,1), (0,0) \rangle$$

is applied. Rather than analyze the electric-circuit behavior, we can simply consult the analysis table:

	q	r	s	Q	
	0	0	0	0	
	0	0	1	1	
start $\longrightarrow$	0	1	0	0	
	0	1	1	U	
	1	0	0	1	end
	1	0	1	1	
	1	1	0	0	
	1	1	1	U	

Starting at the third entry, since $q = 0$ initially and the first input combination is $(r, s) = (1,0)$, we see that the next state ($Q = 0$) is again 0; and since the second input combination is $(r,s) = (0,1)$, the second entry of the analysis table is examined next. Continuing in this manner, one can quickly determine that the memory element is in state 1 at the conclusion of the input sequence.

For obvious reasons, any electronic circuit having two digital inputs r and s and complementary outputs q, $\bar{q}$, with the logical behavior of the above table, is called a *set-reset flip-flop*. The abstract memory elements discussed in the next section represent a deliberate attempt to free ourselves from direct reference to any given electronic circuit. The situation is much the same as that in Chapter 1, where we were not concerned with the particular choice of hardware used in mechanizing our "and" and "or" circuits.

4.3 MEMORY ELEMENTS

Based on the motivation of Sec. 4.2, we define an (n input) *memory element* to be a pair (f, A), where f is a function

$$f{:}B \times A \longrightarrow B$$

and A is a nonempty subset of B^n such that the *induced functions*

$$f_q{:}A \longrightarrow B \qquad (q = 0, 1)$$

are onto (cf. Sec. 0.4) B. Here, f_0 and f_1 are to be defined by

$$f_0(a) = f(0, a) \qquad (4.1)$$

$$f_1(a) = f(1, a) \qquad (4.2)$$

Correlating this definition with our preceding discussion, $n \geq 1$ is the number of inputs, while A is that subset of B^n which specifies the *allowable* input combinations. The requirement that the functions $f_q(q = 0, 1)$ be onto B expresses the desire that it be always possible (with an appropriate input) to either change state or remain in the same state. As an immediate consequence of this requirement, A must have at least two members; hence, each input of a 1-input memory element must be allowable.

EXAMPLE 4.3

For the set-reset flip-flop of Example 4.1, $A = \{(0,0), (0,1), (1,0)\}$ and f is the function

$$(0,(0,0)) \xrightarrow{f} 0$$
$$(0,(0,1)) \xrightarrow{f} 1$$
$$(0,(1,0)) \xrightarrow{f} 0$$
$$(1,(0,0)) \xrightarrow{f} 1$$
$$(1,(0,1)) \xrightarrow{f} 1$$
$$(1,(1,0)) \xrightarrow{f} 0$$

Clearly, f_0 and f_1,

$$(0,0) \xrightarrow{f_0} 0 \qquad (0,0) \xrightarrow{f_1} 1$$
$$(0,1) \xrightarrow{f_0} 1 \qquad (0,1) \xrightarrow{f_1} 1$$
$$(1,0) \xrightarrow{f_0} 0 \qquad (1,0) \xrightarrow{f_1} 0$$

are onto B.

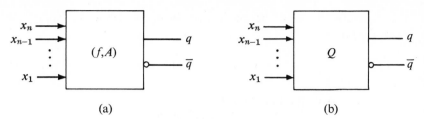

(a)   (b)

FIGURE 4.2

Let (f, A) be a memory element. (Note that we use the symbol f for part of the "name" of the memory element as well as for the name of its function). The function f is called the *characteristic function* of the memory element (f, A). To accompany the symbolic logic elements of Fig. 1.12, we use the symbolic memory element of Fig. 4.2 (with that of Fig. 4.2(b) preferred when the function $f : B \times A \rightarrow B$ is understood) when it is necessary to describe compactly an implementation of a sequential machine.

Now suppose that (f, A) and (f', A') are n-input memory elements. Then we say that (f', A') *covers* (f, A), and we write

$$(f, A) \subseteq (f', A')$$

if $A \subseteq A' \subseteq B^n$ and

$$f(q, a) = f'(q, a)$$

for all $q \in B$ and all $a \in A$. The definition says, in words, that every allowable input for f is allowable for f', and the two memory elements behave in the same way when an input that is allowable for (f, A) is presented to each. Clearly, "covers" is a partial order if we force antisymmetry by adopting the definition

$$(f, A) = (f', A') \Longleftrightarrow \begin{cases} (f, A) \subseteq (f', A') \\ \quad\text{and} \\ (f', A') \subseteq (f, A) \end{cases} \tag{4.3}$$

for equality of two n-input memory elements. Thus, for each integer $n \geq 1$, we have a partially ordered set of memory elements.

EXAMPLE 4.4

Consider the memory element (f', B^2) defined by the analysis table

q	r	s	$Q' = f'(q,(r,s))$
0	0	0	0
0	0	1	1
0	1	0	0
0	1	1	1
1	0	0	1
1	0	1	1
1	1	0	0
1	1	1	0

We see that (f', B^2) covers the set-rest memory element discussed in Example 4.3. It has the same properties as the set-reset element, but in addition, the input $r = s = 1$ causes (f', B^2) to complement itself. For this reason, any electronic realization of f' is called a *complementing flip-flop*.†

*4.4 UNIVERSALITY THEOREM

Having already indicated a quite complicated structure (a partially ordered set for each integer n) for the set of all memory elements, one might expect an enormous difference in the class of sequential machines (we use this term when convenient, even though it will not be defined until Chapter 5) that can be constructed using one type of memory element as opposed to another. The main result of this section is a statement that is quite to the contrary. Before it can be stated, we need the following result, which describes conditions on the logic network F of Fig. 4.3 that are necessary so that the composite logic and memory circuit will itself be a memory element.

Lemma 4.1 Let (g, A) be an n-input memory element

$$g : B \times A \longrightarrow B; \quad A \subseteq B^n$$

and let $F : B \times B^m \rightarrow B^n$ be n-Boolean functions of $m + 1$ variables (cf. Sec. 3.13): $p, x_m, x_{m-1}, \cdots, x_1$ having the properties

(1) $F^{-1}(B^n - A) = \varnothing$.

(2) For each $p, q \in B$, there exists an element $x' \in g_p^{-1}(q)$ such that

$$F_p^{-1}(x') \neq \varnothing$$

where $F_p : B^m \rightarrow B^n (p = 0,1)$ are the functions

$$F_p(x) = F(p, x) \tag{4.4}$$

Furthermore, let $f : B \times B^m \rightarrow B$ be defined by

$$f(q, (x_m, x_{m-1}, \cdots, x_1)) = g(q, F(q, (x_m, x_{m-1}, \cdots, x_1))) \tag{4.5}$$

Then (f, B^m) is an m-input memory element. (See Fig. 4.3.)

PROOF. This is evidently the case if we can show that the induced functions $f_q : B^m \rightarrow B$ are onto B. Suppose they are not. Then, for some $q, Q \in B$, we must have for all $x \in B^m$

$$f_q(x) \neq Q \tag{4.6}$$

But according to Eqs. 4.4 and 4.5, for all $x \in B^m$ we have

†Often (as in Ref. 4-1) called a *j-k* flip-flop with inputs denoted j and k in place of s and r, respectively.

$$f_q(x) = f(q, x) = g(q, F(q, x))$$
$$= g_q(F(q, x))$$
$$= g_q(F_q(x))$$

that is, $f_q = g_q \cdot F_q$. Setting $p = q$ and $q = Q$ in condition (2), there exists an element $x' \in g_q^{-1}(Q)$ such that $F_q^{-1}(x') \neq \emptyset$. So,

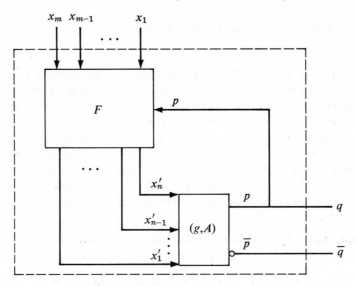

FIGURE 4.3

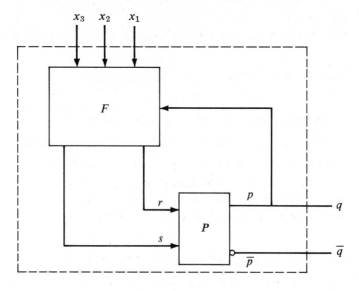

FIGURE 4.4

let $y \in F_q^{-1}(x')$. Then, since $y \in B^m$ and

$$f_q(y) = g_q(F_q(y)) = g_q(x') = Q$$

we have contradicted Eq. 4.6. ∎

Condition (1) was inserted to ensure that F does not generate any inputs that are unallowed by (g, A).

EXAMPLE 4.5

Let (g, A) be the *r-s* memory element; that is,

$$A = \{(0,0), (0,1), (1,0)\}$$

and $g : B \times A \longrightarrow B$ as specified by the analysis table ($n = 2$).

p	r	s	$P = g(p, (r, s))$
0	0	0	0
0	0	1	1
0	1	0	0
0	1	1	U
1	0	0	1
1	0	1	1
1	1	0	0
1	1	1	U

$(0,0) \xrightarrow{g_0} 0 \qquad (0,0) \xrightarrow{g_1} 1$

$(0,1) \xrightarrow{g_0} 1 \qquad (0,1) \xrightarrow{g_1} 1$

$(1,0) \xrightarrow{g_0} 0 \qquad (1,0) \xrightarrow{g_1} 0$

Next, suppose $F: B \times B^3 \longrightarrow B^2$ is given by the truth tables of Table 4.1. Note that we have labeled $F(p,(x_3, x_2, x_1)) = (r, s)$ because of the implied circuit of Fig. 4.4, this being suggested by Fig. 4.3. We observe that (property (1))

$$F^{-1}(B^2 - A) = F^{-1}(\{1,1\}) = \varnothing$$

since $(r, s) = (1,1)$ does not occur in Table 4.1. Furthermore (property (2)),

(i)   If $p = 0$, $q = 0$, there exists an element $x' = (1,0) \in g_0^{-1}(0)$ such that $F_0^{-1}(x') \neq \varnothing$.

p	x_3	x_2	x_1	r	s
0	0	0	0	0	1
0	0	0	1	1	0
0	0	1	0	1	0
0	0	1	1	1	0
0	1	0	0	1	0
0	1	0	1	1	0
0	1	1	0	1	0
0	1	1	1	1	0
1	0	0	0	0	0
1	0	0	1	1	0
1	0	1	0	0	0
1	0	1	1	0	1
1	1	0	0	0	1
1	1	0	1	1	0
1	1	1	0	0	1
1	1	1	1	0	0

TABLE 4.1

q	x_3	x_2	x_1	$Q = f(q, (x_3, x_2, x_1))$
0	0	0	0	1
0	0	0	1	0
0	0	1	0	0
0	0	1	1	0
0	1	0	0	0
0	1	0	1	0
0	1	1	0	0
0	1	1	1	0
1	0	0	0	1
1	0	0	1	0
1	0	1	0	1
1	0	1	1	1
1	1	0	0	1
1	1	0	1	0
1	1	1	0	1
1	1	1	1	1

TABLE 4.2

as seen from observing the function $F_0 : B^3 \longrightarrow B^2$:

$$(0,0,0) \xrightarrow{F_0} (0,1)$$
$$(0,0,1) \xrightarrow{F_0} (1,0)$$
$$(0,1,0) \xrightarrow{F_0} (1,0)$$
$$(0,1,1) \xrightarrow{F_0} (1,0)$$
$$(1,0,0) \xrightarrow{F_0} (1,0)$$
$$(1,0,1) \xrightarrow{F_0} (1,0)$$
$$(1,1,0) \xrightarrow{F_0} (1,0)$$
$$(1,1,1) \xrightarrow{F_0} (1,0)$$

Similarly (property (2)),

(ii)   If $p = 0$, $q = 1$, there exists an element $x' = (0,1) \in g_0^{-1}(1)$ such that $F_0^{-1}(x') = \{(0,0,0)\} \neq \varnothing$.

In like manner, the other two combinations of p, q are checked to see that generally (the condition (2)),

for each $p, q \in B$ there exists $x' \in g_p^{-1}(q)$ such that $F_p^{-1}(x') \neq \varnothing$

holds. (*Note*: If the first entry of Table 4.1 had been $(0,0,0,0) \xrightarrow{F} (0,0)$, then condition (2) would not hold.) The lemma then asserts that (f, B^3) is a memory element if f is defined by Eq. 4.5:

$$f(q, (x_3, x_2, x_1)) = g(q, F(q, (x_3, x_2, x_1)))$$

This definition leads to Table 4.2, and since the induced functions f_0 and f_1 are onto B;

$$(0,0,0) \xrightarrow{f_0} 1 \qquad (0,0,0) \xrightarrow{f_1} 1$$
$$(0,0,1) \xrightarrow{f_0} 0 \qquad (0,0,1) \xrightarrow{f_1} 0$$
$$(0,1,0) \xrightarrow{f_0} 0 \qquad (0,1,0) \xrightarrow{f_1} 1$$
$$(0,1,1) \xrightarrow{f_0} 0 \qquad (0,1,1) \xrightarrow{f_1} 1$$
$$(1,0,0) \xrightarrow{f_0} 0 \qquad (1,0,0) \xrightarrow{f_1} 1$$
$$(1,0,1) \xrightarrow{f_0} 0 \qquad (1,0,1) \xrightarrow{f_1} 0$$
$$(1,1,0) \xrightarrow{f_0} 0 \qquad (1,1,0) \xrightarrow{f_1} 1$$
$$(1,1,1) \xrightarrow{f_0} 0 \qquad (1,1,1) \xrightarrow{f_1} 1$$

(f, B^3) is seen to be a memory element, as claimed. The reader should check the effect of changing the first entry in Table 4.1 as suggested in the parenthetical note above.

In essence, the important theorem we are about to present states that any memory element can be "disguised" as, or made to appear logically equivalent to, a prescribed memory element arbitrarily chosen. The indistinguishability will persist as long as inputs that are allowable to the prescribed memory element are applied. The disguise is accomplished

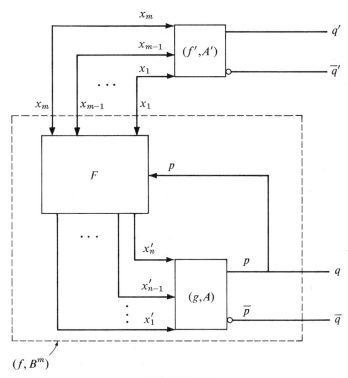

FIGURE 4.5

through the synthesis of an appropriate combinational circuit F, as located in Fig. 4.3. (See Fig. 4.5.)

Theorem 4.2   *Universality Theorem*: Let (f', A') be an m-input memory element and (g, A) be an n-input memory element. Then there exist n Boolean functions

$$F: B \times B^m \longrightarrow B^n$$

of $m + 1$ variables: $p, x_m, x_{m-1}, \cdots, x_1$ such that if

$$f: B \times B^m \longrightarrow B$$

is defined by Eq. 4.5,

$$f(q, (x_m, x_{m-1}, \cdots, x_1)) = g(q, F(q, (x_m, x_{m-1}, \cdots, x_1)))$$

then (f, B^m) is an m-input memory element and

$$(f, B^m) \supseteq (f', A')$$

PROOF.   According to the lemma, if we can find n Boolean functions F satisfying (1) and (2), then (f, B^m) is a memory element.

If $p \in B$ and $x \in A'$, we choose as $F(p, x)$ a definite element $F(p, x) \in g_p^{-1}(f'(p, x))$, a set that is not empty because $f'(p, x) \in B$ and (g, A) is a memory element; that is, g_p is onto B. If $x \notin A'$, we simply choose an element $F(p, x) \in A$. In either event we have

(1′) $F(p, x) \in A$ for all $p \in B$, $x \in B^m$,

for even in the first case $F(p, x) \in g_p^{-1}(B) = A$. Of course this property (1′) is equivalent to (1) of Lemma 4.1. Now let $p, q \in B$. Since (f', A') is a memory element, there exists $x \in B^m$ such that $x \in A'$ and

$$f'(p, x) = f'_p(x) = q$$

and by definition of F, we have

$$F_p(x) = F(p, x) \in g_p^{-1}(f'(p, x)) = g_p^{-1}(q)$$

so that

$$F_p^{-1}(g_p^{-1}(q)) \neq \varnothing$$

That is,

(2′)   There exists an element $x' \in g_p^{-1}(q)$, namely, $x' = F_p(x)$ such that

$$F_p^{-1}(x') \neq \varnothing$$

Hence, (f, B^m) is a memory element, by the lemma.

Now, to show that $(f, B^m) \supseteq (f', A')$, we note first that $A' \subseteq B^m$ because (f', A') is an m-input memory element. Furthermore, if $a' \in A'$ and $q \in B$,

$$f(q, a') = g(q, F(q, a'))$$

where

$$F(q, a') \in g_q^{-1}(f'(q, a'))$$

by the definition of F. Hence,

$$f(q, a') = g_q(F(q, a')) = f'(q, a')$$

so that $(f, B^m) \supseteq (f', A')$ as asserted. ▮

The theorem states that when accompanied by a suitable combinatorial network F, an arbitrary memory element (g, A) can be made indistinguishable from any given memory element (f', A'), (see Fig. 4.5), as long as we only apply inputs that are allowable with respect to (f', A'). Furthermore, in its definition of F, the proof is constructive and therefore provides a means for implementing the required combinational network.

EXAMPLE 4.6

Consider the case where (g, A) is the r-s memory element and (f', A') the complementing memory element (cf. Example 4.4). In order to design the combinational network of Fig. 4.6, we examine the following analysis tables:

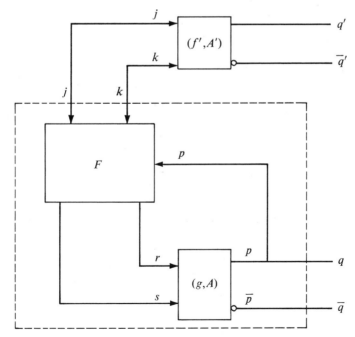

FIGURE 4.6

p	r	s	$P = g(p, (r, s))$		q'	k	j	$Q' = f'(q', (k, j))$
0	0	0	0		0	0	0	0
0	0	1	1		0	0	1	1
0	1	0	0		0	1	0	0
0	1	1	U		0	1	1	1
1	0	0	1		1	0	0	1
1	0	1	1		1	0	1	1
1	1	0	0		1	1	0	0
1	1	1	U		1	1	1	0

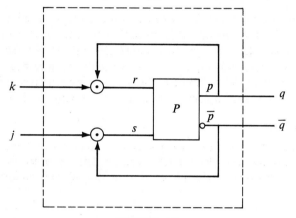

FIGURE 4.7

The definition of F in Theorem 4.2 dictates

p	k	j	$(r, s) = F(p, (k, j))$
0	0	0	(0, 0) or (1, 0)
0	0	1	(0, 1)
0	1	0	(0, 0) or (1, 0)
0	1	1	(0, 1)
1	0	0	(0, 0) or (0, 1)
1	0	1	(0, 0) or (0, 1)
1	1	0	(1, 0)
1	1	1	(1, 0)

which is equivalent to the two incompletely specified (cf. Sec. 3.2) truth tables

p	k	j	r	s
0	0	0	I	0
0	0	1	0	1
0	1	0	I	0
0	1	1	0	1
1	0	0	0	I
1	0	1	0	I
1	1	0	1	0
1	1	1	1	0

whose minimal forms (cf. Sec. 3.3) are computed as in Chapter 3:

$$r = p \cdot k$$
$$s = \bar{p} \cdot j$$

Hence the circuit of Fig. 4.7 behaves as though it were a complementing flip-flop.

4.5 CHARACTERISTIC EQUATIONS

Suppose (f, A) is an n-input memory element. As in Example 4.2, the characteristic function

$$f: B \times A \longrightarrow B$$

or, equivalently, the analysis table of (f, A) may be used to deduce the behavior of the memory element upon receiving a sequence of allowable inputs. Alternatively, this information can be learned from the *characteristic equation Q* of (f, A). This equation is simply the minimal form of the incomplete truth table obtained by replacing U by I in the analysis table. (Actually, this equation may not be uniquely defined, since the incomplete truth table may have several minimal forms; when this is the case, we merely select one of them as the characteristic equation.) Such a replacement is reasonable, for we are interested only in the response of (f, A) to allowable inputs, tacitly assuming that unallowed inputs will not occur.

EXAMPLE 4.7

Again consider the r-s memory element. Replacing U by I in the analysis table of Sec. 4.2, we obtain the incomplete truth table

q	r	s	Q
0	0	0	0
0	0	1	1
0	1	0	0
0	1	1	I
1	0	0	1
1	0	1	1
1	1	0	0
1	1	1	I

By the techniques of Chapter 3,

$$Q = s + \bar{r}q \tag{4.7}$$

is the characteristic equation of the r-s memory element.

To illustrate its usefulness, we again compute the sequence $\langle Q^{(0)}, Q^{(1)}, Q^{(2)}, Q^{(3)}, Q^{(4)}, Q^{(5)} \rangle$ of states of the memory element when it is assumed that

$Q^{(0)} = 0$ and the sequence of allowable inputs $\langle (1,0), (0,1), (0,0), (0,1), (0,0) \rangle$ is applied. (Cf. Example 4.2.) Using Eq. 4.7, we compute

$$Q^{(1)} = 0 + \bar{1} \cdot 0 = 0$$
$$Q^{(2)} = 1 + \bar{0} \cdot 0 = 1$$
$$Q^{(3)} = 0 + \bar{0} \cdot 1 = 1$$
$$Q^{(4)} = 1 + \bar{0} \cdot 1 = 1$$
$$Q^{(5)} = 0 + \bar{0} \cdot 1 = 1$$

so that the memory element is in the state 1 when the input sequence has concluded. Here the notation $Q^{(t)}$ can be thought of as referring to the state of the memory element at discrete times $t = 0, 1, 2, 3, 4, 5$.

We note that the characteristic equation gives no information about the memory element which could not have been learned from the characteristic function or analysis table—its utility derives from its compact representation of the behavior of the memory element.

4.6   SYNTHESIS FUNCTIONS

Again let (f, A) be an n-input memory element, where $A \subseteq B^n$ and $f: B \times A \longrightarrow B$. Then a mapping

$$F: B \times C \longrightarrow C^n$$

$(C = \{0, 1, I\})$ is called a *synthesis function* for (f, A) if for every $(q, Q) \in B \times B$ and every vertex $v \subseteq F(q, Q)$ we have

(1) $v \in A$.
(2) $f(q, v) = Q$.

Concerning these functions, we have the following existence theorem.

Theorem 4.3   Every memory element has a synthesis function.

PROOF.   Let (f, A) be a memory element, where $A \subseteq B^n$ and $f: B \times A \longrightarrow B$. Since $B \times C$ has only six elements, we can define F by a simple enumeration; choose

$$F(0, 0) \in f_0^{-1}(0)$$
$$F(0, 1) \in f_0^{-1}(1)$$
$$F(0, I) \in C^n$$
$$F(1, 0) \in f_1^{-1}(0)$$
$$F(1, 1) \in f_1^{-1}(1)$$
$$F(1, I) \in C^n$$

$$(4.8)$$

Such a definition can be made because (f, A) is a memory element so that $f_q^{-1}(Q) \neq \varnothing$ for all $(q, Q) \in B \times B$. Now suppose $(q, Q) \in B \times B$. Then $F(q, Q)$ has been defined (by Eq. 4.8) to be a vertex in $f_q^{-1}(Q)$; hence

(1) $F(q, Q) \in A$,
(2) $f(q, F(q, Q)) = f_q(F(q, Q)) = Q$,

so that F is a synthesis function. ∎

EXAMPLE 4.8

Suppose (f, A) is the r-s memory element, with characteristic function f and induced functions (cf. Eqs. 4.1 and 4.2)

$$(0, 0) \xrightarrow{f_0} 0 \qquad (0, 0) \xrightarrow{f_1} 1$$
$$(0, 1) \xrightarrow{f_0} 1 \qquad (0, 1) \xrightarrow{f_1} 1$$
$$(1, 0) \xrightarrow{f_0} 0 \qquad (1, 0) \xrightarrow{f_1} 0$$

Since

$$f_0^{-1}(0) = \{(0, 0), (1, 0)\} \qquad f_1^{-1}(0) = \{(1, 0)\}$$
$$f_0^{-1}(1) = \{(0, 1)\} \qquad f_1^{-1}(1) = \{(0, 0), (0, 1)\}$$

we must select (according to Eq. 4.8)

$$F(0, 1) = (0, 1)$$
$$F(1, 0) = (1, 0)$$

(4.9)

But we have two choices for $F(0, 0)$ and $F(1, 1)$. Suppose we take

$$F(0, 0) = (0, 0)$$
$$F(1, 1) = (0, 1)$$

(4.10)

The other two definitions, $F(0, I)$ and $F(1, I)$ may be chosen arbitrarily from among the cells of C^2, say

$$F(0, I) = (I, 1)$$
$$F(1, I) = (I, I)$$

(4.11)

According to Theorem 4.3, Eqs. 4.9 through 4.11 have defined a synthesis function $F: B \times C \longrightarrow C^2$ for (f, A). The significance of this fact will be revealed in Theorem 4.6, where the reasons for naming it a synthesis function will also become apparent. As a preliminary to the theorem, it can be appreciated that in defining $F(q, Q)$ for $(q, Q) \in B \times B$, one asks the question: What inputs (r, s) would cause (f, A) to change from state q to state Q? Thus, in the first of Eqs. 4.10, we ask: What inputs (r, s) would cause the r-s memory element to change from state 0 to state 0, that is, to remain in state 0 if it is already in state 0? The answer is learned from the induced function f_0; we had a choice between $(r, s) = (0, 0)$ or $(r, s) = (1, 0)$. We took the first alternative. Note that these two choices might be combined by taking $(r, s) = (I, 0)$, meaning that "I don't care" or "It doesn't matter" whether r is taken as 0 or 1, but s must be taken as 0. This situation is reflected in the fact that $G: B \times C \longrightarrow C^2$, defined by

$$(0, 0) \xrightarrow{G} (I, 0)$$
$$(0, 1) \xrightarrow{G} (0, 1)$$
$$(0, I) \xrightarrow{G} (I, 1)$$
$$(1, 0) \xrightarrow{G} (1, 0)$$
$$(1, 1) \xrightarrow{G} (0, 1)$$
$$(1, I) \xrightarrow{G} (I, I)$$

is also a synthesis function for the r-s memory element. The reader should check that this is so—according to the definition of a synthesis function.

Now if (f, A) is a memory element and

$$F, G : B \times C \longrightarrow C^n$$

are synthesis functions for (f, A), we say that G *contains* F, $(G \geq F)$ if

$$G(q, Q) \supseteq F(q, Q) \qquad \text{for all } (q, Q) \in B \times C \qquad \textbf{(4.13)}$$

where $\supseteq$ is the inclusion relation of the cellular n cube, C^n. Clearly, $\geq$ is a partial order, and hence the set Ω_f of all synthesis functions for a given memory element (f, A) forms a partially ordered set $(\Omega_f, \geq)$. The memory element (f, A) is said to be *invertable* if $(\Omega_f, \geq)$ has an identity element E:

$$E \geq F \qquad \text{for all } F \in \Omega_f \qquad \textbf{(4.14)}$$

In this case, $E = E_f$ is called the *maximal synthesis function* of f.

EXAMPLE 4.9

With F and G as in Example 4.8, we have $F \leq G$ because

$$G(0, 0) = (I, 0) \supseteq (0, 0) = F(0, 0)$$
$$G(0, 1) = (0, 1) \supseteq (0, 1) = F(0, 1)$$
$$G(0, I) = (I, 1) \supseteq (I, 1) = F(0, I)$$
$$G(1, 0) = (1, 0) \supseteq (1, 0) = F(1, 0)$$
$$G(1, 1) = (0, 1) \supseteq (0, 1) = F(1, 1)$$
$$G(1, I) = (I, I) \supseteq (I, I) = F(1, I)$$

with inclusions taken in C^2. (Cf. Eq. 2.5.) As further practice, the reader should verify that $E : B \times C \to C^2$, defined by

$$(0, 0) \xrightarrow{E} (I, 0)$$
$$(0, 1) \xrightarrow{E} (0, 1)$$
$$(0, I) \xrightarrow{E} (I, I)$$
$$(1, 0) \xrightarrow{E} (1, 0)$$
$$(1, 1) \xrightarrow{E} (0, I)$$
$$(1, I) \xrightarrow{E} (I, I)$$

is another synthesis function for the r-s memory element, and that $E \geq G$. That this synthesis function is an identity element in the partially ordered set of all synthesis functions for the r-s memory element is a consequence of our next theorem, which establishes a necessary and sufficient condition for invertability of a memory element.

Theorem 4.4 A memory element (f, A) is invertible if and only if $f_q^{-1}(Q)$ has $2^{k(q,Q)}$ (for some integer $k = k(q, Q)$) elements or vertices, each belonging to the same k cell, $c = c(q, Q) \in C^n$, for all $(q, Q) \in B \times B$.

PROOF. First suppose that the condition of the theorem is satisfied. Then the function

$$E: B \times C \longrightarrow C^n$$

defined by

$$E(0, 0) = c(0, 0)$$
$$E(0, 1) = c(0, 1)$$
$$E(0, I) = (I, I, \cdots, I)$$
$$E(1, 0) = c(1, 0) \tag{4.15}$$
$$E(1, 1) = c(1, 1)$$
$$E(1, 1) = (I, I, \cdots, I)$$

is an identity element for $(\Omega_f, \geq)$. To see this, let $F \in (\Omega_f, \geq)$ and let $(q, Q) \in B \times C$ (since it is clear that $F(q, I) \subseteq E(q, I) = (I, I, \cdots, I)$, we may assume that $(q, Q) \in B \times B$). Furthermore, suppose v is a vertex of C^n with $v \subseteq F(q, Q)$. Then by (2) in the definition of synthesis function,

$$f_q(v) = f(q, v) = Q$$

so that

$$v \in f_q^{-1}(Q)$$

and by hypothesis, $v \subseteq c(q, Q) = E(q, Q)$.

Since v was arbitrarily chosen in $F(q, Q)$, we have (cf. Prob. 2.26)

$$E(q, Q) \supseteq F(q, Q)$$

for all $(q, Q) \in B \times C$, so that $F \leq E$. But F was arbitrarily chosen in the partially ordered set Ω_f, showing that E is the maximal synthesis function for f; that is, E is an identity element for $(\Omega_f, \geq)$. Thus, the conditions of the theorem imply that (f, A) is invertible. We leave the proof of the converse as an exercise. ∎

EXAMPLE 4.10

Consider once more the r-s memory element (f, A). Since

$$f_0^{-1}(0) = \{(0, 0), (1, 0)\} \qquad k(0, 0) = 1$$
$$f_0^{-1}(1) = \{(0, 1)\} \qquad k(0, 1) = 0$$

$$f_1^{-1}(0) = \{(1, 0)\} \qquad k(1, 0) = 0$$
$$f_1^{-1}(1) = \{(0, 0), (0, 1)\} \qquad k(1, 1) = 1$$

and

$$c(0, 0) = (I, 0)$$
$$c(0, 1) = (0, 1)$$
$$c(1, 0) = (1, 0)$$
$$c(1, 1) = (0, I)$$

Theorem 4.4 asserts that (f, A) is invertable, with the maximal synthesis function

$$E : B \times C \longrightarrow C^2$$

described by Eqs. 4.15:

$$(0, 0) \xrightarrow{E} (I, 0) = c(0, 0)$$
$$(0, 1) \xrightarrow{E} (0, 1) = c(0, 1)$$
$$(0, I) \xrightarrow{E} (I, I)$$
$$(1, 0) \xrightarrow{E} (1, 0) = c(1, 0)$$
$$(1, 1) \xrightarrow{E} (0, I) = c(1, 1)$$
$$(1, I) \xrightarrow{E} (I, I)$$

When the maximal synthesis function of an invertable memory element is arranged in a tabular fashion, exemplified by that of the *r-s* memory element depicted below,

q	Q	r	s
0	0	I	0
0	1	0	1
0	I	I	I
1	0	1	0
1	1	0	I
1	I	I	I

it is called the *synthesis table* of the invertable memory element. If not already apparent to the reader, the reasons for the terminology (synthesis, invertable, etc.) of this section will be made clear by Theorem 4.6 and the examples of Sec. 4.8. We omit the proof of the following corollary.

Corollary 4.5   Let (f, A) be an invertable memory element with maximal synthesis function E:

$$E : B \times C \longrightarrow C^n$$

Then every function

$$F : B \times C \longrightarrow C^n$$

having the property that

$$E(q, Q) \supseteq F(q, Q) \qquad \text{for all } (q, Q) \in B \times C$$

is a synthesis function for (f, A). Conversely, every synthesis function F for (f, A) has this property.

This corollary asserts that every synthesis function for an invertable memory element (f, A) can be obtained by replacing certain I's by 1's and 0's in its synthesis table. Hence, an invertable memory element whose synthesis table contains I's in r locations has 3^r distinct synthesis functions.

4.7 EXAMPLES OF MEMORY ELEMENTS

Of the memory elements commonly encountered by the logical designer, we have already discussed two: the set-reset memory element and its closely related complementing memory element. The reader should take the trouble to show that the complementing memory element is invertable and has the (maximal) synthesis table shown in Table 4.3.

EXAMPLE 4.11

No doubt the simplest (since $n \geq 1$) memory element that one might imagine is the *delay* memory element (f, B), having one input d whose characteristic function $f: B \times B \longrightarrow B$ is given by the following analysis table:

q	d	$Q = f(q, d)$
0	0	0
0	1	1
1	0	0
1	1	1

That (f, B) is an invertable memory element with synthesis table

q	Q	d
0	0	0
0	1	1
0	I	I
1	0	0
1	1	1
1	I	I

is immediately apparent. Its characteristic equation

$$Q = d \qquad (4.16)$$

suggests that a unit-time delay line represents a physical realization of the memory element, thereby accounting for its name. Note that Theorem 4.2 asserts that even this simple memory element is "universal," and hence justifies the often heard statement that "any sequential machine can be constructed from delay elements and Pierce elements alone." (Cf. Prob. 1.22.)

EXAMPLE 4.12

Of a somewhat different character is the *trigger* memory element (g, B), which also has but one input t. Its analysis table

q	t	$Q = g(q, t)$
0	0	0
0	1	1
1	0	1
1	1	0

is also invertable, yielding the synthesis table

q	Q	t
0	0	0
0	1	1
0	I	I
1	0	1
1	1	0
1	I	I

Note that the input $(t = 1)$ causes the memory element to complement itself, that is,

$$Q = q\bar{t} + \bar{q}t \qquad (4.17)$$

We will find it convenient to tabulate (Table 4.3) these examples together with those already introduced, for easy reference in the sequel.

DELAY

Analysis			Synthesis		
q	d	Q	q	Q	d
0	0	0	0	0	0
0	1	1	0	1	1
1	0	0	0	I	I
1	1	1	1	0	0
	$Q = d$		1	1	1
			1	I	I

TRIGGER

Analysis			Synthesis		
q	t	Q	q	Q	t
0	0	0	0	0	0
0	1	1	0	1	1
1	0	1	0	I	I
1	1	0	1	0	1
	$Q = t\bar{q} + \bar{t}q$		1	1	0
			1	I	I

SET-RESET

Analysis				Synthesis			
q	r	s	Q	q	Q	r	s
0	0	0	0	0	0	I	0
0	0	1	1	0	1	0	1
0	1	0	0	0	I	I	I
0	1	1	U	1	0	1	0
1	0	0	1	1	1	0	I
1	0	1	1	1	I	I	I
1	1	0	0				
1	1	1	U				
$Q = s + \bar{r}q$							

COMPLEMENTING

Analysis				Synthesis			
q	k	j	Q	q	Q	k	j
0	0	0	0	0	0	I	0
0	0	1	1	0	1	I	1
0	1	0	0	0	I	I	I
0	1	1	1	1	0	1	I
1	0	0	1	1	1	0	I
1	0	1	1	1	I	I	I
1	1	0	0				
1	1	1	0				
$Q = j\bar{q} + \bar{k}q$							

TABLE 4.3   COMMON INVERTABLE MEMORY ELEMENTS

EXAMPLE 4.13

Table 4.4 is an example of a 3-input memory element that combines the features of the set-reset and trigger elements. Note that it is noninvertable (by Theorem 4.4) because

$$f_0^{-1}(1) = \{(0, 0, 1), (0, 1, 0)\}$$
$$f_1^{-1}(0) = \{(0, 0, 1), (1, 0, 0)\}$$

and these do *not* constitute 1-cells of C^3. Hence, the corresponding partially ordered set $(\Omega_f, \geq)$ does not have an identity element, and there are four maximal synthesis functions, as shown in Table 4.4. We will find in the next section that such situations greatly complicate the synthesis procedures.

SET-RESET-TRIGGER

Analysis

q	r	s	t	Q
0	0	0	0	0
0	0	0	1	1
0	0	1	0	1
0	0	1	1	U
0	1	0	0	0
0	1	0	1	U
0	1	1	0	U
0	1	1	1	U
1	0	0	0	1
1	0	0	1	0
1	0	1	0	1
1	0	1	1	U
1	1	0	0	0
1	1	0	1	U
1	1	1	0	U
1	1	1	1	U

$$Q = s + t\bar{q} + \bar{r}\bar{t}q$$

Synthesis

q	Q	r	s	t
0	0	I	0	0
0	1	0	0	1
0	I	I	I	I
1	0	0	0	1
1	1	0	I	0
1	I	I	I	I

q	Q	r	s	t
0	0	I	0	0
0	1	0	1	0
0	I	I	I	I
1	0	1	0	0
1	1	0	I	0
1	I	I	I	I

q	Q	r	s	t
0	0	I	0	0
0	1	0	0	1
0	I	I	I	I
1	0	1	0	0
1	1	0	I	0
1	I	I	I	I

q	Q	r	s	t
0	0	I	0	0
0	1	0	1	0
0	I	I	I	I
1	0	0	0	1
1	1	0	I	0
1	I	I	I	I

TABLE 4.4

4.8 APPLICATIONS

In the application of a given memory element (f, A) to a particular design problem, it is required that the next state Q of the memory element depend in a fixed way on its present state q and the Boolean values of a finite number (say, t) of other Boolean variables $y_1, y_2, \cdots, y_t$. This motivates the definition of an *application function*

$$f_Q : B \times B^t \longrightarrow C$$

where $C = \{0, 1, I\}$ because we want to admit the case where the conditions of the problem are such that the designer does not care what the next state becomes for particular arguments $(q, (y_t, y_{t-1}, \cdots, y_1))$.

EXAMPLE 4.14

Suppose we wish to design a "nine-state clock," that is, a sequential machine having four memory elements (why not three?) whose states a, b, c, d change in the cyclic fashion:

a	b	c	d	A	B	C	D
0	0	0	0	0	0	0	1
0	0	0	1	0	0	1	0
0	0	1	0	0	0	1	1
0	0	1	1	0	1	0	0
0	1	0	0	0	1	0	1
0	1	0	1	0	1	1	0
0	1	1	0	0	1	1	1
0	1	1	1	1	0	0	0
1	0	0	0	0	0	0	0

and so on, where (a, b, c, d) at time t becomes (A, B, C, D) at time $t + 1$. Then, if (f, A) is a memory element that is to "store" the variable $q = a$, the next state $Q = A$ of the memory element should depend on q and $t = 3$ other Boolean variables $y_1 = b$, $y_2 = c$, $y_3 = d$ according to the application function

$$A = f_A : B \times B^3 \longrightarrow C = \{0, 1, I\}$$

depicted by the incomplete truth table of Table 4.5. Similarly, one can construct application functions for the other three memory elements. Since the

a	b	c	d	A
0	0	0	0	0
0	0	0	1	0
0	0	1	0	0
0	0	1	1	0
0	1	0	0	0
0	1	0	1	0
0	1	1	0	0
0	1	1	1	1
1	0	0	0	0
1	0	0	1	I
1	0	1	0	I
1	0	1	1	I
1	1	0	0	I
1	1	0	1	I
1	1	1	0	I
1	1	1	1	I

TABLE 4.5

states $(a, b, c, d) = (1, 0, 0, 1), (1, 0, 1, 0), \cdots, (1, 1, 1, 1)$ will never occur (provided the machine does not begin in one of these states), the application functions are incompletely specified.

Now we can begin to describe the purpose of the synthesis functions and the synthesis table of a memory element. Consider the first row of Table 4.5, and suppose we ask the question: Which inputs to a memory element storing the variable $q = a$ would cause $a = 0$ to change (here, to remain unchanged) to $A = 0$? Clearly, the answer depends on the type of memory element employed. But if we agree to use an $r\text{-}s$ memory element, we see from its (maximal) synthesis table that we may take $r = 0, s = 0$, or $r = 1, s = 0$ (that is, $r = I, s = 0$). Evidently we could proceed in this manner with each row of Table 4.5 to obtain incompletely specified truth tables for $r = r_A$ and $s = s_A$ as functions of a,b,c,d, which would cause transitions $a \longrightarrow A$ as required by the application function $f_A(a,b,c,d)$. The general validity of such a procedure regardless of the particular synthesis function chosen is guaranteed in our next result, Theorem 4.6(2), in which it is also assured by (1) that such an employment of synthesis functions will give only allowable inputs to the memory element (as with either $r = 0$, $s = 0$, or $r = 1$, $s = 0$ above) in cases where the application function f_Q is specified ($\neq I$).

Theorem 4.6   Let $f_Q : B \times B^t \longrightarrow C$ be an application function for the n-input memory element (f, A), and let $F : B \times C \longrightarrow C^n$ be a synthesis function for (f, A). Then for all $(q, y) \in B \times B^t$ such that $f_Q(q, y) \neq I$, and all vertices $v \subseteq F(q, f_Q(q, y))$, we have

(1) $v \in A$.
(2) $f_Q(q, y) = f(q, v)$.

PROOF.   Suppose the hypothesis is satisfied, that $(q, y) \in B \times B^t$ is such that $f_Q(q, y) \neq I$ (so that we "care" about the value $f_Q(q, y)$) and that $v \subseteq F(q, f_Q(q, y))$ for a vertex $v \in B^n$.
Then

(1′) $v \in A$ because of (1) in the definition of synthesis function, Sec. 4.6
(2′)   By (2) in that definition,

$$f(q, v) = f_Q(q, y)$$

and the theorem is proved immediately. ∎

EXAMPLE 4.15

Consider the application function $f_Q : B \times B^3 \longrightarrow C$, as shown in Table 4.5, and suppose the memory element (f, A) used to store the variable $q = a$ (cf. Example 4.14) is chosen to be an $r\text{-}s$ memory element. Suppose further that the synthesis function $F : B \times C \longrightarrow C^2$ of Example 4.8 is employed:

a	A	r	s
0	0	0	0
0	1	0	1
0	I	I	1
1	0	1	0
1	1	0	1
1	I	I	I

Then for

$$(q, y) = (a, (b, c, d)) = (0, (0, 0, 0))$$

we have

$$F(q, f_Q(q, y)) = F(0, f_A(0, (0, 0, 0))) = F(0, 0) = (0, 0)$$

Now $v \subseteq (0, 0) \Rightarrow v = (0, 0)$, which is an allowable input; furthermore, from Eq. 4.7,

$$f(0, (0, 0)) = 0 + \bar{0} \cdot 0 = 0 + 1 \cdot 0 = 0$$
$$= f_A(0, (0, 0, 0))$$

Thus, the memory element changes (here, leaves unchanged) a, as specified by the first row of Table 4.5, if we put $(r, s) = (0, 0)$ as dictated by our synthesis function (dictated because $a = 0$, $A = 0$ in the first row of Table 4.5). That this coincidence is uniformly true for every row of Table 4.5 *no matter which* synthesis function is chosen is exactly the meaning of Theorem 4.6. When Table 4.6 is completed according to the dictations of the synthesis function, two incompletely specified truth tables result for r_A and s_A. Their synthesis according to the methods of Chapter 3 yields

$$r_A = a$$
$$s_A = bcd$$

and the corresponding logical circuitry will ensure that the memory element a changes as specified by Table 4.5. The importance of a maximal synthesis function derives from the fact that a maximum number of I's would be inserted in Table 4.6—maximum while still being assured that Theorem 4.6 holds. The consequence (generally) of this fact will be appreciated in connection with the use of the minimization theory of Chapter 3.

In summary, we remark that maximal synthesis functions in the partially ordered set $(\Omega_f, \geq)$ correspond to synthesis tables for which no 0 or 1 can be replaced by I while still representing a synthesis function for the memory element. Since the I's in a synthesis table will yield unspecified vertices in the truth tables for the inputs of the memory element, interest is naturally focused on the maximal synthesis functions of the memory element. If the memory element is invertable, there will be a *unique* maximal synthesis function, so that using it, we are certain that the resulting incomplete truth tables for the inputs of the memory element are optimum with respect to unspecified entries. In the noninvertable case, it is not even sufficient to try all maximal synthesis functions and to

a	b	c	d	r_A	s_A
0	0	0	0	0	0
0	0	0	1	0	0
0	0	1	0	0	0
0	0	1	1	0	0
0	1	0	0	0	0
0	1	0	1	0	0
0	1	1	0	0	0
0	1	1	1	0	1
1	0	0	0	1	0
1	0	0	1	I	I
1	0	1	0	I	I
1	0	1	1	I	I
1	1	0	0	I	I
1	1	0	1	I	I
1	1	1	0	I	I
1	1	1	1	I	I

TABLE 4.6

choose the most economical of the resulting solutions, for the optimum solution there may very well depend upon "mixing" entries $F(q, Q)$ from among several maximal synthesis functions F.

EXAMPLE 4.16

To complete the design of the counter of Example 4.14, we repeat the process of Example 4.15 for each memory element, now using the maximal synthesis function (Table 4.3) for r-s memory elements. The results appear in Table 4.7 and we obtain

$$r_A = a$$
$$s_A = bcd$$
$$r_B = bcd$$
$$s_B = \bar{b}cd$$
$$r_C = cd$$
$$s_C = \bar{c}d$$
$$r_D = d$$
$$s_D = \bar{a}\bar{d}$$

which are computed by the methods of Chapter 3.

Hence, the network of Fig. 4.8 will perform the desired counting function, where we have taken advantage of the multiple occurrence of the factors $c \cdot d$, $b \cdot c \cdot d$ in the equations so as to economize further over the straightforward implementation of the minimal forms. In principle, one could apply the techniques of Sec. 3.13 to obtain an optimum multiple output logic net. However, the

a	b	c	d	r_A	s_A	r_B	s_B	r_C	s_C	r_D	s_D
0	0	0	0	I	0	I	0	I	0	0	1
0	0	0	1	I	0	I	0	0	1	1	0
0	0	1	0	I	0	I	0	0	I	0	1
0	0	1	1	I	0	0	1	1	0	1	0
0	1	0	0	I	0	0	I	I	0	0	1
0	1	0	1	I	0	0	I	0	1	1	0
0	1	1	0	I	0	0	I	0	I	0	1
0	1	1	1	0	1	1	0	1	0	1	0
1	0	0	0	1	0	I	0	I	0	I	0
1	0	0	1	I	I	I	I	I	I	I	I
1	0	1	0	I	I	I	I	I	I	I	I
1	0	1	1	I	I	I	I	I	I	I	I
1	1	0	0	I	I	I	I	I	I	I	I
1	1	0	1	I	I	I	I	I	I	I	I
1	1	1	0	I	I	I	I	I	I	I	I
1	1	1	1	I	I	I	I	I	I	I	I

TABLE 4.7

number of variables (12) in the transformed single-output function would probably preclude anything short of a digital computer for its solution.

The synthesis tables and techniques of this section allow for a greatly simplified discussion of the material of Sec. 4.4. Our concluding example, when compared to Example 4.6, will definitely testify to this fact.

EXAMPLE 4.17

Suppose again that we wish to augment the r-s memory element with a logic circuit F, as located in Fig. 4.6, in order that the composite logic and memory circuit be indistinguishable from the complementing memory element. Using the analysis table of the complementing memory element, we obtain an application function $f_P = P$, as shown in the fourth column of the following array:

p	k	j	P	r	s
0	0	0	0	I	0
0	0	1	1	0	1
0	1	0	0	I	0
0	1	1	1	0	1
1	0	0	1	0	I
1	0	1	1	0	I
1	1	0	0	1	0
1	1	1	0	1	0

The synthesis table for the r-s memory element then yields the same incompletely specified truth tables r,s as originally obtained in Example 4.6. But the process here is more mechanical than that in Sec. 4.4. Of course we again conclude that $r = p \cdot k$, $s = \bar{p} \cdot j$ is the required logic circuit.

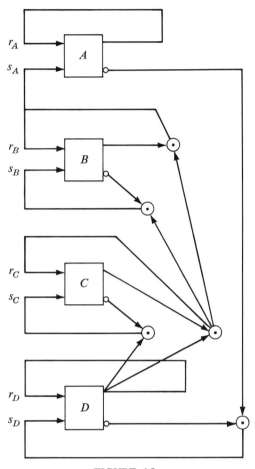

FIGURE 4.8

PROBLEMS

4.1   Every memory element (f, A) has a *transition diagram* consisting of two circles (states) labeled 0 and 1 interconnected by 4 transitional arrows of the form:

$$\textcircled{q} \ \frac{(b_n b_{n-1} \cdots b_1)}{\rule{4cm}{0pt}} \ \textcircled{Q} \qquad (q, Q) \in B^2$$

labeled with all (allowable) input combinations $(b_n, b_{n-1}, \cdots, b_1)$ for which

$$f_q(b_n, b_{n-1}, \cdots, b_1) = Q$$

When (f, A) is the set-reset flip-flop we have the transition diagram:

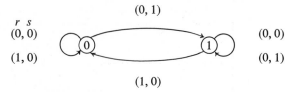

r s
(0, 0)
(1, 0)

(0, 1)

(1, 0)

(0, 0)
(0, 1)

Draw the transition diagram for
(a)   The delay memory element.
(b)   The trigger memory element.
(c)   The complementing $(j\text{-}k)$ flip-flop.
(d)   The set-reset-trigger memory element.

4.2   Why is the following mapping, $f: B \times A \longrightarrow B$,

q	x_2	x_1	$Q = f(q, (x_2, x_1))$
0	0	0	1
0	0	1	0
0	1	0	U
0	1	1	1
1	0	0	0
1	0	1	0
1	1	0	U
1	1	1	0

(where $A = B^2 - \{(1, 0)\}$) *not* a memory element. In what way is its transition diagram "defective?" (See Prob. 4.1.)

4.3   For each of the following memory elements (f, A),

$$f: B \times A \longrightarrow B; \quad A \subseteq B^2$$

q	v	w	$Q = f(q, (v, w))$	q	n	p	$Q = f(q, (n, p))$
0	0	0	0	0	0	0	1
0	0	1	1	0	0	1	0
0	1	0	0	0	1	0	U
0	1	1	1	0	1	1	0
1	0	0	1	1	0	0	1
1	0	1	0	1	0	1	1
1	1	0	0	1	1	0	U
1	1	1	1	1	1	1	0

determine whether (f, A) is invertable. If it is, find its maximal synthesis function (table). If it is not, give all its maximal synthesis functions.

4.4   State the invertability criteria for a memory element (Theorem 4.4) in terms of the labels on the transitional arrows of its transition diagram. (See Prob. 4.1.)

4.5   Using the combinatorial network F in the proof of the universality theorem (Theorem 4.2), augment the first memory element of Prob. 4.3

with combinatorial logic that will make it indistinguishable from the second memory element of Prob. 4.3, provided only allowable inputs for the second are admitted. Conversely, augment' the second memory element with logic, making it indistinguishable from the first.

4.6   Using the method of Prob. 4.5, augment the
      (a) d flip-flop so it behaves as an r-s flip-flop.
      (b) r-s flip-flop so it behaves as a j-k flip-flop.
      (c) r-s flip-flop so it behaves as a t flip-flop.
      (d) j-k flip-flop so it behaves as an r-s-t flip-flop.
      (e) d flip-flop so it behaves as an r-s-t flip-flop.
      (f) t flip-flop so it behaves as a j-k flip-flop.
      (g) j-k flip-flop so it behaves as a t flip-flop.
      (h) r-s-t flip-flop so it behaves as a d flip-flop.
      Repeat, using synthesis functions for the given flip-flops (the ones to be augmented).

4.7   How many distinct 1-input memory elements are there?

4.8   Determine the characteristic equation for each memory element of Prob. 4.3.

4.9   For each memory element of Prob. 4.3, determine the state (0 or 1) in which it would be found at the termination of the sequence of inputs:

$$\langle (1, 1), (0, 1), (0, 0), (0, 1), (0, 0), (1, 1) \rangle$$

(assuming it is initially in the 0 state).

4.10 Prove Corollary 4.5.

4.11 Design counters that count in the sequences

(a) abc	(b) abc	(c) $abcd$
000	000	0001
001	111	0010
010	110	0100
011	101	1000
100	010	1100
101	011	1110
000	100	1111
	000	1001
etc.	etc.	0111
		0011
		0001
		etc.

using r-s memory elements.

4.12 Repeat Prob. 4.11 for (a) j-k memory elements, (b) Trigger memory elements, (c) Delay elements, (d) r-s-t memory elements,

4.13 Repeat Prob. 4.11 for the (a) first memory element of Prob. 4.3, (b) second memory element of Prob. 4.3.

*4.14 Let $g, h \in B(2) - \{f_0, f_{15}\}$. Show that

$$f: B \times B^2 \longrightarrow B$$

given by

$$f(q, (b_2, b_1)) = \bar{q}g(b_2, b_1) + qh(b_2, b_1)$$

is an (abstract) memory element with two inputs for which every input combination is allowable.

*4.15 Let $g, h: B^2 \longrightarrow C$ be i.s.b.f.'s such that

$$(0, 0, 0, 0) \nsubseteq c_g$$

$$(1, 1, 1, 1) \nsubseteq c_g$$

and similarly for h. Suppose also that $c_g \| c_h$. Show that there is a unique memory element (f, A) with $A \subseteq B^2$ having the property

$$f(q, a) = \bar{q}g(a) + qh(a)$$

for all $a \in A$.

4.16 Using the result of Prob. 4.15, compute the number of distinct memory elements with two inputs.

*4.17 Suppose (f, A) and (f', A') are memory elements,
$$f: B \times A \longrightarrow B; \quad A \subseteq B^n$$
$$f': B \times A' \longrightarrow B; \quad A' \subseteq B^n$$
and that we agree to say that (f, A) is *equivalent* to (f', A') (written $(f, A) \sim (f', A')$) if there exists a permutation $\pi: n^+ \longrightarrow n^+$, an element $(b_n, b_{n-1}, \cdots, b_1) \in B^n$, and an element $b \in B$ such that

(a) $(x_n, x_{n-1}, \cdots, x_1) \in A \Longleftrightarrow \left(x_{\pi(n)}^{(b_{\pi(n)})}, x_{\pi(n-1)}^{(b_{\pi(n-1)})}, \cdots, x_{\pi(1)}^{(b_{\pi(1)})}\right) \in A'$

(b) $f_q(x_n, x_{n-1}, \cdots, x_1) = f'^{(b)}_{q^{(b)}}\left(x_{\pi(n)}^{(b_{\pi(n)})}, x_{\pi(n-1)}^{(b_{\pi(n-1)})}, \cdots, x_{\pi(1)}^{(b_{\pi(1)})}\right)$

for all $(x_n, x_{n-1}, \cdots, x_1) \in A$ and $q = 0, 1$.

Show that $\sim$ is an equivalence relation on the (partially ordered) set of all n-input memory elements.

*4.18 Let (f, A) and (f', A') be memory elements

$$f: B \times A \longrightarrow B; \quad A \subseteq B^n$$

$$f': B \times A' \longrightarrow B; \quad A' \subseteq B^n$$

Show that $(f, A) \sim (f', A')$ (cf. Prob. 4.17) if and only if the combinational network F (in the proof of the universality theorem) contains only wires when (f, A) is augmented to behave as (f', A'), and vice versa.

*4.19 For $n = 2$, compute the number of equivalence classes in Prob. 4.17. Hence, determine the number of "essentially different" (see Prob. 4.18) 2-input memory elements. This number should naturally be compared with that obtained in Prob. 4.16.

SUGGESTED REFERENCES

4-1   PHISTER, MONTGOMERY, *Logical Design of Digital Computers* (New York: John Wiley & Sons), 1958.

4-2   HUMPHREY W. S., *Switching Circuits* (New York: McGraw-Hill Book Co.), 1958.

CHAPTER 5   SEQUENTIAL
MACHINE THEORY

5.1 INTRODUCTION

A unification of the material of Chapters 1 through 4 is achieved in the theory of sequential machines. However, one must not be led to think that this theory is a mere composite of those presented previously, since it raises new and important questions and problems of its own.

We have deliberately made liberal use of the as-yet undefined term *sequential machine*, in the hope that the reader will embark on this chapter with a handful of preconceived notions as to their character. Undoubtedly, he already suspects a "black box" characterization

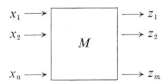

in which binary-valued inputs are transformed into binary-valued outputs in a noncombinational manner; that is, M generally contains memory elements that cause the outputs to depend on the past history of the inputs.

As was characteristic of our treatment of combinational networks, we will be concerned with incompletely specified machines M (those for which the designer is unconcerned as to the behavior of M when certain inputs occur while the memory elements are in certain states) as well as those that are completely specified.

The theory for the latter type is, by now, almost "classical." Although it would be possible to subsume this theory within the more modern framework of the incompletely specified theory, there are good reasons for treating it separately. Indeed, our use of the word "classical" is meant to imply not merely the early date of its development, but also the degree to which the completely specified theory has guided the course of the more recent research and publication.

Before we study either of the synthesis procedures in detail, we will follow the pattern of Chapter 4; that is, we will first analyze a particular machine in order to motivate our abstract definition of "sequential machine."

5.2 ANALYSIS

EXAMPLE 5.1

Consider the logic (and memory) circuit M of Fig. 5.1, which contains two set-reset memory elements Q_2 and Q_1, one input x, and one output z. One can immediately write the Boolean polynomials

$$r_2 = (\bar{x} + \bar{q}_1)q_2$$
$$s_2 = \bar{q}_2 q_1$$
$$r_1 = q_2 + xq_1$$
$$s_1 = \bar{q}_2 \bar{q}_1$$
$$z = \bar{q}_2 q_1 x$$

which describe the dependence of the output z and the inputs to the memory elements on the input x and the states of the memory elements. From the corresponding truth tables,

x	q_2	q_1	r_2	s_2	r_1	s_1	z
0	0	0	0	0	0	1	0
0	0	1	0	1	0	0	0
0	1	0	1	0	1	0	0
0	1	1	1	0	1	0	0
1	0	0	0	0	0	1	1
1	0	1	0	1	1	0	0
1	1	0	1	0	1	0	0
1	1	1	0	0	1	0	0

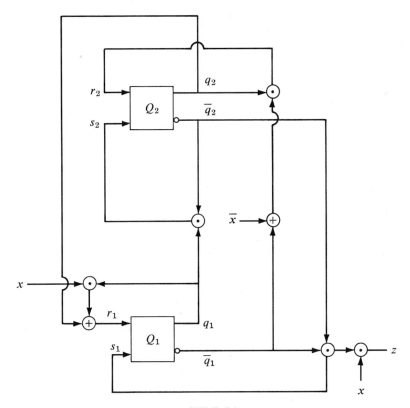

FIGURE 5.1

and the analysis table (cf. Table 4.3) of a set-reset memory element, we obtain the *transition table*

x	q_2	q_1	Q_2	Q_1	z
0	0	0	0	1	0
0	0	1	1	1	0
0	1	0	0	0	0
0	1	1	0	0	0
1	0	0	0	1	1
1	0	1	1	0	0
1	1	0	0	0	0
1	1	1	1	0	0

in a straightforward manner.

With the "black box" characterization,

$$x \longrightarrow \boxed{M} \longrightarrow z$$

one is often little concerned with the knowledge of the states of the individual memory elements. For this reason, the array

x	S	S	z
0	α	β	0
0	β	δ	0
0	γ	α	0
0	δ	α	0
1	α	β	1
1	β	γ	0
1	γ	α	0
1	δ	γ	0

or the rearranged *flow table*

	x	
S	0	1
α	$(\beta,0)$	$(\beta,1)$
β	$(\delta,0)$	$(\gamma,0)$
γ	$(\alpha,0)$	$(\alpha,0)$
δ	$(\alpha,0)$	$(\gamma,0)$

is considered to describe adequately the behavior of the machine.

The flow table of a machine M having r memory elements Q_1, Q_2, $\cdots$, Q_r evidently arises from rearranging the information in its transition table after replacing each composite state $(q_r, q_{r-1}, \cdots, q_1)$ of the r memory elements by a *state* s ($s \in S$) of the machine M. Replacement proceeds according to a 1–1 *encoding function* $\epsilon:B^r \longrightarrow S$, choosing any set S having $|S| = |B^r| = 2^r$ so that ϵ is onto S. Thus, in Example 5.1, we took $S = \{\alpha, \beta, \gamma, \delta\}$ and the encoding function $\epsilon:B^2 \longrightarrow S$ as follows:

$$q_2 \; q_1 \qquad S$$

$$0 \;\; 0 \xrightarrow{\;\epsilon\;} \alpha$$

$$0 \;\; 1 \xrightarrow{\;\epsilon\;} \beta$$

$$1 \;\; 0 \xrightarrow{\;\epsilon\;} \gamma$$

$$1 \;\; 1 \xrightarrow{\;\epsilon\;} \delta$$

The more graphic *state diagram* (recall the transition diagrams for memory elements as introduced in Prob. 4.1) of M can be effective in analysis if $|S|$ is not too large. It is a "graph" in which each state $s \in S$ is enclosed in a circle and the circles are interconnected by *transitional arrows*,

labeled with the input/output information found in the flow table. There should be 2^n arrows leaving each circle (one for each possible input $x \in B^n$) and each arrow should terminate on a circle, perhaps the same circle from which it emanated.

EXAMPLE 5.2

For the flow table of Example 5.1 we obtain the state diagram of Fig. 5.2. Note that the arrow from γ to α is really two arrows in the sense intended above. The same is true of the arrow from α to β.

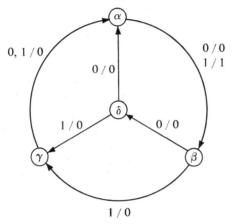

FIGURE 5.2

Each transitional arrow corresponds to an entry in the flow table; thus, the arrow

$$\delta \quad \xrightarrow{\substack{x \ z \\ 0/0}} \quad \alpha$$

corresponds to the entry $(\alpha,0)$ in the bottom row (first column) of the flow table of Example 5.1. The meaning of the arrow or the corresponding entry of the flow table is the same: that is, if M is in the state δ (where according to the encoding function ϵ we have $q_2 = q_1 = 1$), and the input $x = 0$ is applied to M, the "next state" of the machine will be α (where $q_2 = q_1 = 0$), and this change of state is accompanied by an output $z = 0$.

As an illustration of the power of the state diagram (or flow table) in analyzing the behavior of a machine, suppose the input sequence†

$$x = \langle 0,0,1,1,1,0,0,1,1 \rangle = \langle x_1,x_2,x_3,x_4,x_5,x_6,x_7,x_8,x_9 \rangle$$

is applied through the input x at times $t, t + 1, t + 2, \cdots, t + 8$, respectively, with our machine M initially in the state α. Tracing the appropriate transitional arrows of the state diagram, we find that the machine will deliver the output sequence

$$z = \langle 0,0,0,0,1,0,0,1,0 \rangle = \langle z_1,z_2,z_3,z_4,z_5,z_6,z_7,z_8,z_9 \rangle$$

at these times, and that the machine will be found in the state α at the termina-

---

†The reader should be cautioned that here and in much of the theory that follows, the symbol x_j does *not* refer to the jth "physical" input at a fixed time, but to the jth of a sequence of inputs $x = x_j$ on one input line at discrete times $t + j - 1$. A similar remark is appropriate for the symbol z_j.

tion of the input sequence. The reader will observe that while the inputs (x_4 and x_5) to M are the same at the times $t + 3$ and $t + 4$, the outputs are different at these times, illustrating the sequential (as opposed to combinational) nature of its operation.

Questions of the type raised in Example 5.2 can be easily answered from the state diagram (or equivalently, the flow table) of the machine. However, questions concerning input sequences would be very difficult to answer from a mere inspection of Fig. 5.1. The other side of the coin is reflected in the observation that one could, from the description of Fig. 5.1, easily fabricate an electronic circuit whose behavior would correspond to our state diagram; but it is not quite clear how such a circuit could be constructed from the state diagram directly. One would probably try to retrace the steps backward, from state diagram to logic circuit. But even then, how could one be sure that he had arrived at an "economical" such circuit? And what should he take as a measure of economy? These are the synthesis problems that we will study.

5.3 COMPLETELY SPECIFIED MACHINES

If the reader refers to the flow table of Example 5.1, he sees why we define an n-input, m-output, p-state *completely specified sequential machine* (n-m-p c.s.s.m.) $M = (S, \sigma)$ to be a pair (S, σ) in which S is a set, with $|S| = p$, and σ is a mapping

$$\sigma : B^n \times S \longrightarrow S \times B^m \qquad (5.1)$$

Although we restrict S by insisting that it be finite, we do not require that $|S| = 2^r$ for some integer r. When we do not wish to call attention to the number of states in M, we will term it an n-m c.s.s.m.

EXAMPLE 5.3

In Example 5.1 we have a 1–1–4 c.s.s.m. $M = (S, \sigma)$ for which $S = \{\alpha, \beta, \gamma, \delta\}$, and $\sigma : B \times S \longrightarrow S \times B$ is the mapping

$$(0,\alpha) \xrightarrow{\sigma} (\beta,0)$$

$$(0,\beta) \xrightarrow{\sigma} (\delta,0)$$

$$(0,\gamma) \xrightarrow{\sigma} (\alpha,0)$$

$$(0,\delta) \xrightarrow{\sigma} (\alpha,0)$$

$$(1,\alpha) \xrightarrow{\sigma} (\beta,1)$$

$$(1,\beta) \xrightarrow{\sigma} (\gamma,0)$$

$$(1,\gamma) \xrightarrow{\sigma} (\alpha,0)$$

$$(1,\delta) \xrightarrow{\sigma} (\gamma,0)$$

Note that the mapping σ associated with a sequential machine M is simply an abstract characterization of its flow table; as a mapping, it is neither 1–1 nor onto $S \times B^m$, in general.

Roughly speaking, we want to say that two n-m c.s.s.m.'s, $M = (S, \sigma)$ and $N = (T, \tau)$ are "equivalent" if we cannot tell them apart by performing "input-output experiments."[†] To do this, we first define equivalence for states. Let $s \in S$ and $t \in T$. We say that state s is *equivalent* to state t (written $s \sim t$) if for each $k \in Z^+$ and each finite sequence[‡] (cf. Sec. 0.5),

$$\langle x_1, x_2, \cdots, x_k \rangle = \langle x_i \in B^n; 1 \leq i \leq k \rangle$$

we have $z_k = z'_k$ after examining the transitions

$$(x_1, s) \xrightarrow{\sigma} (s_1, z_1) \qquad (x_1, t) \xrightarrow{\tau} (t_1, z'_1)$$

$$(x_2, s_1) \xrightarrow{\sigma} (s_2, z_2) \qquad (x_2, t_1) \xrightarrow{\tau} (t_2, z'_2)$$

$$\vdots \qquad\qquad\qquad \vdots$$

$$(x_k, s_{k-1}) \xrightarrow{\sigma} (s_k, z_k) \qquad (x_k, t_{k-1}) \xrightarrow{\tau} (t_k, z'_k)$$

in the machines M and N, respectively. With such a definition, we see that if M begins in state s and N in an equivalent state t, there is no finite input sequence that can, when applied to each machine simultaneously, cause differing outputs to result. Then, to lend precision to our "rough" definition of machine equivalence, we say that two n-m c.s.s.m.'s, $M = (S, \sigma)$, $N = (T, \tau)$, are *equivalent* (written $M \sim N$) if for each $s \in S$ there exists a state $t \in T$ such that $s \sim t$, and conversely, for each $t \in T$ there is at least one state $u \in S$ such that $t \sim u$.

EXAMPLE 5.4

Consider the 1–1 c.s.s.m. $N = (T, \tau)$, where $T = \{1,2,3,4,5\}$ and τ is the function (see Fig. 5.3)

$$(0,1) \xrightarrow{\tau} (5,0)$$

$$(0,2) \xrightarrow{\tau} (4,0)$$

$$(0,3) \xrightarrow{\tau} (1,0)$$

$$(0,4) \xrightarrow{\tau} (1,0)$$

$$(0,5) \xrightarrow{\tau} (4,0)$$

$$(1,1) \xrightarrow{\tau} (2,1)$$

†E. F. Moore, "Gedanken Experiments on Sequential Machines" (see Ref. 5-1).

‡Generalizing the system of notation used in Example 5.2, we now use the symbol x_j to denote the jth of a sequence of composite inputs $x = x_j = (x_n^{(j)}, x_{n-1}^{(j)}, \cdots, x_1^{(j)})$ on n-input lines $x_n, x_{n-1}, \cdots, x_1$ at discrete times $t + j - 1$. Thus, $x_j \in B^n$. A similar remark is appropriate for our use of the symbol $z_j \in B^m$.

$$(1,2) \xrightarrow{\tau} (3,0)$$
$$(1,3) \xrightarrow{\tau} (1,0)$$
$$(1,4) \xrightarrow{\tau} (3,0)$$
$$(1,5) \xrightarrow{\tau} (3,0)$$

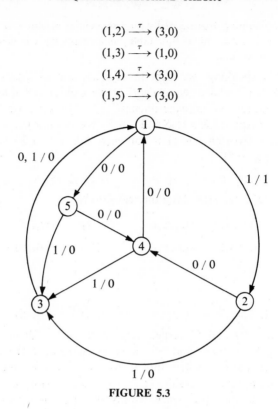

FIGURE 5.3

In Fig. 5.3 we have purposely drawn the state diagram of N with an orientation that suggests a similarity to the state diagram of the machine M shown in Fig. 5.2. In fact, the reader should be able to convince himself (see Example 5.5) that

$$
\begin{array}{ll}
\alpha \sim 1 & 1 \sim \alpha \\
\beta \sim 2 & 2 \sim \beta \\
\gamma \sim 3 & 3 \sim \gamma \\
\delta \sim 4 & 4 \sim \delta \\
& 5 \sim \beta
\end{array}
$$

so that $M \sim N$. Evidently these two machines have identical behavior as far as input-output measurements are concerned. But which of these two machines would we rather build? Recalling the encoding procedure for machine M, it would appear (since $|T| = 5 > 4$) that three memory elements would be required in implementing N, as opposed to two memory elements for M. Considering the hardware (of which Fig. 4.1 is typical) represented by memory elements, preference would quite probably be given to machine M.

Note in our definition of equivalence for states that N may be a "copy" of M. In this case, the definition serves to define equivalence for two states within the same machine M. With this interpretation we formulate the following lemma.

Lemma 5.1. The definition for equivalence among states of a given c.s.s.m. $M = (S, \sigma)$ is an equivalence relation on S. (Thus, S is partitioned (cf. Theorem 0.3) by $\sim$ into disjoint classes of mutually equivalent states.)

PROOF. All except perhaps the transitivity of the relation $\sim$ is obvious, so let $s \sim s'$ and $s' \sim s''$ for elements s, s', $s'' \in S$. Now let $\langle x_1, x_2, \cdots, x_k \rangle$ be any finite input sequence. Assuming that M begins in the various states s, s', s'', the sequence will cause transitions

$$(x_1, s) \xrightarrow{\sigma} (s, z_1) \qquad (x_1, s') \xrightarrow{\sigma} (s'_1, z'_1) \qquad (x_1, s'') \xrightarrow{\sigma} (s''_1, z''_1)$$

$$(x_2, s_1) \xrightarrow{\sigma} (s_2, z_2) \qquad (x_2, s'_1) \xrightarrow{\sigma} (s'_2, z'_2) \qquad (x_2, s''_1) \xrightarrow{\sigma} (s''_2, z''_2)$$

$$\begin{array}{ccc} \cdot & \cdot & \cdot \\ \cdot & \cdot & \cdot \\ \cdot & \cdot & \cdot \end{array}$$

$$(x_k, s_{k-1}) \xrightarrow{\sigma} (s_k, z_k) \qquad (x_k s'_{k-1}) \xrightarrow{\sigma} (s'_k, z'_k) \qquad (x_k, s''_{k-1}) \xrightarrow{\sigma} (s''_k, z''_k)$$

respectively. Now

$$\left. \begin{array}{c} s \sim s' \Longrightarrow z_k = z'_k \\ s' \sim s'' \Longrightarrow z'_k = z''_k \end{array} \right\} \Longrightarrow z_k = z''_k \Longrightarrow s \sim s''$$

so that $\sim$ is transitive. Reflexivity and symmetry being obvious, $\sim$ is an equivalence relation on S. ∎

EXAMPLE 5.5.

For the machine $N = (T, \tau)$ of Example 5.4, we have $5 \sim 2$, whereas states 1,3,4 are equivalent only to themselves. To demonstrate that $3 \nsim 4$, for example, apply the sequence $\langle 1,1 \rangle$ to N, assuming it to begin in the states $s = 3$ and $s' = 4$, respectively. The sequence causes transitions

$$(x_1, s) = (1,3) \xrightarrow{\tau} (1,0) \qquad (x_1, s') = (1,4) \xrightarrow{\tau} (3,0)$$

$$(1,1) \xrightarrow{\tau} (2,1) \qquad\qquad (1,3) \xrightarrow{\tau} (1,0)$$

$$= (s_2, z_2) \qquad\qquad\qquad = (s'_2, z'_2)$$

and since $z_2 \neq z'_2$ we have $3 \nsim 4$. Arguments of a similar nature show that $3 \nsim 1$, $3 \nsim 2$, $3 \nsim 5$; that is, 3 is equivalent only to itself. Similarly, states 1 and 4 are equivalent only to themselves. We have said that $5 \sim 2$ because each input (0 or 1) has exactly the same effect on the states 5 or 2:

$$(0,5) \xrightarrow{\tau} (4,0) \qquad (1,5) \xrightarrow{\tau} (3,0)$$

$$(0,2) \xrightarrow{\tau} (4,0) \qquad (1,2) \xrightarrow{\tau} (3,0)$$

Thus, input sequences of length 1 do not distinguish between states 5 and 2; and sequences of longer length could not do so either because, after the first input of such a sequence, the machine is in the same state regardless of the state in which it started. Thus, T is partitioned by $\sim$ into nonoverlapping classes, which we exhibit in the form

$$\pi = \{\overline{1}; \overline{2,5}; \overline{3}; \overline{4}\}$$

where π is a partition (in the sense of Sec. 0.7) of T. Note that states 5 and 2 have identical rows in the flow table of N:

S	x 0	1
1	(5,0)	(2,1)
2	(4,0)	(3,0)
3	(1,0)	(1,0)
4	(1,0)	(3,0)
5	(4,0)	(3,0)

This condition is sufficient, but *not* necessary in order that two states be equivalent, for in the machine $P = (U, \mu)$ having the flow table

U	x 0	1
1	(5,0)	(2,1)
2	(4,0)	(3,0)
3	(1,0)	(1,0)
4	(1,0)	(3,0)
5	(4,0)	(6,0)
6	(1,0)	(1,0)

we again have $5 \sim 2$, even though rows 2 and 5 are not identical.

Although rows 2 and 5 are not identical in the machine P of the preceding example, it *can* be said that the machine is transformed from state 2 or state 5 into equivalent (if not identical) states when the same input is applied. (Here, $4 \sim 4$ and $3 \sim 6$.) To phrase this necessary condition for state equivalence, it is convenient to introduce for any n-m c.s.s.m. $M = (S, \sigma)$ the *partial functions*

$$\sigma_1 : B^n \times S \longrightarrow S$$
$$\sigma_2 : B^n \times S \longrightarrow B^m$$

defined in such a way that for each $x \in B^n$ and $s \in S$ we have

$$\sigma(x,s) = (\sigma_1(x,s), \sigma_2(x,s)) \tag{5.2}$$

EXAMPLE 5.6

For the machine $P = (U, \mu)$ of Example 5.5, we have the partial functions μ_1 and μ_2 as shown alongside $\mu: B \times S \longrightarrow S \times B$:

$$(0,1) \longrightarrow 5 \qquad (0,1) \longrightarrow 0 \qquad (0,1) \longrightarrow (5,0)$$
$$(0,2) \longrightarrow 4 \qquad (0,2) \longrightarrow 0 \qquad (0,2) \longrightarrow (4,0)$$
$$(0,3) \longrightarrow 1 \qquad (0,3) \longrightarrow 0 \qquad (0,3) \longrightarrow (1,0)$$
$$(0,4) \longrightarrow 1 \qquad (0,4) \longrightarrow 0 \qquad (0,4) \longrightarrow (1,0)$$
$$(0,5) \longrightarrow 4 \qquad (0,5) \longrightarrow 0 \qquad (0,5) \longrightarrow (4,0)$$
$$(0,6) \longrightarrow 1 \qquad (0,6) \longrightarrow 0 \qquad (0,6) \longrightarrow (1,0)$$
$$\mu_1: (1,1) \longrightarrow 2 \qquad \mu_2: (1,1) \longrightarrow 1 \qquad \mu: (1,1) \longrightarrow (2,1)$$
$$(1,2) \longrightarrow 3 \qquad (1,2) \longrightarrow 0 \qquad (1,2) \longrightarrow (3,0)$$
$$(1,3) \longrightarrow 1 \qquad (1,3) \longrightarrow 0 \qquad (1,3) \longrightarrow (1,0)$$
$$(1,4) \longrightarrow 3 \qquad (1,4) \longrightarrow 0 \qquad (1,4) \longrightarrow (3,0)$$
$$(1,5) \longrightarrow 6 \qquad (1,5) \longrightarrow 0 \qquad (1,5) \longrightarrow (6,0)$$
$$(1,6) \longrightarrow 1 \qquad (1,6) \longrightarrow 0 \qquad (1,6) \longrightarrow (1,0)$$

Lemma 5.2. Let $M = (S, \sigma)$ be an n-m c.s.s.m. with $\sigma: B^n \times S \to S \times B^m$ and let $s \sim s'$. Then, for each $x \in B^n$, we have $\sigma_1(x,s) \sim \sigma_1(x,s')$.

PROOF. Suppose we do not have this result; that is, suppose that there exists an input $x \in B^n$ for which $\sigma_1(x,s) \not\sim \sigma_1(x,s')$ where, according to Eq. 5.2, x would cause transitions

$$(x, s) \xrightarrow{\sigma} (\sigma_1(x, s), z) \qquad (x, s') \xrightarrow{\sigma} (\sigma_1(x, s'), z)$$

(Why have we written $\sigma_2(x,s) = \sigma_2(x,s') = z$?) If $\sigma_1(x,s) \not\sim \sigma_1(x,s')$, there exists an input sequence $\langle x_1, x_2, \cdots, x_k \rangle$ such that

$$(x_1, \sigma_1(x, s)) \xrightarrow{\sigma} (s_1, z_1) \qquad (x_1, \sigma_1(x, s')) \xrightarrow{\sigma} (s_1', z_1')$$
$$(x_2, s_1) \xrightarrow{\sigma} (s_2, z_2) \qquad\qquad (x_2, s_1') \xrightarrow{\sigma} (s_2', z_2')$$
$$\vdots \qquad\qquad\qquad\qquad \vdots$$
$$(x_k, s_{k-1}) \xrightarrow{\sigma} (s_k, z_k) \qquad (x_k, s_{k-1}') \xrightarrow{\sigma} (s_k', z_k')$$

and $z_k \neq z_k'$. Clearly, the input sequence $\langle x, x_1, x_2, \cdots, x_k \rangle$ will contradict the equivalence of s and s'. ∎

Theorem 5.3. (Due to Moore): Corresponding to each n-m c.s.s.m, $M = (S, \sigma)$ is a unique (except for machines obtained from N by renaming the states of T; that is, except for machines that are "isomorphic" to N) n-m c.s.s.m. $N = (T, \tau)$ having the properties
(1) $N \sim M$.
(2) If $P = (U, \mu)$ also satisfies $P \sim M, |T| \leq |U|$.
(3) $t, t' \in T$ implies $t \not\sim t'$.

PROOF. A complete proof of this theorem appears in the aforementioned article by Moore (see Ref. 5-1). For our purposes, it suffices to see how N is derived from the given machine M. The reader will then be able to deduce that N has properties (1), (2), and (3).

Let $\bar{s}_1, \bar{s}_2, \cdots, \bar{s}_r$ be the distinct equivalence classes in S induced by the equivalence relation $\sim$ (cf. Theorem 0.3 and Lemma 5.1). According to the fundamental properties (Lemmas 0.1 and 0.2) of the equivalence classes (cf. Eq. 0.47)

$$\bar{s}_j = \{s \in S;\ s \sim s_j\} \tag{5.3}$$

we have

(a) $s, s' \in \bar{s}_j \Longrightarrow s \sim s'$.

(b) $s \in \bar{s}_j, s' \sim s \Longrightarrow s' \in \bar{s}_j$.

(c) $s \in \bar{s}_j \cap \bar{s}_k \Longrightarrow j = k$.

(d) $s \not\sim s', s \in \bar{s}_j \Longrightarrow s' \notin \bar{s}_j$.

(e) $s \in S \Longrightarrow s \in \bar{s}_j$ for some $j (1 \leq j \leq r)$.

Now let the equivalence classes of S be the states of T; that is, put

$$T = \{\bar{s}_1, \bar{s}_2, \cdots, \bar{s}_r\} \qquad (|T| = r)$$

and define

$$\tau : B^n \times T \longrightarrow T \times B^m$$

in accordance with the following procedure: If $\bar{s}_j \in T$, choose any state $s \in \bar{s}_j$ and for each $x \in B^n$ take

$$\tau(x, \bar{s}_j) = (\overline{\sigma_1(x,s)}, \sigma_2(x,s)) \tag{5.4}$$

We must check that τ is well defined by Eq. 5.4; that is, that our definition does not depend on our choice of a particular $s \in \bar{s}_j$. So suppose s' is another state $s' \in \bar{s}_j$. By (a) we have $s \sim s'$, and according to Lemma 5.2, $\sigma_1(x,s) \sim \sigma_1(x,s')$, so that (b) and (e) imply $\overline{\sigma_1(x,s)} = \overline{\sigma_1(x,s')}$. Now we also have $\sigma_2(x,s) = \sigma_2(x,s')$, for otherwise we would not have $s \sim s'$ (simply apply the sequence $\langle x \rangle$ to see this). Thus,

$$(\overline{\sigma_1(x,s)}, \quad \sigma_2(x,s)) = (\overline{\sigma_1(x,s')};\ \sigma_2(x,s'))$$

showing that τ is well defined. We leave to the reader the task of showing that $N = (T, \tau)$ has the required properties. ∎

Our interest in the *reduced form* $N = (T, \tau)$ of the given machine $M = (S, \sigma)$ can be appreciated when properties (1) and (2) are interpreted. Evidently, it is the machine having fewest states that is indistinguishable from M, so far as input-output experiments are concerned. We have already seen that the number of states (r for N) of a machine is directly related to the number of memory elements required in its implementation; hence, this figure is often taken as a criterion for relative economy. While this criterion is not ideal, in that machines may very well exist which are equivalent to M and have more than r states while their total hardware cost (that of memory elements *and* that of logic circuits) is less than that of the reduced form N, the criterion is generally satisfactory and widely used, and the theory surrounding its use is quite extensive.

5.4 HUFFMAN-MEALY-MOORE REDUCTION

Central to the aforementioned theory is the reduction process, discovered independently by Moore and D. A. Huffman[†] (later refined by G. H. Mealy[‡]) for obtaining the equivalence classes of Lemma 5.1. We know from this lemma that a certain partition exists for the set of states of a given c.s.s.m. From Moore's theorem, we know what to do with this partition, but we have not yet given an effective procedure for obtaining it. This is precisely what the Huffman-Mealy-Moore (HMM) procedure accomplishes.

Let $M = (S, \sigma)$ be an n-m c.s.s.m. with $\sigma : B^n \times S \to S \times B^m$. If $s_0, s_0' \in S$, we say that s_0 is i-equivalent to s_0' (written $s_0 \underset{i}{\sim} s_0'$) if, for each input sequence,

$$\langle x_1, x_2, \cdots, x_i \rangle = \langle x_j \in B^n; 1 \le j \le i \rangle \qquad \text{of length } i$$

we have $z_1 = z_1', z_2 = z_2', \cdots, z_i = z_i'$ in the sequence of transitions

$$(x_1, s_0) \xrightarrow{\sigma} (s_1, z_1) \qquad (x_1, s_0') \xrightarrow{\sigma} (s_1', z_1')$$

$$(x_2, s_1) \xrightarrow{\sigma} (s_2, z_2) \qquad (x_2, s_1') \xrightarrow{\sigma} (s_2', z_2')$$

$$\cdot \qquad\qquad\qquad\qquad \cdot$$
$$\cdot \qquad\qquad\qquad\qquad \cdot$$
$$\cdot \qquad\qquad\qquad\qquad \cdot$$

$$(x_i, s_{i-1}) \xrightarrow{\sigma} (s_i, z_i) \qquad (x_i, s_{i-1}') \xrightarrow{\sigma} (s_i', z_i')$$

In terms of the partial function σ_2, we could state the condition for i equivalence more compactly:

$$\sigma_2(x_j, s_{j-1}) = \sigma_2(x_j, s_{j-1}') \qquad (1 \le j \le i) \tag{5.5}$$

One shows as before that $\underset{i}{\sim}$ is an equivalence relation on S. Upon comparison with our original equivalence relation (cf. Sec. 5.3), we see that

$$s \sim s' \longleftrightarrow s \underset{i}{\sim} s' \qquad \text{for all } i \in Z^+ \tag{5.6}$$

That a stronger result holds for machines having a finite number of states is implied by Lemma 5.4. It is well, however, that we establish a few immediate consequences of the definition of i equivalence before proceeding to its statement. Clearly,

$$s \underset{i+1}{\sim} s' \Longrightarrow s \underset{i}{\sim} s' \tag{5.7}$$

[†]D. A. Huffman, "The Synthesis of Sequential Switching Circuits," *J. Franklin Inst.*, 257 (March and April 1954).

[†]G. H. Mealy, "A Method for Synthesizing Sequential Circuits," *Bell System Tech. J.*, 34 (September 1955).

for every integer $i \in Z^+$ and all $s, s' \in S$. Therefore, when we denote by π_i the partition

$$\pi_i = \{A_{i1}, A_{i2}, \cdots, A_{ip_i}\} \tag{5.8}$$

of S induced (Theorem 0.3) by the equivalence relation $\underset{i}{\sim}$, we necessarily have that π_{i+1} is a refinement (cf. Example 1.6) of π_i for each $i \geq 0$ in the lattice $(\Lambda(S), \geq)$ of Sec. 1.4. Here, $\pi_0 = \{S\} = I$ is the identity partition of that lattice, and we summarize these remarks by writing

$$I = \pi_0 \geq \pi_1 \geq \pi_2 \geq \cdots \geq \pi_i \geq \pi_{i+1} \geq \cdots \geq T = \{\bar{s}_1, \bar{s}_2, \cdots, \bar{s}_r\} \tag{5.9}$$

These successive refinements imply that

$$1 = p_0 \leq p_1 \leq p_2 \leq \cdots \leq p_i \leq p_{i+1} \leq \cdots \leq r = |T| \tag{5.10}$$

The HMM procedure is an iterative procedure that computes in succession the partitions π_i. The lemma we are about to state gives information as to the expected length of this computational procedure.

Lemma 5.4.   (Due to Moore): Let $M = (S, \sigma)$ be a c.s.s.m. whose reduced form $N = (T, \tau)$ has r states. Then, for all $s, s' \in S$,

$$s \sim s' \Longleftrightarrow s \underset{r-1}{\sim} s'$$

PROOF.   For each $i \in Z^+$, let π_i be the partition of Eq. 5.8. Then we are required to show that

$$\pi_{r-1} = T = \{\bar{s}_1, \bar{s}_2, \cdots, \bar{s}_r\} \tag{5.11}$$

Suppose that $s_0 \not\sim s_0'$, but that $s_0 \underset{i}{\sim} s_0'$. Then there exists a finite input sequence (and we choose one of minimum length k) $\langle x_1, x_2, \cdots, x_k \rangle$ for some $k > i$ (since $s_0 \underset{i}{\sim} s_0'$) for which

$$\begin{array}{ll} \sigma(x_1, s_0) = (s_1, z_1) & \sigma(x_1, s_0') = (s_1', z_1') \\ \sigma(x_2, s_1) = (s_2, z_2) & \sigma(x_2, s_1') = (s_2', z_2') \\ \quad\vdots & \quad\vdots \\ \sigma(x_k, s_{k-1}) = (s_k, z_k) & \sigma(x_k, s_{k-1}') = (s_k', z_k') \end{array}$$

and $z_k \neq z_k'$. And it follows that $s_{k-i-1} \underset{i+1}{\not\sim} s_{k-i-1}'$ (use the sequence $\langle x_{k-i}, x_{k-i+1}, \cdots, x_k \rangle$ of length $i + 1$ to see this), while $s_{k-i-1} \underset{i}{\sim} s_{k-i-1}'$ because, otherwise, we would contradict the choice of k. This argument,

$$s_0 \not\sim s_0', s_0 \underset{i}{\sim} s_0' \Longrightarrow s_{k-i-1} \underset{i+1}{\not\sim} s_{k-i-1}', s_{k-i-1} \underset{i}{\sim} s_{k-i-1}'$$

shows that (see Eqs. 5.9 and 5.10)

$$\pi_i > T \Longrightarrow \pi_i > \pi_{i+1} \tag{5.12}$$

or, equivalently,

$$\pi_i > T \Longrightarrow p_{i+1} > p_i \tag{5.13}$$

The converse of Eq. 5.13 is obvious; therefore, using Eqs. 5.9 and 5.10,

$$\pi_i = T \Longleftrightarrow p_{i+1} = p_i \tag{5.14}$$

Thus, our problem ($\pi_{r-1} = T$?) is reduced to that of showing $p_r = p_{r-1}$.

If $r = 1$, we obtain $p_1 = p_0 = 1$ from Eq. 5.10, so suppose that $r > 1$. Then we cannot again have $p_1 = p_0 = 1$, for by Eq. 5.14, this would imply that $\pi_0 = T$, and since $|\pi_0| = 1$, this would contradict our assumption that $r > 1$. Thus, $p_1 \geq 2$, and we can infer, more generally, that either of two cases,

Case 1: $$p_i \geq i + 1 \tag{5.15a}$$

or

Case 2: $$\pi_i = T \tag{5.15b}$$

holds for each integer $i \in Z^+$. We use induction on i as follows: Eq. 5.15 has already been established for $i = 1$, so suppose that for some $i \geq 1$ we have that Eq. 5.15 holds. In case 2 we have $\pi_{i+1} = T$ by Eq. 5.9. In case 1 we have, from Eq. 5.10, either

$$p_{i+1} = p_i \tag{5.15a$'$}$$

or

$$p_{i+1} > p_i \tag{5.15b$'$}$$

But according to Eq. 5.14, Eq. 5-15a$'$ implies that $\pi_i = T$, so that also $\pi_{i+1} = T$ because of Eq. 5.9. And Eq. 5.15b$'$ implies that $p_{i+1} > p_i \geq i + 1$, so that $p_{i+1} \geq (i + 1) + 1$. In any case we have shown that i satisfying Eqs. 5.15a or 5.15b implies that $i + 1$ also satisfies Eq. 5.15, completing the inductive proof.

Now we simply take $i = r - 1$ in Eq. 5.15. Since we are finished if $i = r - 1$ satisfies case 2, assume instead that $p_{r-1} \geq r$. Since we also have $p_{r-1} \leq r$, by Eq. 5.10, we obtain $p_{r-1} = r$. But we already established that this is equivalent to saying that $\pi_{r-1} = T$. ∎

As an aid in describing the HMM reduction process, we define for each $i \in Z^+$ yet another equivalence relation $\underset{\tilde{i}}{\simeq}$ on S. Let

$$\pi_i = \{A_{i1}, A_{i2}, \cdots, A_{ip_i}\}$$

be the partitions of Eq. 5.8. For each fixed $s \in S$, let

$$\gamma_i(s) = \langle \overline{\sigma_1(x, s)}; x \in B^n \rangle \tag{5.16}$$

be the sequence (of length 2^n) of $\underset{\tilde{i}}{\sim}$ classes A_{ij} determined by the *next states* $\sigma_1(x,s)$ for $x \in B^n$. We say, then, that s, s' are *strongly i-equivalent* (written $s \underset{\tilde{i}}{\simeq} s'$) if $s \underset{\tilde{i}}{\sim} s'$ and $\gamma_i(s) = \gamma_i(s')$. Here it is important to recall (cf. Sec. 0.5) that two sequences $\langle y_1, y_2, \cdots, y_m \rangle$ and $\langle y'_1, y'_2, \cdots, y'_m \rangle$ of the same length are equal iff $y_i = y'_i$ ($i = 1, 2, \cdots, m$); that is, it is not enough that they be equal as sets. That $\underset{i}{\simeq}$ is an equivalence relation on S and that

$$s \underset{i}{\simeq} s' \Longrightarrow s \underset{i}{\sim} s' \qquad (i > 0) \tag{5.17}$$

are immediate consequences of the definition of strong i-equivalence. Furthermore, the reader will be able to prove the following lemma, which we leave as an exercise.

Lemma 5.5. For all $s, s' \in S$ and $i \geq 0$,

$$s \underset{i+1}{\sim} s' \Longleftrightarrow s \underset{i}{\simeq} s'$$

(Here, one should take $\underset{0}{\simeq}$ to be the relation: $s \underset{0}{\simeq} s'$ iff $\gamma_0(s) = \gamma_0(s')$, where $\gamma_0(s)$ is the sequence

$$\gamma_0(s) = \langle \sigma_2(x, s); x \in B^n \rangle \tag{5.18}$$

of outputs $\sigma_2(x,s)$ for $x \in B^n$.)

Utilizing the two preceding lemmas, the HMM reduction procedure is quite easy to describe. Suppose $M = (S, \sigma)$ is any n-m c.s.s.m. and let $\tilde{\pi}_i$ denote the partition of S resulting from the equivalence relation $\underset{i}{\simeq}$. Then Lemma 5.5 asserts that

$$\tilde{\pi}_i = \pi_{i+1} \tag{5.19}$$

and this is the key to the iterative process that will yield the desired partition $T = \{\bar{s}_1, \bar{s}_2, \cdots, \bar{s}_r\}$: Beginning with

(1) $\pi_0 = \{S\} = \{A_{01}\}$, the iteration

(2) $$\tilde{\pi}_0 = \pi_1$$
$$\tilde{\pi}_1 = \pi_2$$
$$\cdot$$
$$\cdot$$
$$\cdot$$
$$\tilde{\pi}_{r-2} = \pi_{r-1} = T$$

will deliver the equivalence classes $\bar{s}_1, \bar{s}_2, \cdots, \bar{s}_r$ of the relation $\sim$ in at most $r - 1$ steps (by Lemma 5.4). Of course it may happen that for some $i < r - 1$, we have

(3) $$\tilde{\pi}_i = \pi_{i+1} = \pi_i \tag{5.20}$$

and from Eq. 5.14 we know that in this case,

(4) $$\pi_i = T$$

and T has been found sooner than expected.

EXAMPLE 5.7

Consider the state diagram of Fig. 5.4 for a 1–1 c.s.s.m $M = (S, \sigma)$. The HMM procedure is more easily applied to the flow table

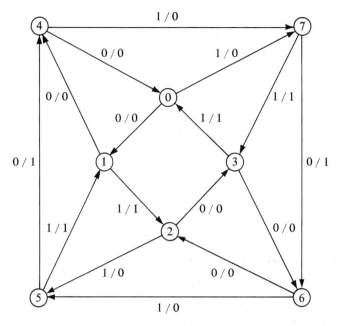

FIGURE 5.4

S	x 0	1
0	(1,0)	(7,0)
1	(4,0)	(2,1)
2	(3,0)	(5,0)
3	(6,0)	(0,1)
4	(0,0)	(7,0)
5	(4,1)	(1,1)
6	(2,0)	(5,0)
7	(6,1)	(3,1)

We begin with step (1),

(i) $\pi_0 = \{S\} = \{\overline{0,1,2,3,4,5,6,7}\}.$
   and then step (2),

(ii)   To compute $\tilde{\pi}_0 = \pi_1$ we first observe from the flow table that (cf. Eq. 5.18)

$$\gamma_0(0) = \langle 0,0 \rangle \qquad \gamma_0(4) = \langle 0,0 \rangle$$
$$\gamma_0(1) = \langle 0,1 \rangle \qquad \gamma_0(5) = \langle 1,1 \rangle$$
$$\gamma_0(2) = \langle 0,0 \rangle \qquad \gamma_0(6) = \langle 0,0 \rangle$$
$$\gamma_0(3) = \langle 0,1 \rangle \qquad \gamma_0(7) = \langle 1,1 \rangle$$

and hence

$$\tilde{\pi}_0 = \overline{\{0,2,4,6; \ \overline{1,3}; \ \overline{5,7}\}} = \pi_1 = \{A_{11},A_{12},A_{13}\}$$

Reinspecting the flow table, we compute (cf. Eq. 5.16)

$$\gamma_1(0) = \langle A_{12},A_{13}\rangle \qquad \gamma_1(4) = \langle A_{11},A_{13}\rangle$$
$$\gamma_1(1) = \langle A_{11},A_{11}\rangle \qquad \gamma_1(5) = \langle A_{11},A_{12}\rangle$$
$$\gamma_1(2) = \langle A_{12},A_{13}\rangle \qquad \gamma_1(6) = \langle A_{11},A_{13}\rangle$$
$$\gamma_1(3) = \langle A_{11},A_{11}\rangle \qquad \gamma_1(7) = \langle A_{11},A_{12}\rangle$$

As an illustration, we have

$$\gamma_1(0) = \langle \overline{\sigma_1(0,0)}, \ \overline{\sigma_1(1,0)}\rangle = \langle \overline{1},\overline{7}\rangle = \langle A_{12},A_{13}\rangle$$

because

$$1 \in A_{12} = \{1,3\}$$
$$7 \in A_{13} = \{5,7\}$$

Thus, by the definition of strong i equivalence,

$$\tilde{\pi}_1 = \overline{\{0,2; \ \overline{1,3}; \ \overline{4,6}; \ \overline{5,7}\}}$$
$$= \pi_2 = \{A_{21},A_{22},A_{23},A_{24}\}$$

Further computation will show, step (3), that

(iii) $\tilde{\pi}_2 = \pi_3 = \pi_2$, so that,
  step 4,

(iv) $\pi_2 = T = \overline{\{0,2; \ \overline{1,3}; \ \overline{4,6}; \ \overline{5,7}\}} = \{\bar{s}_1,\bar{s}_2,\bar{s}_3,\bar{s}_4\} \quad (r = 4)$.

and the HMM process terminates.

The reduced machine $N = (T, \tau)$ thus consists of the set

$$T = \{\bar{s}_1,\bar{s}_2,\bar{s}_3,\bar{s}_4\} = \overline{\{0,2; \ \overline{1,3}; \ \overline{4,6}; \ \overline{5,7}\}}$$

and the mapping τ defined by Eq. 5.4; that is, choosing representatives

$$s_1 = 0, \quad s_2 = 1, \quad s_3 = 4, \quad s_4 = 5$$

of the four equivalence classes, we compute

$$\tau(0,\bar{0}) = \overline{(\overline{\sigma_1(0,0)}, \ \sigma_2(0,0))} = (\bar{1},0)$$
$$\tau(0,\bar{1}) = \overline{(\overline{\sigma_1(0,1)}, \ \sigma_2(0,1))} = (\bar{4},0)$$
$$\tau(0,\bar{4}) = \overline{(\overline{\sigma_1(0,4)}, \ \sigma_2(0,4))} = (\bar{0},0)$$
$$\tau(0,\bar{5}) = \overline{(\overline{\sigma_1(0,5)}, \ \sigma_2(0,5))} = (\bar{4},1)$$
$$\tau(1,\bar{0}) = \overline{(\overline{\sigma_1(1,0)}, \ \sigma_2(1,0))} = (\bar{7},0) = (\bar{5},0)$$
$$\tau(1,\bar{1}) = \overline{(\overline{\sigma_1(1,1)}, \ \sigma_2(1,1))} = (\bar{2},1) = (\bar{0},1)$$
$$\tau(1,\bar{4}) = \overline{(\overline{\sigma_1(1,4)}, \ \sigma_2(1,4))} = (\bar{7},0) = (\bar{5},0)$$
$$\tau(1,\bar{5}) = \overline{(\overline{\sigma_1(1,5)}, \ \sigma_2(1,5))} = (\bar{1},1)$$

Hence, the reduced machine has the state diagram of Fig. 5.5.

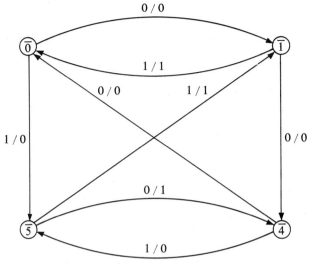

FIGURE 5.5

EXAMPLE 5.8

Let $M = (S, \sigma)$ be a 2–1 c.s.s.m. with flow table

S	x_2x_1 00	01	10	11
a	$(a,0)$	$(d,0)$	$(c,1)$	$(a,0)$
b	$(b,0)$	$(c,0)$	$(c,1)$	$(d,0)$
c	$(a,1)$	$(e,1)$	$(c,0)$	$(d,1)$
d	$(d,0)$	$(d,0)$	$(e,1)$	$(a,0)$
e	$(d,1)$	$(c,1)$	$(e,0)$	$(a,1)$

Then

$$\pi_0 = \{S\} = \overline{\{a,b,c,d,e\}}$$
$$\gamma_0(a) = \langle 0,0,1,0 \rangle$$
$$\gamma_0(b) = \langle 0,0,1,0 \rangle$$
$$\gamma_0(c) = \langle 1,1,0,1 \rangle$$
$$\gamma_0(d) = \langle 0,0,1,0 \rangle$$
$$\gamma_0(e) = \langle 1,1,0,1 \rangle$$
$$\tilde{\pi}_0 = \overline{\{a,b,d;\ c,e\}} = \pi_1 = \{A_{11}, A_{12}\}$$
$$\gamma_1(a) = \langle A_{11}, A_{11}, A_{12}, A_{11} \rangle$$
$$\gamma_1(b) = \langle A_{11}, A_{12}, A_{12}, A_{11} \rangle$$
$$\gamma_1(c) = \langle A_{11}, A_{12}, A_{12}, A_{11} \rangle$$
$$\gamma_1(d) = \langle A_{11}, A_{11}, A_{12}, A_{11} \rangle$$

$$\gamma_1(e) = \langle A_{11}, A_{12}, A_{12}, A_{11} \rangle$$

$$\tilde{\pi}_1 = \{\overline{a,d};\ \overline{b};\ \overline{c,e}\} = \pi_2 = \{A_{21}, A_{22}, A_{23}\}$$

$$\gamma_2(a) = \langle A_{21}, A_{21}, A_{23}, A_{21} \rangle$$

$$\gamma_2(b) = \langle A_{22}, A_{23}, A_{23}, A_{21} \rangle$$

$$\gamma_2(c) = \langle A_{21}, A_{23}, A_{23}, A_{21} \rangle$$

$$\gamma_2(d) = \langle A_{21}, A_{21}, A_{23}, A_{21} \rangle$$

$$\gamma_2(e) = \langle A_{21}, A_{23}, A_{23}, A_{21} \rangle$$

$$\tilde{\pi}_2 = \{\overline{a,d};\ \overline{b};\ \overline{c,e}\} = \pi_3 = \pi_2 = T = \{\bar{s}_1, \bar{s}_2, \bar{s}_3\}$$

Choosing the representatives $s_1 = a$, $s_2 = b$, $s_3 = c$, the reduced machine $N = (T, \tau)$ has the flow table

S	$x_2\,x_1$ 0 0	0 1	1 0	1 1
$\bar{a}$	$(\bar{a},0)$	$(\bar{a},0)$	$(\bar{c},1)$	$(\bar{a},0)$
$\bar{b}$	$(\bar{b},0)$	$(\bar{c},0)$	$(\bar{c},1)$	$(\bar{a},0)$
$\bar{c}$	$(\bar{a},1)$	$(\bar{c},1)$	$(\bar{c},0)$	$(\bar{a},1)$

5.5 GENERATION OF STATE DIAGRAMS

The complete synthesis problem for sequential machines is diagrammatically expressed in Fig. 5.6. So far, we have given an algorithm (the

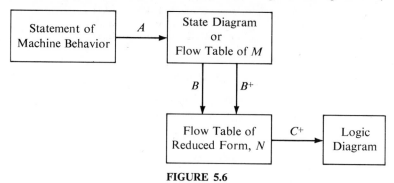

FIGURE 5.6

HMM reduction procedure) for B in case $M = (S, \sigma)$ is a c.s.s.m. We have yet to discuss:

PROBLEM A: The generation of a state diagram or flow table from an English language statement of the desired properties of the machine.

PROBLEM B^+:   The reduction of flow tables of incompletely specified machines.

PROBLEM C^+:   The derivation of a logic circuit (logic elements and memory elements) that economically implements a given (perhaps incompletely specified) flow table.

Ordinarily, Prob. A is dismissed with the rather disheartening statement[†] that success in making such a transition relies heavily on the designer's ingenuity. Certainly there can be no substitute for the experience of a designer in having made such transitions. In order that the reader may quickly develop some facility in this area, we give a few examples here, which highlight features that are common to many design problems.

EXAMPLE 5.9

Often the statement of the machine requirements is such that the machine must always return to some initial "state of anticipation" after receiving a fixed, finite number of inputs. When this is the case, one can construct a state diagram whose topology is that of a branching tree, each new node of which can be labeled with a new state symbol, with the number of branches at each node being equal to the number of inputs possible.

Suppose that a machine is required to receive three binary digits in serial form on a single-input line x and whose output z should indicate (with 1 or 0) whether the three binary digits (with the least significant bit occurring first) correspond to a decimal number that is or is not a multiple of 3. Letting a denote the state of anticipation, the reasoning of the preceding paragraph leads the designer to the state diagram of Fig. 5.7, where it should be observed that, beginning at state a, all paths return to a after three transitions. The machine thereby examines inputs "three at a time," making its decision ($z = 1$ or $z = 0$) only when the last of a sequence $\langle x_1, x_2, x_3 \rangle$ of three inputs has been received. Enumerating all eight possible occurrences in the form of a "truth table,"

x_3 x_2 x_1	z	
0–0 0 0	1	$(0 = 3 \cdot 0)$
1–0 0 1	0	
2–0 1 0	0	
3–0 1 1	1	$(3 = 3 \cdot 1)$
4–1 0 0	0	
5–1 0 1	0	
6–1 1 0	1	$(6 = 3 \cdot 2)$
7–1 1 1	0	

we can appreciate the labels on the transitional arrows. Note that this "truth table" differs from those considered in Chapter 1 in that the information

---

[†]Some hope for improving this situation lies in the theory of "regular expressions"—R. McNaughton and H. Yamada, "Regular Expressions and State Graphs for Automata," *IRE Trans. on Electronic Computers*, EC-9, 1 (March 1960). (See also Ref. 5-4.)

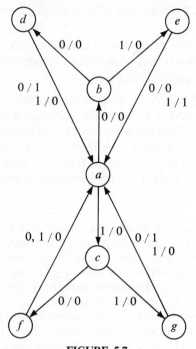

FIGURE 5.7

(x_3, x_2, x_1) is not simultaneously available to the machine. This is why memory elements are required.

From the flow table

S	x 0	1
a	(b,0)	(c,0)
b	(d,0)	(e,0)
c	(f,0)	(g,0)
d	(a,1)	(a,0)
e	(a,0)	(a,1)
f	(a,0)	(a,0)
g	(a,1)	(a,0)

we can immediately conclude that $d \sim g$ (since these two rows are identical). The HMM procedure would show that this is the only pair of equivalent states in S. Thus, we need not be unduly concerned about the number of states we draw, for the HMM procedure will tell us when we have drawn too many.

EXAMPLE 5.10

Suppose we try to devise a state diagram for a machine that differs from that of the preceding example in that it looks at an infinite sequence x and its output is 1 whenever its last three (including its current input) inputs correspond to a decimal number that is a multiple of 3. In so doing, it is convenient to begin at the state 0, which is defined by the condition that two or more consecutive zeros have been received. We may then begin the diagram with the transitional arrow for if three or more consecutive zeros have been received, it is certainly

true that two or more consecutive zeros have been received; and our last three inputs would have been (0,0,0) corresponding to a multiple of 3 (see row 0 of the truth table for Example 5.9). In a similar way, we might postulate the existence of a state 1 in which two or more consecutive 1's have occurred. We then draw an appropriate transitional arrow since 7 is not a multiple of 3. With

these two states alone we have accounted for four of the eight possibilities for the three most recent inputs—those corresponding to the first two and the last two combinations in the truth table of Example 5.9. Letting states 2, 3, 4, 5 represent the other four possibilities, we obtain the state diagram of Fig. 5.8.

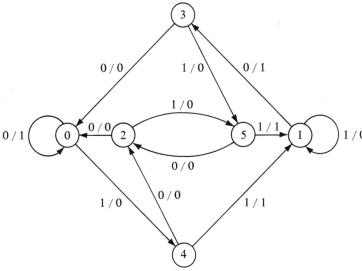

FIGURE 5.8

(Can this state diagram be reduced?) By way of illustration, suppose the most recent three inputs were $\langle x_1, x_2, x_3 \rangle = \langle 1,1,0 \rangle$ so that the machine is in state 3 (see the truth table of Example 5.9). Next suppose that $x = x_4 = 0$. Then we have the transition

$$(0, 3) \xrightarrow{\sigma} (0, 0) \quad \text{or} \quad 3 \xrightarrow{0/0} 0$$

since $\langle x_1, x_2, x_3, x_4 \rangle = \langle 1,1,0,0 \rangle$ and the most recent three inputs are $\langle x_2, x_3, x_4 \rangle$

$= \langle 1,0,0 \rangle$ (1 is not a multiple of 3 and we have had two or more successive zeros). On the other hand, if $x_4 = 1$, $\langle x_2, x_3, x_4 \rangle = \langle 1,0,1 \rangle$, and we write

$$(1,3) \xrightarrow{\ \sigma\ } (5,0) \quad \text{or} \quad 3 \xrightarrow{\ 1/0\ } 5$$

EXAMPLE 5.11

The preceding examples illustrate the importance of deciding upon an "initial" state for the machine, from which the state diagram can be conveniently derived. For machines of the "combination lock" variety, in which an output 1 is to occur whenever a specified "unlocking" sequence has been received, it is often helpful to choose an initial state that cannot, by its definition, be in the midst of an "unlocking" sequence. From this initial state, one can apply the "unlocking" sequence, defining new states along the way and providing a skeleton for the state diagram.

Suppose the specifications for a single-input–single-output machine are such that its output $z = 1$ iff the sequence $\langle 0,1,0 \rangle$ has been its three prior (including its current) inputs.

Evidently we cannot be in the midst of an unlocking sequence if two or more successive ones have occurred as most recent inputs. This observation suggests the initial state:

$$\alpha \equiv \text{two or more successive ones}$$

and the partial diagram

$$\alpha \quad 1/0$$

from which we can apply an unlocking sequence

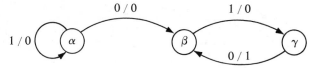

The reason here for returning to β is contained in the definition

$$\beta \equiv \text{one or more successive zeros}$$

Using this skeleton, the state diagram of Fig. 5.9 is close at hand.

If we had not returned to β above, but had defined a new state δ, the

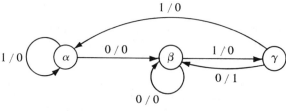

FIGURE 5.9

resulting state diagram would have had more states than necessary. Such redundancy is not serious, however, since superfluous states are eliminated in the HMM reduction process.

5.6 DERIVATION OF LOGIC CIRCUITS

In order that its definition incorporate an allowance for incomplete flow tables, we say that an *n-m-p incompletely specified sequential machine* (*n-m-p* i.s.s.m.) is a pair $M = (S, \sigma)$ in which S is a set with $|S| = p$ and σ is a mapping

$$\sigma: B^n \times S \longrightarrow S^+ \times C^m \qquad (5.21)$$

where

$$C = \{0, 1, I\}$$

and for any set S with $I \notin S$,

$$S^+ = S \cup \{I\}$$

Henceforth, the term *sequential machine* without further qualification will mean "incompletely specified sequential machine" unless otherwise noted. We have introduced the i.s.s.m.'s before discussing Prob. C$^+$ because the solution to the corresponding Problem C for c.s.s.m.'s is only a special case of that for incompletely specified machines. Moreover, we need make no assumption that the machines under consideration be in reduced form.

Let $M = (S, \sigma)$ be an *n-m-p* sequential machine. A 1–1 mapping

$$\alpha: S \longrightarrow B^h$$

for some integer h with $p \le 2^h$ (otherwise α could not possibly be 1–1) is called a *state assignment* (or simply, an *assignment*) for M. If, in addition,

$$2^{h-1} < p \le 2^h \qquad (5.22)$$

so that (cf. Prob. 0.27)

$$h = [\log_2 p] \qquad (5.23)$$

we say that α is a *minimal* state assignment. The reader will quickly see that state assignments have a purpose that is reciprocal to that of encoding functions in analysis—that of effecting the translation of an abstract sequential machine into a logic network having the behavior of that machine.

EXAMPLE 5.12

If $S = \{1,2,3\}$, $\alpha: S \longrightarrow B^3$ as given by

$$1 \xrightarrow{\alpha} (0,1,1)$$

$$2 \xrightarrow{\alpha} (1,0,0)$$

$$3 \xrightarrow{\alpha} (1,0,1)$$

is a state assignment. It is not a minimal assignment because $|S| = p = 3$ and $h = 3$, so that we do not have $2^{h-1} < p$. We would have to take $h = [\log_2 3] = 2$ in order to obtain a minimal assignment. Thus, any 1–1 mapping $\alpha:S \longrightarrow B^2$, say,

$$1 \longrightarrow (0,0)$$
$$2 \longrightarrow (1,0)$$
$$3 \longrightarrow (1,1)$$

is minimal. The reason for this terminology is obvious: When $M = (S, \sigma)$ has p states, *at least* $h = [\log_2 p]$ memory elements will be needed in order that the h memory elements have p or more composite states.

Now if $\sigma:B^n \times S \longrightarrow S^+ \times C^m$ and $\alpha:S \longrightarrow B^h$ is any state assignment, we extend it to a mapping $\alpha:S^+ \longrightarrow C^h$ by taking

$$\alpha(I) = (\overbrace{I, I, \cdots, I}^{h})$$

Then α induces a mapping

$$\sigma': B^n \times B^h \longrightarrow C^h \times C^m \tag{5.24}$$

as given by

$$\sigma'(x, b) = \begin{cases} (\alpha(\sigma_1(x, \alpha^{-1}(b))), \sigma_2(x, \alpha^{-1}(b))) & \text{if } b \in \alpha(S) \\ ((\underbrace{I, I, \cdots, I}_{h}), (\underbrace{I, I, \cdots, I}_{m})) & \text{if } b \notin \alpha(S) \end{cases} \tag{5.25}$$

This mapping σ' simultaneously defines h application functions (cf. Sec. 4.8):

$$f_i: B \times B^t \longrightarrow C \qquad (i = 1, 2, \cdots, h) \tag{5.26}$$

where $t = n + h - 1$, and m output functions

$$z_j: B^{n+h} \longrightarrow C \qquad (j = 1, 2, \cdots, m)$$

in a straightforward (though perhaps not obvious) manner. Using these and the results of Theorem 4.6, one can choose memory elements $(f_1, A_1), (f_2, A_2), \cdots, (f_h, A_h)$ to implement the machine $M = (S, \sigma)$. To see how this comes about, it is best that we consider an example.

EXAMPLE 5.13

Suppose $M = (S, \sigma)$ is to be a 2–2 sequential machine, one of whose outputs $z_1 = 1$ if both inputs $x_1 = x_2 = 1$ *and* x_1 was 1 before x_2 was 1. Similarly, the other output z_2 should be 1 if both $x_1 = x_2 = 0$ *and* x_1 was 0 before x_2 was 0. Additionally, suppose it is known that the two inputs will not change simultaneously.

As further practice in generating state diagrams from word descriptions, we might postulate four states:

$$①\equiv [x_1 = x_2 = 0 \text{ and } x_1 = 0 \text{ first}]$$
$$②\equiv [x_1 = x_2 = 0 \text{ and } x_2 = 0 \text{ first}]$$
$$③\equiv [x_1 = x_2 = 1 \text{ and } x_1 = 1 \text{ first}]$$
$$④\equiv [x_1 = x_2 = 1 \text{ and } x_2 = 1 \text{ first}]$$

with the resulting starting point

for our state diagram. Since inputs change one at a time, by hypothesis, one is led to include two other states, 5 and 6, and the transitions of Fig. 5.10. From each state there is an input combination that never occurs, so that the flow table is incomplete and $M = (S, \sigma)$ is incompletely specified.

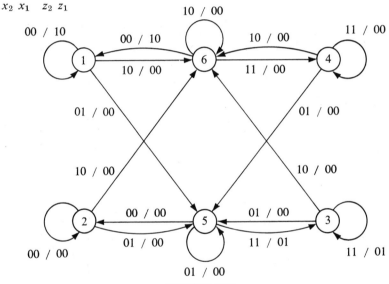

FIGURE 5.10

S	$x_2 x_1$ 0 0	0 1	1 0	1 1
1	(1,(1,0))	(5,(0,0))	(6,(0,0))	(I,(I,I))
2	(2,(0,0))	(5,(0,0))	(6,(0,0))	(I,(I,I))
3	(I,(I,I))	(5,(0,0))	(6,(0,0))	(3,(0,1))
4	(I,(I,I))	(5,(0,0))	(6,(0,0))	(4,(0,0))
5	(2,(0,0))	(5,(0,0))	(I,(I,I))	(3,(0,1))
6	(1,(1,0))	(I,(I,I))	(6,(0,0))	(4,(0,0))

is incomplete and $M = (S, \sigma)$ is incompletely specified.

Now let $\alpha:S \longrightarrow B^3$ be the (minimal) state assignment:

$$S \qquad Q_3\ Q_2\ Q_1$$

$$1 \overset{\alpha}{\longrightarrow} 0\ \ 0\ \ 0$$

$$2 \overset{\alpha}{\longrightarrow} 0\ \ 0\ \ 1$$

$$3 \xrightarrow{\alpha} 0 \quad 1 \quad 0$$

$$4 \xrightarrow{\alpha} 0 \quad 1 \quad 1$$

$$5 \xrightarrow{\alpha} 1 \quad 0 \quad 0$$

$$6 \xrightarrow{\alpha} 1 \quad 0 \quad 1$$

The mapping $\sigma: B^2 \times S \longrightarrow S^+ \times C^2$ of the flow table together with α induces the mapping

$$\sigma': B^2 \times B^3 \longrightarrow C^3 \times C^2$$

of Table 5,1, according to the prescription of Eq. 5.25. By way of illustration, consider the sixth row of that table, in which $x = (x_2, x_1) = (0,0)$ and $b = (q_3, q_2, q_1) = (1,0,1)$. Since $b \in \alpha(S)$ and

$$\alpha^{-1}(b) = 6$$

x_2 x_1	q_3 q_2 q_1	Q_3 Q_2 Q_1	z_2 z_1	k_3 j_3	k_2 j_2	k_1 j_1
0 0	0 0 0	0 0 0	1 0	I 0	I 0	I 0
0 0	0 0 1	0 0 1	0 0	I 0	I 0	0 I
0 0	0 1 0	I I I	I I	I I	I I	I I
0 0	0 1 1	I I I	I I	I I	I I	I I
0 0	1 0 0	0 0 1	0 0	1 I	I 0	I 1
0 0	1 0 1	0 0 0	1 0	1 I	I 0	1 I
0 0	1 1 0	I I I	I I	I I	I I	I I
0 0	1 1 1	I I I	I I	I I	I I	I I
0 1	0 0 0	1 0 0	0 0	I 1	I 0	I 0
0 1	0 0 1	1 0 0	0 0	I 1	I 0	1 I
0 1	0 1 0	1 0 0	0 0	I 1	1 I	I 0
0 1	0 1 1	1 0 0	0 0	I 1	1 I	1 I
0 1	1 0 0	1 0 0	0 0	0 I	I 0	I 0
0 1	1 0 1	I I I	I I	I I	I I	I I
0 1	1 1 0	I I I	I I	I I	I I	I I
0 1	1 1 1	I I I	I I	I I	I I	I I
1 0	0 0 0	1 0 1	0 0	I 1	I 0	I 1
1 0	0 0 1	1 0 1	0 0	I 1	I 0	0 I
1 0	0 1 0	1 0 1	0 0	I 1	1 I	I 1
1 0	0 1 1	1 0 1	0 0	I 1	1 I	0 I
1 0	1 0 0	I I I	I I	I I	I I	I I
1 0	1 0 1	1 0 1	0 0	0 I	I 0	0 I
1 0	1 1 0	I I I	I I	I I	I I	I I
1 0	1 1 1	I I I	I I	I I	I I	I I
1 1	0 0 0	I I I	I I	I I	I I	I I
1 1	0 0 1	I I I	I I	I I	I I	I I
1 1	0 1 0	0 1 0	0 1	I 0	0 I	I 0
1 1	0 1 1	0 1 1	0 0	I 0	0 I	0 I
1 1	1 0 0	0 1 0	0 1	1 I	I 1	I 0
1 1	1 0 1	0 1 1	0 0	1 I	I 1	0 I
1 1	1 1 0	I I I	I I	I I	I I	I I
1 1	1 1 1	I I I	I I	I I	I I	I I

σ'

TABLE 5.1

we obtain, from Eq. 5.25 and the flow table,

$$\sigma'(x, b) = (\alpha(\sigma_1(x, \alpha^{-1}(b))), \sigma_2(x, \alpha^{-1}(b)))$$
$$= (\alpha(\sigma_1((0, 0), 6)), \sigma_2((0, 0), 6))$$
$$= (\alpha(1), (1, 0))$$
$$= ((0, 0, 0), (1, 0))$$

Thus, we have taken $(Q_3, Q_2, Q_1) = (0,0,0)$ and $(z_2, z_1) = (1,0)$ in the sixth row. In contrast, the seventh row has $x = (x_2, x_1) = (0,0)$ and $b = (q_3, q_2, q_1) = (1,1,0)$. Since $b \notin \alpha(S)$, we must, according to Eq. 5.25, write

$$\sigma'(x,b) = ((I,I,I), (I,I))$$

and these are the entries we have written for (Q_3, Q_2, Q_1) and (z_2, z_1) in the seventh row.

The reader should not have difficulty understanding that the first ten columns of Table 5.1 are merely a representation of the flow-table specifications, couched in the new language of the composite binary memory element states rather than that of the machine states, the translation being provided by the state assignment α. The mapping σ' merely formalizes this translation. Having proceeded this far, we are left with a problem that was solved in Chapter 4; that is, after deciding on a particular type (here j-k) of memory element, the three application functions

$$Q_i = f_i : B \times B^4 \longrightarrow C \qquad (i = 1, 2, 3)$$

obtained by properly interpreting the first five columns and (one at a time) one of the next three in Table 5.1, will necessitate the derivation of six incomplete truth tables for the inputs j_i, k_i of the various memory elements. Following the procedure of Sec. 4.8 and using maximal synthesis functions for the j-k flip-flops, we obtain the last six columns of Table 5.1.

Using the techniques of Chapter 3, we interpret these last six columns as being i.s.b.f.'s of the variables of the first five columns, and obtain the minimal forms:

$$\begin{aligned}
k_3 &= x_2 x_1 + \bar{x}_2 \bar{x}_1 & j_3 &= \bar{x}_2 x_1 + x_2 \bar{x}_1 \\
k_2 &= \bar{x}_2 + \bar{x}_1 & j_2 &= x_2 x_1 \\
k_1 &= \bar{x}_2 x_1 + \bar{x}_2 q_3 & j_1 &= \bar{x}_1 q_3 + x_2 \bar{x}_1 \\
z_2 &= \bar{x}_2 \bar{x}_1 \bar{q}_3 \bar{q}_1 + \bar{x}_2 q_3 q_1 & z_1 &= x_2 x_1 \bar{q}_1
\end{aligned} \qquad (5.27)$$

From these it is a simple matter to draw a logic circuit having three j-k memory elements wired with the logic of Eqs. 5.27.

The reader may have noticed in our original flow table the possibility (since unspecified entries may be arbitrarily assigned) of "merging" row 1,4,6, and 2,3,5, to obtain the reduced table

T	$x_2 \, x_1$ 0 0	0 1	1 0	1 1
a	$(a,(1,0))$	$(b,(0,0))$	$(a,(0,0))$	$(a,(0,0))$
b	$(b,(0,0))$	$(b,(0,0))$	$(a,(0,0))$	$(b,(0,1))$

where a replaces $1, 4, 6$, and b replaces $2, 3, 5$. If this had been done, we could have used the state assignment (for *one* memory element Q)

$$\alpha: T \longrightarrow B$$

given by

$$
\begin{array}{cc}
T & Q \\
a \xrightarrow{\alpha} 0 \\
b \xrightarrow{\alpha} 1
\end{array}
$$

The mapping $\tau : B^2 \times T \longrightarrow T^+ \times C^2$ of the reduced flow table, taken with α, gives a map $\tau' : B^2 \times B \longrightarrow C \times C^2$, namely:

x_2 x_1	q	Q	z_2 z_1	k	j
0 0	0	0	1 0	I	0
0 0	1	1	0 0	0	I
0 1	0	1	0 0	I	1
0 1	1	1	0 0	0	I
1 0	0	0	0 0	I	0
1 0	1	0	0 0	1	I
1 1	0	0	0 0	I	0
1 1	1	1	0 1	0	I

Using again a j-k flip-flop and the methods of Chapters 3 and 4, we obtain minimal forms

$$
\begin{array}{cc}
k = x_2\bar{x}_1 & j = \bar{x}_2 x_1 \\
z_2 = \bar{x}_2\bar{x}_1\bar{q} & z_1 = x_2 x_1 q
\end{array}
\tag{5.28}
$$

and the circuit of Fig. 5.11.

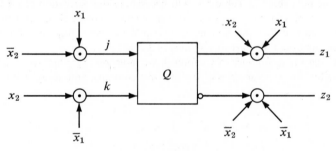

FIGURE 5.11

The reader has only to compare the cost of this circuit with that of one constructed from Eqs. 5.27 to appreciate the need for a satisfactory solution to Prob. B^+—the reduction of incompletely specified flow tables is not generally so obvious as was that in our example, so that quite sophisticated techniques are needed. We will devote the next two sections to the study of this problem.

Another problem in machine synthesis is intimately connected with Prob. C^+, but we have managed to overlook it until now. When $M = (S, \sigma)$ is a given sequential machine, reduced or not, there are a great many 1–1 mappings $\alpha : S \longrightarrow B^h$, even when p is fixed so that α is a minimal assignment. When $|S| = 2^h$ so that α is essentially a permutation (cf. Example

0.13) of S, there are $(2^h)!$ distinct state assignments. (If $h = 3$, this number is 40,320.) Now it is clear that the induced mapping σ' of Eq. 5.25 depends upon our choice of the assignment. Since σ' in turn determines the truth tables for the outputs as well as those for the inputs to memory elements, we see that *the cost of implementing a given sequential machine will depend on the state assignment chosen.* In the face of the large numbers involved, the question is: How can we select an assignment that might be expected to yield an economical circuit realization? This is the so-called *state assignment problem for sequential machines,* and we will undertake to study this question in Sec 5.9.

EXAMPLE 5.14

To illustrate the existence of the state assignment problem, consider the 2-1-4 c.s.s.m. $M = (S, \sigma)$ with the following flow table:

S	$x_2\,x_1$ $0\,0$	$0\,1$	$1\,0$	$1\,1$
a	$(a,1)$	$(b,1)$	$(c,1)$	$(d,1)$
b	$(c,1)$	$(d,1)$	$(a,1)$	$(b,1)$
c	$(b,0)$	$(a,0)$	$(d,0)$	$(c,0)$
d	$(d,0)$	$(c,0)$	$(b,0)$	$(a,0)$

If $\alpha:S \longrightarrow B^2$ is the state assignment,

$$S \qquad Q_2\,Q_1$$
$$a \xrightarrow{\ \alpha\ } 0 \quad 0$$
$$b \xrightarrow{\ \alpha\ } 1 \quad 0$$
$$c \xrightarrow{\ \alpha\ } 1 \quad 1$$
$$d \xrightarrow{\ \alpha\ } 0 \quad 1$$

then the induced mapping $\sigma': B^2 \times B^2 \longrightarrow C^2 \times C^2$ is as depicted in Table 5.2(a) and the use of delay memory elements (cf. Example 4.11) for Q_2 and Q_1 leads to the equations

$$d_2 = Q_2 = \bar{q}_2\bar{x}_2x_2 + \bar{q}_2x_2\bar{x}_1 + q_2\bar{x}_2\bar{x}_1 + q_2x_2x_1$$
$$d_1 = Q_1 = \bar{q}_2\bar{q}_1x_2 + \bar{q}_2q_1\bar{x}_2 + q_2\bar{q}_1\bar{x}_2 + q_2q_1x_2 \qquad (5.29)$$
$$z = \bar{q}_1$$

On the other hand, the assignment β,

$$S \qquad Q_2\,Q_1$$
$$a \xrightarrow{\ \beta\ } 0 \quad 0$$
$$b \xrightarrow{\ \beta\ } 0 \quad 1$$
$$c \xrightarrow{\ \beta\ } 1 \quad 0$$
$$d \xrightarrow{\ \beta\ } 1 \quad 1$$

q_2	q_1	x_2	x_1	Q_2	Q_1	z		q_2	q_1	x_2	x_1	Q_2	Q_1	z
0	0	0	0	0	0	1		0	0	0	0	0	0	1
0	0	0	1	1	0	1		0	0	0	1	0	1	1
0	0	1	0	1	1	1		0	0	1	0	1	0	1
0	0	1	1	0	1	1		0	0	1	1	1	1	1
0	1	0	0	0	1	0		0	1	0	0	1	0	1
0	1	0	1	1	1	0		0	1	0	1	1	1	1
0	1	1	0	1	0	0		0	1	1	0	0	0	1
0	1	1	1	0	0	0		0	1	1	1	0	1	1
1	0	0	0	1	1	1		1	0	0	0	0	1	0
1	0	0	1	0	1	1		1	0	0	1	0	0	0
1	0	1	0	0	0	1		1	0	1	0	1	1	0
1	0	1	1	1	0	1		1	0	1	1	1	0	0
1	1	0	0	1	0	0		1	1	0	0	1	1	0
1	1	0	1	0	0	0		1	1	0	1	1	0	0
1	1	1	0	0	1	0		1	1	1	0	0	1	0
1	1	1	1	1	1	0		1	1	1	1	0	0	0

Part (a)   Part (b)

TABLE 5.2

leads to Table 5.2(b) and the equations

$$d_2 = Q_2 = \bar{q}_1 x_2 + q_1 \bar{x}_2$$

$$d_1 = Q_1 = \bar{q}_2 x_1 + q_2 \bar{x}_1 \qquad (5.30)$$

$$z = \bar{q}_2$$

A comparison of these two sets of equations reveals the strong effect that a state assignment can have on the relative simplicity of the logic circuits required to implement a machine.

5.7 INCOMPLETELY SPECIFIED MACHINES

We have already seen (Example 5.13) that i.s.s.m.'s exist. At first sight, it would appear that the classical theory would be applicable if, difficult though such a task might be, we were to replace exhaustively all unspecified entries by all possible states or outputs, or both, obtaining c.s.s.m.'s for which the HMM reduction procedure could be applied, choosing that reduced machine having fewest states among all reduced machines so obtained. The following example shows that this is not the case.

EXAMPLE 5.15

If we were to asign the unspecified entry of the flow table

	x	
S	0	1
a	(a,I)	$(b,1)$
b	$(c,1)$	$(a,1)$
c	$(b,0)$	$(a,1)$

in each of the two possible ways, we obtain

	x				x	
S	0	1		S	0	1
a	$(a,0)$	$(b,1)$		a	$(a,1)$	$(b,1)$
b	$(c,1)$	$(a,1)$	or	b	$(c,1)$	$(a,1)$
c	$(b,0)$	$(a,1)$		c	$(b,0)$	$(a,1)$

and the reader can verify that neither of these completely specified flow tables may be reduced. (Use the HMM procedure to see this.) Yet, a machine having *two* states *can* be constructed so that it will agree with the behavior of the given flow table when it is specified, for consider the two-state flow table

	x	
T	0	1
B	$(C,1)$	$(B,1)$
C	$(B,0)$	$(B,1)$

in which $B = \{a,b\}$ and $C = \{a,c\}$; that is, we have "merged" the given flow table in accordance with a set system (cf. Example 1.6)

$$\gamma = \overline{\{a,b;\ a,c\}}$$

of S rather than a partition of S, as was the case with the "classical" reduction theory. In so doing, the reader will be able to see that our reduced machine behaves in agreement with the original flow table in the following sense: For each state a, b, or c, there exists a state (B or C) of the reduced machine for which every input sequence (when applied to the two machines after beginning in these states) will give outputs from the reduced machine such as to agree with those of the original machine whenever the latter are specified. Simply take B for b, C for c, and either B or C for a to see this.

The foregoing example illustrates that we cannot directly extend the completely specified theory of sequential machines to the incompletely specified situation. Nevertheless, we will find the classical theory to be a valuable intuitive aid in formulating a more general theory for i.s.s.m. reduction. But it is clear from the way in which unspecified state entries arise (from various input combinations that are assumed never to occur while the machine is in certain states) that we should limit our attention to input sequences which are "applicable" in the following sense: If $M = (S, \sigma)$ is a sequential machine with

$$\sigma: B^n \times S \longrightarrow S^+ \times C^m$$

the input sequence $\langle x_1, x_2, \cdots, x_k \rangle = \langle x_i \in B^n; 1 \leq i \leq k \rangle$ is said to be *applicable to the state* $s \in S$ if the resulting transitions

$$\sigma(x_1,s) = (s_1,z_1)$$
$$\sigma(x_2,s_1) = (s_2,z_2)$$
$$\vdots$$
$$\sigma(x_{k-1},s_{k-2}) = (s_{k-1},z_{k-1})$$

involve only specified state entries, that is, if $s_i \in S$ ($s_i \neq I$) for each $i = 1, 2, \cdots, k - 1$. We do *not* make a corresponding restriction on the z_i. (Why?) In this way, we are at least sure of which state the machine is in when the last input is received.

Now, to replace the concept for equivalence of states in the classical theory, suppose $M = (S, \sigma)$ and $N = (T, \tau)$ are two *n-m* machines and that $s \in S$, $t \in T$. We say that t *covers* s (written $t \geq s$) if each input sequence $\langle x_1, x_2, \cdots, x_k \rangle$ that is applicable to s is applicable also to t, and if in the resulting transitions

$$\sigma(x_1,s) = (s_1,z_1) \qquad \tau(x_1,t) = (t_1,z_1')$$
$$\sigma(x_2,s_1) = (s_2,z_2) \qquad \tau(x_2,t_1) = (t_2,z_2')$$
$$\vdots \qquad\qquad \vdots$$
$$\sigma(x_k,s_{k-1}) = (s_k,z_k) \qquad \tau(x_k,t_{k-1}) = (t_k,z_k')$$

we have $z_i' \subseteq z_i$ ($i = 1, 2, \cdots, k$), with inclusion taken in the partially ordered set C^m. Since this is the case, the outputs from N agree with those of M whenever the latter are specified. We continue by generalizing the concept of machine equivalence, saying that N *covers* M (written $N \geq M$) if for each $s \in S$ there exists a state $t \in T$ with $t \geq s$. Theorem 5.6 asserts that these covering relations are the proper extensions of the equivalence relations that proved to be so important in the completely specified theory. It can be seen that if N and M are c.s.s.m.'s $N \sim M$ iff $N \geq M$ and $N \leq M$.

If $A, A' \in \mathscr{P}(S)$, we say that A *implies* A' (written $A \Longrightarrow A'$) if for some fixed $x \in B^n$ we have

$$A' = \{\sigma_1(x,s) \in S; s \in A\} \tag{5.31}$$

EXAMPLE 5.16

We have $A = \{3,4,5\} \Longrightarrow \{5,1\} = A'$ in the flow table

| | x | |
S	0	1
1	(2,0)	(3,1)
2	(1,1)	(5,0)
A $\begin{cases} 3 \\ 4 \\ 5 \end{cases}$ 3	(5,1)	$(I,1)$
4	$(I,0)$	(I,I)
5	(1,0)	(4,0)

because

$$\{5,1\} = \{\sigma_1(0,s) \in S; s \in \{3,4,5\}\}$$

The impression has been given that the partitions of the classical theory will be replaced by set systems in merging the states of an incompletely specified flow table σ. Among the set systems of S, attention will be focused on those that are σ-closed in the sense that the blocks A_i of the covering

$$\lambda = \{A_1, A_2, \cdots, A_q\}$$

satisfy

PROPERTY 1 $(A_i \Longrightarrow A) \Longrightarrow A \subseteq A_j$ for some $j = 1, 2, \cdots, q$.

PROPERTY 2   For each $i = 1, 2, \cdots, q$ and each $x \in B^n$

$$\prod_{s \in A_i} \sigma_2(x,s) \neq 0$$

with multiplication (intersection) taken in the lattice $(C^m, +, \cdot)$

EXAMPLE 5.17

In the 2-2-5 i.s.s.m $M = (S,\sigma)$ having the following flow table,

| | $x_2\, x_1$ | | | |
S	0 0	0 1	1 0	1 1
1	(3,(0,0))	(5,(1,1))	$(I,(I,1))$	$(1,(I,0))$
2	(3,(0,0))	$(5,(I,I))$	$(I,(I,I))$	$(4,(I,0))$
3	$(2,(I,0))$	(3,(0,0))	(1,(1,0))	(2,(0,0))
4	(2,(0,0))	$(3,(I,I))$	(5,(0,1))	$(I,(I,I))$
5	$(I,(I,I))$	(5,(0,0))	$(1,(1,I))$	$(I,(0,I))$

the set system

$$\lambda = \{\overline{1,2,4};\ \overline{2,3,5}\} = \{A_1,A_2\}$$

of S is σ-closed. To see this, observe that, Property 1 holds:

(i) $A_1 \Longrightarrow \{2,3\} \subseteq A_2$ $A_2 \Longrightarrow \{2,3\} \subseteq A_2$

       $A_1 \Longrightarrow \{3,5\} \subseteq A_2$ $A_2 \Longrightarrow \{3,5\} \subseteq A_2$

       $A_1 \Longrightarrow \{5\} \ \ \subseteq A_2$ $A_2 \Longrightarrow \{1\} \ \ \subseteq A_1$

       $A_1 \Longrightarrow \{1,4\} \subseteq A_1$ $A_2 \Longrightarrow \{2,4\} \subseteq A_1$

and, Property 2 holds:

(ii)
$$\prod_{s \in A_1} \sigma_2((0,0),s) = (0,0)\cdot(0,0)\cdot(0,0) = (0,0)$$

$$\prod_{s \in A_1} \sigma_2((0,1),s) = (1,1)\cdot(I,I)\cdot(I,I) = (1,1)$$

$$\prod_{s \in A_1} \sigma_2((1,0),s) = (I,1)\cdot(I,I)\cdot(0,1) = (0,1)$$

$$\prod_{s \in A_1} \sigma_2((1,1),s) = (I,0)\cdot(I,0)\cdot(I,I) = (I,0)$$

and similarly

$$\prod_{s \in A_2} \sigma_2(x,s) \neq 0 \qquad \text{for all } x \in B^2$$

When taken with the next theorem, this information will imply that M can be reduced ($N \geq M$) to the 2–2–2 machine $N = (T, \tau)$ having flow table

T	$x_2 x_1$ $0\ 0$	$0\ 1$	$1\ 0$	$1\ 1$
A_1	$(A_2,(0,0))$	$(A_2,(1,1))$	$(A_2,(0,1))$	$(A_1,(I,0))$
A_2	$(A_2,(0,0))$	$(A_2,(0,0))$	$(A_1,(1,0))$	$(A_1,(0,0))$

EXAMPLE 5.18

The set system $\lambda = \{\overline{a,b}; \overline{a,c}\}$ of $S = \{a,b,c\}$ is σ-closed if $M = (S,\sigma)$ is the machine of Example 5.15.

EXAMPLE 5.19

If $M = (S,\sigma)$ is any completely specified machine and π is the partition of S resulting from the equivalence relation $\sim$, then π is σ-closed.

Recalling Theorem 5.3, the following result indicates that the σ-closed set systems of S replace the partitions of the completely specified theory.

Theorem 5.6. (Due to Paull-Unger): Corresponding to each n-m i.s.s.m. $M = (S, \sigma)$ is a (not necessarily unique) machine $N = (T, \tau)$ having the properties

(a) $N \geq M$.
(b) If $P = (U, \mu)$ also satisfies $P \geq M$, then $|T| \leq |U|$.

Associated with each such machine $N = (T, \tau)$ is a σ-closed set system $\lambda = \{A_1, A_2, \cdots, A_r\}$ of S with $|\lambda| = r$ minimal among all σ-closed set systems of S. We have $T = \{t_1, t_2, \cdots, t_r\}$ with $t_i \geq s$ for all $s \in A_i$ ($i = 1, 2, \cdots, r$).

Conversely, to each σ-closed set system $\lambda = \{A_1, A_2, \cdots, A_q\}$ of S, there corresponds an n-m-q machine $P = (U, \mu)$ for which $P \geq M$.

PROOF.   A complete proof of this theorem is quite lengthy[†] and we will therefore concentrate instead on its constructive aspect—the method for deriving from a σ-closed set system λ with minimum $|\lambda|$ a machine having properties (a) and (b). This construction will be analogous to that given in lieu of a complete proof of Moore's theorem.

Suppose $\lambda = \{A_1, A_2, \cdots, A_r\}$ is a σ-closed set system of S (that $|\lambda|$ be minimal is really not essential to the construction). Put

$$T = \lambda = \{A_1, A_2, \cdots, A_r\}$$

and define

$$\tau \colon B^n \times T \longrightarrow T^+ \times C^m$$

in accordance with the following procedure (we did it in Example 5.17!): Consider any pair (x, t) with $x \in B^n$ and $t = A_i \in T$.

(i)   If $\sigma_1(x, s) = I$ for each $s \in A_i$, put $\tau_1(x, t) = I$. If $\sigma_1(x, s) \neq I$ for some $s \in A_i$, then examine the states (cf. Eq. 5.31)

$$A_i' = \{\sigma_1(x, s) \in S; s \in A_i\}$$

According to Property 1, we have

$$A_i' \subseteq A_j \qquad \text{for some } j = 1, 2, \cdots, r$$

and thus we put

$$\tau_1(x, t) = A_j$$

(ii)   Take

$$\tau_2(x, t) = \prod_{s \in A_i} \sigma_2(x, s)$$

which, according to Property 2 is a k cell ($k \geq 0$) in C^m.

Now we simply write

$$\tau(x, t) = (\tau_1(x, t), \tau_2(x, t))$$

to complete the definition of the machine $N = (T, \tau)$. ∎

5.8   PAULL-UNGER-GINSBURG REDUCTION

The reduction procedure that replaces HMM in the incompletely specified theory is that (PUG) introduced simultaneously in the afore-mentioned work (see footnote, p. 000) of M. C. Paull and S. H. Unger and

†M. C. Paull and S. H. Unger, "Minimizing the Number of States in Incompletely Specified Sequential Switching Functions," *IRE Trans. on Electronic Computers*, EC-8, 3 (September 1959).

in that of S. Ginsburg.[†] (An earlier, though less complete treatment of the problem is that of D. D. Aufenkamp.[‡]) In the light of Theorem 5.6, interest is centered upon the minimal σ-closed set systems λ of S. Intuitively, one would expect such coverings to contain fewer blocks if the size of the blocks were large. The PUG reduction process exploits this intuitive notion.

We begin by introducing for a given i.s.s.m. $M = (S, \sigma)$ a simplicial complex (cf. Sec. 3.14) denoted by (S, Γ_S) consisting of the set S of states of M and the collection $\Gamma = \Gamma_S$ of simplexes A (subsets of S) defined according to the rule

$$A \in \Gamma \Longleftrightarrow \begin{cases} \text{there exist subsets } A_1, A_2, \cdots, A_q \text{ of } S \\ \text{for which } \lambda = \{A, A_1, A_2, \cdots, A_q\} \text{ is a} \\ \sigma\text{-closed covering of } S \end{cases} \qquad (5.32)$$

(We leave to the reader the task of verifying that (S, Γ_S) is actually a complex; see Prob. 5.30.) The interpretation is clear: A is a simplex of Γ iff there is a machine $N = (T, \tau)$ with $N \geq M$ in which the states of A may be "merged." This is, in fact, our reason for defining the rule (Eq. 5.32) as we have. According to Eq. 3.46, this simplicial complex induces a compatibility relation (we call it $\approx$ rather than $\underset{\Gamma}{\approx}$) on S, namely,

$$s \approx s' \Longleftrightarrow \{s, s'\} \in \Gamma \qquad (5.33)$$

But if we are to exploit the notion that our intuition has suggested, we must be interested in obtaining the collection

$$\gamma = \{A \in \Gamma; \; A \text{ is a basic simplex of } K\} \qquad (5.34)$$

of basic simplexes (cf. Eq. 3.43) of the complex $K = (S, \Gamma_S)$. In this connection, the next theorem is of central importance, particularly when the consequences of Theorem 3.16 are reviewed. We precede its statement with two relatively easy lemmas.

Lemma 5.7. If $A \in \Gamma$ and $A \Longrightarrow A'$, then $A' \in \Gamma$.

PROOF. Suppose $A = A_0 \in \Gamma$. Then, by Eq. 5.32, there exists a σ-closed covering $\lambda = \{A_0, A_1, A_2, \cdots, A_q\}$ of S. Now suppose also that $A \underset{x}{\Longrightarrow} A'$ (where we specifically call attention to an element $x \in B^n$ of Eq. 5.31). Now, according to Property 1, Sec 5.7, $A' \subseteq A_j$ for some $j = 0, 1, \cdots, q$. The diagram

---

†S. Ginsburg, "A Technique for the Reduction of a Given Machine to a Minimal State Machine," *IRE Trans. on Electronic Computers*, EC-8, 3 (September 1959).

‡D. D. Aufenkamp, "Analysis of Sequential Machines II," *IRE Trans. on Electronic Computers*, EC-7, 4 (December 1958).

$$A' \underset{x}{\Longrightarrow} A''$$

$$\cap | \qquad \cap |$$

$$A_j \underset{x}{\Longrightarrow} B \subseteq A_k \qquad (0 \leq k \leq q)$$

shows that the covering $\lambda' = \{A', A_0, A_1, A_2, \cdots, A_q\}$ satisfies Property 1. But $A' \subseteq A_j$ shows also that Property 2 is satisfied; that is,

$$\prod_{s \in A'} \sigma_2(x, s) \supseteq \prod_{s \in A_j} \sigma_2(x, s) \neq 0$$

Hence, λ' is σ-closed and $A' \in \Gamma$ by Eq. 5.32. ∎

Lemma 5.8 Γ is a σ-closed covering of S.

PROOF.   That Property 2 is met by Γ is obvious. So suppose $A_i \in \Gamma$ and $A_i \Longrightarrow A$. Then, by Lemma 5.7, $A \in \Gamma$, which is enough to conclude Property 1. Thus, Γ is σ-closed *if* it is a covering. But for each $x \in S$ we have $\{x\} \in \Gamma$ (why?), so this reservation can be removed. ∎

Theorem 5.9.   (Due to Paull-Unger): Let $M = (S, \sigma)$ be a sequential machine. Then the corresponding simplicial complex (S, Γ_S) is inductive.

PROOF.   Let

$$\Lambda = \{A \in \mathscr{P}(S); A' \subseteq A, A' \in \Gamma^1 \Longrightarrow A \in \Gamma\}$$

be the collection of all subsets A of S, pairs of whose states are compatible. We will show that $\Gamma \cup \Lambda$ is σ-closed; this will prove the theorem, for we need to show (cf. Eq. 3.47) that $A \in \Lambda \Longrightarrow A \in \Gamma$, and we will be able to use $\Gamma \cup \Lambda$ for the required covering λ in Eq. 5.32.

For subsets $A \in \Gamma$ it is obvious that Properties 1 and 2 are satisfied, so we may restrict our attention to subsets $A \in \Lambda$.

(1)   If $A \underset{x}{\Longrightarrow} B$ and $\beta = \{b_1, b_2\} \subseteq B$, there is a 2-element subset $\alpha = \{a_1, a_2\} \subseteq A$ with $\alpha \underset{x}{\Longrightarrow} \beta$. But $\alpha \in \Gamma$ by the definition of Λ, so that $\beta \in \Gamma$ by Lemma 5.7. Since β was any 2-element subset of B, we have shown that $B \in \Lambda$. Thus, $\Gamma \cup \Lambda$ satisfies Property 1.

(2)
$$\prod_{s \in A} \sigma_2(x, s) = \prod_{\alpha \subseteq A} [\sigma_2(x, a_i) \cdot \sigma_2(x, a_j)] \neq 0$$

(cf. Prob. 3.41) with the latter product taken over all 2-element subsets α of A—each product $\sigma_2(x, a_i) \cdot \sigma_2(x, a_j) \neq 0$, by the definition of Λ.

We have now shown that $\Gamma \cup \Lambda$ is σ-closed, and this completes the proof. ∎

In using this result (see the discussion following Theorem 3.16) to obtain the collection γ of basic simplexes, we must have a means for deciding whether or not each pair of states $s, s' \in S$, is compatible ($s \approx s'$). Recalling the process (HMM) for deciding whether or not $s \sim s'$ in a c.s.s.m., and preparatory to the determination of the compatibility matrix $(r_{ij}; \ i > j)$ for the relation $\approx$ on $S = \{s_1, s_2, \cdots, s_p\}$, we assert:

(a) Certain of these elements r_{ij} may be immediately designated 0 by an inspection of rows i and j of the flow table of $M = (S, \sigma)$; for if $\sigma_2(x, s_i) \cdot \sigma_2(x, s_j) = 0$ for some $x \in B^n$, we cannot have Property 2 for $\{s_i, s_j\}$, and of necessity we conclude that $r_{ij} = 0$.

(b) For each pair $\alpha_{ij} = \{s_i, s_j\}$ with $r_{ij} \neq 0$ (at least, not yet 0), we determine the set

$$\gamma_{ij} = \{\{s_u, s_v\} = \beta_{uv} \neq \alpha_{ij}; \ \alpha_{ij} \Longrightarrow \beta_{uv}\} \qquad (5.35)$$

of 2-element subsets of S, and

(c) Put $r_{ij} = 0$ if $r_{uv} = 0$ for some $\beta_{uv} \in \gamma_{ij}$.

Since (c) adds new zeros to the matrix, we repeat (c) until no new zeros are obtained. Finally, we

(d) Put $r_{ij} = 1$ if $r_{ij} \neq 0$ after the repetitions of (c).

By construction, the resulting matrix $(r_{ij}; \ i > j)$ has the property

$$r_{ij} = 1 \Longleftrightarrow s_i \approx s_j \qquad (5.36)$$

that is, it is the compatibility matrix of the relation $\approx$.

EXAMPLE 5.20

Consider the following flow table for a machine $M = (S, \sigma)$:

S	$x_2 x_1$ 0 0	0 1	1 0	1 1
1	(2,I)	(3,0)	(I,I)	(4,I)
2	(3,0)	(5,0)	(I,I)	(I,I)
3	(4,I)	(6,I)	(3,I)	(I,I)
4	(5,1)	(3,0)	(I,I)	(1,I)
5	(I,I)	(6,0)	(I,I)	(I,I)
6	(I,I)	(I,1)	(4,I)	(2,I)

After step (a) of the process, we have the partially completed compatibility matrix

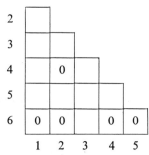

In step (b) we compute

$\gamma_{21} = \{\{3,2\}, \{5,3\}\}$

$\gamma_{31} = \{\{4,2\}, \{6,3\}\}$ $\gamma_{32} = \{\{4,3\}, \{6,5\}\}$

$\gamma_{41} = \{\{5,2\}\}$ $\gamma_{43} = \{\{5,4\}, \{6,3\}\}$

$\gamma_{51} = \{\{6,3\}\}$ $\gamma_{52} = \{\{6,5\}\}$ $\gamma_{53} = \varnothing$ $\gamma_{54} = \{\{6,3\}\}$

                                  $\gamma_{63} = \{\{4,3\}\}$

As a matter of convenience, these pairs are often entered instead on the partially completed compatibility matrix:

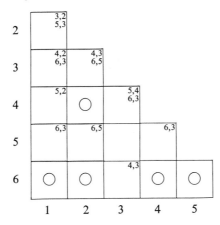

In step (c), we put

$r_{31} = 0$ because $\{4,2\} \in \gamma_{31}$ and $r_{42} = 0$

$r_{32} = 0$ because $\{6,5\} \in \gamma_{32}$ and $r_{65} = 0$

$r_{52} = 0$ because $\{6,5\} \in \gamma_{52}$ and $r_{65} = 0$

Repeating step (c), we put

$r_{21} = 0$ because $\{3,2\} \in \gamma_{21}$ and $r_{32} = 0$

$r_{41} = 0$ because $\{5,2\} \in \gamma_{41}$ and $r_{52} = 0$

The third pass through (c) yields no new zeros, so the process terminates with (d) in the compatibility matrix:

	1	2	3	4	5
2	0				
3	0	0			
4	0	0	1		
5	1	0	1	1	
6	0	0	1	0	0

According to Theorems 3.16 and 5.9, the collection

$$\gamma = \{\overline{1,5};\ \overline{2};\ \overline{3,4,5};\ \overline{3,6}\}$$

of maximal compatibles (as determined by the process given in Sec. 0.10) is also the collection γ of basic simplexes of the complex $K = (S, \Gamma_S)$. Thus, the complex is as depicted in Fig. 5.12.

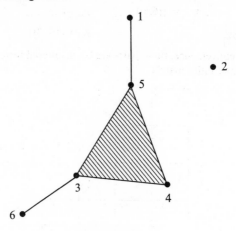

FIGURE 5.12

This example will serve as an illustration of our next theorem, which we precede by an estimate due to Ginsburg. The latter gives bounds for the number r of states in any reduced machine $N = (T, \tau)$ occurring in Theorem 5.6. But the estimate is partially phrased in the language of the *dual complex* $\tilde{K} = (S, \tilde{\Gamma}_S)$ whose collection $\tilde{\Gamma} = \tilde{\Gamma}_S$ of simplexes (subsets of S) is defined by

$$A \in \tilde{\Gamma} \Longleftrightarrow \begin{cases} A = \{s\} \text{ for some } s \in S \text{ or} \\ s \not\approx s' \text{ for all 2-element subsets } \{s, s'\} \subseteq A \end{cases} \tag{5.37}$$

Lemma 5.10. $A \in \tilde{\Gamma} \Longrightarrow r \geq |A|$.

PROOF. Suppose $A \in \tilde{\Gamma}$. Since $r \geq 1$ is obvious, we will suppose that A has more than one element. Now let $\lambda = \{A_1, A_2, \cdots, A_r\}$ be any σ-closed set system of S (not necessarily having minimum $|\lambda| = r$.). Since $s \not\approx s'$ for each pair of elements in A, each element of A must be in a different block of λ. Hence, $r \geq |A|$, as was to be proved. ∎

It is more convenient to visualize $\tilde{\Gamma}$ in its abbreviated form,

$$\tilde{\gamma} = \{A \in \tilde{\Gamma};\ A \text{ is a basic simplex of } \tilde{K}\} \tag{5.38}$$

when stating the corollary:

Corollary 5.11. (Due to Ginsburg): $|\gamma| \geq r \geq \langle \tilde{\gamma} \rangle$.

PROOF.   Half of this proof follows directly from Lemma 5.10, and since we learn from Lemma 5.8 that γ is σ-closed, we have $|\gamma| \geq r$. ∎

Theorem 5.12.   If the collection γ of basic simplexes = maximal compatibles of $K = (S, \Gamma_s)$ is an irredundant covering of S, then

$$|\gamma| = r.$$

PROOF.   If $\gamma = \{A_1, A_2, \cdots, A_t\}$ is irredundant, there exist elements $s_i \in A_i$ $(i = 1, 2, \cdots, t)$ with $s_i \not\approx s_j$ $(1 \leq i, j \leq t)$. Putting $A = \{s_i; 1 \leq i \leq t\}$, we have $A \in \tilde{\Gamma}$ so that $r \geq t$ by Lemma 5.10. But $r \leq t$ by Corollary 5.11. Hence, $r = t = |\gamma|$. ∎

EXAMPLE 5.21

Since $\gamma = \{\overline{1,5}; \overline{2}; \overline{3,4,5}; \overline{3,6}\} = \{A_1, A_2, A_3, A_4\}$ is an irredundant covering of $S = 6^+$ in Example 5.20, we learn from Theorem 5.12 that $r = |\gamma| = 4$; that is, that every σ-closed set system of S has at least four blocks. Thus, the covering γ may be used to merge rows of the flow table and obtain a minimal state machine $N = (T, \tau)$ with $N \geq M$. By the usual process, we derive its flow table:

T	$x_2\,x_1$ $0\,0$	$0\,1$	$1\,0$	$1\,1$
A_1	(A_2,I)	$(A_4,0)$	(I,I)	(A_3,I)
A_2	$(A_3,0)$	$(A_3,0)$	(I,I)	(I,I)
A_3	$(A_3,1)$	$(A_4,0)$	(A_3,I)	(A_1,I)
A_4	(A_3,I)	$(A_4,1)$	(A_3,I)	(A_2,I)

In this particular example, the Ginsburg upper and lower bounds agree, since

$$\tilde{\gamma} = \{\overline{1,2,3}; \overline{1,2,4,6}; \overline{2,5,6}\}$$

(These "maximal incompatibles" are obtained by finding the maximal compatibles of the matrix $(s_{ij}) = (\bar{r}_{ij})$) and $\langle \tilde{\gamma} \rangle = 4 = |\gamma|$.

In general, we are not so fortunate as we were in Examples 5.20 and 5.21. If γ is redundant (it will still be a grouping), we must consider all subgroupings λ (cf. Example 1.6) of γ. Of these, some will be σ-closed; others will not be. We must select a *minimal σ-closed subgrouping* of γ. Also, it may be that $|\gamma|$ is greater than the number p of rows in the original flow table, so that the Ginsburg upper bound is of no use; moreover, the Ginsburg lower bound is not always attainable, so that considerable enumeration may be necessary to prove that one has achieved a *minimal σ-closed subgrouping*. Paull and Unger have constructed a number of pathological examples (see the article cited in footnote, p. 313) that attest to the reality of these complications. But instead of dwelling on these, we prefer to give two more examples, which illustrate the application of our recent theoretical results.

EXAMPLE 5.22

For the flow table

S	$x_2\,x_1$ 0 0	0 1	1 0	1 1
1	$(7,I)$	(I,I)	$(3,0)$	$(6,1)$
2	$(3,0)$	$(6,1)$	(I,I)	(I,I)
3	$(5,1)$	$(1,0)$	(I,I)	(I,I)
4	(I,I)	(I,I)	$(7,1)$	$(5,0)$
5	$(3,0)$	$(4,1)$	(I,I)	(I,I)
6	$(5,1)$	$(7,0)$	$(2,1)$	$(6,0)$
7	$(1,I)$	(I,I)	$(6,1)$	$(5,0)$

we obtain the compatibility matrix

2	1					
3	1	0				
4	0	1	1			
5	1	0	0	1		
6	0	0	0	0	0	
7	0	1	1	0	1	0
	1	2	3	4	5	6

and thus

$$\gamma = \{\overline{6}; \overline{5,7}; \overline{4,5}; \overline{3,7}; \overline{3,4}; \overline{2,7}; \overline{2,4}; \overline{1,5}; \overline{1,2}; \overline{1,3}\}$$

$$\tilde{\gamma} = \{\overline{1,4,6,7}; \overline{2,3,5,6}; \overline{3,5,6}\}$$

Since $|\gamma| = 10 > 7$, the Ginsburg upper bound gives no information. But $\langle \tilde{\gamma} \rangle = 4$ and thus, if we find a σ-closed subgrouping of γ containing four blocks, it is necessarily minimal.

Evidently $\{6\}$ is a member of every σ-closed covering. Since there are six remaining states and there are no 2-simplexes in $K = (S, \Gamma_s)$, the only hope of achieving the lower bound of four blocks lies in finding a σ-closed subgrouping

$$\lambda = \{\overline{6}; \overline{a,b}; \overline{c,d}; \overline{e,f}\}$$

where a, b, c, d, e, f are distinct. From the implications $\{7,5\} \Longleftrightarrow \{1,3\}$ together with the fact that $\{2,4\}$ implies no 2-element subsets, we obtain the σ-closed subgrouping $\lambda = \{\overline{6}; \overline{5,7}; \overline{1,3}; \overline{2,4}\}$ and the estimate of Ginsburg gives a proof of its minimality.

EXAMPLE 5.23

For the flow table

S	x	
	0	1
a	$(I,0)$	(f,I)
b	(f,I)	(I,I)
c	(I,I)	$(I,0)$
d	$(e,1)$	(c,I)
e	(I,I)	(d,I)
f	$(I,0)$	(I,I)

we obtain the compatibility matrix

b	1				
c	1	1			
d	0	1	1		
e	0	1	1	1	
f	1	1	1	0	1
	a	b	c	d	e

and thus

$$\gamma = \overline{\{a,b,c,f;\ b,c,d,e;\ b,c,e,f\}} \qquad |\gamma| = 3$$
$$\tilde{\gamma} = \overline{\{a,d;\ a,e;\ b;\ c;\ d,f\}} \qquad \langle\tilde{\gamma}\rangle = 2$$

The subgrouping

$$\lambda = \overline{\{a,b,c,f;\ d,e\}}$$

is not σ-closed because $\{d,e\} \underset{1}{\Longrightarrow} \{c,d\}$. But if we take

$$\lambda = \overline{\{a,b,c,f;\ c,d,e\}}$$

we obtain a σ-closed (minimal, since $|\lambda| = \langle\tilde{\gamma}\rangle = 2$) subgrouping.

*5.9   PARTITION PAIRS AND REDUCED DEPENDENCY

We begin this discussion by noting in Example 5.14 that for the assignment β, we have Q_2 independent of q_1 and Q_1 independent of q_2, which must certainly have contributed to the relative simplicity of Eqs. 5.30. Assuming for the time being that we are dealing with an (not necessarily reduced) n-m-p completely specified machine $M = (S, \sigma)$, we will attempt to concentrate on those state assignments $\alpha:S \to B^h$ ($p \leq 2^h$) that cause one or more of the application functions (cf. Eq. 5.26)

$$Q_i = f_i: B \times B^t = B^n \times B^h \longrightarrow C$$

to be *independent of* certain variables q_k $(1 \leq k \leq h)$ in the sense that

$$Q_i(b, (b_h, b_{h-1}, \cdots, \overset{k}{0}, \cdots, b_1)) = Q_i(b, (b_h, b_{h-1}, \cdots, \overset{k}{1}, \cdots, b_1)) \tag{5.39}$$

for all $b \in B^n$ and all $(b_h, b_{h-1}, \cdots, \hat{b}_k, \cdots, b_1) \in B^{h-1}$. Any assignment α that has this property for some i and k $(1 \leq i, k \leq h)$ will be called an assignment with *reduced dependency*. Such reductions in dependency will be found to be contingent upon making a judicious choice of *partial assignments* $A \overset{\alpha}{\longrightarrow} c$ (also written $\alpha(A) = c$ and abbreviated (A, c) as if it were an element of $\mathscr{P}(S) \times C^h$)) for subsets $A \subseteq S$ and cells $c \in C^h$ with $\log_2 |A| \leq \theta(c) < h$. Two such partial assignments (A_1, c_1), (A_2, c_2),

$$A_i \overset{\alpha}{\longrightarrow} a_i \qquad\qquad \log_2 |A_i| \leq \theta(c_i) < h \qquad (i = 1, 2)$$

are said to be *compatible* $((A_1, c_1) \approx (A_2, c_2))$ if there exist sets $A_i' \supseteq A_i$ (not necessarily subsets of S) with

(1) $|A_i'| = 2^{\theta(c_i)}$ $(i = 1, 2)$.
(2) $|A_1' \cap A_2'| = 2^{\theta(c_1 \cdot c_2)}$

More generally, a collection $\{(A_1, c_1), (A_2, c_2), \cdots, (A_t, c_t)\}$ of partial assignments

$$A_i \longrightarrow c_i \qquad\qquad \log_2 |A_i| \leq \theta(c_i) < h \qquad (1 \leq i \leq t)$$

are said to be *consistent* (see Prob. 5.31) if there exist sets $A_i' \supseteq A_i$ (not necessarily subsets of S) with

$$\left| \bigcup_{i=1}^{t} A_i' \right| \leq 2^h \tag{5.40}$$

$$\left| \bigcap_{j \in J} A_j' \right| = 2^{\theta\left(\prod_{j \in J} c_j\right)} \qquad \text{for every } J \subseteq t^+ \tag{5.41}\dagger$$

When $t = 2$, the definitions of compatibility and consistency are seen to coincide.

The Hartmanis theorems of the next section establish a close connection between these desirable assignments with reduced dependency and the so-called partition pairs of the given machine. In the lattice $\Lambda(S) \times \Lambda(S)$ (cf. Eq. 0.48, Theorem 1.5, and Theorem 1.9), an element (λ, λ') is called a *partition pair* (PP) of M if (cf. Theorem 0.3)

$$s_i \underset{\lambda}{\sim} s_j \Longrightarrow \sigma_1(x, s_i) \underset{\lambda'}{\sim} \sigma_1(x, s_j) \tag{5.42}$$

for all $x \in B^n$. In words, the definition insists that whenever two states s_i and s_j are in the same block of the partition λ, we have as a consequence that $\sigma_1(x, s_i)$ and $\sigma_1(x, s_j)$ are in the same block of λ' no matter which

----

†Here and in (2) above, it is reasonable to postulate that $|\phi| = 1/2$, since $\theta(0) = -1$ in Sec. 2.2.

input $x \in B^n$ is applied. When (λ, λ) is a partition pair of M, the partition λ is itself called a *partition with the substitution property* (PSP).

EXAMPLE 5.24

Consider the partitions

$$\lambda = \{\overline{a,b};\ \overline{c,d}\}$$
$$\lambda' = \{\overline{a,c};\ \overline{b,d}\}$$

of $S = \{a,b,c,d\}$ in the machine of Example 5.14. Since $a \underset{\lambda}{\approx} b$ and

$$\sigma_1((0,0),a) = a \underset{\lambda'}{\approx} c = \sigma_1((0,0),b)$$
$$\sigma_1((0,1),a) = b \underset{\lambda'}{\approx} d = \sigma_1((0,1),b)$$
$$\sigma_1((1,0),a) = c \underset{\lambda'}{\approx} a = \sigma_1((1,0),b)$$
$$\sigma_1((1,1),a) = d \underset{\lambda'}{\approx} b = \sigma_1((1,1),b)$$

and also

$$\sigma_1(x,c) \underset{\lambda'}{\approx} \sigma_1(x,d) \qquad \text{for all } x \in B^2$$

we conclude that (λ, λ') is a partition pair of M.

Now the partial assignments

$$A = \{a,b\} \xrightarrow{\beta} (0,I) \quad \text{and} \quad B = \{a,c\} \xrightarrow{\beta} (I,0)$$

are compatible for taking $A' = A$ and $B' = B$; we have

$$|A'| = |A| = 2 = 2^{\theta(0,\,I)}, \quad |B'| = |B| = 2 = 2^{\theta(I,0)}$$

and

$$|A' \cap B'| = |\{a\}| = 1 = 2^{\theta((0,\,I)\cdot(I,0))}$$

The reader should see that these partial assignments lead directly to the assignment β chosen in Example 2.14. (Note that these two partial assignments imply a third: $\{a\} \xrightarrow{\beta} (0,0)$. This in turn forces us to write $\{b\} \xrightarrow{\beta} (0,1)$, $\{c\} \xrightarrow{\alpha} (1,0)$, and finally $\{d\} \longrightarrow (1,1)$.) The relationship of the two partial assignments to the partitions λ and λ' should also be noted.

EXAMPLE 5.25

If $S = \{1,2,3,4,5,6,7\}$, the partial assignments

$$A = \{1,2,3,4\} \xrightarrow{\alpha} (1,I,I) = c$$
$$B = \{1,5,6,7\} \xrightarrow{\alpha} (I,1,I) = d$$

are not compatible, for

$$A' \supseteq A, |A'| = 2^{\theta(c)} = 4 \Longrightarrow A' = A$$
$$B' \supseteq B, |B'| = 2^{\theta(d)} = 4 \Longrightarrow B' = B$$

while

$$|A' \cap B'| = |A \cap B| = 1 \neq 2 = 2^{\theta(c\cdot d)}$$

Intuitively speaking, the incompatibility of these two partial assignments is due to the geometric fact that two 2-cells of a 3-cube must intersect in a

1-cell, for otherwise they are disjoint. On the other hand, if $B = \{1,6,7\}$, the two partial assignments would be compatible; take $B' = \{1,2,6,7\}$ to see this.

EXAMPLE 5.26

Consider the collection $\{(A_1,c_1), (A_2,c_2), (A_3,c_3)\}$ of partial assignments for $S = \{a,b,c,d,e,f,g,h\}$ as shown:

$$A_1 = \{a,b,c,d\} \xrightarrow{\alpha} (1,I,I) = c_1$$
$$A_2 = \{a,b,e,f\} \xrightarrow{\alpha} (I,1,I) = c_2$$
$$A_3 = \{a,b,g,h\} \xrightarrow{\alpha} (I,I,1) = c_3$$

It is clear that each pair of partial assignments is compatible, but the three partial assignments are not consistent. To see this, we note that

$$A_i' \supseteq A_i, \quad |A_i'| = 2^{\theta(c_i)} = 2^2 = 4 \Longrightarrow A_i' = A_i \quad (i = 1, 2, 3)$$

so that, taking $J = \{1,2,3\} = 3^+$, we have

$$\left| \bigcap_{j \in J} A_j' \right| = \left| \bigcap_{j=1}^{3} A_j' \right| = |\{a, b\}|$$

$$= 2 \neq 1 = 2^0 = 2^{\theta\left(\prod_{j=1}^{3} c_j\right)} = 2^{\theta\left(\prod_{j \in J} c_j\right)}$$

and thus Eq. 5.41 is not satisfied.

Before we can establish the precise connection between PP's and assignments with reduced dependency, it will be necessary to develop several of the algebraic properties of partition pairs, the first of which we formulate in the following lemma.

Lemma 5.13. Let (λ, λ') be a PP for the c.s.s.m. $M = (S, \sigma)$ and suppose that $\lambda_0 \leq \lambda$ and $\lambda' \leq \lambda_0'$ in the partially ordered set $\Lambda(S)$. Then (λ_0, λ') and (λ, λ_0') are also PP's for M.

PROOF. Suppose, as given, that (λ, λ') is a partition pair for $M = (S, \sigma)$. Then

$$s_i \underset{\lambda_0}{\sim} s_j \Longrightarrow s_i \underset{\lambda}{\sim} s_j \Longrightarrow \sigma_1(x, s_i) \underset{\lambda'}{\sim} \sigma_1(x, s_j)$$

for every $x \in B^n$, showing that (λ_0, λ') is a PP. Similarly, it is shown that (λ, λ_0') is a PP if $\lambda' \leq \lambda_0'$. ∎

Next we demonstrate by a lemma that the partition pairs (λ, λ') on a sequential machine have a lattice structure.

Lemma 5.14. If $M = (S, \sigma)$ is a sequential machine, the set

$$P(S) = \{(\lambda, \lambda'); (\lambda,\lambda') \text{ a PP of } M\} \subseteq \Lambda(S) \times \Lambda(S) \qquad (5.43)$$

forms a sublattice of $\Lambda(S) \times \Lambda(S)$.

PROOF. We must show that the property "(λ, λ') is a PP" is preserved under $+$, $\cdot$ in the lattice $\Lambda(S) \times \Lambda(S)$. So suppose (λ, λ') and $(\gamma, \gamma') \in P(S)$. Using Eq. 1.20,

$$s_i \underset{\lambda \cdot \gamma}{\widetilde{\sim}} s_j \implies \begin{Bmatrix} s_i \underset{\lambda}{\widetilde{\curvearrowright}} s_j \\ \text{and} \\ s_i \underset{\gamma}{\widetilde{\curvearrowright}} s_j \end{Bmatrix} \implies \begin{Bmatrix} \sigma_1(x, s_i) \underset{\lambda'}{\widetilde{\curvearrowright}} \sigma_1(x, s_j) \\ \text{and} \\ \sigma_1(x, s_i) \underset{\gamma'}{\widetilde{\curvearrowright}} \sigma_1(x, s_j) \end{Bmatrix}$$

$$\implies \sigma_1(x, s_i) \underset{\lambda' \cdot \gamma'}{\widetilde{\sim}} \sigma_1(x, s_j)$$

which shows that $(\lambda, \lambda') \cdot (\gamma, \gamma') = (\lambda \cdot \gamma, \lambda' \cdot \gamma') \in P(S)$. Then, using Eq. 1.21,

$$s_i \underset{\lambda + \gamma}{\widetilde{\sim}} s_j \implies \begin{cases} \text{there exist two chain-connected blocks} \\ \{A_i, A_j\} \subseteq \lambda \cup \gamma \text{ in the set } \lambda \cup \gamma \text{ with} \\ s_i \in A_i, s_j \in A_j \end{cases}$$

and this in turn implies that there exists a sequence

$$\langle A_i = A_{(1)}, A_{(2)}, \cdots, A_{(r)} = A_j \rangle$$

of sets of $\lambda \cup \gamma$ and a sequence

$$\langle s_i = s_{(1,2)} \, s_{(2,3)}, \cdots, s_{(r-1,r)} = s_j \rangle$$

of states of S such that

$$s_{(t-1,t)} \underset{\lambda}{\widetilde{\curvearrowright}} s_{(t,t+1)} \quad \text{or} \quad s_{(t-1,t)} \underset{\gamma}{\widetilde{\curvearrowright}} s_{(t,t+1)}$$

for $t = 2, 3, \cdots, r - 1$, and

$$s_{(t-1,t)} \in A_{(t-1)} \cap A_{(t)}$$

$t = 2, 3, \cdots, r$.

Now it follows from the fact that (λ, λ') and (γ, γ') are PP's that

$$s'_{(t-1,t)} = \sigma_1(x, s_{(t-1,t)}) \underset{\lambda'}{\widetilde{\curvearrowright}} \sigma_1(x, s_{(t,t+1)})$$
$$= s'_{(t,t+1)}$$

or

$$s'_{(t-1,t)} = \sigma_1(x, s_{(t-1,t)}) \underset{\gamma'}{\widetilde{\curvearrowright}} \sigma_1(x, s_{(t,t+1)})$$
$$= s'_{(t,t+1)}$$

for all $x = b_n, b_{n-1}, \cdots, b_1) \in B^n$ and for all $t = 2, 3, \cdots, r - 1$. Choosing blocks

$$\langle B_i = B_{(1)}, B_{(2)}, \cdots, B_{(r)} = B_j \rangle$$

from among the union $\lambda' \cup \gamma'$ to satisfy

$$s'_{(t-1,t)} \in B_{(t-1,t)} \cap B_{(t)} \quad (t = 2, 3, \cdots, r)$$

we see that

$$s'_i = s'_{(1,2)} \underset{\lambda' + \gamma'}{\widetilde{\sim}} s'_{(r-1,r)} = s'_j$$

Hence, $(\lambda + \gamma, \lambda' + \gamma')$ is a PP, so that $P(S)$ is definitely a sublattice of $\Lambda(S) \times \Lambda(S)$. ∎

Now if $\lambda \in \Lambda(S)$, we define

$$M(\lambda) = \sum_{(\lambda_\alpha, \lambda) \in P(S)} \lambda_\alpha \qquad (5.44)$$

$$m(\lambda) = \prod_{(\lambda, \lambda_\alpha) \in P(S)} \lambda_\alpha \qquad (5.45)$$

where the sum and product are taken in the lattice $\Lambda(S)$. These definitions would assert that $M(\lambda)$ is the "largest" partition γ for which (γ, λ) is a PP, while $m(\lambda)$ is the smallest partition τ such that (λ, τ) is a PP. The following lemma then shows how these definitions assure the existence of PP's for any sequential machine.

Lemma 5.15. $M(\lambda)$ and $m(\lambda)$ exist for any partition $\lambda \in \Lambda(S)$. Moreover,

$$(M(\lambda), \lambda) \quad \text{and} \quad (\lambda, m(\lambda))$$

are partition pairs.

PROOF. The assertions that

$$(M(\lambda), \lambda) \quad \text{and} \quad (\lambda, m(\lambda))$$

are PP's is an immediate consequence of the preceding lemma unless the sums and products of Eqs. 5.44 and 5.45 were taken over an empty set of indices. But the fact that

$$(0, \lambda) \in P(S) \quad \text{and} \quad (\lambda, I) \in P(S)$$

for any partition λ shows that this is not possible. ∎

*5.10 THE HARTMANIS[†] THEOREMS

We are now in possession of the algebraic machinery necessary for relating the PP's to assignments with reduced dependency. First, we proceed in the direction toward analyzing a machine that is known to have an assignment with reduced dependency. Illustrative of this situation is the machine of Example 5.14 and its assignment β. We showed in Example 5.24 that a partition pair existed for this machine. That this implication is perfectly general is the subject of the following theorem.

Theorem 5.16. (Due to Hartmanis): Let $M = (S, \sigma)$ be an n-m-p c.s.s.m. and $\alpha : S \to B^h$ an assignment with reduced dependency in that Q_i is independent of q_k $(1 \le i, k \le h)$. Then there exists a partition pair (λ, λ') for M in which

$$s \underset{\lambda}{\sim} t \iff \begin{cases} \alpha(s) = (b_h, b_{h-1}, \cdots, b_k, \cdots, b_1) \\ \alpha(t) = (b_h, b_{h-1}, \cdots, \bar{b}_k, \cdots, b_1) \end{cases} \qquad (5.46)$$

for some $(b_h, b_{h-1}, \cdots, \hat{b}_k, \cdots, b_1) \in B^{h-1}$.

†J. Hartmanis and R. E. Stearns, "On the State Assignment Problem for Sequential Machines, II," *IRE Trans. on Electronic Computers*, EC-10, 4 (December 1961).

PROOF.   When α is given with Q_i independent of q_k, define the partition λ of S according to Eq. 5.46. Next define the partition λ' in accordance with

$$s \underset{\lambda'}{\sim} s \Longleftrightarrow \begin{cases} \alpha(s) = (a_h, a_{h-1}, \cdots, a_i, \cdots, a_1) \\ \alpha(t) = (a'_h, a'_{h-1}, \cdots, a'_i, \cdots, a'_1) \end{cases} \tag{5.47}$$

and $a_i = a'_i$. Now let $s \underset{\lambda}{\sim} t$ and consider any input $x = (x, {}_nx_{n-1}, \cdots, x_1) \in B^n$. If we denote $\sigma_1(x, s) = u$ and $\sigma_1(x, t) = v$, and consider the "codes" for s, t, u, v,

$$\alpha(s) = (b_h, b_{h-1}, \cdots, b_k, \cdots, b_1)$$
$$\alpha(t) = (b_h, b_{h-1}, \cdots, \bar{b}_k, \cdots, b_1)$$
$$\alpha(u) = (a_h, a_{h-1}, \cdots, a_i, \cdots, a_1)$$
$$\alpha(v) = (a'_h, a'_{h-1}, \cdots, a'_i, \cdots, a'_1)$$

we have, using Eq. 5.39,

$$a_i = Q_i(x, (b_h, b_{h-1}, \cdots, b_k, \cdots, b_1))$$
$$= Q_i(x, (b_h, b_{h-1}, \cdots, \bar{b}_k, \cdots, b_1)) = a'_i$$

Thus, by Eq. 5.47, we see that $u = \sigma_1(x, s) \underset{\lambda'}{\sim} \sigma_1(x, t) = v$, showing that (λ, λ') is a PP. ∎

More generally, the reader can verify the following corollary.

Corollary 5.17.   Under the hypothesis of Theorem 5.16, excepting that Q_i is independent of $q_{k_1}, q_{k_2}, \cdots, q_{k_\rho} (\rho \geq 1$ and $1 \leq i, k_1, k_2, \cdots, k_\rho \leq h)$, there exists a partition pair (λ, λ') for M in which

$$s \underset{\lambda}{\sim} t \Longleftrightarrow \begin{cases} \alpha(s) \text{ and } \alpha(t) \text{ agree for coordinates} \\ \text{other than those with indices } k_1, k_2, \cdots, k_\rho \end{cases}$$

EXAMPLE 5.27

In analyzing a sequential machine having the transition table (cf. Sec. 5.2)

x	q_3	q_2	q_1	Q_3	Q_2	Q_1	z
0	0	0	0	0	0	0	0
0	0	0	1	0	0	1	1
0	0	1	0	1	0	0	0
0	0	1	1	1	1	1	0
0	1	0	0	0	0	1	1
0	1	0	1	0	1	1	0
0	1	1	0	0	1	1	0
0	1	1	1	1	0	1	1
1	0	0	0	1	0	0	1
1	0	0	1	1	0	0	0
1	0	1	0	1	1	0	0
1	0	1	1	0	1	0	0
1	1	0	0	1	0	0	1
1	1	0	1	1	0	1	1
1	1	1	0	0	0	0	0
1	1	1	1	1	1	1	1

we would obtain, after selecting an encoding function $\epsilon: B^3 \longrightarrow 8^+ = S$, say,

$$(0,0,0) \xrightarrow{\epsilon} 1$$
$$(0,0,1) \xrightarrow{\epsilon} 2$$
$$(0,1,0) \xrightarrow{\epsilon} 3$$
$$(0,1,1) \xrightarrow{\epsilon} 4$$
$$(1,0,0) \xrightarrow{\epsilon} 5$$
$$(1,0,1) \xrightarrow{\epsilon} 6$$
$$(1,1,0) \xrightarrow{\epsilon} 7$$
$$(1,1,1) \xrightarrow{\epsilon} 8$$

the flow table

	x	
S	0	1
1	(1,0)	(5,1)
2	(2,1)	(5,0)
3	(5,0)	(7,0)
4	(8,0)	(3,0)
5	(2,1)	(5,1)
6	(4,0)	(6,1)
7	(4,0)	(1,0)
8	(6,1)	(8,1)

Since Q_1 is independent of q_2, that is,

$$Q_1(x,(q_3,0,q_1)) = Q_1(x,(q_3,1,q_1))$$

for all $x \in B$ and all $(q_3,q_1) \in B^2$, we should be able to find a partition pair (λ, λ') for this machine, in which

$$s \overset{\sim}{\lambda} t \Longleftrightarrow \begin{cases} \epsilon^{-1}(s) = (b_3,b_2,b_1) \\ \\ \epsilon^{-1}(t) = (b_3,\bar{b}_2,b_1) \end{cases} \quad \text{for some} \quad (b_3,b_1) \in B^2$$

Evidently Eq. 5.46 tells us that

$$\lambda = \{\overline{1,3}; \overline{2,4}; \overline{5,7}; \overline{6,8}\}$$

is such a partition, and we can use Eq. 5.47 with $i = 1$ to find the corresponding λ'. Thus, $1 \overset{\sim}{\lambda'} 3 \overset{\sim}{\lambda'} 5 \overset{\sim}{\lambda'} 7$ and $2 \overset{\sim}{\lambda'} 4 \overset{\sim}{\lambda'} 6 \overset{\sim}{\lambda'} 8$. The reader should verify that with $\lambda' = \{\overline{1,3,5,7}; \overline{2,4,6,8}\}$, we have a partition pair (λ, λ').

We are, of course, greatly interested in knowing whether or not Theorem 5.16 has a converse, since we are hoping that our partition pairs can detect the existence of assignments with reduced dependency. Fortunately, Hartmanis has shown this to be the case. In his theorem, which follows, we augment the notations $|\lambda|$ and $\langle\lambda\rangle$ of Eqs. 0.41 and 0.42 to include also, when $\lambda \leq \gamma$,

$$|\gamma, \lambda| = \begin{cases} \text{the number of blocks of } \lambda \text{ that are contained} \\ \text{in a block of } \gamma \text{ which contains a maximum} \\ \text{number of } \lambda \text{ blocks} \end{cases} \quad \textbf{(5.48)}$$

Also, a partition γ is said to be *primary* if $|\gamma| = 2$, and a partition pair (λ, λ') is said to be a *primary partition pair* (PPP) if λ' is a primary partition.

EXAMPLE 5.28

If
$$\lambda = \{\overline{1}; \overline{2}; \overline{3,4,5}; \overline{6,7}; \overline{8}\} \leq \{\overline{1,2,6,7}; \overline{3,4,5,8}\} = \gamma$$
we have $|\gamma, \lambda| = 3$, while γ is primary.

Even before stating the Hartmanis theorem, we must explain that its constructive proof shows how the partial assignments are to be realized; therefore, a careful study of the argument is essential to the applications.

Theorem 5.18. (Due to Hartmanis): Let $M = (S, \sigma)$ be an *n-m-p* c.s.s.m. and suppose (λ, λ') is a nontrivial $(\lambda \neq 0)$ PPP for M. Then there exists a (minimal) assignment $\alpha : S \rightarrow B^h$ with reduced dependency in that for some $i (1 \leq i \leq h)$, Q_i is independent of $q_{k_1}, q_{k_2}, \cdots, q_{k_\rho}(1 \leq \rho = h - [\log_2 |\lambda|])$ if

(1) $[\log_2 \langle \lambda' \rangle] = h - 1$,

(2) $[\log_2 |\lambda|] + [\log_2 \langle \lambda \rangle] = h$,

and either

(3a) $\lambda + \lambda' = \lambda'$,
$$[\log_2 |\lambda|] = [\log_2 |\lambda', \lambda|] + 1$$

or

(3b) $\lambda + \lambda' = I$,
$$[\log_2 |\lambda \cdot \lambda'|] + [\log_2 \langle \lambda \cdot \lambda' \rangle] = h$$
$$[\log_2 |\lambda \cdot \lambda'|] = [\log_2 \langle \lambda', \lambda \cdot \lambda'|] + 1$$
$$= [\log_2 |\lambda, \lambda \cdot \lambda'|] + [\log_2 |\lambda|]$$

PROOF. Since (λ, λ') is a PPP, λ' is a primary partition, and we write $\lambda' = \{A_0, A_1\}$. This is sufficient to conclude that in the lattice $\Lambda(S)$, λ' is maximal in the sense that
$$\lambda' \leq \gamma, \quad \lambda' \neq \gamma \Longrightarrow \gamma = I$$

Hence, the two cases

(a) $\lambda + \lambda' = \lambda'$,

(b) $\lambda + \lambda' = I$,

are the only situations that can arise.

Case (a) If $\lambda + \lambda' = \lambda'$, we have $\lambda \leq \lambda'$ from Lemma 1.2, and we choose partial assignments (that they are partial assignments follows from condition (1)):

$$\alpha(A_b) = a_b \quad (b = 0, 1)$$

with (cf. Sec. 2.3)

$$\theta(\alpha(A_b)) = h - 1, \tag{5.49a}$$

$$\alpha(A_0) \| \alpha(A_1). \tag{5.49b}$$

Denoting $\lambda = \{B_1, B_2, \cdots, B_q\}$, we temporarily rename its blocks

$$\lambda = \{B_1, B_2, \cdots, B_q\}$$
$$= \{B_1^{(0)}, B_2^{(0)}, \cdots, B_{q_0}^{(0)}, B_1^{(1)}, B_2^{(1)}, \cdots, B_{q_1}^{(1)}\}$$

(with $q_0 + q_1 = q$) arbitrarily, except for insisting that

$$B_j \subseteq A_b \Longrightarrow B_j = B_k^{(b)} \quad \text{for some } k \ (1 \le k \le q_b)$$

We note that $|\lambda| = q$ and $|\lambda', \lambda| = \max\{q_0, q_1\}$, so that the conditions of (3a) will ensure the existence of 1–1 mappings

$$\tau_b: \{B_k^{(b)}; k = 1, 2, \cdots, q_b\} \longrightarrow B^{[\log_2 q] - 1}$$

for $b = 0, 1$ (we do not claim that these mappings are onto); for we could only fail to find such mappings if for some $b = 0, 1$

$$2^{[\log_2 q] - 1} < q_b$$

But then

$$2^{[\log_2 |\lambda|] - 1} < |\lambda, \lambda'|$$

and

$$[\log_2 |\lambda|] - 1 < \log_2 |\lambda, \lambda'| \le [\log_2 |\lambda, \lambda'|]$$

which contradicts (3a).

Using the mappings τ_b, we can construct partial assignments

$$\alpha(B_j) = b_j \quad (j = 1, 2, \cdots, q)$$

with the properties

$$\theta(\alpha(B_j)) = [\log_2 \langle \lambda \rangle] \tag{5.50a}$$

$$\alpha(B_i) \| \alpha(B_j) \tag{5.50b}$$

$$B_j \subseteq A_b \Longleftrightarrow \alpha(B_j) \subseteq \alpha(A_b) \tag{5.50c}$$

This can be done because we specify one coordinate of the B_j according to Eq. 5.49, so that Eq. 5.50c follows. We then specify $[\log_2 |\lambda|] - 1$ others (in the same coordinates so that we obtain Eq. 5.50b) as determined by $\tau_b(B_j)$, leaving a difference of

$$h - 1 - ([\log_2 |\lambda|] - 1) = h - [\log_2 |\lambda|]$$
$$= [\log_2 \langle \lambda \rangle]$$

(Notice our use of condition (2)) coordinates unspecified; hence, we have Eq. 5.50a.

Having done this, we must check that the total (those of Eqs. 5.49 and those of Eqs. 5.50) collection

$$\{(A_0, a_0), (A_1, a_1), (B_1, b_1), (B_2, b_2), \cdots, (B_q, b_q)\}$$

of partial assignments is consistent. To do this, we choose sets $B'_j \supseteq B_j$ with $|B'_j| = 2^{h - \lceil \log_2 q \rceil} = 2^{\theta(\alpha(B_j))}$ by Eqs. 5.50b; we can choose them to be mutually disjoint because λ is a partition. (The sets B'_j need not be subsets of S.) Then we take

$$A'_b = \bigcup_{B_j = B_k{}^{(b)}} B'_j \qquad (b = 0, 1)$$

and see that in Eq. 5.40,

$$|A'_0 \cup A'_1 \cup B'_1 \cup B'_2 \cup \cdots \cup B'_q| = \left| \bigcup_{j=1}^{q} B'_i \right|$$
$$= q 2^{h - \lceil \log_2 q \rceil}$$
$$= 2^{\log_2 q + h - \lceil \log_2 q \rceil}$$
$$\leq 2^h$$

When we try to verify Eq. 5.41, we need only consider 2-set intersections of the form $A'_b \cap B'_j$ for sets $B_j = B_k^{(b)}$ (for otherwise, it is clear from Eqs. 5.49 and 5.50 that Eq. 5.41 becomes $|\varnothing| = \frac{1}{2} = 2^{\theta(0)}$ in accordance with the footnote for Eq. 5.41). And even then, the necessary equality follows:

$$|A'_b \cap B'_j| = |B'_j| = 2^{\theta(\alpha(B_j))} = 2^{\theta(b_j)} = 2^{\theta(a_b \cdot b_j)}$$

so that we have made consistent partial assignments.

We have yet to show that these partial assignments lead to an assignment with the asserted reduction in variable dependency. Without loss of generality, suppose that Eqs. 5.49 specify the hth coordinate and that Eqs. 5.50 specify, in addition, the coordinates $h - 1, h - 2, \cdots, h - \lceil \log_2 |\lambda| \rceil + 1$. Then we will show that Q_h is independent of the variables $q_1, q_2, \cdots, q_{h - \lceil \log_2 |\lambda| \rceil}$. Consider any variable $q_i (1 \leq i \leq h - \lceil \log_2 |\lambda| \rceil = t)$ and any input $x = (x_n, x_{n-1}, \cdots, x_1)$. Then, for $b \in B$, $Q_h(x, (b_h, b_{h-1}, \cdots, b_t, \cdots, \overset{i}{b}, \cdots, b_1))$ is found by first computing

$$\alpha^{-1}(b_h, b_{h-1}, \cdots, b_t, \cdots, \overset{i}{b}, \cdots, b_1) = s_b$$

Now, if

$$\sigma_1(x, s_b) = s'_b \qquad (5.51)$$

in the flow table, and

$$\alpha(s'_b) = (b_h^{(b)}, b_{h-1}^{(b)}, \cdots, b_1^{(b)})$$

we have

$$Q_h(x, (b_h, b_{h-1}, \cdots, b_t, \cdots, \overset{i}{b}, \cdots, b_1)) = b_h^{(b)}$$

and we are interested to know if $b_h^{(0)} = b_h^{(1)}$. But $s_0 \underset{\lambda}{\frown} s_1$ because of

Eqs. 5.50, and since (λ, λ') is a PP, we have from Eq. 5.51 $s'_0 \sim s'_1$ and Eqs. 5.49 assure us that $b_h^{(0)} = b_h^{(1)}$, so that Q_h is independent of q_i.

Case (b). In case $\lambda + \lambda' = I$, we repeat Eqs. 5.49. Using any 1–1 mapping (why does one exist?) $\tau:\lambda \longrightarrow B^{[\log_2 q]}$, we again take partial assignments as in Eqs. 5.50, but we are here assigning one more coordinate with τ than we did with the mappings τ_b (assuming the same $[\log_2 q]$, of course). We leave to the reader the task of showing that once more we obtain consistent partial assignments and that the variable Q_i specified in Eqs. 5.49 is again independent of $h - [\log_2 |\lambda|]$ variables, namely, q_i together with those unassigned by Eqs. 5.49 and 5.50. ∎

We now compensate for having given only an outline of the proof of case (b), by taking as our first example a machine with PPP satisfying conditions (1), (2), (3b) of Theorem 5.18.

EXAMPLE 5.29

To illustrate this important theorem, consider the 2–1–6 c.s.s.m. $M = (S, \sigma)$, where $S = \{a,b,c,d,e,f\}$ and σ is described by the flow table

S	$x_2\,x_1$ 0 0	0 1	1 0	1 1
a	$(f,0)$	$(c,0)$	$(b,0)$	$(d,0)$
b	$(e,0)$	$(b,0)$	$(d,0)$	$(a,0)$
c	$(b,0)$	$(d,0)$	$(b,0)$	$(f,0)$
d	$(a,0)$	$(b,0)$	$(d,0)$	$(d,0)$
e	$(f,1)$	$(e,1)$	$(b,1)$	$(b,1)$
f	$(c,0)$	$(d,0)$	$(d,0)$	$(a,0)$

The reader will observe that

$$(\lambda, \lambda') = (\{\overline{b,c,f};\ \overline{a,d,e}\},\ \{\overline{a,f};\ \overline{b,c,d,e}\})$$

is a PPP for M. (In the next section, we show how all PPP's for a machine can be computed.) And if $\alpha: S \longrightarrow B^h$ is to be minimal, then we must have

$$h = [\log_2 p] = [\log_2 6] = 3$$

and verifying condition (1),

$$[\log_2 \langle\lambda'\rangle] = [\log_2 4] = 2 = h - 1$$

verifying condition (2),

$$[\log_2 |\lambda|] + [\log_2 \langle\lambda\rangle] = [\log_2 2] + [\log_2 3]$$
$$= 1 + 2 = h,$$

so that Theorem 5.18 may apply. Furthermore we have condition (3b),

$$\lambda + \lambda' = I, \quad \lambda \cdot \lambda' = \{\overline{a};\ \overline{b,c};\ \overline{d,e};\ \overline{f}\}$$
$$[\log_2 |\lambda \cdot \lambda'|] + [\log_2 \langle\lambda \cdot \lambda'\rangle] = [\log_2 4] + [\log_2 2]$$
$$= 2 + 1 = h$$

$$[\log_2 |\lambda \cdot \lambda'|] = [\log_2 4] = 2$$
$$= [\log_2 2] + 1 = [\log_2 |\lambda', \lambda \cdot \lambda'|] + 1$$
$$= [\log_2 2] + [\log_2 2]$$
$$= [\log_2 |\lambda, \lambda \cdot \lambda'|] + [\log_2 |\lambda|]$$

so that Theorem 5.18 implies the existence of an assignment with reduced dependency.

Using Eqs. 5.49, we denote

$$\lambda' = \{\overline{a,f};\ \overline{b,c,d,e}\} = \{A_0, A_1\}$$

and take partial assignments

$$\{a,f\} \xrightarrow{\alpha} (0,I,I)$$
$$\{b,c,d,e\} \xrightarrow{\alpha} (1,I,I)$$

Denoting

$$\lambda = \{\overline{b,c,f};\ \overline{a,d,e}\} = \{B_1, B_2\}$$

we have $q = 2$ and $[\log_2 q] = [\log_2 2] = 1$. Using any 1–1 mapping $\tau : \lambda \to B^{[\log_2 q]} = B$, say

$$B_1 \longrightarrow 0$$
$$B_2 \longrightarrow 1$$

as suggested in the outline of the proof of case (b), we take partial assignments

$$\{b,c,f\} \xrightarrow{\alpha} (I,0,I)$$
$$\{a,d,e\} \xrightarrow{\alpha} (I,1,I)$$

satisfying Eqs. 5.50. The diagram of our partial assignments

$$Q_3\ Q_2\ Q_1$$

$$a \xrightarrow{\alpha} 0\quad 1$$

$$b \xrightarrow{\alpha} 1\quad 0$$

$$c \xrightarrow{\alpha} 1\quad 0$$

$$d \xrightarrow{\alpha} 1\quad 1$$

$$e \xrightarrow{\alpha} 1\quad 1$$

$$f \xrightarrow{\alpha} 0\quad 0$$

shows that the blocks of $\lambda \cdot \lambda' = \{\overline{a};\ \overline{b,c};\ \overline{d,e};\ \overline{f}\}$ have been distinguished; that is,

$$Q_3 = 0,\quad Q_2 = 0 \qquad \text{iff } \alpha(s) = f$$
$$Q_3 = 0,\quad Q_2 = 1 \qquad \text{iff } \alpha(s) = a$$
$$Q_3 = 1,\quad Q_2 = 0 \qquad \text{iff } \alpha(s) = b \text{ or } c$$
$$Q_3 = 1,\quad Q_2 = 1 \qquad \text{iff } \alpha(s) = d \text{ or } e$$

Any completion of this diagram which represents an assignment in that it is 1–1 (such completions exist because our partial assignments are consistent) will have the property: Q_3 is independent of q_3 and q_1. To illustrate, suppose the assignment is completed as follows:

$$
\begin{array}{rccc}
 & Q_3 & Q_2 & Q_1 \\
a \xrightarrow{\alpha} & 0 & 1 & 0 \\
b \xrightarrow{\alpha} & 1 & 0 & 0 \\
c \xrightarrow{\alpha} & 1 & 0 & 1 \\
d \xrightarrow{\alpha} & 1 & 1 & 0 \\
e \xrightarrow{\alpha} & 1 & 1 & 1 \\
f \xrightarrow{\alpha} & 0 & 0 & 0
\end{array}
$$

Then the flow table for $M = (S, \sigma)$ is transformed into the application functions shown in the truth tables of Table 5.3.

Computing $Q_3 = Q_3(q_3, q_2, q_1, x_2, x_1)$ according to the methods of Chapter 3, we find

$$Q_3 = \bar{q}_2 \bar{x}_2 + \bar{q}_2 \bar{x}_1 + q_2 x_2 + q_2 x_1$$

so that Q_3 is indeed independent of q_3 and q_1.

EXAMPLE 5.30

For the same machine as that in Example 5.29,

$$(\lambda, \lambda') = (\{\overline{a,e};\ \overline{b,f};\ \overline{c};\ \overline{d}\},\ \{\overline{a,c,e};\ \overline{b,d,f}\})$$

is also a PPP. And the reader can verify that conditions (1), (2), (3a) of Theorem 5.18 are satisfied. In agreement with Eqs. 5.49, we take partial assignments

$$\{a,c,e\} \longrightarrow (0,I,I)$$
$$\{b,d,f\} \longrightarrow (1,I,I)$$

Now denoting

$$\lambda' = \{\overline{a,c,e};\ \overline{b,d,f}\} = \{A_0, A_1\}$$

we write

$$\lambda = \{\overline{a,e};\ \overline{b,f};\ \overline{c};\ \overline{d}\} = \{B_1^{(0)},\ B_1^{(1)},\ B_2^{(0)},\ B_2^{(1)}\}$$

and choose 1–1 mappings $\tau_b: \{B_k^{(b)}\} \longrightarrow B^{[\log_2 q]-1} = B$,

$$
\begin{array}{ll}
\{a,e\} = B_1^{(0)} \xrightarrow{\tau_0} 0 & \{b,f\} \xrightarrow{\tau_1} 0 \\
\{c\} = B_2^{(0)} \xrightarrow{\tau_0} 1 & \{d\} \xrightarrow{\tau_1} 1
\end{array}
$$

for use in making partial assignments

$$
\begin{array}{l}
\{a,e\} \xrightarrow{\alpha} (0,0,I) \\
\{b,f\} \xrightarrow{\alpha} (1,0,I) \\
\{c\} \xrightarrow{\alpha} (0,1,I) \\
\{d\} \xrightarrow{\alpha} (1,1,I)
\end{array}
$$

q_3	q_2	q_1	x_2	x_1	Q_3	Q_2	Q_1	z
0	0	0	0	0	1	0	1	0
0	0	0	0	1	1	1	0	0
0	0	0	1	0	1	1	0	0
0	0	0	1	1	0	1	0	0
0	0	1	0	0	I	I	I	I
0	0	1	0	1	I	I	I	I
0	0	1	1	0	I	I	I	I
0	0	1	1	1	I	I	I	I
0	1	0	0	0	0	0	0	0
0	1	0	0	1	1	0	1	0
0	1	0	1	0	1	0	0	0
0	1	0	1	1	1	1	0	0
0	1	1	0	0	I	I	I	I
0	1	1	0	1	I	I	I	I
0	1	1	1	0	I	I	I	I
0	1	1	1	1	I	I	I	I
1	0	0	0	0	1	1	1	0
1	0	0	0	1	1	0	0	0
1	0	0	1	0	1	1	0	0
1	0	0	1	1	0	1	0	0
1	0	1	0	0	1	0	0	0
1	0	1	0	1	1	1	0	0
1	0	1	1	0	1	0	0	0
1	0	1	1	1	0	0	0	0
1	1	0	0	0	0	1	0	0
1	1	0	0	1	1	0	0	0
1	1	0	1	0	1	1	0	0
1	1	0	1	1	1	1	0	0
1	1	1	0	0	0	0	0	1
1	1	1	0	1	1	1	1	1
1	1	1	1	0	1	0	0	1
1	1	1	1	1	1	0	0	1

TABLE 5.3

which satisfy the conditions of Eq. 5.50. The reader can complete the diagram

$$Q_3 \; Q_2 \; Q_1$$

$$a \xrightarrow{\alpha} 0 \quad 0$$

$$b \xrightarrow{\alpha} 1 \quad 0$$

$$c \xrightarrow{\alpha} 0 \quad 1$$

$$d \xrightarrow{\alpha} 1 \quad 1$$

$$e \xrightarrow{\alpha} 0 \quad 0$$

$$f \xrightarrow{\alpha} 1 \quad 0$$

in such a way that an assignment results for which Q_3 is independent of q_1.

In concluding this section, we wish to point out that when a non-trivial partition pair (λ, λ') exists for a sequential machine M, it is not necessary that conditions (1), (2), and (3) of Theorem 5.18 hold in order that M possess an assignment with reduced dependency. These conditions are meant only to ensure that a minimal ($h = [\log_2 p]$) such assignment exist. If one is willing to consider assignments involving more than the minimal number of variables, Theorem 5.18 can be altered appropriately.

*5.11 COMPUTATION OF PARTITION PAIRS

Using the definition of partition pair together with Lemmas 5.13 and 5.15 and Theorem 5.18, we now describe a procedure that can be used for obtaining all PPP (λ, λ') leading to assignments with reduced dependency. If $M = (S, \sigma)$, where $S = \{s_1, s_2, \cdots, s_p\}$, the procedure involves the partitions

$$\lambda_{ij} = \{\overline{s_i, s_j}; \bar{s}_1; \bar{s}_2; \cdots \hat{s}_i; \cdots \hat{s}_j; \cdots \bar{s}_p\} \tag{5.52}$$

where $i < j$. *Note*: Interchangeable with this notation λ_{ij} will be the symbol $\lambda_{s_i s_j}$ and similarly with λ'_{ij} in the procedure that follows:

(1) Compute $m(\lambda_{ij})$ for all $1 \leq i < j \leq p$ (cf. Eq. 5.45).
(2) List all primary partitions $\lambda' = \lambda'_{ij} \geq m(\lambda_{ij})$ for which $[\log_2 \langle \lambda' \rangle]$ $= h - 1$ (condition (1) of Theorem 5.18), where $h = [\log_2 p]$.
(3) List all partitions (cf. Eq. 5.44)

$$M(\lambda') = \sum_{m(\lambda_{ij}) \leq \lambda'} \lambda_{ij} \tag{5.53}$$

(4) Then each pair (λ, λ') with $0 < \lambda \leq M(\lambda')$ is a PPP. (Cf. Lemmas 5.13 and 5.15.) One may discard (λ, λ') in case λ fails to satisfy condition (2) of Theorem 5.18:

$$[\log_2 |\lambda|] + [\log_2 \langle \lambda \rangle] = h$$

(5) Test the PPP retained in procedure (4) to see whether either of the conditions (3a) or (3b) of Theorem 5.18 are met. Those for which one of the conditions is met represent the PPP's leading to assignments with reduced dependency.

EXAMPLE 5.31

We illustrate this procedure with the machine M of Example 5.29. Using the partitions (see "Note" above)

$$\lambda_{ab} = \{\overline{a,b}; \bar{c}; \bar{d}; \bar{e}; \bar{f}\}$$
$$\lambda_{ac} = \{\overline{a,c}; \bar{b}; \bar{d}; \bar{e}; \bar{f}\}$$
$$\lambda_{ad} = \{\overline{a,d}; \bar{b}; \bar{c}; \bar{e}; \bar{f}\}$$

and so on, we compute:

(i) The list of Table 5.4. For example, consider $m(\lambda_{bd})$. From Eq. 5.45 we have

$$m(\lambda_{ab}) = \{\overline{a,b,c,d};\ \overline{e,f}\} \qquad m(\lambda_{bc}) = \{\overline{a,f};\ \overline{b,d,e};\ \overline{c}\}$$
$$m(\lambda_{ac}) = \{\overline{a};\ \overline{b,c,d,f};\ \overline{e}\} \qquad m(\lambda_{bd}) = \{\overline{a,d,e};\ \overline{b};\ \overline{c};\ \overline{f}\}$$
$$m(\lambda_{ad}) = \{\overline{a,f};\ \overline{b,c,d};\ \overline{e}\} \qquad m(\lambda_{be}) = \{\overline{a,b,d,e,f};\ \overline{c}\}$$
$$m(\lambda_{ae}) = \{\overline{a};\ \overline{b,d};\ \overline{c,e};\ \overline{f}\} \qquad m(\lambda_{bf}) = m(\lambda_{ae})$$
$$m(\lambda_{af}) = \{\overline{a,b,c,d,f};\ \overline{e}\} \qquad m(\lambda_{cd}) = \{\overline{a,b,d,f};\ \overline{c};\ \overline{e}\}$$
$$m(\lambda_{ce}) = \{\overline{a};\ \overline{b,f};\ \overline{c};\ \overline{d,e}\}$$
$$m(\lambda_{cf}) = m(\lambda_{ad})$$
$$m(\lambda_{de}) = m(\lambda_{bc})$$
$$m(\lambda_{df}) = \{\overline{a,b,c,d};\ \overline{e};\ \overline{f}\}$$
$$m(\lambda_{ef}) = \{\overline{a,b,d,e};\ \overline{c,f}\}$$

TABLE 5.4

$$m(\lambda_{bd}) = \prod_{(\lambda_{bd},\ \lambda_\alpha)\,\in\,P(S)} \lambda_\alpha$$

In order that $(\lambda_{bd}, \lambda_\alpha)$ be a PP, we must have (consulting the flow table for M) $e \underset{\lambda_\alpha}{\sim} a,\, a \underset{\lambda_\alpha}{\sim} d$ and hence, by transitivity, $e \underset{\lambda_\alpha}{\sim} d$, so that $\{a,d,e\}$ must be contained in a block of λ_α. Since $\{\overline{a,d,e};\ \overline{b};\ \overline{c};\ \overline{f}\}$ is the smallest partition with this property, we evidently have $m(\lambda_{bd}) = \{\overline{a,d,e};\ \overline{b};\ \overline{c};\ \overline{f}\}$ as listed in Table 5.4. This computation is typical.

(ii)   Since $h = [\log_2 p] = [\log_2 6] = 3$, we are looking for partitions

$$\lambda' = \lambda'_{s_i s_j} \geq m(\lambda_{s_i s_j})$$

with $[\log_2 \langle\lambda'\rangle] = h - 1 = 2$. (This means, of course, that the largest block of λ' should consist of three or four states.) Thus, for certain partitions $(m(\lambda_{af}))$ is an example) found in (i), we will not be able to find any such partitions λ', while for others we may obtain several.

Consider $m(\lambda_{ad}) = \{\overline{a,f};\ \overline{b,c,d};\ \overline{e}\}$. Both $\{\overline{a,e,f};\ \overline{b,c,d}\}$ and $\{\overline{a,f};\ \overline{b,c,d,e}\}$ qualify as partitions λ'_{ad} so we list each of them. Using this sort of reasoning, the reader can verify the list of Table 5.5, which omits duplications.

(iii) The lists of Tables 5.4 and 5.5 are used in obtaining for each λ'_k in (ii) the partition

$\lambda'_1 = \{\overline{a,b,c,d};\ \overline{e,f}\}$	$\lambda'_9 = \{\overline{a,c,f};\ \overline{b,d,e}\}$
$\lambda'_2 = \{\overline{a,e};\ \overline{b,c,d,f}\}$	$\lambda'_{10} = \{\overline{a,d,e};\ \overline{b,c,f}\}$
$\lambda'_3 = \{\overline{a,e,f};\ \overline{b,c,d}\}$	$\lambda'_{11} = \{\overline{a,b,d,e};\ \overline{c,f}\}$
$\lambda'_4 = \{\overline{a,f};\ \overline{b,c,d,e}\}$	$\lambda'_{12} = \{\overline{a,c,d,e};\ \overline{b,f}\}$
$\lambda'_5 = \{\overline{a,b,d};\ \overline{c,e,f}\}$	$\lambda'_{13} = \{\overline{a,d,e,f};\ \overline{b,d}\}$
$\lambda'_6 = \{\overline{a,c,e};\ \overline{b,d,f}\}$	$\lambda'_{14} = \{\overline{a,b,f};\ \overline{c,d,e}\}$
$\lambda'_7 = \{\overline{a,b,d,f};\ \overline{c,e}\}$	$\lambda'_{15} = \{\overline{a,c};\ \overline{b,d,e,f}\}$
$\lambda'_8 = \{\overline{a,c,e,f};\ \overline{b,d}\}$	$\lambda'_{16} = \{\overline{a,b,c,f};\ \overline{d,e}\}$

TABLE 5.5

$$M(\lambda'_k) = \sum_{m(\lambda_{ij}) \leq \lambda'_k} \lambda_{s_i s_j}$$

For example, consider $\lambda'_7 = \{\overline{a,b,d,f}; \overline{c,e}\}$. Since $m(\lambda_{bf}) = m(\lambda_{ae}) \leq \lambda'_7$ and also $m(\lambda_{cd}) \leq \lambda'_7$, while there are no others,

$$M(\lambda'_7) = \lambda_{bf} + \lambda_{ae} + \lambda_{cd} = \{\overline{a,e}; \overline{b,f}; \overline{c,d}\}$$

Similarly, one obtains the other partitions in the list of Table 5.6.

$M(\lambda'_1) = \{\overline{a,b}; \overline{c}; \overline{d,f}; \overline{e}\}$	$M(\lambda'_9) = \{\overline{a}; \overline{b,c}; \overline{d,e}; \overline{f}\}$
$M(\lambda'_2) = \{\overline{a,c}; \overline{b}; \overline{d}; \overline{e}; \overline{f}\}$	$M(\lambda'_{10}) = \{\overline{a}; \overline{b,d}; \overline{c,e}; \overline{f}\}$
$M(\lambda'_3) = \{\overline{a,d}; \overline{b}; \overline{c,f}; \overline{e}\}$	$M(\lambda'_{11}) = \{\overline{a}; \overline{b,d}; \overline{c}; \overline{e,f}\}$
$M(\lambda'_4) = \{\overline{a,d,e}; \overline{b,c,f}\}$	$M(\lambda'_{12}) = M(\lambda'_{10})$
$M(\lambda'_5) = \{\overline{a,e}; \overline{b,f}; \overline{c}; \overline{d}\}$	$M(\lambda'_{13}) = \{\overline{a}; \overline{b,d}; \overline{c}; \overline{e}; \overline{f}\}$
$M(\lambda'_6) = M(\lambda'_5)$	$M(\lambda'_{14}) = \{\overline{a}; \overline{b}; \overline{c,e}; \overline{d}; \overline{f}\}$
$M(\lambda'_7) = \{\overline{a,e}; \overline{b,f}; \overline{c,d}\}$	$M(\lambda'_{15}) = M(\lambda'_{14})$
$M(\lambda'_8) = M(\lambda'_5)$	$M(\lambda'_{16}) = M(\lambda'_{14})$

TABLE 5.6

(iv) The pairs (λ, λ'_k), where $0 < \lambda \leq M(\lambda'_k)$, may not represent partition pairs that satisfy condition (2) in Theorem 5.18. For example,

$$[\log_2 |M(\lambda'_2)|] + [\log_2 \langle M(\lambda'_2) \rangle] = [\log_2 5] + [\log_2 2]$$
$$= 3 + 1 = 4 > 3 = h$$

and the same can be said for all λ with $0 < \lambda \leq M(\lambda'_2)$.

On the other hand, a consideration of such pairs may lead to several partition pairs satisfying condition (2), as is the case with $M(\lambda'_4)$. For each of the partitions

$$\lambda = \{\overline{a,d,e}; \overline{b,c,f}\}, \{\overline{a}; \overline{d,e}; \overline{b}; \overline{c,f}\}, \{\overline{a}; \overline{d,e}; \overline{b,f}; \overline{c}\}$$
$$\{\overline{a}; \overline{d,e}; \overline{b,c}; \overline{f}\}, \{\overline{a,e}; \overline{d}; \overline{b}; \overline{c,f}\}, \{\overline{a,e}; \overline{d}; \overline{b,f}; \overline{c}\}$$
$$\{\overline{a,e}; \overline{d}; \overline{b,c}; \overline{f}\}, \{\overline{a,d}; \overline{e}; \overline{b}; \overline{c,f}\}, \{\overline{a,d}; \overline{e}; \overline{b,f}; \overline{c}\}$$
$$\{\overline{a,d}; \overline{e}; \overline{b,c}; \overline{f}\}$$

we can assert that $0 < \lambda \leq M(\lambda'_4)$ and that condition (2), Theorem 5.18 is satisfied:

$$[\log_2 |\lambda|] + [\log_2 \langle \lambda \rangle] = 3 = h$$

If we let P_i denote the set

$$P_i = \{\lambda; 0 < \lambda \leq M(\lambda'_i), \lambda \text{ satisfies condition (2)}\}$$

we obtain the sets of Table 5.7.

(v) For the nonempty sets P_i of Table 5.7, we have made a notation ((a) or (b)) as to whether, for $\lambda_i \in P_i$, we have

Type (a): $\qquad\qquad\qquad\qquad \lambda_i + \lambda'_i = \lambda'_i$

(b) $P_1 = \{\{\overline{a,b};\ \overline{c};\ \overline{d,f};\ \overline{e}\}\}$

  $P_2 = \phi$

(b) $P_3 = \{\{\overline{a,d};\ \overline{b};\ \overline{c,f};\ \overline{e}\}\}$

(b) $P_4 = \{\{\overline{a,d,e};\ \overline{b,c,f}\},\ \{\overline{a};\ \overline{d,e};\ \overline{b};\ \overline{c,f}\},\ \{\overline{a};\ \overline{d,e};\ \overline{b,f};\ \overline{c}\},$
  $\{\overline{a};\ \overline{d,e};\ \overline{b,c};\ \overline{f}\},\ \{\overline{a,e};\ \overline{d};\ \overline{b};\ \overline{c,f}\},\ \{\overline{a,e};\ \overline{d};\ \overline{b,f};\ \overline{c}\},$
  $\{\overline{a,e};\ \overline{d};\ \overline{b,c};\ \overline{f}\},\ \{\overline{a,d};\ \overline{e};\ \overline{b};\ \overline{c,f}\},\ \{\overline{a,d};\ \overline{e};\ \overline{b,f};\ \overline{c}\},$
  $\{\overline{a,d};\ \overline{e};\ \overline{b,c};\ \overline{f}\}\}$

(b) $P_5 = \{\{\overline{a,e};\ \overline{b,f};\ \overline{c};\ \overline{d}\}\}$

(a) $P_6 = P_5$

(b) $P_7 = \{\{\overline{a,e};\ \overline{b,f};\ \overline{c,d}\},\ \{\overline{a};\ \overline{e};\ \overline{b,f};\ \overline{c,d}\},$
  $\{\overline{a,e};\ \overline{b};\ \overline{f};\ \overline{c,d}\},\ \{\overline{a,e};\ \overline{b,f};\ \overline{c};\ \overline{d}\}\}$

(b) $P_8 = P_5$

(b) $P_9 = \{\{\overline{a};\ \overline{b,c};\ \overline{d,e};\ \overline{f}\}\}$

(b) $P_{10} = \{\{\overline{a};\ \overline{b,d};\ \overline{c,e};\ \overline{f}\}\}$

(b) $P_{11} = \{\{\overline{a};\ \overline{b,d};\ \overline{c};\ \overline{e,f}\}\}$

(b) $P_{12} = P_{10}$

  $P_{13} = P_{14} = P_{15} = P_{16} = \phi$

TABLE 5.7

or

Type (b): $\lambda_i + \lambda_i' = I$

Only for $P_6 = \{\{\overline{a,e};\ \overline{b,f};\ \overline{c};\ \overline{d}\}\}$ and $\lambda_6' = \{\overline{a,c,e};\ \overline{b,d,f}\}$ do we have type (a). Hence, we check that if $\lambda_6 = \{\overline{a,e};\ \overline{b,f};\ \overline{c};\ \overline{d}\}$,

$$[\log_2 |\lambda_6|] = 3 = 2 = 1 + 1 = [\log_2 |\lambda_6', \lambda_6|] + 1$$

so that condition (3a), Theorem 5.18, is satisfied and $(\{\overline{a,e};\ \overline{b,f};\ \overline{c};\ \overline{d}\},\ \{\overline{a,c,e};\ \overline{b,d,f}\})$ is a partition pair leading to an assignment with reduced dependency.

With the other pairs of (iv) yet to be considered, we must test condition (3b) of Theorem 5.18. Evidently we need for this purpose the products $\lambda_i \cdot \lambda_i'$ for $\lambda_i \in P_i$. Omitting any consideration of P_6 as well as P_i for which $P_i = \phi$, we denote the sequence (rather than set, since duplications may occur) of all such intersections by P_i'. This gives Table 5.8.

Deleting partitions λ_i from the P_i and $\lambda_i \cdot \lambda_i'$ from the P_i' that fail to satisfy condition 3(b):

$$[\log_2 |\lambda_i \cdot \lambda_i'|] + [\log_2 \langle \lambda_i \cdot \lambda_i' \rangle] = 3$$

we have remaining

$P_3 = \{\{\overline{a,d};\ \overline{b};\ \overline{c,f};\ \overline{e}\}\} = \{\lambda_3\}$

$P_4 = \{\{\overline{a,d,e};\ \overline{b,c,f}\},\ \{\overline{a,e};\ \overline{d};\ \overline{b};\ \overline{c,f}\},$
  $\{\overline{a,e};\ \overline{d};\ \overline{b,f};\ \overline{c}\},\ \{\overline{a,d};\ \overline{e};\ \overline{b};\ \overline{c,f}\},\ \{\overline{a,d};\ \overline{e};\ \overline{b,f};\ \overline{c}\}\}$
  $= \{\lambda_4,\ \lambda_{4,1},\ \lambda_{4,2},\ \lambda_{4,3},\ \lambda_{4,4}\}$

$$P'_1 = \langle \{\overline{a,b}; \bar{c}; \bar{d}; \bar{e}; \bar{f}\} \rangle$$
$$P'_3 = \langle \{\bar{a}; \bar{b}; \bar{c}; \bar{d}; \bar{e}; \bar{f}\} \rangle$$
$$P'_4 = \langle \{\bar{a}; \overline{b,c}; \overline{d,e}; \bar{f}\}, \{\bar{a}; \bar{b}; \bar{c}; \overline{d,e}; \bar{f}\}, \{\bar{a}; \bar{b}; \bar{c}; \overline{d,e}; \bar{f}\},$$
$$\{\bar{a}; \overline{b,c}; \bar{d}; \bar{e}; \bar{f}\}, \{\bar{a}; \bar{b}; \bar{c}; \bar{d}; \bar{e}; \bar{f}\}, \{\bar{a}; \bar{b}; \bar{c}; \bar{d}; \bar{e}; \bar{f}\},$$
$$\{\bar{a}; \overline{b,c}; \bar{d}; \bar{e}; \bar{f}\}, \{\bar{a}; \bar{b}; \bar{c}; \bar{d}; \bar{e}; \bar{f}\}, \{\bar{a}; \bar{b}; \bar{c}; \bar{d}; \bar{e}; \bar{f}\},$$
$$\{\bar{a}; \overline{b,c}; \bar{d}; \bar{e}; \bar{f}\} \rangle$$
$$P'_5 = \langle \{\bar{a}; \bar{b}; \bar{c}; \bar{d}; \bar{e}; \bar{f}\} \rangle$$
$$P'_7 = \langle \{\bar{a}; \overline{b,f}; \bar{c}; \bar{d}; \bar{e}\}, \{\bar{a}; \overline{b,f}; \bar{c}; \bar{d}; \bar{e}\},$$
$$\{\bar{a}; \bar{b}; \bar{c}; \bar{d}; \bar{e}; \bar{f}\}, \{\bar{a}; \overline{b,f}; \bar{c}; \bar{d}; \bar{e}\} \rangle$$
$$P'_8 = \langle \{\overline{a,e}; \bar{b}; \bar{c}; \bar{d}; \bar{f}\} \rangle$$
$$P'_9 = \langle \{\bar{a}; \bar{b}; \bar{c}; \overline{d,e}; \bar{f}\} \rangle$$
$$P'_{10} = \langle \{\bar{a}; \bar{b}; \bar{c}; \bar{d}; \bar{e}; \bar{f}\} \rangle$$
$$P'_{11} = \langle \{\bar{a}; \overline{b,d}; \bar{c}; \bar{e}; \bar{f}\} \rangle$$
$$P'_{12} = \langle \{\bar{a}; \bar{b}; \overline{c,e}; \bar{d}; \bar{f}\} \rangle$$

TABLE 5.8

$$P_5 = \{\{\overline{a,e}; \overline{b,f}; \bar{c}; \bar{d}\}\} = \{\lambda_5\}$$
$$P_7 = \{\{\overline{a,e}; \bar{b}; \bar{f}; \overline{c,d}\}\} = \{\lambda_6\}$$
$$P_{10} = \{\{\bar{a}; \overline{b,d}; \overline{c,e}; \bar{f}\}\} = \{\lambda_7\}$$

and their corresponding products with λ'_i:

$$P'_3 = \langle 0 \rangle$$
$$P'_4 = \langle \{\bar{a}; \overline{b,c}; \overline{d,e}; \bar{f}\}, 0, 0, 0, 0 \rangle$$
$$P'_5 = \langle 0 \rangle$$
$$P'_7 = \langle 0 \rangle$$
$$P'_{10} = \langle 0 \rangle$$

Now, for $\lambda_3 = \{\overline{a,d}; \bar{b}; \overline{c,f}; \bar{e}\}$, we have

$$[\log_2 | \lambda_3 \cdot \lambda'_3 |] + [\log_2 \langle 0 \rangle] = 3$$
$$[\log_2 | \lambda'_3, \lambda_3 \cdot \lambda'_3 |] + 1 = [\log_2 3] + 1 = 2 + 1 = 3$$
$$[\log_2 | \lambda_3, \lambda_3 \cdot \lambda'_3 |] + [\log_2 | \lambda_3 |] = [\log_2 2] + [\log_2 4] \qquad (5.54)$$
$$= 1 + 2 = 3$$

so that all conditions of (3b) in Theorem 5.18 are met by the partition pair

$$(\{\overline{a,d}; \bar{b}; \overline{c,f}; \bar{e}\}, \{\overline{a,e,f}; \overline{b,c,d}\})$$

and this pair will lead to an assignment with reduced dependency. Checking the computations of the form of Eqs. 5.54 for all remaining partitions λ_i or $\lambda_{i,j}$ and pairs (λ_i, λ'_i) or $(\lambda_{i,j}, \lambda'_i)$, we find that each satisfies condition (3b), so the complete list of ten partition pairs that lead (by Theorem 5.18) to assignments with reduced dependency is as follows:

Type (a):

$$(\{\overline{a,e}; \overline{b,f}; \bar{c}; \bar{d}\}, \{\overline{a,c,e}; \overline{b,d,f}\})$$

Type (b)

$$(\{\overline{a,d};\ \overline{b};\ \overline{c,f};\ \overline{e}\},\ \{\overline{a,e,f};\ \overline{b,c,d}\})$$
$$(\{\overline{a,d,e};\ \overline{b,c,f}\},\ \{\overline{a,f};\ \overline{b,c,d,e}\})$$
$$(\{\overline{a,e};\ \overline{d};\ \overline{b};\ \overline{c,f}\},\ \{\overline{a,f};\ \overline{b,c,d,e}\})$$
$$(\{\overline{a,e};\ \overline{d};\ \overline{b,f};\ \overline{c}\},\ \{\overline{a,f};\ \overline{b,c,d,e}\})$$
$$(\{\overline{a,d};\ \overline{e};\ \overline{b};\ \overline{c,f}\},\ \{\overline{a,f};\ \overline{b,c,d,e}\})$$
$$(\{\overline{a,d};\ \overline{e};\ \overline{b,f};\ \overline{c}\},\ \{\overline{a,f};\ \overline{b,c,d,e}\})$$
$$(\{\overline{a,e};\ \overline{b,f};\ \overline{c};\ \overline{d}\},\ \{\overline{a,b,d};\ \overline{c,e,f}\})$$
$$(\{\overline{a,e};\ \overline{b};\ \overline{f};\ \overline{c,d}\},\ \{\overline{a,b,d,f};\ \overline{c,e}\})$$
$$(\{\overline{a};\ \overline{b,d};\ \overline{c,e};\ \overline{f}\},\ \{\overline{a,d,e};\ \overline{b,c,f}\})$$

Note that the PPP's of Examples 5.29 and 5.30 have appeared among our list. Since Theorem 5.18 asserts that Q_i is independent of more variables when $[\log_2|\lambda|]$ is small (where (λ, λ') is used to achieve reduction in variable dependency), we see that the partition pair $(\{\overline{a,d,e};\ \overline{b,c,f}\},\ \{\overline{a,f};\ \overline{b,c,d,e}\})$ used in Example 5.29 is optimum in the sense that independence of two variables can be achieved for some Q_i; indeed, we have shown how this can be done. For all other partition pairs, independence of but one variable would result. Nevertheless, we will be able to improve on our original assignment for machine M, using the material to be developed in the next section.

*5.12 MULTIPLE REDUCTION OF VARIABLE DEPENDENCY[†]

Without having had his direct attention called to it, the reader has probably sensed the existence of a problem concerning assignments for reduced dependency, whose precise statement (as well as its solution) has not yet been given. The problem is that of determining "consistent" combinations of PPP's that lead to a maximum total reduction in variable dependency among the variables Q_i. Such combinations would not necessarily include a PPP (λ, λ') having minimum $[\log_2|\lambda|]$, for attention should naturally shift to those PPP's that are "compatible" with others.

If $M = (S, \sigma)$ is a c.s.s.m., let

$$\bar{P} = \bar{P}(S) = \left\{ \begin{matrix} (\lambda,\lambda');\ (\lambda,\lambda')\ \text{is a PPP of } M \text{ for which} \\ \text{Theorem 5.18 applies} \end{matrix} \right\} \quad (5.55)$$
$$\subseteq P(S)$$

and suppose that we agree to call a collection (a subset of $\bar{P}$)

$$\mathscr{C} = \{(\lambda_i,\lambda_i') \in \bar{P}(S); \lambda_i' = \{A_0^{(i)},A_1^{(i)}\},\ 1 \le i \le k\} \quad (5.56)$$

of such PPP's *consistent* if the associated partial assignments, say,

†H. A. Curtis, "Multiple Reduction of Variable Dependency in Sequential Machines," *J. Assn. for Computing Mach.*, 9, 3 (July 1962).

$$A_b^{(i)} \xrightarrow{\alpha} (I,I, \cdots, I, \overset{h-i+1}{b}, I, \cdots, I) \qquad (5.57)$$

together with those required for the blocks of λ_i can be made in accordance with Eqs. 5.49 and 5.50 in such a way that the total collection of partial assignments is consistent. When $\mathscr{C}$ consists of but two PPP's, we say that its PPP's are *compatible* $((\lambda_1,\lambda_1') \approx (\lambda_2,\lambda_2'))$ if $\mathscr{C}$ is consistent. With each collection $\mathscr{C}$, consistent or not, as long as the λ_i' are distinct, we associate an integer $w(\mathscr{C})$,

$$w(\mathscr{C}) = h(h - k) + \sum_{i=1}^{k} [\log_2 |\lambda_i|] \qquad (5.58)$$

called the *weight* of $\mathscr{C}$, which represents the total number of state variables that would appear (counting duplications) in the application equations

$$Q_j = Q_j(x_n, x_{n-1}, \cdots, x_1, q_h, q_{h-1}, \cdots, q_1)$$

$(1 \leq j \leq h)$ if the collection were consistent.

EXAMPLE 5.32

Consider the collection $\mathscr{C} = \{(\lambda, \lambda'), (\gamma, \gamma')\}$, where

$$(\lambda, \lambda') = (\{\overline{a,e}; \overline{b}; \overline{f}; \overline{c,d}\}, \{\overline{a,b,d,f}; \overline{c,e}\})$$
$$(\gamma, \gamma') = (\{\overline{a,d,e}; \overline{b,c,f}\}, \{\overline{a,f}; \overline{b,c,d,e}\})$$

are two of the primary PP's found in Example 5.31. Although the partial assignments of Eq. 5.57 are compatible (cf. Prob. 5.21), since

(a) $\quad [\log_2 \langle \lambda' \cdot \gamma' \rangle] = [\log_2 \langle \{\overline{a,f}; \overline{b,d}; \overline{c,e}\} \rangle]$
$$= [\log_2 2] = 1 = h - 2 \, (h = [\log_2 6] = 3)$$

(b) $\quad [\log_2 |\lambda', \lambda' \cdot \gamma'|] = [\log_2 |\gamma', \lambda' \cdot \gamma'|]$
$$= [\log_2 2] = 1$$

it can nevertheless be seen that $(\lambda, \lambda') \napprox (\gamma, \gamma')$, for consider the partially completed assignment

	Q_3	Q_2	Q_1
$a \longrightarrow$		0	0
$b \longrightarrow$		0	1
$c \longrightarrow$		1	1
$d \longrightarrow$		0	1
$e \longrightarrow$		1	1
$f \longrightarrow$		0	0

resulting from Eq. 5.57. Since (λ, λ') is of type (b), Eqs. 5.50 require that each block of λ be assigned to a 1-cell of C^3. This cannot be arranged for the block $\{a,e\}$, no matter how our assignment is completed. Neither can it be accomplished if we permute and/or complement the partial assignments made in Eq. 5.57. Thus, $\mathscr{C}$ is not a consistent collection.

EXAMPLE 5.33

In Example 5.31, the type (b) primary PP's,

$$(\lambda, \lambda') = (\{\overline{a}; \overline{b,d}; \overline{c,e}; \overline{f}\}, \{\overline{a,d,e}; \overline{b,c,f}\})$$

$$(\gamma, \gamma') = (\{\overline{a,d,e}; \overline{b,c,f}\}, \{\overline{a,f}; \overline{b,c,d,e}\})$$

are compatible. The test of Prob. 5.21 shows that the assignments of Eq. 5.57 are compatible. Furthermore, the partially completed assignment

$$Q_3\ Q_2\ Q_1$$

$$a \xrightarrow{\alpha} 0\ \ 0$$
$$b \xrightarrow{\alpha} 1\ \ 1$$
$$c \xrightarrow{\alpha} 1\ \ 1$$
$$d \xrightarrow{\alpha} 0\ \ 1$$
$$e \xrightarrow{\alpha} 0\ \ 1$$
$$f \xrightarrow{\alpha} 1\ \ 0$$

can be completed in such a way (the blocks of $\gamma = \lambda'$ are already assigned),

$$\{a\} \xrightarrow{\alpha} (I,0,0)$$
$$\{b,d\} \xrightarrow{\alpha} (I,1,1)$$
$$\{c,e\} \xrightarrow{\alpha} (I,1,0)$$
$$\{f\} \xrightarrow{\alpha} (I,0,1)$$

that Eqs. 5.50 are satisfied, and these assignments are consistent with those of Eq. 5.57. This example demonstrates that multiple reduction of variable dependency is possible for the machine $M = (S, \sigma)$ introduced in Example 5.29. Indeed, we should have, using the collection $\mathscr{C} = \{(\lambda, \lambda'), (\gamma, \gamma')\}$ with $k = 2$, the reductions: Q_3 independent of q_3; Q_2 independent of q_2, q_1. This would leave a total of

$$w(\mathscr{C}) = 3(3 - 2) + [\log_2|\lambda|] + [\log_2|\gamma|]$$
$$= 3 + 2 + 1 = 6$$

state variables entering into the application equations.

Now the reader should have anticipated our definition (cf. Sec. 3.14) of a simplicial complex $K = (\bar{P}; \Gamma_{\bar{P}})$, whose collection $\Gamma = \Gamma_{\bar{P}}$ of simplexes $\mathscr{C}$ is determined by

$$\mathscr{C} \in \Gamma \longleftrightarrow \begin{cases} \mathscr{C} \text{ is a consistent collection of PPP} \\ (\lambda_i, \lambda_i') \in \bar{P} \text{ having distinct } \lambda_i' \end{cases} \quad (5.59)$$

for the precise statement of the "optimum multiple reduction in variable dependency" problem can then be phrased: *Find a basic simplex of* K *having minimum weight.* Having encountered simplicial complexes often enough in our previous work, the reader will be able to understand the method of solution to this problem after a careful consideration of our examples.

EXAMPLE 5.34

Consider once more the 2–1–6 c.s.s.m. $M = (S, \sigma)$ introduced in Example 5.29. The set $\bar{P} = \bar{P}(S)$ was computed in Example 5.31, that is,

$$\bar{P} = \{(\lambda_1, \lambda_1'), (\lambda_2, \lambda_2'), \cdots, (\lambda_{10}, \lambda_{10}')\}$$

with

$$(\lambda_1, \lambda_1') = (\{\overline{a,e};\ \overline{b,f};\ \overline{c};\ \overline{d}\}, \{\overline{a,c,e};\ \overline{b,d,f}\})$$
$$(\lambda_2, \lambda_2') = (\{\overline{a,d};\ \overline{b};\ \overline{c,f};\ \overline{e}\}, \{\overline{a,e,f};\ \overline{b,c,d}\})$$
$$(\lambda_3, \lambda_3') = (\{\overline{a,d,e};\ \overline{b,c,f}\}, \{\overline{a,f};\ \overline{b,c,d,e}\})$$
$$(\lambda_4, \lambda_4') = (\{\overline{a,e};\ \overline{d};\ \overline{b};\ \overline{c,f}\}, \{\overline{a,f};\ \overline{b,c,d,e}\})$$
$$(\lambda_5, \lambda_5') = (\{\overline{a,e};\ \overline{d};\ \overline{b,f};\ \overline{c}\}, \{\overline{a,f};\ \overline{b,c,d,e}\})$$
$$(\lambda_6, \lambda_6') = (\{\overline{a,d};\ \overline{e};\ \overline{b};\ \overline{c,f}\}, \{\overline{a,f};\ \overline{b,c,d,e}\})$$
$$(\lambda_7, \lambda_7') = (\{\overline{a,d};\ \overline{e};\ \overline{b,f};\ \overline{c}\}, \{\overline{a,f};\ \overline{b,c,d,e}\})$$
$$(\lambda_8, \lambda_8') = (\{\overline{a,e};\ \overline{b,f};\ \overline{c};\ \overline{d}\}, \{\overline{a,b,d};\ \overline{c,e,f}\})$$
$$(\lambda_9, \lambda_9') = (\{\overline{a,e};\ \overline{b};\ \overline{f};\ \overline{c,d}\}, \{\overline{a,b,d,f};\ \overline{c,e}\})$$
$$(\lambda_{10}, \lambda_{10}') = (\{\overline{a};\ \overline{b,d};\ \overline{c,e};\ \overline{f}\}, \{\overline{b,c,f};\ \overline{a,d,e}\})$$

As usual, we construct the compatibility matrix

	1	2	3	4	5	6	7	8	9
2	0								
3	1	0							
4	0	0	0						
5	1	0	0	0					
6	0	0	0	0	0				
7	0	0	0	0	0	0			
8	1	0	0	0	0	0	0		
9	0	0	0	0	0	0	0	0	
10	1	0	1	1	1	1	1	1	0

of the relation $\underset{\bar{r}}{\approx}$ (cf. Eq. 3.46) on elements of $\bar{P}$. Some pairs of PP's are incompatible because (as with $(\lambda_3, \lambda_3') \underset{\bar{r}}{\not\approx} (\lambda_4, \lambda_4')$) the λ_i' are the same; others (as with $(\lambda_1, \lambda_1') \underset{\bar{r}}{\not\approx} (\lambda_9, \lambda_9')$) are incompatible because the partial assignments of Eq. 5.57 are not compatible; still others (as with $(\lambda_3, \lambda_3') \underset{\bar{r}}{\not\approx} (\lambda_9, \lambda_9')$—cf. Example 5.32) are incompatible even though the assignments of Eq. 5.57 are compatible. By the usual procedure (cf. Sec. 0.10) we obtain the maximal compatibles

$$\gamma^2 = \{\overline{1,3,10};\ \overline{1,5,10};\ \overline{1,8,10};\ \overline{2};\ \overline{4,10};\ \overline{6,10};\ \overline{7,10};\ \overline{9}\}$$
$$= \{\mathscr{C}_1,\ \mathscr{C}_2,\ \mathscr{C}_3,\ \mathscr{C}_4,\ \mathscr{C}_5,\ \mathscr{C}_6,\ \mathscr{C}_7,\ \mathscr{C}_8\}$$

These are not necessarily basic simplexes, however; K is not generally an inductive complex (cf. Eq. 3.47). Nevertheless, we compute the weights, which show

$$w(\mathscr{C}_1) = 5$$
$$w(\mathscr{C}_i) \geq 6 \qquad (2 \leq i \leq 8)$$

and thus, if $\mathscr{C}_1$ is a basic simplex (that is, if it is a consistent collection), it represents the unique "optimum" solution to the problem. That the partial assignments of Eq. 5.57 give a complete assignment

$$\begin{array}{ccc} & Q_3\ Q_2\ Q_1 \\ a \xrightarrow{\ \alpha\ } & 0\ \ 0\ \ 1 \\ b \xrightarrow{\ \alpha\ } & 1\ \ 1\ \ 0 \end{array}$$

$$c \xrightarrow{\alpha} 0 \ 1 \ 0$$
$$d \xrightarrow{\alpha} 1 \ 1 \ 1$$
$$e \xrightarrow{\alpha} 0 \ 1 \ 1$$
$$f \xrightarrow{\alpha} 1 \ 0 \ 0$$

satisfying Eqs. 5.49 and 5.50 verifies that $\mathscr{C}_1$ is consistent. Theorem 5.18 shows that we should expect the reductions: Q_3 independent of q_2; Q_2 independent of q_3 and q_2; Q_1 independent of q_1. Indeed, the assignment α transforms the flow table into the application functions of Table 5.9, where we find

q_3	q_2	q_1	x_2	x_1	Q_3	Q_2	Q_1	z
0	0	0	0	0	I	I	I	I
0	0	0	0	1	I	I	I	I
0	0	0	1	0	I	I	I	I
0	0	0	1	1	I	I	I	I
0	0	1	0	0	1	0	0	0
0	0	1	0	1	0	1	0	0
0	0	1	1	0	1	1	0	0
0	0	1	1	1	1	1	1	0
0	1	0	0	0	1	1	0	0
0	1	0	0	1	1	1	1	0
0	1	0	1	0	1	1	0	0
0	1	0	1	1	1	0	0	0
0	1	1	0	0	1	0	0	1
0	1	1	0	1	0	1	1	1
0	1	1	1	0	1	1	0	1
0	1	1	1	1	1	1	0	1
1	0	0	0	0	0	1	0	0
1	0	0	0	1	1	1	1	0
1	0	0	1	0	1	1	1	0
1	0	0	1	1	0	0	1	0
1	0	1	0	0	I	I	I	I
1	0	1	0	1	I	I	I	I
1	0	1	1	0	I	I	I	I
1	0	1	1	1	I	I	I	I
1	1	0	0	0	0	1	1	0
1	1	0	0	1	1	1	0	0
1	1	0	1	0	1	1	1	0
1	1	0	1	1	0	0	1	0
1	1	1	0	0	0	0	1	0
1	1	1	0	1	1	1	0	0
1	1	1	1	0	1	1	1	0
1	1	1	1	1	1	1	1	0

TABLE 5.9

$$Q_3 = \bar{q}_3\bar{q}_1 + q_1x_2 + q_3\bar{x}_2x_1 + x_2\bar{x}_1 + \bar{q}_3\bar{x}_1$$
$$Q_2 = \bar{x}_2\bar{x}_1 + \bar{q}_1\bar{x}_1 + q_1x_2$$

$$Q_1 = q_3\bar{q}_2x_1 + q_3q_2\bar{x}_1 + \bar{q}_2x_2x_1 + \bar{q}_3q_2\bar{x}_2x_1 + q_3x_2$$

exhibiting the variable dependence reductions predicted above.

EXAMPLE 5.35

Consider the 1–1–6 c.s.s.m. $M = (S, \sigma)$ with flow table

S	x	
	0	1
a	$(e,0)$	$(b,0)$
b	$(d,0)$	$(a,0)$
c	$(a,1)$	$(d,1)$
d	$(f,0)$	$(c,0)$
e	$(b,0)$	$(c,0)$
f	$(c,0)$	$(b,0)$

As practice in the computations of Sec. 5.11, the reader should verify that

$$\bar{P} = \bar{P}(S) = \{(\lambda_i, \lambda_i')\}$$

consists of the PPP's, each of type (a),

$$(\lambda_1,\lambda_1') = (\{\overline{a,b};\ \bar{c};\ \bar{d};\ \overline{e,f}\},\ \{\overline{a,b,c};\ \overline{d,e,f}\})$$
$$(\lambda_2,\lambda_2') = (\{\overline{a,b,f};\ \overline{c,d,e}\},\ \{\overline{a,b,f};\ \overline{c,d,e}\})$$
$$(\lambda_3,\lambda_3') = (\{\overline{a,c};\ \overline{b,d};\ \bar{e};\ \bar{f}\},\ \{\overline{a,c,e};\ \overline{b,d,f}\})$$
$$(\lambda_4,\lambda_4') = (\{\overline{a,d};\ \overline{b,c};\ \overline{e,f}\},\ \{\overline{a,d};\ \overline{b,c,e,f}\})$$
$$(\lambda_5,\lambda_5') = (\{\overline{a,d};\ \overline{b,c};\ \overline{e,f}\},\ \{\overline{a,b,c,d};\ \overline{e,f}\})$$
$$(\lambda_6,\lambda_6') = (\{\overline{a,d};\ \overline{b,c};\ \overline{e,f}\},\ \{\overline{a,d,e,f};\ \overline{b,c}\})$$
$$(\lambda_7,\lambda_7') = (\{\bar{a};\ \overline{b,e};\ \overline{c,f};\ \bar{d}\},\ \{\overline{a,c,f};\ \overline{b,d,e}\})$$
$$(\lambda_8,\lambda_8') = (\{\bar{a};\ \bar{b};\ \overline{c,d};\ \overline{e,f}\},\ \{\overline{a,e,f};\ \overline{b,c,d}\})$$

together with all PP's (λ,λ_i') with $0 < \lambda \le \lambda_i$, which satisfy conditions (2) and (3a) of Theorem 5.18.

Constructing the compatibility matrix for the complex $K = (\bar{P}, \Gamma_{\bar{P}})$, we find that

$$\mathscr{C} = \{(\lambda_2,\lambda_2'), (\lambda_4,\lambda_4'), (\lambda_5,\lambda_5')\}$$

is the minimum weight ($w(\mathscr{C}) = 5$), basic simplex of K. The resulting assignment

$$
\begin{array}{cccc}
& Q_3 & Q_2 & Q_1 \\
a \longrightarrow & 0 & 0 & 0 \\
b \longrightarrow & 0 & 1 & 0 \\
c \longrightarrow & 1 & 1 & 0 \\
d \longrightarrow & 1 & 0 & 0 \\
e \longrightarrow & 1 & 1 & 1 \\
f \longrightarrow & 0 & 1 & 1 \\
\end{array}
$$

yields the application equations

$$Q_3 = \bar{q}_3\bar{x} + q_3x$$
$$Q_2 = q_1 + \bar{q}_2$$
$$Q_1 = \bar{q}_2\bar{x}$$

Note that these simple equations have the properties:

(i) Q_3 is dependent only on variables in $\{q_3\}$ and inputs.

(ii) Q_2 and Q_1 are dependent only on variables in $\{q_2, q_1\}$ and inputs.

Assignments having the consequence that there exists a proper subset $J \subset h^+$ such that

$$j \in J \Longrightarrow Q_j \text{ is dependent only on } \{q_j; j \in J\} \text{ and inputs}$$

are called *assignments with self-dependent subsets*. The assignment of Example 5.35 has two self-dependent subsets, $\{q_3\}$ and $\{q_2, q_1\}$, and thus behaves (see Fig. 5.13, where delay memory elements have been used) as

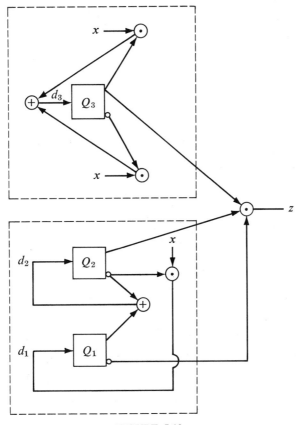

FIGURE 5.13

though it were two machines operating in parallel. Observe that the partitions

$$\lambda_2 = \overline{\{a,b,f;\ c,d,e\}}$$
$$\lambda_4 = \lambda_5 = \overline{\{a,d;\ b,c;\ e,f\}}$$

have the substitution property (cf. Sec. 5.9). This is not accidental, as the following corollary[†] shows. The reader should not have difficulty verifying it if he reviews Theorems 5.17 and 5.18.

Corollary 5.19.   (Due to Hartmanis[‡]): A necessary and sufficient condition that an *n-m-p* c.s.s.m. $M = (S,\sigma)$ possess a minimal ($h = [\log_2 p]$) assignment $\alpha : S \rightarrow B^h$ with a self-dependent subset is that there be a nontrivial ($\lambda \neq 0,I$)PSP satisfying

$$[\log_2 |\lambda|] + [\log_2 \langle\lambda\rangle] = h$$

Since the study of sequential machines having assignments with self-dependent subsets is subsumed by the study of those having assignments with reduced dependency, we have not placed a great emphasis on the former.

PROBLEMS

5.1   Obtain a flow table and state diagram for the following sequential machines:

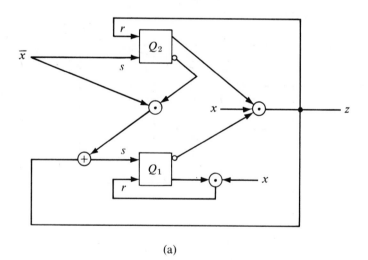

(a)

[†]Chronologically, the PSP's and assignments with self-dependent subsets represented the earliest attack on the state-assignment problem. Subsequently, the PPP's and assignments with reduced dependency were seen to cast the problem and its solution in a more general framework.

[‡]J. Hartmanis, "On the State Assignment Problem for Sequential Machines, I," *IRE Trans. on Electronic Computers*, EC-10, 2 (June 1961).

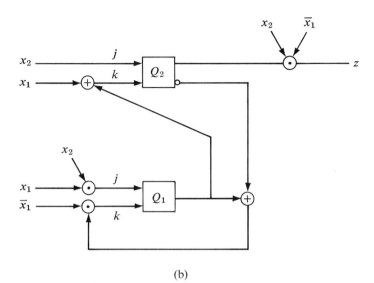

(b)

5.2 Determine the sequence of outputs z that are obtained (a) if the machine of Prob. 5.1(a) is given the input sequence $x = \langle 0,0,1,1,1,0,1,0,1,1 \rangle$; (b) if the machine of Prob. 5.1(b) is given the input sequence (x_2,x_1) $= \langle (0,1),(1,0),(1,1),(1,1),(0,0),(0,1),(0,1) \rangle$. Assume in both (a) and (b) that the machine begins the sequence with $Q_2 = Q_1 = 0$.

5.3 Prove Lemma 5.5.

5.4 Compute the number of (essentially different, in the sense of the definition of equivalence for sequential machines) c.s.s.m.'s $M = (S, \sigma)$ for which $S = \{s_1,s_2\}$ and $\sigma : B^2 \times S \longrightarrow S \times B$.

5.5 Clarify the statement: Every (abstract) memory element is an (abstract) sequential machine.

5.6 Without comparing the answers, why should the number obtained in Prob. 5.4 be larger than that obtained in Prob. 4.19? (See Prob. 5.5.)

5.7 Using minimal state assignments and j-k memory elements, derive logic circuits for the sequential machines having the state diagram of (a) Fig. 5.5, (b) Fig. 5.7, (c) Fig. 5.8, and (d) Fig. 5.9.

5.8 Derive state diagrams and flow tables for sequential machines having the following specifications:
   (a) The machine is required to receive groups of four binary digits in serial form on the line x. Its output z should indicate (with 1 or 0) that the four binary digits do or do not correspond to a prime decimal number. Decisions are made for successive groups of four.
   (b) The machine is similar to (a) except that its output should be 1 whenever its last four (including its current input) inputs correspond to a prime decimal number.

(c) The machine is a single-input–single-output "combination lock" with unlocking sequence 1,1,0,1.

(d) The machine is a two-input–single-output "combination lock" with unlocking sequence (1,1),(1,0),(0,1).

(e) The machine is a counter that simply counts the number of times that its (single) input changes. It begins counting anew after 12 changes have occurred. One of its outputs is 1 iff the total number of changes is divisible by 3. The other is 1 iff the total number of changes is divisible by 12.

(f) The machine examines groups of five inputs in serial form on a single line x. Its output $z = 1$ iff exactly one consecutive group of 1's appeared among the five inputs. Decisions are made for successive groups of five.

5.9 Use the HMM procedure to remove superfluous states in the diagrams obtained in Prob. 5.8.

5.10 Using minimal state assignments and r-s flip-flops, derive logic circuits for the sequential machines obtained in Prob. 5.9.

5.11 Use the HMM procedure to find the flow table of the reduced form of the sequential machine having flow table:

(a)

	x	
	0	1
a	$(b,0)$	$(a,1)$
b	$(d,1)$	$(c,0)$
c	$(a,1)$	$(b,1)$
d	$(e,0)$	$(d,1)$
e	$(a,1)$	$(c,0)$

(b)

	x	
	0	1
a	$(b,0)$	$(c,0)$
b	$(e,1)$	$(c,0)$
c	$(d,0)$	$(a,0)$
d	$(e,1)$	$(a,0)$
e	$(e,1)$	$(e,0)$

(c)

	x	
	0	1
a	$(a,1)$	$(a,0)$
b	$(a,1)$	$(f,0)$
c	$(d,0)$	$(e,0)$
d	$(a,1)$	$(g,0)$
e	$(b,0)$	$(c,0)$
f	$(d,0)$	$(e,0)$
g	$(b,0)$	$(c,0)$

(d)

	$x_2 x_1$			
	0 0	0 1	1 0	1 1
a	$(c,1)$	$(e,0)$	$(a,1)$	$(b,0)$
b	$(f,1)$	$(i,0)$	$(b,1)$	$(a,0)$
c	$(e,1)$	$(d,1)$	$(a,0)$	$(g,0)$
d	$(g,1)$	$(a,0)$	$(g,0)$	$(e,1)$
e	$(a,0)$	$(a,1)$	$(i,1)$	$(g,1)$
f	$(i,1)$	$(g,1)$	$(b,0)$	$(h,0)$
g	$(g,1)$	$(a,0)$	$(d,0)$	$(i,1)$
h	$(d,1)$	$(a,1)$	$(d,0)$	$(e,1)$
i	$(a,0)$	$(a,1)$	$(e,1)$	$(d,1)$

(e)

	x	
	0	1
a	$(e,1)$	$(h,1)$
b	$(g,1)$	$(d,0)$
c	$(e,1)$	$(b,1)$
d	$(f,1)$	$(b,0)$
e	$(c,1)$	$(d,1)$
f	$(i,0)$	$(e,0)$
g	$(f,0)$	$(a,0)$
h	$(i,1)$	$(d,0)$
i	$(f,0)$	$(a,0)$

5.12 Use the PUG reduction procedure to reduce the following flow tables to ones that have fewest states.

(a)

	$x_2 x_1$			
	0 0	0 1	1 0	1 1
a	(I,I)	$(b,1)$	(I,I)	(I,I)
b	(m,I)	(I,I)	$(I,1)$	$(I,1)$
c	$(I,0)$	(g,I)	(I,I)	(I,I)
d	$(I,1)$	$(I,0)$	(f,I)	(I,I)
e	(I,I)	(I,I)	(I,I)	(m,I)
f	(I,I)	(c,I)	$(I,0)$	$(I,0)$
g	(I,I)	$(I,1)$	$(I,0)$	$(j,0)$
h	$(d,1)$	(I,I)	$(I,1)$	$(I,0)$
i	(I,I)	(I,I)	$(e,1)$	(I,I)
j	(I,I)	(h,I)	(I,I)	$(I,1)$
k	(i,I)	$(I,0)$	(I,I)	$(I,0)$
m	$(a,1)$	(I,I)	(I,I)	$(c,0)$

(b)

	$x_2 x_1$			
	0 0	0 1	1 0	1 1
a	$(I,0)$	$(d,1)$	$(c,0)$	(I,I)
b	(e,I)	$(j,0)$	$(a,0)$	$(I,0)$
c	$(I,0)$	(f,I)	(I,I)	$(c,1\cdot)$
d	$(k,0)$	(f,I)	(I,I)	$(c,1)$
e	$(i,0)$	(h,I)	(I,I)	$(I,0)$
f	$(k,0)$	(f,I)	(I,I)	(c,I)
g	(i,I)	$(h,1)$	(I,I)	$(c,0)$
h	$(i,0)$	(h,I)	(g,I)	$(I,0)$
i	$(i,0)$	$(I,1)$	(g,I)	(c,I)
j	(I,I)	$(k,1)$	(k,I)	$(I,1)$
k	(f,I)	$(I,1)$	(c,I)	$(k,1)$

(c)

$x_2\,x_1$			
0 0	0 1	1 0	1 1
a $(b,0)$	$(c,0)$	(I,I)	$(d,1)$
b $(c,0)$	$(e,0)$	(I,I)	(I,I)
c $(d,1)$	$(f,0)$	$(c,1)$	(I,I)
d $(e,1)$	$(c,0)$	(I,I)	$(a,1)$
e (I,I)	$(f,0)$	(I,I)	(I,I)
f (I,I)	(I,I)	$(d,1)$	$(b,0)$

(d)

$x_2\,x_1$			
0 0	0 1	1 0	1 1
a $(b,1)$	$(d,1)$	$(c,1)$	(I,I)
b (I,I)	(I,I)	(I,I)	$(d,0)$
c (I,I)	(I,I)	$(f,1)$	$(f,0)$
d $(e,1)$	$(a,0)$	$(f,0)$	(I,I)
e (I,I)	$(b,1)$	(I,I)	(I,I)
f $(c,1)$	$(b,0)$	(I,I)	$(c,0)$

5.13 Using minimal state assignments and delay memory elements, derive logic circuits for the reduced machines of Prob. 5.12.

5.14 Obtain the maximal compatibles and maximal incompatibles for the following compatibility tables:

(a)

2	1
3	0 1
4	1 0 0
5	0 0 0 1
6	0 1 1 1 1
7	0 1 0 1 0 1

1 2 3 4 5 6

(b)

2	1
3	0 1
4	1 0 1
5	1 1 0 0
6	0 1 1 0 1
7	0 1 0 0 1 1
8	0 0 1 0 0 1 1

1 2 3 4 5 6 7

(c)

2	0
3	1 0
4	1 1 1
5	0 1 1 1
6	0 0 1 0 1

1 2 3 4 5

5.15 Supposing that the compatibility matrices of Prob. 5.14 have resulted from the PUG reduction procedure, compute $|\gamma|$, $\langle\tilde{\gamma}\rangle$ and thereby obtain the Ginsburg bounds on r. Which (if any) of the groupings γ is irredundant?

5.16 If $M = (S, \sigma)$ has the flow table

S	$x_2\,x_1$			
	0 0	0 1	1 0	1 1
a	$(b,1)$	$(c,1)$	$(d,1)$	$(a,1)$
b	$(a,0)$	$(d,0)$	$(c,0)$	$(b,0)$
c	$(c,0)$	$(b,0)$	$(a,0)$	$(d,0)$
d	$(d,1)$	$(a,1)$	$(b,1)$	$(c,1)$

show that $(\{\overline{a,d};\ \overline{b,c}\}, \{\overline{a,c};\ \overline{b,d}\})$ is a PP and $\{\overline{a,b};\ \overline{c,d}\}$ is a PSP. Are there other nontrivial PP's?

5.17 Prove Corollary 5.17.

5.18 If

$$\pi = \{\overline{1,2,3};\ \overline{4,5};\ \overline{6,7,8}\}$$
$$\gamma = \{\overline{1,3,6};\ \overline{2,7};\ \overline{4,5,8}\}$$
$$\rho = \{\overline{1,2};\ \overline{3,4};\ \overline{5,6};\ \overline{7};\ \overline{8}\}$$

compute

(a) $[\log_2|\pi, \pi\cdot\gamma|]$.

(b) $[\log_2|\gamma, \pi\cdot\gamma|]$.

(c) $[\log_2|\pi|]$.

(d) $[\log_2\langle\rho\rangle]$.

(e) $[\log_2|\rho, \pi + \rho|]$.

(f) $[\log_2|\rho, \gamma + \rho|]$.

(g) $[\log_2\langle\gamma + \rho\rangle]$.

(h) $[\log_2\langle\gamma\cdot\rho\rangle]$.

5.19 Show how Theorem 5.18 should be restated if one is to allow assignments involving more than the minimal number $h = [\log_2 p]$ of state variables.

*5.20 Prove the (b) part of Theorem 5.18 in complete detail.

5.21 Let (λ,λ') and (γ,γ') be PPP's for an n-m-p c.s.s.m. in which

$$\lambda' = \{A_0, A_1\} \neq \{B_0, B_1\} = \gamma'$$

Show that the partial assignments

$$A_b \xrightarrow{\alpha} (b, I, I, \cdots, I)$$
$$B_b \xrightarrow{\alpha} (I, b, I, \cdots, I)$$

$(b = 0, 1)$ are compatible iff

(a) $\qquad [\log_2\langle\lambda'\cdot\gamma'\rangle] = h - 2, (h = [\log_2 p])$.

(b) $\qquad [\log_2|\lambda',\lambda'\cdot\gamma'|] = [\log_2|\gamma',\lambda'\cdot\gamma'|] = 1$.

*5.22 Let $\mathscr{C} = \{(\lambda_i,\lambda'_i); 1 \leq i \leq k\}$ be a collection of PPP's for an n-m-p c.s.s.m. in which the $\lambda'_i = \{A_0^{(i)}, A_1^{(i)}\}$ are distinct. Show that, as necessary conditions for the consistency of the partial assignments

$$A_b^{(i)} \longrightarrow (I, I, \cdots, \overset{h-i+1}{b}, I, \cdots, I)$$

$(b = 0, 1)$, we must have

(a) $[\log_2\langle\prod_{i=1}^{k} \lambda'_i\rangle] = h - k, (h = [\log_2 p])$ and

(b) $[\log_2|\prod_{i\neq j} \lambda'_i, \prod_{i=1}^{k} \lambda'_i|] = 1, (j = 1, 2, \cdots, k)$.

Are these also sufficient conditions?

*5.23 For a c.s.s.m. $M = (S, \sigma)$ and $s_i, s_j \in S$, let $\lambda(s_i,s_j)$ denote the "smallest" PSP λ for which $s_i \underset{\lambda}{\sim} s_j$; that is,

$$\lambda(s_i,s_j) = \prod_{\substack{s_i \underset{\lambda}{\sim} s_j \\ \lambda \text{ a PSP}}} \lambda$$

Show that $\lambda(s_i,s_j)$ can be computed according to the following program:

(1) Put $\lambda_0 = \lambda_{s_i s_j}$ (cf. Eq. 5.52).

(2) Let $\lambda_1 = m(\lambda_0) = m(\lambda_{s_i s_j})$ (see (i) in Example 5.31).

$$\vdots$$

(k) Put $\lambda_k = \prod_{s \underset{\lambda_{k-1}}{\sim} t} m(\lambda_{st})$

$$\vdots$$

where the process is halted when $\lambda_k = \lambda_{k-1}$ for some k, this repeating partition being $\lambda(s_i,s_j)$.

*5.24 Prove that the set of all PSP's for a c.s.s.m. $M = (S, \sigma)$ forms a sublattice of $\Lambda(S)$.

*5.25 Show that every PSP λ for an n-m-p c.s.s.m. has the form $\lambda = \sum \lambda(s_i,s_j)$ for a sum taken over some nonempty subset of the $\frac{1}{2}p \cdot (p - 1)$ partitions $\lambda(s_i,s_j)$. (See Prob. 5.23.)

5.26 Using the results of Prob. 5.25, give a procedure for finding all PSP's for a sequential machine.

5.27 Find all PSP's for the machines having flow tables

(a)

S	x 0	1
a	$(b,1)$	$(g,1)$
b	$(d,0)$	$(e,0)$
c	$(e,0)$	$(e,0)$
d	$(g,0)$	$(b,0)$
e	$(f,0)$	$(c,0)$
f	$(h,0)$	$(a,0)$
g	$(a,0)$	$(a,0)$
h	$(c,0)$	$(g,0)$

(b)

S	$x_2 x_1$ 0 0	0 1	1 0	1 1
a	$(d,1)$	$(b,1)$	$(c,1)$	$(d,1)$
b	$(a,1)$	$(d,1)$	$(c,1)$	$(d,1)$
c	$(a,1)$	$(b,1)$	$(d,1)$	$(d,1)$
d	$(a,0)$	$(b,0)$	$(c,0)$	$(d,0)$

using the procedure of Prob. 5.26.

*5.28 Prove Corollary 5.19.

*5.29 Obtain assignments with self-dependent subsets for the machines of Prob. 5.27 and derive the logic of their state variables.

5.30 Show that (S, Γ_S) is a simplicial complex.

*5.31 Let $\{(A_1,c_1), (A_2,c_2), \cdots, (A_t,c_t)\}$ be a collection of partial assignments with $A_i \subseteq S$, $c_i \in C^h$ and $\log_2|A_i| \leq \theta(c_i) < h$ $(1 \leq i \leq t)$. Show that the collection is consistent iff there exists an assignment $\alpha : S \longrightarrow B^h$ such that for each $i = 1, 2, \cdots, t$, we have $\alpha(a) \subseteq c_i$ for all $a \in A_i$.

5.32 Use the procedure of Sec. 5.11 to find all PPP's leading to assignments with reduced dependency for the following flow tables:

(a)

	$x_2 x_1$ 0 0	0 1	1 0	1 1
a	$(b,1)$	$(c,1)$	$(d,1)$	$(a,1)$
b	$(a,0)$	$(d,0)$	$(c,0)$	$(b,0)$
c	$(c,0)$	$(b,0)$	$(a,0)$	$(d,0)$
d	$(d,1)$	$(a,1)$	$(b,1)$	$(c,1)$

(b)

	$x_2 x_1$ 0 0	0 1	1 0	1 1
a	$(a,1)$	$(b,1)$	$(c,1)$	$(a,1)$
b	$(a,1)$	$(e,1)$	$(b,1)$	$(d,1)$
c	$(c,0)$	$(b,0)$	$(c,0)$	$(e,0)$
d	$(e,0)$	$(a,0)$	$(b,0)$	$(d,0)$
e	$(c,0)$	$(e,0)$	$(b,0)$	$(d,0)$

(c) The flow table of Prob. 5.27(a).

(d) The flow table of Prob. 5.27(b).

5.33 Use the procedure of Sec. 5.12 to find an assignment that maximizes the reduction of variable dependency and obtain the logic for the state variables, taking the results of Prob. 5.32.

SUGGESTED REFERENCES

5-1 SHANNON C. E., and J. McCARTHY, eds., *Automata Studies* (Princeton New Jersey: Princeton University Press), 1956.

5-2 GILL, A., *Introduction to the Theory of Finite State Machines* (New York: McGraw-Hill Book Co.), 1962.

5-3 GINSBURG, S., *An Introduction to Mathematical Machine Theory* (Reading, Mass.: Addison-Wesley Pub. Co.), 1962.

5-4 MILLER R. E., *Switching Theory* Vol. II (New York: John Wiley & Sons), 1966.

5-5 HARTMANIS, J. and STEARNS, R.E., *Algebraic Structure Theory of Sequential Machines* (Englewood Cliffs, N.J.: Prentice-Hall, Inc.), 1966.

CHAPTER 6 | TREE CIRCUITS

6.1 INTRODUCTION

In Chapter 3 we studied the problem of determining the most economical 2-level implementation of a Boolean function $f(x_n, x_{n-1}, \cdots, x_{-1})$. For fairly large n (say, $n \geq 5$), however, it can be argued that these circuits often fail to be consistent with practical engineering requirements, since they have an exceedingly large number of inputs to "and" and "or" gates. For this and other reasons, a redirection† of effort has taken place in combinatorial switching theory. When carried to its ultimate conclusion, this redirection may be approximately described as an attempt to replace the "two-level unlimited-input-per-gate" minimization problem by an "unlimited-level two-input-per-gate" minimization problem. To be

†See Ref. 7-1.

sure, the degree to which this new problem is solved (or even understood) is considerably less than the earlier problem. Nevertheless, in defense of our last two chapters, we will show that an approximate solution to the new problem is quite often preferable (from an economical, as well as an engineering standpoint) to an exact solution of the former problem.

In this chapter we develop certain procedures for obtaining economical two-input-per-gate circuits of a particular variety—those that have come to be known as "tree circuits." These procedures will be particularly attractive when used in conjunction with the decomposition theory of the following chapter. As in Chapter 3, we will make every effort to extend our results to incompletely specified and multiple-output functions.

As a dual objective, we will discuss certain upper bounds and cost estimates for general use in switching theory. But our direct application of these bounds and estimates will be toward assisting in obtaining economical tree circuits and economical decompositions of Boolean functions. Moreover, they will provide a most convincing justification for the aforementioned redirection of effort in switching theory.

6.2 TWO-INPUT-PER-GATE CIRCUITS

In Chapter 1 we learned that any Boolean function $f: B^n \longrightarrow B$ can be fabricated from subcircuits of the type (two-input, complementary output "and" and "or" circuits) depicted in Fig. 6.1. Such logic networks

FIGURE 6.1

N will be termed *two-input-per-gate circuits*. The *diode cost* $\tau(N)$ of such circuits should be taken as twice the number of gates employed; we will do that here. One such circuit is immediately at hand (and it is not always uneconomical) when a minimal form of f has been computed. If f has a minimal form

$$g = \sum_{j=1}^{k} p_j$$

for Boolean products p_j, we may construct these products with "cascaded" two-input and gates; similarly, for the sum of the products, cascaded two-input or gates may be used.

EXAMPLE 6.1

If $f: B^4 \longrightarrow B$ has the minimal form

$$g = x_4 \bar{x}_3 x_2 \bar{x}_1 + x_3 \bar{x}_2 x_1 + \bar{x}_4 \bar{x}_3 + x_4 x_3 x_2 x_1$$

we may implement f as shown in Fig. 6.2. Note that $M(f) = 17$, while the circuit of Fig. 6.2 has the diode cost 24.

Generally, if a minimal form g of f has k products, p_j and $m(p_j)$ denotes, as usual, the number of literals in the product p_j, this *two-input-per-gate equivalent of the minimal form* of f will have a diode cost (cf. Eqs. 3.10 and 3.14)

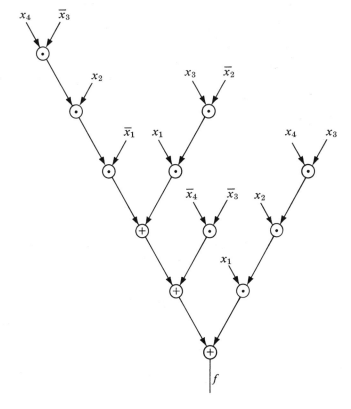

FIGURE 6.2

$$M'(f) = 2[(k - 1) + \sum_{j=1}^{k} (m(p_j) - 1)]$$
$$= 2[M(f) - k - 1]$$
$$= 2[\sum_{j=1}^{k} m(p_j) - 1]$$
$$= 2[\mu_1(g) - 1]$$

$$(6.1)$$

Now if we were to attempt an imitation of Chapter 3 (see the definition of minimal form) for two-input-per-gate circuits, we would try to solve the *unlimited-level two-input-per-gate minimization problem:* Given $f: B^n \to C$, find a two-input-per-gate circuit $N \in FL(n)$ (cf. Example 1.19) for which

(1) $v_{p^{-1}(N)} \subseteq c_f$.
(2) $\left. \begin{array}{l} v_{p^{-1}(N')} \subseteq c_f \\ N' \text{ a two-input-per-gate circuit} \end{array} \right\} \Longrightarrow \tau(N) \leq \tau(N').$

Except for very special types of functions, the solution to this problem is not known. Thus, we restrict our attention to a class of two-input-per-gate circuits which, though not guaranteed to contain a solution to this minimization problem, at least provides a circuit N satisfying (1) and having at the same time a diode cost $T(f)$, which we will show to be uniformly bounded by Eq. 6.1, that is, $T(f) \leq M'(f)$ for each Boolean function f. The members of this restricted class of circuits are called "tree circuits," and we will soon be able to describe their nature.

6.3 PARTIAL EXPANSIONS

If $f: B^n \to B$, our characterization of tree circuits will be made to depend upon the *i*th *partial expansions* $f_i: B^{n-1} \to B^n$, defined by

$$f_i(b_n, b_{n-1}, \cdots, \hat{b}_i, \cdots, b_1)$$
$$= (f(b_n, b_{n-1}, \cdots, \overset{i}{0}, \cdots, b_1), f(b_n, b_{n-1}, \cdots, \overset{i}{1}, \cdots, b_1))$$

$$(6.2)$$

for each $i = 1, 2, \cdots, n.\dagger$

EXAMPLE 6.2

If $f: B^4 \to B$ has the truth table

†As mentioned previously, the caret (^) over b_i is understood to mean that the argument b_i is missing within the parentheses.

x_4	x_3	x_2	x_1	f
0	0	0	0	0
0	0	0	1	0
0	0	1	0	1
0	0	1	1	0
0	1	0	0	1
0	1	0	1	1
0	1	1	0	1
0	1	1	1	1
1	0	0	0	0
1	0	0	1	0
1	0	1	0	0
1	0	1	1	0
1	1	0	0	1
1	1	0	1	1
1	1	1	0	0
1	1	1	1	0

we have four partial expansions:

$x_4\ x_3\ x_2$		$x_4\ x_3\ x_1$		$x_4\ x_2\ x_1$		$x_3\ x_2\ x_1$	
0 0 0 $\longrightarrow$ 00		0 0 0 $\longrightarrow$ 01		0 0 0 $\longrightarrow$ 01		0 0 0 $\longrightarrow$ 00	
0 0 1 $\longrightarrow$ 10		0 0 1 $\longrightarrow$ 00		0 0 1 $\longrightarrow$ 01		0 0 1 $\longrightarrow$ 00	
0 1 0 11		0 1 0 11		0 1 0 11		0 1 0 10	
f_1: 0 1 1 : 11		f_2: 0 1 1 : 11		f_3: 0 1 1 : 01		f_4: 0 1 1 : 00	
1 0 0 . 00		1 0 0 . 00		1 0 0 . 01		1 0 0 . 11	
1 0 1 00		1 0 1 00		1 0 1 01		1 0 1 11	
1 1 0 11		1 1 0 10		1 1 0 00		1 1 0 10	
1 1 1 $\longrightarrow$ 00		1 1 1 $\longrightarrow$ 10		1 1 1 $\longrightarrow$ 00		1 1 1 $\longrightarrow$ 10	

Streamlining our notation a bit, we abbreviate these functions as

	x_1		x_2		x_3		x_4
	00		01		01		00
	10		00		01		00
	11		11		11		10
f_1: $x_4x_3x_2$	11	f_2: $x_4x_3x_1$	11	f_3: $x_4x_2x_1$	01	f_4: $x_3x_2x_1$	00
	00		00		01		11
	00		00		01		11
	11		10		00		10
	00		10		00		10

and in this form† they are known as the $2^{n-1} \times 2$ *matrix representations* of f or as the $2^{n-1} \times 2$ *charts* for f. Clearly, these matrix representations are nothing more than rearrangements of the truth table entries.

†Some authors prefer to write these matrices horizontally; that is

f_1	$x_4x_3x_2$
x_1	0 1 1 1 0 0 1 0
	0 0 1 1 0 0 1 0

and so on, but we would rather retain the close relationship to the form of the truth table of f.

Now let $g_i(x_n, x_{n-1}, \cdots, \hat{x}_i, \cdots, x_1)$ and $h_i(x_n, x_{n-1}, \cdots, \hat{x}_i, \cdots, x_1)$ be the functions (of $n-1$ variables) whose truth table entries are respectively the left and right columns of the ith $2^{n-1} \times 2$ matrix representation of f; that is, let g_i and h_i be defined by

$$f_i(b_n, b_{n-1}, \cdots, \hat{b}_i, \cdots, b_1)$$
$$= (g_i(b_n, b_{n-1}, \cdots, \hat{b}_i, \cdots, b_1), h_i(b_n, b_{n-1}, \cdots, \hat{b}_i, \cdots, b_1))$$

(6.3)

Here, g_i and h_i are called the ith *partial functions* associated with f. By comparison with Eq. 6.2 we have

$$f(x_n, x_{n-1}, \cdots, x_1)$$
$$= g_i(x_n, x_{n-1}, \cdots, \hat{x}_i, \cdots, x_1)\bar{x}_i + h_i(x_n, x_{n-1}, \cdots, \hat{x}_i, \cdots, x_1)x_i$$

(6.4)

for each $i = 1, 2, \cdots, n$, and this provides n decompositions of f of the form (see Fig. 6.3)

$$f(x_n, x_{n-1}, \cdots, x_1)$$
$$= F(g_i(x_n, x_{n-1}, \cdots, \hat{x}_i, \cdots, x_1), h_i(x_n, x_{n-1}, \cdots, \hat{x}_i, \cdots, x_1), x_i)$$

(6.5)

where

$$F(g_i, h_i, x_i) = g_i\bar{x}_i + h_i x_i$$

(6.6)

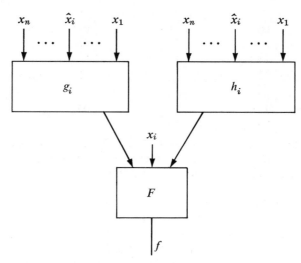

FIGURE 6.3

6.4 THE TREE CIRCUIT THEOREM

In Sec. 6.5 we list (See Tables 1.7 and 6.1) the tree circuit costs $T(f)$ for each $f: B^n \longrightarrow B$ ($n = 2$ and $n = 3$). For all $n \geq 2$, the "tree circuit theorem" that follows provides for each $i = 1, 2, \cdots, n$ a *tree circuit decomposition* (G_i, H_i, and F_i, not necessarily equal to g_i, h_i, and F, respectively)

$$f(x_n, x_{n-1}, \cdots, x_1)$$
$$= F_i(G_i(x_n, x_{n-1}, \cdots, \hat{x}_i, \cdots, x_1), H_i(x_n, x_{n-1}, \cdots, \hat{x}_i, \cdots, x_1), x_i))$$
$$(6.7)$$

as dictated by the corresponding $2^{n-1} \times 2$ matrix representation of f. Since it is assumed that $T(f)$ is well defined for $f: B^m \longrightarrow B$ with $m < n$, we list in this theorem certain formulas

$$\tau_i(f) = T(F_i) + T(G_i, H_i) \qquad (6.8)$$

in which $T(F_i)$ is determined from Table 6.1 and $T(G_i, H_i) \leq T(G_i) + T(H_i)$.

Taking

$$T(f) = \min_{1 \leq i \leq n} \tau_i(f) \qquad (6.9)$$

one obtains a criterion ($\tau_j(f) = T(f)$) for selecting the variable x_j for which the tree circuit theorem should be applied. (In case $f: B^n \longrightarrow C$ is incompletely specified, we take

$$T(f) = \min_{\substack{g_0: B^n \to B \\ v_0 \subseteq c_f}} T(g) \qquad (6.10)$$

and choose x_j and g accordingly.)

The tree circuit theorem itself is a variation of a theorem due to Curtis,† and since the reader is encouraged to consult his proof, we abbreviate ours by examining in detail only one of the 15 cases that might arise.

Theorem 6.1   (Tree Circuit Theorem): Every Boolean function $f: B^n \longrightarrow B$ can be decomposed (for each $i = 1, 2, \cdots, n$) in the form of Eq. 6.7 where the functions F_i, G_i, H_i are dictated by f.

PROOF.   Since we may take $G_i = g_i$, $H_i = h_i$, and $F_i = F$, the existence (by Eq. 6.5) of such decompositions for f is not at all in doubt. But we are interested in learning to what extent the character of f

†H. A. Curtis, "A Functional Canonical Form," *J. Assn. for Computing Mach.*, 6, 2 (April 1959).

determines or dictates the choice of suitable G_i, H_i, and F_i (some of which may be different from the obvious choices $G_i = g_i$, $H_i = h_i$, $F_i = F$). Toward this end we consider the ith partial expansion f_i or, equivalently, the ith $2^{n-1} \times 2$ matrix representation of f; we then discuss separately the *cases* 1, 2, 3, 4, in which the matrix has 1, 2, 3, 4 distinct rows. (Since B^2 has but 4 elements, these are the only cases that can arise.) With all but case 4 we also tabulate the various subcases corresponding to the exact types of rows that might occur in the individual cases. This tabulation will be found in Appendix Table II (see columns ①, ②, ③, ④, and ⑤ there; column ⑥ will be discussed in Sec. 6.6, and columns ⑦ and ⑧ are essentially the result of Probs. 3.3 through 3.8.) except for the trivial case 1 tabulated below.

Case 1: One Distinct Row.

(i) row (0,0)	(ii) row (0,1)	(iii) row (1,0)	(iv) row (1,1)
$G_i = 0$	$G_i = 0$	$G_i = 0$	$G_i = 0$
$H_i = 0$	$H_i = 0$	$H_i = 0$	$H_i = 0$
$F_i = 0$	$F_i = x_i$	$F_i = \bar{x}_i$	$F_i = 1$
$T(F_i) = 0$	$T(F_i) = 0$	$T(F_i) = 0$	$T(F_i) = 0$
$\tau_i(f) = 0$	$\tau_i(f) = 0$	$\tau_i(f) = 0$	$\tau_i(f) = 0$

Consider now Case 3(ii) in Appendix Table II; that is, suppose that the ith $2^{n-1} \times 2$ matrix representation of f has only the three types of rows: (0,0), (0,1), (1,1). In this case the functions g_i and h_i stand in the relation $g_i \leq h_i$ so that $g_i + h_i = h_i$. Furthermore, we have $g_i \bar{h}_i = 0$. Thus, if $h_i': B^{n-1} \to B$ is such that

$$\bar{g}_i h_i \leq h_i' \leq h_i$$

we must have

$$g_i + x_i h_i' \geq g_i \geq g_i \bar{x}_i$$
$$g_i + x_i h_i' \geq g_i x_i + x_i h_i' = x_i(g_i + h_i')$$
$$\geq x_i(g_i + \bar{g}_i h_i) = x_i(g_i + h_i) = x_i h_i$$

so by the definition of the least upper bound (sum) of $g_i \bar{x}_i$ and $x_i h_i$, we conclude that

$$g_i + x_i h_i' \geq g_i \bar{x}_i + h_i x_i$$

Conversely,

$$g_i \bar{x}_i + h_i x_i \geq h_i x_i \geq h_i' x_i$$
$$g_i \bar{x}_i + h_i x_i = (g_i + x_i)(h_i + \bar{x}_i) \geq g_i(h_i + \bar{x}_i) = g_i$$

because $g_i \leq h_i \leq h_i + \bar{x}_i$, so again by the definition of addition for Boolean functions we conclude that

$$g_i \bar{x}_i + h_i x_i \geq g_i + x_i h_i'$$

From the antisymmetry of Boolean algebras, these last two conclusions imply that

$$f = g_i \bar{x}_i + h_i x_i = g_i + x_i h'_i$$

Thus we may choose

$$G_i = g_i$$
$$\bar{g}_i h_i \leq H'_i \leq h_i$$
$$F_i = G_i + x_i H'_i$$

A dual analysis will show that the choice

$$g_i \leq G'_i \leq g_i + \bar{g}_i \bar{h}_i$$
$$H_i = h_i$$
$$F_i = H_i (x_i + G'_i)$$

can also be made. Thus

$$T(F_i) = 4$$
$$\tau_i(f) = 4 + \min\{T(G_i) + T(H'_i), T(G'_i) + T(H_i)\}$$

as quoted in columns ④ and ⑤ of Appendix Table II. ∎

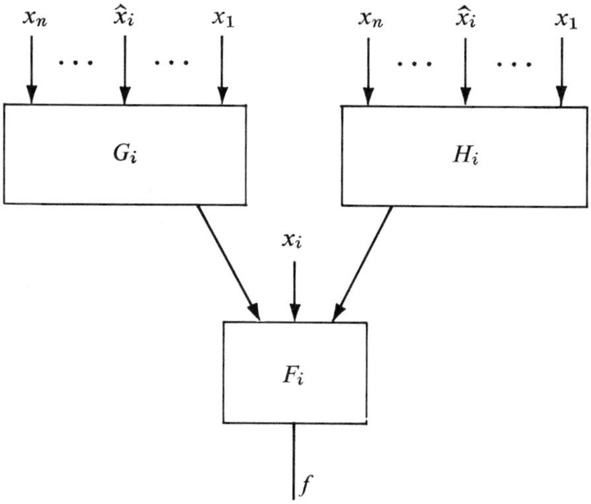

FIGURE 6.4

The term *tree circuit* will refer to a cirucit that is constructed by iterated application of Theorem 6.1. After one application (for some i) of Theorem 6.1, we have the structure of Fig. 6.4. The single exception is that (due to Case 4 of Theorem 6.1) we sometimes allow the structure of Fig. 6.5. In any event, the subfunctions G_i, H_i (and K_i in the exceptional

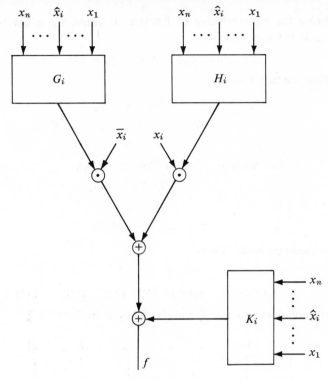

FIGURE 6.5

case) are functions of $n - 1$ variables and may be decomposed in the same manner as was done with f. Since F_i has in every case an obvious two-input-per-gate circuit (cf. Sec. 6.5) and the subfunctions are functions of $n - 1$ variables, we can conclude by induction that tree circuits are two-input-per-gate circuits, provided we have available two-input-per-gate circuits for functions of two variables. (There being only 16 such functions, we will analyze this situation exhaustively in the next section.)

EXAMPLE 6.3

Consider the Boolean function $f: B^4 \longrightarrow B$ whose $2^{4-1} \times 2$ matrices were constructed in Example 6.2. We note that the third matrix

$$
x_4 x_2 x_1 \quad
\begin{array}{c}
x_3 \\
\hline
\begin{array}{|c|}
\hline
01 \\
01 \\
11 \\
01 \\
01 \\
01 \\
00 \\
00 \\
\hline
\end{array}
\end{array}
$$

contains only three distinct rows $(0, 0)$, $(0, 1)$, $(1, 1)$ so that we find ourselves in case 3 (ii) of Table II. Hence

$$f(x_4, x_3, x_2, x_1) = F_3(G_3, H'_3, x_3) = G_3 + x_3 H'_3$$

where G_3 and H'_3 have truth tables (H'_3 is incompletely specified)

x_4	x_2	x_1	G_3	H'_3
0	0	0	0	1
0	0	1	0	1
0	1	0	1	I
0	1	1	0	1
1	0	0	0	1
1	0	1	0	1
1	1	0	0	0
1	1	1	0	0

Alternatively, we may write

$$f(x_4, x_3, x_2, x_1) = H_3(x_3 + G'_3)$$

where G'_3 and H_3 have the truth tables

x_4	x_2	x_1	G'_3	H_3
0	0	0	0	1
0	0	1	0	1
0	1	0	1	1
0	1	1	0	1
1	0	0	0	1
1	0	1	0	1
1	1	0	I	0
1	1	1	I	0

A satisfactory tree circuit algorithm should give criteria for choosing between such alternatives (as well as choosing the variable x_j for which the tree circuit

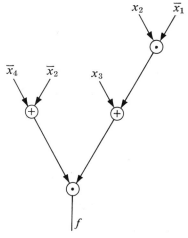

FIGURE 6.6

theorem should be applied). If the second alternative were chosen, it would not be difficult to see that a second application of Theorem 6.1 to the subfunctions G_3', H_3 could lead (if the appropriate variables x_j were selected by the tree circuit algorithm) to the tree circuit of Fig. 6.6, which has diode cost $4(2) = 8$. Note that $M(f) = 10$, as evidenced by the minimal form circuit of Fig. 6.7.

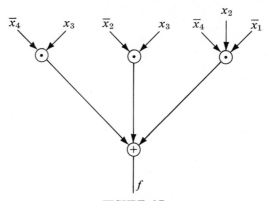

FIGURE 6.7

6.5 TWO- AND THREE-VARIABLE TREE CIRCUITS

The basic inequality ($T(f) \leq M'(f)$ for all $f: B^n \longrightarrow B$) of the next section requires an inductive proof. Thus, one is aided in proving or understanding this inequality by a thorough consideration of the two-variable tree circuit costs. Using the class decomposition (cf. Sec. 1.16)

$$\lambda_4 = \{A, B, C, D, E, F\}$$

of $B(2)$, an exhaustive treatment requires only the computation of the tree circuit costs of representatives of the classes A, B, C, D, E.

EXAMPLE 6.4

Consider $f_1 \in A$ in Tables 1.3 or 1.7. Since f_1 has the matrix representations

$$x_2 \begin{array}{c} x_1 \\ \begin{array}{|c|} \hline 10 \\ \hline 00 \\ \hline \end{array} \end{array} \qquad x_1 \begin{array}{c} x_2 \\ \begin{array}{|c|} \hline 10 \\ \hline 00 \\ \hline \end{array} \end{array}$$

in each matrix we have case 2(ii) of Theorem 6.1. Thus

$$G_1 = g_1 = \bar{x}_2 \qquad G_2 = g_2 = \bar{x}_1$$
$$H_1 = 0 \qquad H_2 = 0$$

$$F_1 = G_1 \bar{x}_1 = \bar{x}_2 \bar{x}_1 \qquad F_2 = G_2 \bar{x}_2 = \bar{x}_1 \bar{x}_2$$

so that the tree circuit form of f_1 is indentical with its minimal circuit (cf. Fig. 1.16) and with its minimal (sum of products) form.

This behavior is generally true for $f: B^2 \longrightarrow B$, as a consideration of representatives of the other classes would reveal. Since each minimal circuit for $f: B^2 \longrightarrow B$ is a two-input-per-gate circuit we have a corollary.

Corollary 6.2 $T(f) = M'(f) = M(f) = m(f)$ for all $f: B^2 \longrightarrow B$.

When considering Boolean functions $f: B^3 \longrightarrow B$, one is aided by the equivalence relation $\cong$ (cf. Secs. 1.15 and 2.11) on $B(3)$. For the 22 equivalence classes, one may choose representatives as shown in Table 6.1 and compute the tree circuit costs of each.

EXAMPLE 6.5

Consider $f = f_{67} \in \text{III}_2$ (Table 6.1) and examine its matrix representations:

$$
x_3 x_2
\begin{array}{|c|}
\hline
\begin{array}{c} x_1 \\ \hline 11 \\ 00 \\ 00 \\ 10 \end{array} \\
\hline
\end{array}
\qquad
x_3 x_1
\begin{array}{|c|}
\hline
\begin{array}{c} x_2 \\ \hline 10 \\ 10 \\ 01 \\ 00 \end{array} \\
\hline
\end{array}
\qquad
x_2 x_1
\begin{array}{|c|}
\hline
\begin{array}{c} x_3 \\ \hline 10 \\ 10 \\ 01 \\ 00 \end{array} \\
\hline
\end{array}
$$

Case   3(iii)   3(i)   3(i)

In the first matrix we have Case 3(iii) of Theorem 6.1 so that

$$\tau_1(f) = 4 + \min\{T(G_1) + T(H_1'), T(G_1') + T(H_1)\} = 4 + \min\{6, 4\} = 8$$

because the truth tables

x_3	x_2	G_1	H_1'	G_1'	H_1
0	0	1	1	I	1
0	1	0	I	0	0
1	0	0	I	0	0
1	1	1	0	1	0

imply (using Corollary 6.2 and the material of Secs. 1.18 and 3.16)

$$T(G_1) = 6$$
$$T(H_1') = 0$$
$$T(G_1') = 2$$
$$T(H_1) = 2$$

The last two matrices are identical, so that we need only consider the first of these. Using the formulas in Case 3(i) of Theorem 6.1 we obtain truth tables

x_3	x_1	G_2'	H_2''	G_2''	H_2'	G_2	H_2
0	0	1	1	1	0	1	0
0	1	1	1	1	0	1	0
1	0	0	1	1	1	0	1
1	1	I	0	0	I	0	0

			CLASS NAME: O_1	I_1	II_1	II_2	II_3	III_1	III_2	III_3	IV_1	IV_2	IV_3	IV_4	IV_5	IV_6	V_1	V_2	V_3	VI_1	VI_2	VI_3	VII_1	VIII_1
x_3	x_2	x_1	f_0	f_1	f_3	f_9	f_{129}	f_7	f_{67}	f_{41}	f_{15}	f_{23}	f_{39}	f_{135}	f_{195}	f_{105}	f_{248}	f_{214}	f_{188}	f_{252}	f_{246}	f_{126}	f_{254}	f_{255}
0	0	0	0	1	1	1	1	1	1	1	1	1	1	1	1	1	0	0	0	0	0	0	0	1
0	0	1	0	0	1	0	0	1	1	0	1	1	1	1	1	0	0	1	0	0	1	1	1	1
0	1	0	0	0	0	0	0	1	0	0	1	1	1	1	0	0	0	1	1	1	1	1	1	1
0	1	1	0	0	0	1	0	0	0	1	1	0	0	0	0	1	1	0	1	1	0	1	1	1
1	0	0	0	0	0	0	0	0	0	0	0	1	0	0	0	0	1	1	1	1	1	1	1	1
1	0	1	0	0	0	0	0	0	0	1	0	0	1	0	0	1	1	0	1	1	1	1	1	1
1	1	0	0	0	0	0	0	0	1	0	0	0	0	0	1	1	1	1	0	1	1	1	1	1
1	1	1	0	0	0	0	1	0	0	0	0	0	0	1	1	0	1	1	1	1	1	0	1	1
$M(f_i)$			0	3	2	8	8	6	7	12	0	9	6	10	6	16	4	13	9	2	7	9	3	0
$M'(f_i)$			0	4	2	10	10	6	8	16	0	10	6	12	6	22	4	16	10	2	8	10	4	0
$T(f_i)$			0	4	2	8	10	4	8	12	0	8	6	8	6	12	4	12	8	2	8	10	4	0

TABLE 6.1.

370

so that

$$T(G_2') = 0 \qquad T(G_2'') = 2 \qquad T(G_2) = 0$$

$$T(H_2'') = 2 \qquad T(H_2') = 0 \qquad T(H_2) = 2$$

and

$$\tau_2(f) = \tau_3(f) = \min \{8 + 0 + 2, 8 + 2 + 0, 6 + 0 + 2\} = 8$$

Then, according to Eq. 6.9,

$$T(f) = T(f_{67}) = 8$$

which accounts for one of the entries in Table 6.1. One of the resulting tree circuits for f_{67}, having cost 8, is shown in Fig. 6.8—that arising from the first matrix representation.

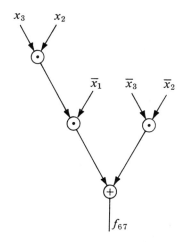

FIGURE 6.8

In a similar way one computes $T(f_i)$ for the other representatives of Table 6.1, the procedure being exactly as we have indicated for f_{67}, that is, using the formulas of the tree circuit theorem and the minimal two-variable circuits. Scanning the figures in the last two rows of Table 6.1, we conclude (because of Theorem 1.16) the following corollary.

Corollary 6.3. $T(f) \leq M'(f)$ for all $f: B^3 \rightarrow B$.

6.6 THE TREE CIRCUIT INEQUALITY

Since the functions G_i, H_i (and perhaps K_i) that appear in the formulas (those of the form of Eq. 6.8) of Theorem 6.1 are themselves functions of $n - 1$ variables, Eq. 6.9 serves by recursion to define unambiguously a unique (even) integer $T(f)$ for each $f: B^n \longrightarrow B$. (If $f: B^n \longrightarrow C$, one uses Eq. 6.10 with Eq. 6.9.) To extend the results of the preceding section, there are obvious technical difficulties inherent in any attempt to compute $T(f)$ when n is even moderately large, owing to its recursive definition (from the "last stage in," so to speak). Nevertheless we can assert the following theorem.

Theorem 6.4   (The Tree Circuit Inequality): $T(f) \leq M'(f)$ for all $f: B^n \longrightarrow B$.

This theorem asserts that tree circuit representations are uniformly preferable (among the class of two-input-per-gate circuits) to those that arise from the more conventional minimization techniques. While its proof† uses simple mathematical induction and the initial arguments ($n = 2$, $n = 3$) can be seen from the results of the preceding section, the tree circuit theorem and the propositions claimed in Probs. 3.3 through 3.8 must all be employed. Owing to the length of the proof, we content ourselves instead with a discussion of its application to the problem of obtaining economical tree-circuit representations.

When attempting to synthesize economical tree-circuit representations for Boolean functions $f: B^n \longrightarrow B$ ($n \geq 4$), one might choose to observe the following hierarchy:

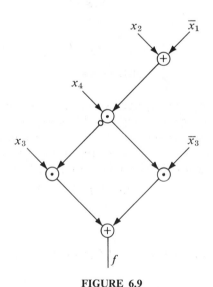

FIGURE 6.9

†R.E. Prather, "On Tree Circuits," *IEEE Trans. on Electronic Computers*, EC-14, 6(December 1965).

Case 1
Case 2(iii)
Case 2(i), (ii), (v), (vi)
Case 2(iv)
Case 3(ii), (iii)
Case 3(i), (iv)
Case 4

In using this convention, one applies Theorem 6.1 with respect to that variable x_i whose $2^{n-1} \times 2$ matrix has rows corresponding to the case of highest ranking among the n variables $x_1, x_2, \cdots, x_n$.

EXAMPLE 6.6

If $f: B^4 \longrightarrow B$ has the truth table and matrices

x_4	x_3	x_2	x_1	f
0	0	0	0	0
0	0	0	1	0
0	0	1	0	0
0	0	1	1	0
0	1	0	0	1
0	1	0	1	1
0	1	1	0	1
0	1	1	1	1
1	0	0	0	1
1	0	0	1	0
1	0	1	0	1
1	0	1	1	1
1	1	0	0	0
1	1	0	1	1
1	1	1	0	0
1	1	1	1	0

x_1 ($x_4 x_3 x_2$):

| 00 |
| 00 |
| 11 |
| 11 |
| 10 |
| 11 |
| 01 |
| 00 |

Case 4

x_2 ($x_4 x_3 x_1$):

| 00 |
| 00 |
| 11 |
| 11 |
| 11 |
| 01 |
| 00 |
| 10 |

Case 4

x_3 ($x_4 x_2 x_1$):

| 01 |
| 01 |
| 01 |
| 01 |
| 10 |
| 01 |
| 10 |
| 10 |

Case 2(iv)

x_4 ($x_3 x_2 x_1$):

| 01 |
| 00 |
| 01 |
| 01 |
| 10 |
| 11 |
| 10 |
| 10 |

Case 4

we choose to apply Theorem 6.1 with respect to the variable x_3, writing

$$f(x_4, x_3, x_2, x_1) = F_3(G_3, H_3, x_3) = G_3 \bar{x}_3 + \bar{G}_3 x_3$$

with

$$G_3 = g_3 = \bar{h}_3$$
$$H_3 = \bar{g}_3 = h_3$$

Using the most economical tree circuit for g_3 (of cost 4, since $g_3 \cong f_7$ in Table 6.1), we obtain the circuit of Fig. 6.9, which has cost 10. (Note that $M(f) = 15$ and $M'(f) = 20$.)

The shortcoming of the foregoing selection procedure is immediately apparent: Particularly for large n—the problems of greatest interest—one has to expect that it will often happen that case 4 is obtained for every $2^{n-1} \times 2$ matrix. In such instances, our "course" selection criterion gives no preference. But here (and wherever "ties" occur in the application of the "course" criteria arising from the hierarchy of cases) is where the practical significance of the tree circuit inequality (Theorem 6.4) is realized.

Since $T(f) \leq M'(f)$ for each $f: B^n \longrightarrow B$, we approximate the figures $\tau_i(f)$ occurring in column ⑤ of Appendix Table II by appropriate figures $t_i(f)$ as shown in column ⑥, and replace Eq. 6.9 by

$$T'(f) = \min_{1 \leq i \leq n} t_i(f) \tag{6.11}$$

Our "fine" selection criterion may then be stated: Choose x_j (for application of Theorem 6.1) for which $t_j(f) = T'(f)$. This refined estimation procedure is to be used whenever "ties" occur in the application of the "course" selection process. Since $M(G_i)$, $M(H_i)$, etc., may be computed according to the methods of Chapter 3, the estimates $t_i(f)$ are readily obtainable with the help of Eq. 6.1.

EXAMPLE 6.7

Consider the Boolean function $f: B^5 \longrightarrow B$ having 16×2 matrices as follows:

	x_1		x_2		x_3		x_4		x_5
	00		00		01		01		00
	01		01		00		00		01
	10		10		00		01		00
	01		01		11		10		10
	10		11		11		11		10
	10		00		01		01		01
	11		11		11		01		00
$x_5x_4x_3x_2$	11	$x_5x_4x_3x_1$	11	$x_5x_4x_2x_1$	01	$x_5x_3x_2x_1$	11	$x_4x_3x_2x_1$	10
	01		00		00		01		11
	00		10		11		10		00
	01		00		00		01		11
	00		10		00		01		01
	10		11		10		00		10
	11		01		01		11		11
	01		00		10		00		10
	01		11		11		01		11

Clearly, we have case 4 of Table II for each variable x_i. In computing the estimates $t_i(f)$, one finds (using Eq. 6.1 and the methods of Chapter 3)

$M'(G_1) = 12$	$M'(G_2) = 18$	$M'(G_3) = 18$	$M'(G_4) = 24$	$M'(G_5) = 22$
$M'(H_1) = 20$	$M'(H_2) = 22$	$M'(H_3) = 16$	$M'(H_4) = 24$	$M'(H_5) = 22$
$M'(G_1') = 8$	$M'(G_2') = 14$	$M'(G_3') = 10$	$M'(G_4') = 2$	$M'(G_5') = 10$
$M'(H_1') = 14$	$M'(H_2') = 10$	$M'(H_3') = 12$	$M'(H_4') = 14$	$M'(H_5') = 10$
$M'(K_1) = 10$	$M'(K_2) = 10$	$M'(K_3) = 22$	$M'(K_4) = 28$	$M'(K_5) = 16$
$t_1(f) = 38$	$t_2(f) = 42$	$t_3(f) = 40$	$t_4(f) = 52$	$t_5(f) = 44$

so that

$$T'(f) = 38 = t_1(f)$$

and Theorem 6.1 is to be applied with respect to the variable x_1.

This gives Fig. 6.10, in which $g(x_5, x_4, x_3, x_2)$ and $h(x_5, x_4, x_3, x_2)$ have the

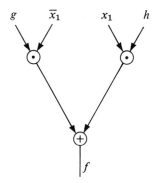

$g \qquad \bar{x}_1 \qquad x_1 \qquad h$

FIGURE 6.10

following 8×2 matrices:

For g:

	x_2		x_3		x_4		x_5
$x_5x_4x_3$	00 10 11 11 00 00 11 00	$x_5x_4x_2$	01 00 11 11 00 00 10 10	$x_5x_3x_2$	01 01 11 01 01 01 00 00	$x_4x_3x_2$	00 00 10 00 11 11 10 10

For h:

	x_2		x_3		x_4		x_5
$x_5x_4x_3$	01 01 00 11 10 10 01 11	$x_5x_4x_2$	00 11 01 01 11 00 01 11	$x_5x_3x_2$	00 10 01 11 10 01 11 01	$x_4x_3x_2$	01 10 01 10 00 01 11 11

respectively. At this stage, the exact formulas for $\tau_i(g)$ and $\tau_i(h)$ could be used in conjunction with the figures of Table 6.1. If this is done, we have, by the formulas of Theorem 6.1,

Case 3(iii) $\tau_2(g) = 4 + \min\{6 + 0, 2 + 4\} = 10$

Case 4: $\tau_3(g) = \min\{6 + 0 + 4, 8 + 0 + 2 + 2\} = 10$

Case 3(ii): $\tau_4(g) = 4 + \min\{4 + 2, 2 + 2\} = 8$

Case 3(iii): $\tau_5(g) = 4 + \min\{4 + 0, 4 + 2\} = 8$

Case 4: $\tau_2(h) = \min\{6 + 6 + 8, 8 + 2 + 6 + 2\} = 18$

Case 3(ii): $\tau_3(h) = 4 + \min\{12 + 0, 4 + 8\} = 16$

Case 4: $\tau_4(h) = \min\{6 + 6 + 4, 8 + 6 + 4 + 0\} = 16$

Case 4: $\tau_5(h) = \min\{6 + 6 + 8, 8 + 2 + 6 + 2\} = 18$

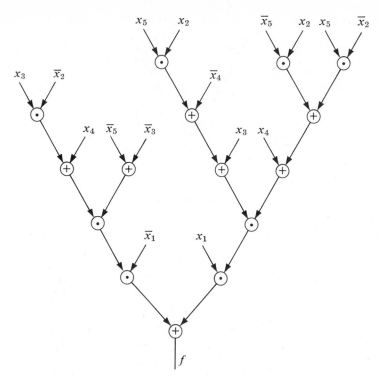

FIGURE 6.11

showing that a tree circuit having diode cost $6 + 8 + 16 = 30$ will result if Theorem 6.1 is applied to g with respect to either x_4 or x_5 and to h with respect to either x_3 or x_4. One such circuit is shown in Fig. 6.11, where the variables x_4 and x_3 were selected respectively. It is interesting to point out that the estimates $t_i(g)$ and $t_i(h)$ for $i = 2, 3, 4, 5$ are in complete agreement with the exact figures $\tau_i(g)$ and $\tau_i(h)$ listed above; the reader may want to test his understanding of the estimation formulas t_i by verifying this statement.

6.7 MULTIPLE-OUTPUT AND INCOMPLETELY SPECIFIED PROBLEMS

In a typical application of Theorem 6.1 to a Boolean function $f(x_n, x_{n-1}, \cdots, x_1)$, there result *two* Boolean functions $G_i(x_n, x_{n-1}, \cdots, \hat{x}_i, \cdots, x_1)$ and $H(x_n, x_{n-1}, \cdots, \hat{x}_i, \cdots, x_1)$ of *the same* $n - 1$ variables, and (as a glance at, say, case 3(ii) reveals) the functions G_i and H_i are, in general, *incompletely specified*. Thus, even when we begin the synthesis of *one completely specified* function, we are inevitably led to a consideration of the multiple-output, incompletely specified synthesis problem. The need for revised techniques is all the more apparent if we have an incompletely specified, multiple-output problem to begin with. There is every reason to suppose that specialized techniques which acknowledge the existence of these two new complications might yield more satisfactory implementations.

EXAMPLE 6.8

Consider the family $F = \{f_1, f_2, f_3, f_4\}$ of functions $f_j : B^3 \rightarrow C$, shown in the following truth tables:

x_3	x_2	x_1	f_1	f_2	f_3	f_4
0	0	0	0	1	0	0
0	0	1	1	1	1	1
0	1	0	I	0	1	0
0	1	1	0	0	1	1
1	0	0	I	0	I	0
1	0	1	I	0	1	0
1	1	0	0	0	0	0
1	1	1	1	1	1	1

Using the cell

$$c_{f_1} = (1, 0, I, I, 0, I, 1, 0) \in C^8$$

$$C_{f_1} = D(c_{f_1}) = (130, 182)$$

and the computations of Sec. 2.9 (cf. Example 2.18) we can compute all the decimal vertices:

$$
\begin{array}{ccccccc}
 & & 4 & 16 & 32 & & \\
130 & / & 134 & 146 & 162 & / & 150 \\
 & & & 166 & 178 & / & 182
\end{array}
$$

of the 3-cell $C_{f_1} = D(c_{f_1})$. These decimal vertices correspond to the characteristic numbers $\eta(g) = D(v_g) = V_g$ of the $2^3 = 8$ c.s.b.f.'s g, which have the property $v_g \subseteq c_{f_1}$. These functions g belong to certain classes $[g]$ having certain tree circuit costs

$\eta(g) = V_g$	$[g]$	$T(g)$
130	II_2	8
134	III_3	12
146	III_3	12
162	III_1	4
150	IV_6	12
166	IV_4	8
178	IV_2	8
182	V_2	12

as determined by Appendix Table I and Table 6.1, respectively. Thus, if we were only interested in finding the most economical tree circuit for f_1, we could have (from Eq. 6.10) $T(f_1) = 4$ by choosing the unspecified entries according to $162 = V_{F_1}$ where F_1 is the c.s.b.f. of the first of the four truth tables:

x_3	x_2	x_1	F_1	$F_2 = f_2$	F_3	F_4
0	0	0	0	1	0	0
0	0	1	1	1	1	1
0	1	0	0	0	1	0
0	1	1	0	0	1	1
1	0	0	0	0	0	0
1	0	1	1	0	1	0
1	1	0	0	0	0	0
1	1	1	1	1	1	1

Similarly, the c.s.b.f.'s $F_2 \in \text{III}_2$, $F_3 \in \text{V}_1$, and $F_4 \in \text{III}_1$ will lead to minimum cost tree circuits for f_2, f_3, and f_4, having costs 8, 4, and 4, respectively. Thus the four separate tree circuits would have total cost $4 + 8 + 4 + 4 = 20$.

But suppose instead that the unspecified entries were chosen so that we have c.s.b.f.'s F'_i in place of F_i ($i = 1, 2, 3, 4$) as shown:

x_3	x_2	x_1	F'_1	F'_2	F'_3	F'_4
0	0	0	0	1	0	0
0	0	1	1	1	1	1
0	1	0	0	0	1	0
0	1	1	0	0	1	1
1	0	0	0	0	1	0
1	0	1	0	0	1	0
1	1	0	0	0	0	0
1	1	1	1	1	1	1

Then, when considering their 4×2 matrices with respect to x_1, we find

$$F'_1: \quad x_1 \qquad F'_2: \quad x_1 \qquad F'_3: \quad x_1 \qquad F'_4: \quad x_1$$

	x_1
	01
	00
x_3x_2	00
	01

g_1h_1

Case 2(i)

	x_1
	11
	00
x_3x_2	00
	01

g_2h_2

Case 3(ii)

	x_1
	01
	11
x_3x_2	11
	01

g_3h_3

Case 2(v)

	x_1
	01
	01
x_3x_2	00
	01

g_4h_4

Case 2(i)

so that Theorem 6.1 gives the formulas:

$$F'_1 = H_1 x_1 \qquad\qquad H_1 = h_1$$

$$F'_2 = H_2(x_1 + G'_2) \qquad g_2 \le G'_2 \le g_2 + \bar{g}_2\bar{h}_2$$

$$H_2 = h_2 = h_1$$

$$F'_3 = G_3 + x_1 \qquad G_3 = g_3 = \bar{h}_1$$

$$F'_4 = H_4 x_1 \qquad H_4 = h_4$$

Now, if we implement

$$G'_2 = \bar{x}_2 \in F$$

$$h_1 \in E$$
$$h_4 \in C$$

a multiple-output circuit can be constructed (see Fig. 6.12) having cost $2 + 4 + 2 + 2$ plus the cost of the classes CE. But according to Table 1.8, this cost is 6, so that by considering the partial expansions of each function F_i' with respect to x_1, we have found a multiple-output tree circuit costing 4 less than does the total cost of the four separate minimal tree circuits.

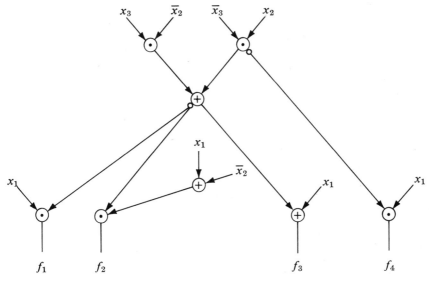

FIGURE 6.12

A quite general approach to the multiple-output, incompletely specified problem can be given after we list the tree-circuit upper bounds, which are to be incorporated as estimates in our tree-circuit synthesis algorithm. This approach will utilize the outstanding characteristic of the preceding example—that considerable economy is likely to be achieved in synthesizing a family $F = \{f_1, f_2, \cdots, f_m\}$ of i.s.b.f.'s if Theorem 6.1 is applied with respect to the *same variable x_i for each* function. This becomes apparent when we realize that the subfunctions G_i, H_i (roughly $2n$ in number) arising from the tree circuit theorem will then be functions of the same $n - 1$ variables. We then have the possibility that several of these may be equal or at least compatible (cf. Sec. 3.15), so that fewer than the expected (say, $2n$) number of subfunctions need to be implemented. It is this prospect that will serve as our inspiration for treating multiple-output functions as being other than m separate single-output circuits to synthesize.

6.8 TREE-CIRCUIT UPPER BOUNDS

We are interested in finding integers $B_T(n, k)$ for which it can be said that if $F = \{f_1, f_2, \cdots, f_k\}$ is a family of k c.s.b.f.'s $f_j : B^n \to B$ ($j = 1, 2, \cdots, k$) of the same n variables, a multiple-output tree circuit exists for F whose cost is less than or equal to $B_T(n, k)$. Ideally, one would hope that these upper bounds would be so "tight" that for each pair of integers n and k, there actually exist a family F of k functions of n variables whose least expensive tree circuit has $B_T(n, k)$ as its cost. (When this is the case, we write $\bar{B}_T(n, k)$ rather than $B_T(n, k)$.) We will be able to achieve this desirable situation when $n \leq 3$.

k	$\bar{B}_T(2, k)$
1	6
2	6
3	8
4	8
5	10
6	10
7	10
.	.
.	.
.	.

TABLE 6.2

For $n = 2$ there is no difficulty. We simply translate the information of Table 1.8 into that of Table 6.2. Using the philosophy embodied in the discussion of the preceding section, the integers $\bar{B}_T(3, k)$ have been determined†; we tabulate the results in Table 6.3. Note that $\bar{B}_T(2, k) < k\bar{B}_T(2, 1)$ and, similarly, $\bar{B}_T(3, k) < k\bar{B}_T(3, 1)$ as befits the multiple-output approach outlined in Sec. 6.7. The reader should also observe the "saturation" effects; that is, that

$$\bar{B}_T(2, k) = \bar{B}_T(2, 5) \qquad \text{for } k > 5$$

$$\bar{B}_T(3, k) = \bar{B}_T(3, 123) \qquad \text{for } k > 123$$

The first of these can be explained when it is observed that we could have no worse situation than the problem of implementing all five classes ABCDE of functions of two variables; and this problem has 10 as its cost

†R.E. Prather, "Three-Variable Multiple Output Tree Circuits," *IEEE Trans. on Electronic Computers*, EC-15, 1 (February 1966).

k	$\bar{B}_T(3, k)$	k	$\bar{B}_T(3, k)$	k	$\bar{B}_T(3, k)$	k	$\bar{B}_T(3, k)$
1	12	33	202	65	362	97	484
2	18	34	208	66	366	98	488
3	26	35	212	67	372	99	490
4	34	36	218	68	376	100	494
5	40	37	224	69	380	101	498
6	46	38	228	70	386	102	500
7	52	39	234	71	390	103	504
8	58	40	240	72	394	104	508
9	64	41	244	73	400	105	510
10	70	42	250	74	404	106	512
11	76	43	256	75	408	107	514
12	82	44	260	76	412	108	516
13	88	45	266	77	416	109	518
14	94	46	272	78	418	110	520
15	100	47	276	79	422	111	522
16	106	48	282	80	428	112	524
17	112	49	288	81	430	113	526
18	118	50	292	82	434	114	528
19	124	51	296	83	438	115	528
20	130	52	302	84	440	116	530
21	136	53	306	85	444	117	532
22	142	54	310	86	448	118	532
23	148	55	316	87	450	119	534
24	154	56	320	88	454	120	536
25	160	57	324	89	458	121	536
26	164	58	330	90	460	122	538
27	170	59	334	91	464	123	540
28	176	60	338	92	468	124	540
29	180	61	344	93	470	125	540
30	186	62	348	94	474	126	.
31	192	63	352	95	478	127	.
32	196	64	358	96	480	128	.

TABLE 6.3

(cf. Table 1.8). The upper limit 540 in Table 6.3 has a similar meaning; the reader should consult the aforementioned reference for a more complete understanding.

Now, for the bounds $B_T(n, k)$, $n \geq 4$, we use the inequality

$$\bar{B}_T(n, k) \leq 6k + B_T(n - 1, 2k) \qquad (6.12)$$

to recursively define upper bounds ($n \geq 4$)

$$B_T(n, k) = 6k + B_T(n - 1, 2k) \qquad (6.13)$$

The reasoning behind the inequality of Eq. 6.12 is found in the tree circuit theorem. Let $F = \{f_1, f_2, \cdots, f_k\}$ be a family of k functions of the same n variables. In an application of Theorem 6.1 to these k functions in the "worst case" we would have case 4 of that theorem with respect to every variable x_i. Assuming that none of the $2k$ functions G_i, H_i is compatible ($i = 1, 2, \cdots, n$), we have

$$\tau_i(f_j) \leq 6 + \tau(G_i) + \tau(H_i)$$

for all i, j. There being k such functions, we accumulate a cost $6k$ together with the cost of implementing the $2k$ functions G_i, H_i. Since the latter is estimated by $B_T(n - 1, 2k)$, owing to the fact that the subfunctions G_i, H_i are of $n - 1$ variables, we obtain Eq. 6.12. A partial listing of the bounds $B_T(n, k)$ obtained from Eq. 6.13 is shown in Table 6.4.

k \ n	4	5	6	7	8	9	10
1	24	52	100	196	382	746	1302
2	46	94	190	376	740	1296	
3	64	136	280	552	1038		
4	82	178	364	718	1284		
5	100	220	450	878			
6	118	262	534	1020			
7	136	302	614	1154			
8	154	340	694	1260			
9	172	380	762				
10	190	420	848				
11	208	458	916				
12	226	498	984				
13	242	536	1054				
14	260	572	1112				
15	276	608	1164				
16	292	646	1212				
17	310	682					
18	326	718					
19	342	754					
20	360	788					
21	376	818					
22	392	850					
23	410	882					
24	426	912					
25	442	944					
26	458	976					
27	472	1002					
28	488	1028					
29	504	1050					
30	518	1074					
31	534	1098					
32	550	1116					
33	564						
34	580						
35	596						
36	610						

k \ n	4
37	626
38	640
39	652
40	668
41	680
42	692
43	706
44	718
45	730
46	744
47	756
48	768
49	782
50	794
51	806
52	820
53	830
54	840
55	850
56	860
57	868
58	876
59	886
60	894
61	902
62	912
63	918
64	924

TABLE 6.4

6.9 TREE CIRCUITS VERSUS MINIMAL FORMS

The tree circuit inequality (Theorem 6.4) provides one sort of comparison between tree circuits and minimal (sums of products) forms, although the cost $M'(f)$ occurring in that theorem is the cost of the two-input-per-gate equivalent of the minimal form rather than $M(f)$ itself. In this section we will obtain another comparison (which is in a sense, more direct) between these two types of circuit realizations of a Boolean function f.

Lemma 6.5   For each integer n there exists a c.s.b.f. $f^{(n)}: B^n \to B$ having the properties:
  (1) $|K^0(f^{(n)})| = 2^{n-1}$.
  (2) $\Delta(v, v') > 1$ for all $v, v' \in K^0(f^{(n)})$.

PROOF.   To see this, we proceed inductively, defining

$$f^{(1)} = x_1$$

$$f^{(2)} = x_2 \oplus x_1 = x_1 \bar{x}_2 + \bar{x}_1 x_2$$

and, in general, supposing that $f^{(n-1)}$ has been defined, we put

$$f^{(n)} = f^{(n-1)} \bar{x}_n + \bar{f}^{(n-1)} x_n$$

(The resulting truth tables for $n = 3, 4$ are shown in Table 6.5.) Properties (1) and (2) are verified by mathematical induction; we leave the details as an exercise. ∎

x_3	x_2	x_1	$f^{(3)}$	x_4	x_3	x_2	x_1	$f^{(4)}$
0	0	0	0	0	0	0	0	0
0	0	1	1	0	0	0	1	1
0	1	0	1	0	0	1	0	1
0	1	1	0	0	0	1	1	0
1	0	0	1	0	1	0	0	1
1	0	1	0	0	1	0	1	0
1	1	0	0	0	1	1	0	0
1	1	1	1	0	1	1	1	1
				1	0	0	0	1
				1	0	0	1	0
				1	0	1	0	0
				1	0	1	1	1
				1	1	0	0	0
				1	1	0	1	1
				1	1	1	0	1
				1	1	1	1	0

TABLE 6.5

Since $f^{(n)}$ has a 0-skeleton $K^0(f^{(n)})$ consisting of 2^{n-1} mutually nonadjacent vertices, each vertex is itself an essential cell, so that

$$M(f^{(n)}) = 2^{n-1} + \sum_{j=1}^{2^{n-1}} n = 2^{n-1} + n \cdot 2^{n-1} = (n+1)2^{n-1} \quad (6.14)$$

and, according to Eq. 6.1,

$$M'(f^{(n)}) = 2[M(f^{(n)}) - 2^{n-1} - 1] = n2^n - 2 \quad (6.15)$$

It is also clear that if $f: B^n \longrightarrow B$ has more than 2^{n-1} vertices in $K^0(f)$, $K^0(f)$ must have a pair of adjacent vertices. Thus,

$$M(f) \leq M(f^{(n)}) \quad (6.16)$$

for all $f: B^n \longrightarrow B$ and similarly for the cost M'. If we were to introduce a *least* upper bound $\bar{B}_M(n)$ for the minimal form cost $M(f)$ of functions $f: B^n \longrightarrow B$, it would then necessarily (because of Eq. 6.16) agree with the figure found in Eq. 6.14; that is,

$$\bar{B}_M(n) = (n+1)2^{n-1} \quad (6.17)$$

and, similarly,

$$\bar{B}_{M'}(n) = n2^n - 2 \quad (6.18)$$

for the least upper bound on the cost of the two-input-per-gate equivalent. If we tabulate a few of these figures (see Table 6.6) together with

$$B_T(n) \equiv B_T(n, 1) \quad (6.19)$$

as determined from Table 6.4, a comparison most definitely favors tree circuits over minimal forms. This comparison could be taken with the tree circuit inequality as the justification for devoting an entire chapter to the study of tree circuits.

n	$\bar{B}_M(n)$	$\bar{B}_{M'}(n)$	$B_T(n)$
2	6	6	6
3	16	22	12
4	40	62	24
5	96	158	52
6	224	382	100
7	512	894	196
8	1152	2046	382
9	2560	4616	746
10	5632	10238	1302

TABLE 6.6

6.10   TREE-CIRCUIT ESTIMATES

It has been observed (cf. Example 6.8) that when synthesizing a family $F = \{f_1, f_2, \cdots, f_m\}$ of i.s.b.f.'s $f_j: B^n \longrightarrow C$ of the same n variables, one is likely to achieve economy by applying the tree circuit theorem with respect to the *same variable* x_i *for each* function. Suppose the ith partial expansions (or their $2^{n-1} \times 2$ matrices) for each function are drawn; and to each function $f \in F$ we assign an integer $d_i(f)$ as determined by Table 6.7. When a c.s.b.f. $f(x_n, x_{n-1}, \cdots, x_1)$ has the tree circuit decomposition of Eq. 6.7, this integer $d_i(f)$ is given by

$$d_i(f) = \min T(F_i) \tag{6.20}$$

DESCRIPTION		CASE	$d_i(f)$
I	One distinct row or $g_i \approx h_i$ (in the sense of Prob. 3.42)	1 or 2(iii)	0
II	Two distinct rows other than the pair $(0, 1)$, $(1, 0)$	2(i), (ii), (v) or (vi)	2
III	Three distinct rows not including the pair $(0, 1)$, $(1, 0)$	3(ii) or (iii)	4
IV	Both rows $(0, 1)$ and $(1, 0)$ appear	2(iv) or 3(i), (iv), or 4	6

TABLE 6.7

with the minimum taken over all allowable tree circuit representations with respect to x_i. If f is incompletely specified, we have taken (in Table 6.7)

$$d_i(f) = \min_{\substack{v_g \subseteq c_f \\ g : B^n \to B}} d_i(g) \tag{6.21}$$

so that for an i.s.b.f. f, one simply tests the descriptions of Table 6.7 in descending order until one achieves a "match" in the sense that an assignment to the unspecified entries will result in one of the cases having the description under consideration. We might point out that $d_i(f) = 6$ automatically if the ith partial expansion contains both rows $(0, 1)$ and $(1, 0)$.

EXAMPLE 6.9

Consider the function $f: B^4 \longrightarrow C$, one of whose 8×2 matrices is

$$
\begin{array}{cc}
& x_2 \\
& \begin{array}{|c|} \hline
01 \\
1I \\
11 \\
0I \\
I0 \\
01 \\
I1 \\
0I \\
\hline
\end{array} \\
x_4 x_3 x_1 & \\
& g_2 h_2
\end{array}
$$

It is evidently not possible to assign elements of B to the unspecified entries in such a way that one distinct row will result (this is obvious because we must have the two different rows: (0, 1) and (1, 1) no matter how the unspecified entries are assigned). Neither is $g_2 \approx h_2$ (cf. Prob. 3.42), so that description I in Table 6.7 cannot be satisfied.

If we were to have only two distinct rows, they would have to be (0, 1) and (1, 1), but the fifth row could not be made into one of these. Hence, description II cannot be met.

Now, if the two of the five unspecified entries are assigned in such a way that the matrix becomes

$$
x_4 x_3 x_1 \quad
\begin{array}{c}
x_2 \\
\hline
01 \\
11 \\
11 \\
0I \\
00 \\
01 \\
I1 \\
0I \\
\hline
\end{array}
$$

it is then apparent that description III can be achieved, for any assignment to the remaining entries will produce a matrix having three distinct rows, (0, 0), (0, 1), (1, 1), in which *the pair* of rows (0, 1), (1, 0) does not appear. Thus, $d_2(f) = 4$. This figure is the tree circuit cost of $F_2(G_2, H_2, x_2)$ in either of the allowable tree circuits for case 3(ii) of Table II.

Next suppose that a minimal covering μ (cf. Sec. 3.15) is obtained for the simplicial complex $(F_i \, \Gamma_{F_i})$ arising from the family†

$$
F_i = \{ g_i^{(1)}, h_i^{(1)}, g_i^{(2)}, h_i^{(2)}, \cdots, g_i^{(m)}, h_i^{(m)} \}
$$

of incompletely specified ith partial functions for $f_1, f_2, \cdots, f_m$. (Cf. Eq. 6.3.) If $|\mu| = \rho_i$, we expect (if Theorem 6.1 is applied with respect to the variable x_i) to have ρ_i functions of $n - 1$ variables to implement. Thus, we estimate our multiple-output tree circuit cost (assuming the application of Theorem 6.1 with respect to x_i) by the figure

$$
\sigma_i(F) = \sum_{j=1}^{m} d_i(f_j) + B_T(n - 1, \rho_i) \tag{6.22}
$$

and put

$$
S(F) = \min_{1 \leq i \leq n} \sigma_i(F) \tag{6.23}
$$

EXAMPLE 6.10

If $F = \{f_1, f_2, f_3\}$ is a family of functions $f_j: B^4 \longrightarrow C$ for which the third partial expansions have matrices

†Here we do not include those partial functions that are compatible with the identity function or with the zero function. In case $n = 3$ $(n - 1 = 2)$ we do not include those partial functions that are compatible with functions of the class F.

$$f_1 : x_3 \qquad f_2 : x_3 \qquad f_3 : x_3$$

$$x_4 x_2 x_1 \begin{array}{|c|} \hline I1 \\ 00 \\ 01 \\ I0 \\ 01 \\ 11 \\ I0 \\ 00 \\ \hline \end{array} \qquad x_4 x_2 x_1 \begin{array}{|c|} \hline 00 \\ 1I \\ I1 \\ II \\ 11 \\ I0 \\ 00 \\ 1I \\ \hline \end{array} \qquad x_4 x_2 x_1 \begin{array}{|c|} \hline I1 \\ 01 \\ 1I \\ I0 \\ 1I \\ II \\ 01 \\ 01 \\ \hline \end{array}$$

$$g_3^{(1)} h_3^{(1)} \qquad\qquad g_3^{(2)} h_3^{(2)} \qquad\qquad g_3^{(3)} h_3^{(3)}$$

then the reader will check that

$$d_3(f_1) = 4 \qquad d_3(f_2) = 2 \qquad d_3(f_3) = 4$$

Now observe that the family

$$F_3 = \{g_3^{(1)}, h_3^{(1)}, g_3^{(2)}, h_3^{(2)}, g_3^{(3)}, h_3^{(3)}\}$$

is identical with the family of six functions studied in Example 3.25. There we found (cf. Example 3.27) a minimal covering μ for the complex (F_3, Γ_{F_3}) with $|\mu| = 3$. Hence,

$$\sigma_3(F) = 4 + 2 + 4 + B_T(3, 3) = 10 + 26 = 36$$

6.11 ALGORITHM FOR DETERMINING ECONOMICAL TREE CIRCUITS

In this section we present an algorithm that is not guaranteed to deliver the most economical tree circuit for a given function or family of functions, but which will generally produce a tree circuit realization that compares favorably in cost with a minimal two-level realization while possessing the several engineering advantages alluded to at the opening of the chapter. In so doing, we take our cue from the selection criteria of Sec. 6.6 (cf. Examples 6.6 and 6.7).

Again we consider a family $F = \{f_1, f_2, \cdots, f_m\}$ of i.s.b.f.'s $f_j : B^n \to C$ $(j = 1, 2, \cdots, m)$ of the same n variables. If n is large and m is small (and particularly so when the percentage of unspecified entries is small), one is likely to have

$$\sigma_i(F) = \sigma_j(F) \qquad \text{(all } 1 \le i, j \le n) \tag{6.24}$$

in estimating the various tree circuit costs with the "course" estimate σ_i of Eq. 6.22. This situation will naturally occur if both:

(I) $\rho_i = 2m$,

(II) $d_i(f_j) = 6$ (all $1 \le i \le n$, $1 \le j \le m$), for then, from Eqs. 6.22 and 6.13, we have

$$\sigma_i(F) = 6m + B_T(n-1, 2m) = B_T(n, m)$$

for each $i = 1, 2, \cdots, n$. Clearly, these conditions

(I') None of the partial functions is compatible,

(II') Both rows (0, 1) and (1, 0) appear in each partial function

are likely to be simultaneously satisfied as n becomes large while m becomes small.

In those instances in which Eq. 6.24 is satisfied, our *course estimates* $\sigma_i(F)$ are of no help as a criterion for deciding which variable x_i to use in applying Theorem 6.1. Even when $\sigma_i(F) = S(F)$ for more than 1, but not all indices i, we are in need of a "finer" selection criterion for breaking "ties." Imitating the reasoning (primarily suggested by the tree circuit inequality) that lead us to write Eq. 6.11, we define the ith *fine estimate* by ($n > 3$; see Eq. 6.29)

$$s_i(F) = \sum_{j=1}^{m} d_i(f_j) + \min_{g \in F_i'} \sum M'(g) \tag{6.25}$$

and replace Eq. 6.23 by

$$S'(F) = \min_{\sigma_i(F)=S(F)} s_i(F) \tag{6.26}$$

where $F_i' = F_i'(\mu) = \{g_1, g_2, \cdots, g_{\rho_i}\}$ is the family of functions that results from merging the "blocks" of compatible i.s.b.f.'s in a minimal covering μ (cf. Sec. 6.10) of the simplicial complex (F_i, Γ_{F_i}), and the minimum of Eq. 6.25 is taken over all such minimal coverings μ.

In most applications of Eq. 6.25, we will be computing $s_i(F)$ only because $\rho_i = 2m$; that is, because none of the partial functions are compatible. When this is the case,

$$F_i' = \{g_i^{(1)}, h_i^{(1)}, g_i^{(2)}, h_i^{(2)}, \cdots, g_i^{(m)}, h_i^{(m)}\} = F_i$$

so that Eq. 6.25 becomes simply

$$s_i(F) = \sum_{j=1}^{m} d_i(f_j) + \sum_{j=1}^{m} M'(g_i^{(j)}) + \sum_{j=1}^{m} M'(h_i^{(j)})$$

$$= \sum_{j=1}^{m} [d_i(f_j) + M'(g_i^{(j)}) + M'(h_i^{(j)})] \tag{6.27}$$

Still more specifically, we might need to compute $s_i(F)$ when F contains only one function; that is, $F = \{f\}$. If g_i and h_i are its ith partial functions, then Eq. 6.27 reduces to

$$s_i(F) = d_i(f) + M'(g_i) + M'(h_i) \approx t_i(f) \tag{6.28}$$

Since it requires only slightly more effort, one should probably compute $t_i(f)$ rather than $s_i(F)$ in this event.

One more situation should perhaps be treated specially—that in which F is a family of functions of three variables with $m > 1$. Since we have solved (cf. Sec. 3.16) the two-variable minimization problem in full generality, it seems reasonable to replace Eq. 6.25 by

$$s_i(F) = \sum_{j=1}^{m} d_i(f_j) + m(F_i) \qquad (6.29)$$

when $n = 3$. (Here, $m(F_i)$ is the cost of implementing the family $F_i = \{g_i^{(1)}, h_i^{(1)}, g_i^{(2)}, h_i^{(2)}, \cdots, g_i^{(m)}, h_i^{(m)}\}$ of functions of two variables as determined by the methods of Sec. 3.16.)

With all these estimating formulas as machinery, we now state our *tree circuit algorithm* for synthesizing a multiple-output logic network for a family† $F = \{f_1, f_2, \cdots, f_m\}$ with $f_j : B^n \longrightarrow C$ ($j = 1, 2, \cdots, m$).

(1) Compute $\sigma_i(F)$ for $i = 1, 2, \cdots, n$ (Eq. 6.22).

(2) (a) If there is a unique index $i = i_*$ for which $\sigma_i(F) = S(F)$, then execute step (5) for this index.
    (b) If not execute step (3).

(3) (a) If $m > 1$, compute $s_i(F)$ for each index i having $\sigma_i(F) = S(F)$ (Eqs. 6.25, 6.27, or 6.29, depending on the circumstances).
    (b) If $m = 1$ so that $F = \{f\}$, compute $t_i(f)$ for each index i having $\sigma_i(F) = S(F)$ and let this be taken as $s_i(F)$ (Sec. 6.6).

(4) Choose any index $i = i_*$ for which $s_i(F) = S'(F)$ and execute step (5) for this index.

(5) Apply Theorem 6.1 with respect to the variable i_* to each function $f_j \in F$. There remains a new family $F'_{i_*} = \{g_1, g_2, \cdots, g_{\rho_{i_*}}\}$ of i.s.b.f.'s of $n - 1$ variables.
    (a) If $n - 1 > 2$, repeat the algorithm for the new family, beginning at Step (1).
    (b) If $n - 1 = 2$, implement a minimal circuit for this new family (Sec. 3.16).

EXAMPLE 6.11

Consider the family $F = \{f_1, f_2, f_3, f_4\}$ of incomplete truth tables depicted in Table 6.8. Using the test of Prob. 3.25, it can be seen that the functions are mutually incompatible. In Table 6.9 we have listed the corresponding partial functions, and after "naming" them with integers, the compatibility matrices have been drawn in Table 6.10. From the latter we obtain (cf. Sec. 3.15) the maximal compatibles γ_i^2 for the variable x_i partial expansions

$$\gamma_1^2 = \{\overline{3, 7, 8}; \overline{5, 8}; \overline{3, 4}; \overline{2, 3}; \overline{1, 3}; \overline{6}\}$$

$$\gamma_2^2 = \{\overline{9, 11}; \overline{9, 12}; \overline{10, 16}; \overline{12, 16}; \overline{13, 14}; \overline{15}\}$$

---

†We assume that the members of F are mutually incompatible. The reader will be able to suggest an obvious modification or initialization process as being appropriate in case the functions are not pairwise incompatible.

x_4	x_3	x_2	x_1	f_1	f_2	f_3	f_4
0	0	0	0	0	I	1	1
0	0	0	1	1	I	0	1
0	0	1	0	I	0	0	0
0	0	1	1	0	I	1	I
0	1	0	0	1	1	0	I
0	1	0	1	I	0	0	0
0	1	1	0	I	I	1	1
0	1	1	1	0	1	I	I
1	0	0	0	1	1	I	I
1	0	0	1	I	I	1	I
1	0	1	0	0	I	1	0
1	0	1	1	0	0	0	I
1	1	0	0	1	I	1	1
1	1	0	1	0	0	0	1
1	1	1	0	1	1	0	1
1	1	1	1	I	0	1	I

TABLE 6.8

$$\gamma_3^2 = \{\overline{17, 19};\ \overline{18, 19};\ \overline{19, 20};\ \overline{19, 21};\ \overline{19, 23};\ \overline{23, 24};\ \overline{22}\}$$
$$\gamma_4^2 = \{\overline{25, 29};\ \overline{25, 32};\ \overline{26, 27, 31};\ \overline{26, 28, 31};\ \overline{30}\}$$

and the corresponding collections γ_i^3 of basic simplexes

$$\gamma_1^3 = \{\overline{3, 7};\ \overline{3, 8};\ \overline{7, 8};\ \overline{5, 8};\ \overline{3, 4};\ \overline{2, 3};\ \overline{1, 3};\ \overline{6}\}$$
$$\gamma_2^3 = \gamma_2^2$$
$$\gamma_3^3 = \gamma_3^2$$
$$\gamma_4^3 = \gamma_4^2$$

Thus, the complexes (F_i, Γ_{F_i}) have minimal coverings

$i = 1$: $\mu_1^{(1)} = \{\overline{6};\ \overline{1, 3};\ \overline{2, 3};\ \overline{3, 4};\ \overline{5, 8};\ \overline{7, 8}\}$

$\qquad\quad \mu_1^{(2)} = \{\overline{6};\ \overline{1, 3};\ \overline{2, 3};\ \overline{3, 4};\ \overline{5, 8};\ \overline{7, 8}\}$ $\qquad \rho_1 = 6$

$i = 2$: $\mu_2^{(1)} = \{\overline{15};\ \overline{13, 14};\ \overline{10, 16};\ \overline{9, 11};\ \overline{9, 12}\}$

$\qquad\quad \mu_2^{(2)} = \{\overline{15};\ \overline{13, 14};\ \overline{10, 16};\ \overline{9, 11};\ \overline{12, 16}\}$ $\qquad \rho_2 = 5$

$i = 3$: $\mu_3 = \{\overline{22};\ \overline{23, 24};\ \overline{19, 21};\ \overline{19, 20};\ \overline{18, 19};\ \overline{17, 19}\}$ $\qquad \rho_3 = 6$

$i = 4$: $\mu_4 = \gamma_4^3 = \gamma_4^2$ $\qquad \rho_4 = 5$

Then, from the tabulations of $d_i(f_j)$,

$\diagdown\ \ ^{j}$ $_{i}$	1	2	3	4	$\sum_j d_i(f_j)$
1	6	4	6	4	20
2	4	4	6	4	18
3	4	4	6	6	20
4	4	4	6	4	18

	$g_1^{(1)}$	$h_1^{(1)}$	$g_1^{(2)}$	$h_1^{(2)}$	$g_1^{(3)}$	$h_1^{(3)}$	$g_1^{(4)}$	$h_1^{(4)}$
	0	1	I	I	1	0	1	1
	I	0	0	I	0	1	0	I
	1	I	1	0	0	0	I	0
$x_4x_3x_2$	I	0	I	1	1	I	1	I
	1	I	1	I	I	1	I	I
	0	0	I	0	1	0	0	I
	1	0	I	0	1	0	1	1
	1	I	1	0	0	1	1	I
	1	2	3	4	5	6	7	8

	$g_2^{(1)}$	$h_2^{(1)}$	$g_2^{(2)}$	$h_2^{(2)}$	$g_2^{(3)}$	$h_2^{(3)}$	$g_2^{(4)}$	$h_2^{(4)}$
	0	I	I	0	1	0	1	0
	1	0	I	I	0	1	1	I
	1	I	1	I	0	1	I	1
$x_4x_3x_1$	I	0	0	1	0	I	0	I
	1	0	1	I	I	1	I	0
	I	0	I	0	1	0	I	I
	1	1	I	1	1	0	1	1
	0	I	0	0	0	1	1	I
	9	10	11	12	13	14	15	16

	$g_3^{(1)}$	$h_3^{(1)}$	$g_3^{(2)}$	$h_3^{(2)}$	$g_3^{(3)}$	$h_3^{(3)}$	$g_3^{(4)}$	$h_3^{(4)}$
	0	1	I	1	1	0	1	I
	1	I	I	0	0	0	1	0
	I	I	0	I	0	1	0	1
$x_4x_2x_1$	0	0	I	1	1	I	I	I
	1	1	1	I	I	1	I	1
	I	0	I	0	1	0	I	1
	0	1	I	1	1	0	0	1
	0	I	0	0	0	1	I	I
	17	18	19	20	21	22	23	24

	$g_4^{(1)}$	$h_4^{(1)}$	$g_4^{(2)}$	$h_4^{(2)}$	$g_4^{(3)}$	$h_4^{(3)}$	$g_4^{(4)}$	$h_4^{(4)}$
	0	1	I	1	1	I	1	I
	1	I	I	I	0	1	1	I
	I	0	0	I	0	1	0	0
$x_3x_2x_1$	0	0	I	0	1	0	I	I
	1	1	1	I	0	1	I	1
	I	0	0	0	0	0	0	1
	I	1	I	1	1	0	1	1
	0	I	1	0	I	1	I	I
	25	26	27	28	29	30	31	32

TABLE 6.9

2	0						
3	1	1					
4	0	0	1				
5	0	0	0	0			
6	0	0	0	0	0		
7	0	0	1	0	0	0	
8	0	0	1	0	1	0	1
	1	2	3	4	5	6	7

10	0						
11	1	0					
12	1	0	0				
13	0	0	0	0			
14	0	0	0	0	1		
15	0	0	0	0	0	0	
16	0	1	0	1	0	0	0
	9	10	11	12	13	14	15

18	0						
19	1	1					
20	0	0	1				
21	0	0	1	0			
22	0	0	0	0	0		
23	0	0	1	0	0	0	
24	0	0	0	0	0	0	1
	17	18	19	20	21	22	23

26	0						
27	0	1					
28	0	1	0				
29	1	0	0	0			
30	0	0	0	0	0		
31	0	1	1	1	0	0	
32	1	0	0	0	0	0	0
	25	26	27	28	29	30	31

TABLE 6.10

and the figures ρ_i, we compute (cf. Eq. 6.22) the course estimates

$$\sigma_1(F) = 20 + B_T(3, 6) = 66$$
$$\sigma_2(F) = 18 + B_T(3, 5) = 58$$
$$\sigma_3(F) = 20 + B_T(3, 6) = 66$$
$$\sigma_4(F) = 18 + B_T(3, 5) = 58$$

Thus, on completing step (1) of the tree circuit algorithm, we have a "tie" between the indices $i = 2, 4$, so that we must execute step (3), computing the fine estimates $s_2(F)$ and $s_4(F)$.

We tabulate the results of having computed $M'(g)$ for each $g \in F_2'(\mu_2^{(1)})$, $F_2'(\mu_2^{(2)})$, $F_4'(\mu_4)$, as follows

For $\mu_2^{(1)}$:

	$\overline{15}$	$\overline{13, 14}$		$\overline{10, 16}$		$\overline{9, 11}$		$\overline{9, 12}$	
	1	1	0	0	0	0	0	0	0
	1	0	1	0	0	1	1	1	1
	I	0	1	1	1	1	1	1	1
$x_4x_3x_1$	0	0	1	0	0	0	0	1	1
	I	0	1	0	0	1	1	1	1
	I	1	0	0	0	I	I	0	0
	1	1	0	1	1	1	1	1	1
	1	0	1	I	I	0	0	0	0
$M'(g)$	2	16		2		8		8	$\Sigma = 36$

For $\mu_2^{(2)}$:

	$\overline{15}$	$\overline{13,14}$	$\overline{10,16}$	$\overline{9,11}$	$\overline{12,16}$
	1	1 0	0 0	0 0	0 0
	1	0 1	0 0	1 1	I I
	I	0 1	1 1	1 1	1 1
$x_4x_3x_1$	0	0 1	0 0	0 0	1 1
	I	0 1	0 0	1 1	0 0
	I	1 0	0 0	I I	0 0
	1	1 0	1 1	1 1	1 1
	1	0 1	I I	0 0	0 0
$M'(g)$	2	16	2	8	6

$\Sigma = 34$

For μ_4:

	$\overline{25,29}$	$\overline{25,32}$	$\overline{26,27,31}$	$\overline{26,28,31}$	$\overline{30}$
	0 1	0 0	1 1 1	1 1 1	I
	1 0	1 1	1 1 1	1 1 1	1
	1 0	0 0	0 0 0	0 0 0	1
$x_4x_3x_2$	0 1	0 0	0 0 0	0 0 0	0
	1 0	1 1	1 1 1	1 1 1	1
	1 0	1 1	0 0 0	0 0 0	0
	0 1	1 1	1 1 1	1 1 1	0
	0 1	0 0	1 1 1	0 0 0	1
$M'(g)$	12	6	8	6	16

$\Sigma = 48$

Using Eq. 6.25, we write

$$s_2(F) = 18 + 34 = 52$$
$$s_4(F) = 18 + 48 = 66$$

so that

$$S'(F) = 52 = s_2(F)$$

and we should apply Theorem 6.1 with respect to the variable x_2.

Utilizing the minimal covering $\mu = \mu_2^{(2)} = \{\overline{15}; \overline{13,14}; \overline{10,16}; \overline{9,11}; \overline{12,16}\}$, one might wish to consider the two refinements (cf. Sec. 3.15)

$$\pi_1 = \{\overline{15}; \overline{13,14}; \overline{10,16}; \overline{9,11}; \overline{12}\}$$
$$\pi_2 = \{\overline{15}; \overline{13,14}; \overline{10}; \overline{9,11}; \overline{12,16}\}$$

and their corresponding "merged" partial functions (see Table 6.9):

For π_1:

	$g_2^{(1)}$ $h_2^{(1)}$	$g_2^{(2)}$ $h_2^{(2)}$	$g_2^{(3)}$ $h_2^{(3)}$	$g_2^{(4)}$ $h_2^{(4)}$
	0 0	0 0	1 0	1 0
	1 0	1 I	0 1	1 0
	1 1	1 I	0 1	I 1
$x_4x_3x_1$	0 0	0 1	0 1	0 0
	1 0	1 I	0 1	I 0
	I 0	I 0	1 0	I 0
	1 1	1 1	1 0	1 1
	0 I	0 0	0 1	1 I
	9 10	11 12	13 14	15 16
$d_2(f_j)$	4	4	6	4

For π_2:

	$g_2^{(1)}$	$h_2^{(1)}$	$g_2^{(2)}$	$h_2^{(2)}$	$g_2^{(3)}$	$h_2^{(3)}$	$g_2^{(4)}$	$h_2^{(4)}$
	0	I	0	0	1	0	1	0
	1	0	1	I	0	1	1	I
	1	I	1	1	0	1	I	1
$x_4x_3x_1$	0	0	0	1	0	1	0	1
	1	0	1	0	0	1	I	0
	I	0	I	0	1	0	I	0
	1	1	1	1	1	0	1	1
	0	I	0	0	0	1	1	0
	9	10	11	12	13	14	15	16
$d_2(f_j)$	4		6		6		6	

Preference would be given to π_1 when we recompute the integers $d_2(f_j)$ for each refinement. When enough unspecified entries are chosen to ensure these figures $d_2(f_j)$ for the refinement π_1, we obtain partial functions as follows:

	$g_2^{(1)}$	$h_2^{(1)}$	$g_2^{(2)}$	$h_2^{(2)}$	$g_2^{(3)}$	$h_2^{(3)}$	$g_2^{(4)}$	$h_2^{(4)}$
	0	0	0	0	1	0	1	0
	1	0	1	1	0	1	1	0
	1	1	1	1	0	1	1	1
$x_4x_3x_1$	0	0	0	1	0	1	0	0
	1	0	1	1	0	1	I	0
	I	0	0	0	1	0	I	0
	1	1	1	1	1	0	1	1
	0	0	0	0	0	1	1	0
	9	10	11	12	13	14	15	16
Case	3(iii)		3(ii)		2(iv)		3(iii)	

In this table we chose the unspecified entry in $h_2^{(1)}$ to be 0 in order that the row (0, 1) not appear in the columns $g_2^{(1)}h_2^{(1)}$, for if this were to happen, we would have $d_2(f_1) = 6$ rather than 4. But this necessitates that the same choice be made for the unspecified entry in $h_2^{(4)}$ if we are to retain the compatibility relation $h_2^{(1)} \approx h_2^{(4)}$. Similar reasoning guided our choice for other unspecified entries. If it came to a choice between increasing $\sum d_i(f_j)$ by 2 or ρ_i by 1, we would naturally prefer the former. We say this because of the greater effect such an increase in ρ_i has on the "course" tree-circuit estimate (Eq. 6.22), at least when $n \geq 4$ $(n - 1 \geq 3)$ and m is small. (See Tables 6.3 and 6.4.) (If n were 3, we would normally prefer the latter alternative. Why?)

Applying Theorem 6.1, we write

$$f_1 = G_1(\bar{x}_2 + H_1')$$
$$f_2 = G_2 + x_2H_2'$$
$$f_3 = G_2 \oplus x_2 \tag{6.30}$$
$$f_4 = G_4(\bar{x}_2 + H_4')$$

with the assurance that we need implement no more than $\rho_2 = 5$ functions in order to synthesize the seven incomplete truth tables shown below:

x_4	x_3	x_1	G_1	H'_1	G_2	H'_2	G_3	G_4	H'_4
0	0	0	0	I	0	0	1	1	0
0	0	1	1	0	1	I	0	1	0
0	1	0	1	1	1	I	0	1	1
0	1	1	0	I	0	1	0	0	I
1	0	0	1	0	1	I	0	I	0
1	0	1	I	0	0	0	1	I	0
1	1	0	1	1	1	I	1	1	1
1	1	1	0	0	0	0	0	1	0
			a	b	c	d	e	f	g

Interestingly enough, when we construct a compatibility matrix

	a	b	c	d	e	f
b	0					
c	1	0				
d	0	1	0			
e	0	0	0	0		
f	0	0	0	1	0	
g	0	1	0	1	0	0

we find the maximal compatibles = collection of basic simplexes

$$\mu = \gamma^2 = \{\overline{a, c};\ \overline{b, d, g};\ \overline{d, f};\ \overline{e}\}$$

is the unique minimal covering μ, so that four rather than five functions will suffice. This phenomenon occurred because the tree circuit theorem introduced new unspecified entries in the tables for $h_2^{(1)}$, $h_2^{(2)}$, and $h_2^{(4)}$. Using this information, we select one of the refinements (say, π)

$$\pi = \{\overline{a, c};\ \overline{b, g};\ \overline{d, f};\ \overline{e}\}$$
$$\pi' = \{\overline{a, c};\ \overline{b, d, g};\ \overline{f};\ \overline{e}\}$$

to "merge" functions a, b, c, d, e, f, g. Then, as shown by Eqs. 6.30, we have a partial circuit (Fig. 6.13) for the given family $F = \{f_1, f_2, f_3, f_4\}$ in which the four functions $f^{(i)}: B^3 \longrightarrow C$

x_4	x_3	x_1	f^1	f^2	f^3	f^4
0	0	0	0	0	0	1	1
0	0	1	1	0	0	1	0
0	1	0	1	1	0	1	0
0	1	1	0	I	1	0	0
1	0	0	1	0	I	I	0
1	0	1	1	0	0	1	1
1	1	0	1	1	0	1	1
1	1	1	0	0	0	1	0
			$\overline{a, c}$	$\overline{b, g}$	$\overline{d, f}$	$\overline{e}$

remain to be synthesized.

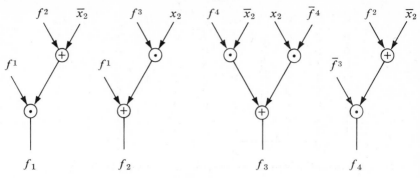

FIGURE 6.13

Since $n - 3 > 2$, we repeat the tree circuit algorithm for the new family

$$G = \{f^{(1)}, f^{(2)}, f^{(3)}, f^{(4)}\}$$

beginning at step (1). From the partial functions and compatibility matrices (see the footnote, page 000, regarding the definition of the families F_i),

$x_4 x_3$

$g_1^1\ h_1^1$	$g_1^2\ h_1^2$	$g_1^3\ h_1^3$	$g_1^4\ h_1^4$
0 1	0 0	0 0	1 0
1 0	1 I	0 1	0 0
1 0	0 0	I 0	0 1
1 0	1 0	0 0	1 0
1 2	3 4	5 6	7 8

	1	2	6	7
2	1			
6	0	0		
7	0	0	0	
8	0	0	0	0

$x_4 x_1$

$g_3^1\ h_3^1$	$g_3^2\ h_3^2$	$g_3^3\ h_3^3$	$g_3^4\ h_3^4$
0 1	0 1	0 0	1 0
1 0	0 I	0 1	0 0
1 1	0 1	I 0	0 1
0 0	0 0	0 0	1 0
9 10	11 12	13 14	15 16

	9	14	15
14	0		
15	1	0	
16	0	0	0

$x_3 x_1$

$g_4^1\ h_4^1$	$g_4^2\ h_4^2$	$g_4^3\ h_4^3$	$g_4^4\ h_4^4$
0 1	0 0	0 I	1 0
1 0	0 0	0 0	0 1
1 1	1 1	0 0	0 1
0 0	I 0	1 0	0 0
17 18	19 20	21 22	23 24

	17	20	21	23
20	0			
21	0	0		
23	0	0	0	
24	1	0	0	0

we compute the integers $d_i(f^j)$ for $i = 1, 3, 4$

i \ j	1	2	3	4	Σ
1	6	2	2	6	16
3	6	2	2	6	16
4	6	0	2	6	14

and the minimal coverings μ_i of the complexes (F_i, Γ_{F_i}):

$$\mu_1 = \{\overline{1, 2};\ \overline{6};\ \overline{7};\ \overline{8}\} \qquad \rho_1 = 4$$
$$\mu_3 = \{\overline{9, 15};\ \overline{14};\ \overline{16}\} \qquad \rho_2 = 3$$
$$\mu_4 = \{\overline{17, 24};\ \overline{20};\ \overline{21};\ \overline{23}\} \qquad \rho_4 = 4$$

From these figures we obtain

$$\sigma_1(G) = 16 + B_T(2, 4) = 24$$
$$\sigma_3(G) = 16 + B_T(2, 3) = 24$$
$$\sigma_4(G) = 14 + B_T(2, 4) = 22$$

so that the tree circuit theorem should be applied to the family G with respect to the variable x_4.

In order to ensure that

$$\sum_{j=1}^{4} d_4(f^j) = 14$$

the unspecified entries are chosen in such a way that we have partial functions

	$g_4^1\ h_4^1$	$g_4^2\ h_4^2$	$g_4^3\ h_4^3$	$g_4^4\ h_4^4$
	0 1	0 0	0 0	1 0
	1 0	0 0	0 0	0 1
$x_3 x_1$	1 1	1 1	0 0	0 1
	0 0	0 0	1 0	0 0
Case:	4	2(iii)	2(ii)	3(i)

Applying Theorem 6.1, we write (see Fig. 6.14)

$$f^1 = G_1 \bar{x}_4 + H_1 x_4$$
$$f^2 = G_2$$
$$f^3 = G_3 \bar{x}_4 \qquad\qquad (6.31)$$
$$f^4 = G_4 \bar{x}_4 + H_4 x_4$$

where the subfunctions are

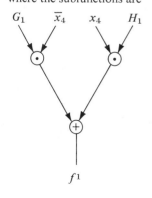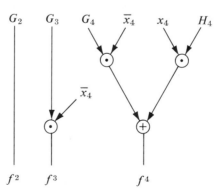

FIGURE 6.14

x_3	x_1	G_1	H_1	G_2	G_3	G_4	H_4
0	0	0	1	0	0	1	0
0	1	1	0	0	0	0	1
1	0	1	1	1	0	0	1
1	1	0	0	0	1	0	0

Using the methods of Sec. 3.16 (or Sec. 1.18, since all functions are completely specified), we obtain the minimal circuit of Fig. 6.15. If Figs. 6.13, 6.14, and 6.15 are now "wired together," we obtain the multiple-output circuit of Fig. 6.16, having cost 40.

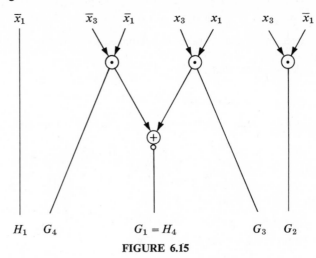

$$\overline{x}_1 \qquad \overline{x}_3 \quad \overline{x}_1 \qquad x_3 \quad x_1 \qquad x_3 \quad \overline{x}_1$$

$$H_1 \quad G_4 \qquad\qquad G_1 = H_4 \qquad\qquad G_3 \quad G_2$$

FIGURE 6.15

It is necessary that we make a few closing remarks for this chapter, primarily with the intention of placing the material of this section in its proper perspective. The reader has no doubt observed, in following the arguments given in Example 6.11, that the so-called 'tree circuit algorithm' is not an algorithm in the strict sense of the word, for we have not given a precise "recipe" with mechanizable instructions for synthesizing a definite tree circuit for an arbitrary family F of i.s.b.f.'s. Rather, we have given a roughly outlined procedure whose "steps" definitely rely, in some measure, on the designer's ingenuity.

With this rough outline as a basis, it would be possible to write a genuine algorithm with clearly defined "micro-instructions" for arriving at *some* tree circuit implementation. But the theory does not entirely reveal the optimum procedure to follow. Consider our fine estimate $s_i(F)$. We hesitate to introduce a more all-inclusive estimate (in lieu of Eq. 6.25),

$$s_i(F) = \sum_{j=1}^{m} d_i(f_j) + \underbrace{\min_{\pi \text{ a refinement of}}}_{\substack{\pi \text{ a refinement of} \\ \text{some minimal covering } \mu}} \sum_{g \in F'_i} M'(g)$$

in the face of the increased computations that this revision would entail,

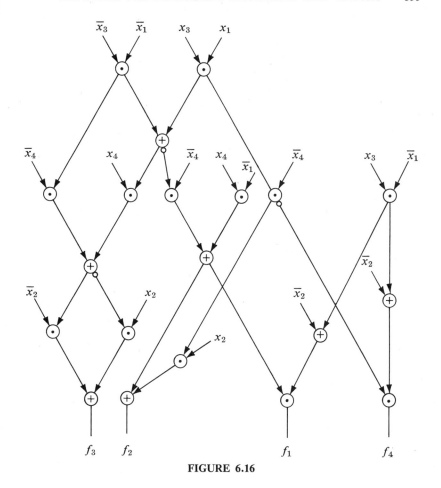

FIGURE 6.16

and of the lack of theoretical justification for doing so. Yet, one can produce examples for which this revision would allow a more economical realization. As another case in point, recall our dilemma of whether to prefer an increase in $\sum d_i(f_j)$ or an increase in ρ_i; while definite sub-algorithms could be set down for deciding such matters, we would then be faced with increased computations and, a lack of theoretical evidence supporting one particular decision criterion over another. We could go on citing our failure to suggest criteria for preferring one allowable tree circuit form (see Case 3(ii), for example) over another, and our omission of theoretical material that would have provided *minimal* three-variable, multiple-output circuits, etc.. But the thought behind this summary is clear, namely, that some sort of compromise is called for.

Thus we have tried to present a partially organized procedure, which at least can claim

(i)   Acknowledgement of the two fundamental theoretical results:
       (a)   The tree circuit theorem.
       (b)   The tree circuit inequality.
(ii)   An incorporation of the tree circuit upper bounds $B_T(n, k)$.
(iii) A framework from which additional research may be suggested.

Because of these features we can expect some measure of success from the "algorithm" in spite of its being, shall we say, "incompletely specified".

PROBLEMS

*6.1   Show that

$$\lim_{n\to\infty} \left\{ \max_{f \in B(n)} \left[\frac{M'(f)}{M(f)} \right] \right\} = 2$$

Hint: Use the functions $f^{(n)}$ of Lemma 6.5.

6.2   From the four 8×2 matrix representations for the Boolean function $f: B^4 \longrightarrow B$ with $\mathscr{K}^0(f) = \{2, 3, 8, 9, 10, 13\}$, determine the four corresponding cases of the tree circuit theorem. Using the methods of Sec. 6.6, obtain an economical tree circuit for f.

6.3   Derive the formulas F_i, G_i, H_i in Theorem 6.1: (a) case 2(ii), (b) case 2(iv), (c) case 3(i), (d) case 3(iii), (e) case 3(iv), and (f) case 4.

6.4   Verify the entry $T(f_i)$ in Table 6.1 when (a) $f_i \in II_2$, (b) $f_i \in II_3$, (c) $f_i \in III_3$, (d) $f_i \in IV_4$, (e) $f_i \in V_2$, and (f) $f_i \in VI_3$.

6.5   Compute the expected (average) cost:

$$\frac{1}{256} \sum_{f \in B(3)} T(f)$$

for a three-variable tree circuit. Repeat for $M(f)$; for $M'(f)$.
Hint: See Table 2.3.

6.6   Compute $T(f)$ and derive a tree circuit having this cost for $f: B^3 \longrightarrow B$ in which:
        (a) $\mathscr{K}^0(f) = \{3, 4\}$.   (d) $\mathscr{K}^0(f) = \{1, 2, 4, 7\}$.
        (b) $\mathscr{K}^0(f) = \{0, 3, 5\}$.   (e) $\mathscr{K}^0(f) = \{2, 4\}$.
        (c) $\mathscr{K}^0(f) = \{1, 2, 4, 5\}$.   (f) $\mathscr{K}^0(f) = \{0, 2, 3, 6\}$.

*6.7   Verify the entry $\bar{B}_T(3, 2) = 18$ in Table 6.3.

6.8   Complete the proof of Lemma 6.5.

6.9   Show that if $f: B^n \longrightarrow C$, then $M(f) \leq M(f^{(n)})$.

*6.10   Verify the tree circuit inequality $T(f) \leq M'(f)$ for $f: B^n \longrightarrow B$ in the event that for some index i ($i = 1, 2, \cdots, n$) the ith $2^{n-1} \times 2$ matrix representation of f gives (a) case 2(ii), (b) case 2(iv), (c) case 3(i), (d) case 3(iii), (e) case 3(iv), and (f) case 4 of the tree circuit theorem. *Hint*: See Probs. 3.3 through 3.8.

6.11 Compute $M'(f)$ for the functions f in Prob. 3.23.

6.12 Compute $M'(f)$ for f as defined in (a) Prob. 3.30(a), (b) Prob. 3.30(b), (c) Prob. 3.31(a), and (d) Prob. 3.31(b).

6.13 Compute $T(f)$ if f is the function of Example 6.2. Compute $M(f)$ and $M'(f)$ for this same function.

6.14 Prove Corollary 6.2.

6.15 Compute $T'(f)$ for each function of Prob. 6.12. According to the selection criteria of Sec. 6.6, for which variable should one first apply Theorem 6.1 in the case of these functions?

6.16 Compute $T(f)$ for the i.s.b.f. f shown in (a) Prob. 3.16 and (b) Prob. 3.17. Derive a tree circuit for f having the cost $T(f)$ for each function.

6.17 Assuming that the truth tables of Prob. 3.36, taken two at a time, are the fourth partial functions $g_4^{(i)}$, $h_4^{(i)}$ of four i.s.b.f.'s $f_i : B^4 \longrightarrow C$ ($i = 1$, 2, 3, 4), compute the estimate $\sigma_4(F)$ for the family $F = \{f_1, f_2, f_3, f_4\}$.

6.18 Repeat Prob. 6.17 with the truth tables of Prob. 3.37.

6.19 Use the tree circuit algorithm to derive economical tree circuits for the function or family of functions in (a) Prob. 3.31(a), (b) Prob. 3.31(b), (c) Prob. 3.32, (d) Prob. 3.33(a), (e) Prob. 3.33(b), and (f) Prob. 3.36.

6.20 Using the tree circuit algorithm, determine economical tree circuits for the following pairs of functions:

				(a)		(b)	
x_4	x_3	x_2	x_1	f_1	f_2	f_1	f_2
0	0	0	0	0	1	1	1
0	0	0	1	1	1	0	0
0	0	1	0	I	0	0	1
0	0	1	1	I	I	1	1
0	1	0	0	0	0	0	0
0	1	0	1	1	0	0	1
0	1	1	0	1	I	1	0
0	1	1	1	I	1	1	0
1	0	0	0	0	0	0	1
1	0	0	1	0	0	1	1
1	0	1	0	1	1	1	1
1	0	1	1	I	0	0	1
1	1	0	0	0	I	0	1
1	1	0	1	I	I	1	0
1	1	1	0	0	1	0	0
1	1	1	1	1	0	0	1

6.21 Using the tree circuit algorithm, determine economical tree circuits for the functions

$$f: B^5 \longrightarrow B$$

where

(a) $\mathcal{K}^0(f) = \{0, 1, 2, 4, 6, 9, 10, 14, 17, 19, 22, 25, 28, 30, 31\}$.

(b) $\mathcal{K}^0(f) = \{4, 5, 6, 7, 9, 11, 14, 17, 18, 19, 20, 25, 26, 27, 29\}$.

(c) $\mathcal{K}^0(f) = \{1, 3, 5, 7, 8, 9, 11, 12, 14, 16, 17, 18, 23, 24, 26, 27, 31\}$.

6.22 Construct a "catalog" of three-variable tree circuits, one having cost $T(f_i)$ for each representative function f_i in Table 6.1.

CHAPTER 7 | DECOMPOSITION THEORY

7.1 INTRODUCTION

In this closing chapter we introduce the elements of a relatively recent approach to switching theory, which is due primarily to the investigations of R. L. Ashenhurst, and their extensions, by H. Allen Curtis (Ref. 7-1). In direct contrast to the conventional minimization theory of Chapter 3, this new approach emphasizes the structure of a Boolean function $f(x_n, x_{n-1}, \cdots, x_1)$ as it is composed of subfunctions of fewer than n variables. When such a decomposition is known, one can concentrate on the implementation of these subfunctions. The original synthesis problem for f then becomes more manageable, since the subfunctions (which depend on fewer than n variables) are each more easily synthesized than is the original function.

The situation here is not unlike that which the reader has encountered in the calculus of functions of n real variables. There, when studying a function $f(x, y, z)$, for example, considerable simplification in the analysis is often achieved if it is known that $f(x, y, z)$ possesses the "decomposition"

$$f(x, y, z) = F(u(x,), v(y, z))$$

as is the case with

$$f(x, y, z) = \exp(\cos x + \sqrt{y^2 + z^2})$$

where

$$v(y, z) = \sqrt{y^2 + z^2}$$
$$u(x) = \cos x$$
$$F(u, v) = e^{u+v}$$

Typical of the simplifications afforded in the analysis of such functions are the so-called chain rules for differentiation of composite functions. In these, and other ways, many analytical properties (differentiability, periodicity, etc.) of the composite function f can be learned from studying the subfunctions u, v, and F.

Ideally, one might like to decompose each Boolean function $f(x_n, x_{n-1}, \cdots, x_1)$ in such a way that each subfunction would be a function of at most two variables. If this were possible, decomposition theory might be expected to yield economical two-input-per-gate realizations of Boolean functions. With the "disjunctive" decompositions introduced in Sec. 7.2, this objective is not always possible, for we will see that a given Boolean function $f: B^n \longrightarrow B$ may not be "disjunctively decomposable," as defined there. Or f may itself be decomposable in that sense, but one or more of its subfunctions may fail to be "disjunctively decomposable." For this reason, a more general "compound disjunctive" decomposability is introduced in Sec. 7.7; it includes the tree circuit decompositions of Chapter 6 as a special case. The compound disjunctive decomposition theory is then applicable to every Boolean function $f: B^n \longrightarrow B$, and when applied in conjunction with the estimates of Sec. 7.8 (which have as their basis the tree circuit estimates of Sec. 6.10), may be expected to yield economical two-input-per-gate realizations of Boolean functions.

7.2 DISJUNCTIVE DECOMPOSITIONS

Among the functional decompositions (cf. Sec. 0.4) found in mathematics, we will naturally be concerned here with *Boolean decompositions*, that is, with the decompositions

$$f = F \cdot \sigma \tag{7.1}$$

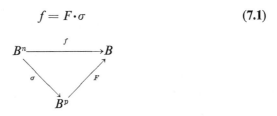

of a Boolean function $f: B^n \to B$. The implication in writing $f = F \cdot \sigma$ is that an n-input, single-output, combinatorial logic circuit may thereby be replaced by the structure of Fig. 7.1. Depending on the cost of this configuration as compared with a conventional implementation of f, we may have much to gain by considering such decompositions.

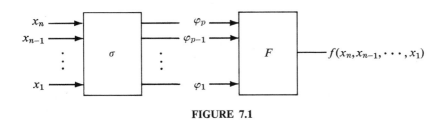

FIGURE 7.1

EXAMPLE 7.1

A Boolean decomposition is depicted in Table 7.1, where $n = 4$ and $p = 3$.

x_4	x_3	x_2	x_1	f	x_4	x_3	x_2	x_1	φ_3	φ_2	φ_1
0	0	0	0	1	0	0	0	0	0	0	0
0	0	0	1	0	0	0	0	1	0	0	1
0	0	1	0	1	0	0	1	0	0	1	0
0	0	1	1	0	0	0	1	1	0	1	1
0	1	0	0	0	0	1	0	0	1	0	0
0	1	0	1	0	0	1	0	1	1	0	1
0	1	1	0	1	0	1	1	0	1	1	0
0	1	1	1	1	0	1	1	1	1	1	1
1	0	0	0	0	1	0	0	0	1	0	0
1	0	0	1	0	1	0	0	1	1	0	1
1	0	1	0	1	1	0	1	0	1	1	0
1	0	1	1	1	1	0	1	1	1	1	1
1	1	0	0	1	1	1	0	0	0	0	0
1	1	0	1	0	1	1	0	1	0	0	1
1	1	1	0	1	1	1	1	0	0	1	0
1	1	1	1	0	1	1	1	1	0	1	1

TABLE 7.1

φ_3	φ_2	φ_1	F
0	0	0	1
0	0	1	0
0	1	0	1
0	1	1	0
1	0	0	0
1	0	1	0
1	1	0	1
1	1	1	1

TABLE 7.1 (Cont'd)

Note that f has the minimal form

$$f(x_4, x_3, x_2, x_1) = \bar{x}_4\, x_3\, x_2 + x_4\, \bar{x}_3\, x_2 + \bar{x}_4\, \bar{x}_3\, \bar{x}_1 + x_4\, x_3\, \bar{x}_1$$

and $M(f) = 16$. However, f can be factored as

$$f = (\bar{x}_4\, x_3 + x_4\, \bar{x}_3)x_2 + (\bar{x}_4\, \bar{x}_3 + x_4\, x_3)\bar{x}_1$$
$$= (x_4 \oplus x_3)x_2 + (\overline{x_4 \oplus x_3})\bar{x}_1$$
$$= F(\varphi_3(x_4, x_3),\, \varphi_2(x_2),\, \varphi_1(x_1))$$

where

$$\varphi_3(x_4, x_3) = x_4 \oplus x_3$$
$$= \bar{x}_4\, x_3 + x_4\, \bar{x}_3$$
$$\varphi_2(x_2) = x_2 \qquad\qquad (7.2)$$
$$\varphi_1(x_1) = x_1$$
$$F(\varphi_3, \varphi_2, \varphi_1) = \bar{\varphi}_3\, \bar{\varphi}_1 + \varphi_3\, \varphi_2$$

This decomposition of f suggests the circuit of Fig. 7.2, having cost $12 < 16$. We present this example as an illustration of the practical importance of decomposition theory. In addition, the example will motivate several preliminary definitions important to a theoretical treatment of disjunctive decompositions.

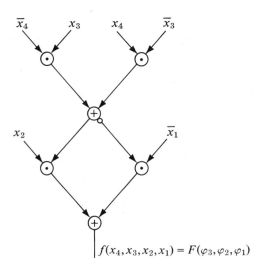

$$f(x_4, x_3, x_2, x_1) = F(\varphi_3, \varphi_2, \varphi_1)$$

FIGURE 7.2

The term "disjunctive" in decomposition theory refers, as in Example 7.1, to the fact that the subfunctions $\varphi_1, \varphi_2, \cdots, \varphi_p$ do not have variables in common. More precisely, the disjunctive decompositions observe a partition $\lambda = \{A_1, A_2, \cdots, A_p\}$ of $S_n = \{x_n, x_{n-1}, \cdots, x_1\}$ in that the *subfunctions* φ_i $(i = 1, 2, \cdots, p)$ are functions only of the variables appearing in the block A_i, a feature that we indicate by the notation $\varphi_i(A_i)$. Then we have $\varphi_i : B^{|A_i|} \longrightarrow B$.

The mapping σ of Eq. 7.1 is required to be the Cartesian product mapping (cf. Eq. 0.22)

$$\sigma = \prod_{i=1}^{p} \varphi_i \tag{7.3}$$

in the decomposition theory we are about to develop. But, as such, the set B^n on which σ is defined must be reinterpreted as $B^n = B^{|A_1|} \times B^{|A_2|} \times \cdots \times B^{|A_p|}$.

EXAMPLE 7.2

In Example 7.1, Eqs. 7.2 reveal that with[†]

$$\lambda = \{A_1, A_2, A_3\} = \{\overline{x_1}; \overline{x_2}; \overline{x_3, x_4}\}$$

the functions $\varphi_i : B^{|A_i|} \longrightarrow B$ $(i = 1, 2, 3)$ are

x_4	x_3	φ_3	x_2	φ_2	x_1	φ_1
0	0	0	0	0	0	0
0	1	1	1	1	1	1
1	0	1				
1	1	0				

while the Cartesian product $\sigma = \varphi_3 \times \varphi_2 \times \varphi_1 : B^4 \longrightarrow B^3$ of Eq. 7.3 has the following description:

$$((0, 0), 0, 0) \xrightarrow{\sigma} (\varphi_3, (0, 0), \varphi_2(0), \varphi_1(0)) = (0, 0, 0)$$
$$((0, 0), 0, 1) \xrightarrow{\sigma} (\varphi_3, (0, 0), \varphi_2(0), \varphi_1(1)) = (0, 0, 1)$$
$$((0, 0), 1, 0) \xrightarrow{\sigma} (0, 1, 0)$$
$$((0, 0), 1, 1) \xrightarrow{\sigma} (0, 1, 1)$$
$$((0, 1), 0, 0) \xrightarrow{\sigma} (1, 0, 0)$$
$$((0, 1), 0, 1) \xrightarrow{\sigma} (1, 0, 1)$$
$$((0, 1), 1, 0) \xrightarrow{\sigma} (1, 1, 0)$$
$$((0, 1), 1, 1) \xrightarrow{\sigma} (1, 1, 1)$$
$$((1, 0), 0, 0) \xrightarrow{\sigma} (1, 0, 0)$$
$$((1, 0), 0, 1) \xrightarrow{\sigma} (1, 0, 1)$$
$$((1, 0), 1, 0) \xrightarrow{\sigma} (1, 1, 0)$$
$$((1, 0), 1, 1) \xrightarrow{\sigma} (1, 1, 1)$$

[†]Here, the notation $\bar{x}_i$ should not be mistaken as the "complement of x_i." Instead, we are employing the convention introduced in Sec. 0.7, which denotes subsets of a partition by overscores.

$$((1, 1), 0, 0) \xrightarrow{\sigma} (0, 0, 0)$$
$$((1, 1), 0, 1) \xrightarrow{\sigma} (0, 0, 1)$$
$$((1, 1), 1, 0) \xrightarrow{\sigma} (0, 1, 0)$$
$$((1, 1), 1, 1) \xrightarrow{\sigma} (0, 1, 1)$$

in agreement with the three truth tables φ_3, φ_2, φ_1 of Table 7.1.

Motivated by Examples 7.1 and 7.2 and using the notation introduced above, we say that a c.s.b.f. $f : B^n \longrightarrow B$ is *disjunctively decomposable* if there exists a nontrivial ($\lambda \neq 0, I$) partition $\lambda = \{A_1, A_2, \cdots, A_p\}$ of $S_n = \{x_n, x_{n-1}, \cdots, x_1\}$ and functions

$$\varphi_j : B^{|A_j|} \longrightarrow B \qquad (j = 1, 2, \cdots, p)$$
$$F : B^p \longrightarrow B$$

for which

$$f = F \cdot \prod_{j=1}^{p} \varphi_j \tag{7.4}$$

(In Prob. 7.23 the reader is asked to explain why we restrict our attention to nontrivial partitions of S_n.) Equation 7.4 is equivalent to writing

$$f(x_n, x_{n-1}, \cdots, x_1) = F(\varphi_p(A_p), \varphi_{p-1}(A_{p-1}), \cdots, \varphi_1(A_1)) \tag{7.5}$$

If $|A_j| > 1$ for exactly one index j, Eq. 7.5 is termed a *simple* disjunctive decomposition. If, on the other hand, we have $|A_j| > 1$ for more than one index, the decomposition is said to be a *multiple* disjunctive decomposition. Evidently the decomposition of Examples 7.1 and 7.2 was a simple one.

7.3 PARTITION FUNCTIONS, MATRICES, AND CHARTS

In the next section, we give Ashenhurst's important criterion for deciding whether or not a Boolean function f admits a disjunctive decomposition. In order to phrase this criterion and in order to present the tools for its effective application, we must first introduce functions and matrices that are direct generalizations of the ith partial expansions and associated matrix representations of Sec. 6.3.

Suppose $f : B^n \longrightarrow B$ and $A \subseteq S_n = \{x_n, x_{n-1}, \cdots, x_1\}$ is such that $1 \leq |A| \leq n - 1$, so that $\lambda_A = \{A, S_n - A\}$ is a primary (cf. Sec 5.10) partition of S_n. Treating A and $S_n - A$ as sequences,

$$A = \langle x_{i_{|A|}}, x_{i_{|A|-1}}, \cdots, x_{i_1} \rangle$$

$$S_n - A = \langle x_{j_{|S_n-A|}}, x_{j_{|S_n-A|-1}}, \cdots, x_{j_1} \rangle$$

with $1 \leq i_1 < i_2 < \cdots < i_{|A|} \leq n$ and also $1 \leq j_1 < j_2 < \cdots < j_{|S_n-A|}$

$\leq n$, we define a permutation (cf. Example 0.13) $\pi_A : n^+ \longrightarrow n^+$ by writing

$$\pi_A(i_{|A|}) = n \qquad\qquad \pi_A(j_{|S_n-A|}) = n - |A|$$
$$\pi_A(i_{|A|-1}) = n - 1 \qquad \pi_A(j_{|S_n-A|-1}) = n - |A| - 1$$

$$\qquad\qquad \cdot \qquad\qquad\qquad\qquad \cdot$$
$$\qquad\qquad \cdot \qquad\qquad\qquad\qquad \cdot$$
$$\qquad\qquad \cdot \qquad\qquad\qquad\qquad \cdot$$

$$\pi_A(i_1) = n - |A| + 1 \qquad \pi_A(j_1) = 1$$

Using the induced vertex map (cf. Eq. 2.46) $t_{\pi_A} = t^b_{\pi_A} : B^n \longrightarrow B^n$ with $b = (1, 1, \cdots, 1)$,

$$t_{\pi_A}(b_n, b_{n-1}, \cdots, b_1) = (b_{\pi_A(n)}, b_{\pi_A(n-1)}, \cdots, b_{\pi_A(1)}) \qquad (7.6)$$

we define the *partition function* f_A *of* f *with respect to* A

$$f_A : B^{|A|} \longrightarrow B^{2^{n-|A|}}$$

according to the prescription

$$f_A(b_{|A|}, b_{|A|-1}, \cdots, b_1) = (f \cdot t_{\pi_A}(b_{|A|}, b_{|A|-1}, \cdots, b_1, \overbrace{0, 0, \cdots, 0, 0}^{n-|A|}),$$
$$f \cdot t_{\pi_A}(b_{|A|}, b_{|A|-1}, \cdots, b_1, 0, 0, \cdots, 0, 1),$$
$$f \cdot t_{\pi_A}(b_{|A|}, b_{|A|-1}, \cdots, b_1, \overbrace{1, 1, \cdots, 1, 1}^{n-|A|})) \qquad (7.7)$$

The corresponding $2^{|A|} \times 2^{n-|A|}$ matrix having the $f_A(b_{|A|}, b_{|A|-1}, \cdots, b_1)$ as its rows is called the *partition matrix of* f *with respect to* A.

EXAMPLE 7.3

For $f : B^5 \longrightarrow B$, as shown in Table 7.2, take $A = \{x_4, x_2, x_1\}$ so that

$$\lambda_A = \{A, S_5 - A\} = \{\overline{x_4, x_2, x_1}; \overline{x_5, x_3}\}$$

Then $\pi_A : 5^+ \longrightarrow 5^+$ is the permutation

$$4 \xrightarrow{\pi_A} 5 \qquad 5 \xrightarrow{\pi_A} 2$$
$$2 \xrightarrow{\pi_A} 4 \qquad 3 \xrightarrow{\pi_A} 1$$
$$1 \xrightarrow{\pi_A} 3$$

and we have shown the effect of the vertex map t_{π_A} in Table 7.2.

Using Eq. 7.7, we compute

$$f_A(0,0,0) = (f \cdot t_{\pi_A}(0,0,0,0,0), f \cdot t_{\pi_A}(0,0,0,0,1), f \cdot t_{\pi_A}(0,0,0,1,0),$$
$$f \cdot t_{\pi_A}(0,0,0,1,1))$$

$$= f(0,0,0,0,0), f(0,0,1,0,0), f(1,0,0,0,0), f(1,0,1,0,0))$$
$$= (1,0,0,0)$$
$$f_A(0,0,1) = (0,0,1,1)$$
$$f_A(0,1,0) = (1,0,0,0)$$
$$f_A(0,1,1) = (0,1,0,1)$$

x_5	x_4	x_3	x_2	x_1	f	$t_{\pi_A}(x_5, x_4, x_3, x_2, x_1)$				
0	0	0	0	0	1	0	0	0	0	0
0	0	0	0	1	0	0	0	1	0	0
0	0	0	1	0	1	1	0	0	0	0
0	0	0	1	1	0	1	0	1	0	0
0	0	1	0	0	0	0	0	0	0	1
0	0	1	0	1	0	0	0	1	0	1
0	0	1	1	0	0	1	0	0	0	1
0	0	1	1	1	1	1	0	1	0	1
0	1	0	0	0	0	0	0	0	1	0
0	1	0	0	1	0	0	0	1	1	0
0	1	0	1	0	1	1	0	0	1	0
0	1	0	1	1	1	1	0	1	1	0
0	1	1	0	0	1	0	0	0	1	1
0	1	1	0	1	0	0	0	1	1	1
0	1	1	1	0	1	1	0	0	1	1
0	1	1	1	1	0	1	0	1	1	1
1	0	0	0	0	0	0	1	0	0	0
1	0	0	0	1	1	0	1	1	0	0
1	0	0	1	0	0	1	1	0	0	0
1	0	0	1	1	0	1	1	1	0	0
1	0	1	0	0	0	0	1	0	0	1
1	0	1	0	1	1	0	1	1	0	1
1	0	1	1	0	0	1	1	0	0	1
1	0	1	1	1	1	1	1	1	0	1
1	1	0	0	0	0	0	1	0	1	0
1	1	0	0	1	1	0	1	1	1	0
1	1	0	1	0	0	1	1	0	1	0
1	1	0	1	1	0	1	1	1	1	0
1	1	1	0	0	1	0	1	0	1	1
1	1	1	0	1	1	0	1	1	1	1
1	1	1	1	0	1	1	1	0	1	1
1	1	1	1	1	0	1	1	1	1	1

TABLE 7.2

$$f_A(1,0,0) = (0,1,0,1)$$
$$f_A(1,0,1) = (0,0,1,1)$$
$$f_A(1,1,0) = (1,1,0,1)$$
$$f_A(1,1,1) = (1,0,0,0)$$

so that the corresponding 8×4 partition matrix of f with respect to A is written

$$
A
\begin{array}{c}
S_5 - A \\
\begin{bmatrix}
1 & 0 & 0 & 0 \\
0 & 0 & 1 & 1 \\
1 & 0 & 0 & 0 \\
0 & 1 & 0 & 1 \\
0 & 1 & 0 & 1 \\
0 & 0 & 1 & 1 \\
1 & 1 & 0 & 1 \\
1 & 0 & 0 & 0
\end{bmatrix}
\end{array}
\quad \text{or} \quad x_4 x_2 x_1
\begin{array}{c}
x_5 x_3 \\
\begin{bmatrix}
1 & 0 & 0 & 0 \\
0 & 0 & 1 & 1 \\
1 & 0 & 0 & 0 \\
0 & 1 & 0 & 1 \\
0 & 1 & 0 & 1 \\
0 & 0 & 1 & 1 \\
1 & 1 & 0 & 1 \\
1 & 0 & 0 & 0
\end{bmatrix}
\end{array}
$$

EXAMPLE 7.4

If $f: B^4 \rightarrow B$ is the function of Example 7.1 and $A = \{x_4, x_3\}$, the 4×4 partition matrix of f with respect to A is

$$
\begin{array}{c}
\quad x_2x_1 \\
x_4x_3\ \begin{array}{|cccc|}
\hline
1 & 0 & 1 & 0 \\
0 & 0 & 1 & 1 \\
0 & 0 & 1 & 1 \\
1 & 0 & 1 & 0 \\
\hline
\end{array}
\end{array}
$$

Observe that if $A = \{x_4, x_3, x_1\}$, the partition matrix

$$
\begin{array}{c}
\quad x_2 \\
x_4x_3x_1\ \begin{array}{|cc|}
\hline
1 & 1 \\
0 & 1 \\
0 & 1 \\
1 & 1 \\
0 & 0 \\
0 & 1 \\
0 & 1 \\
0 & 0 \\
\hline
\end{array}
\end{array}
$$

of f with respect to A is identical with the second partial expansion of f.

Since S_n has $2^n - 2$ proper subsets A, there are $2^n - 2$ partition matrices for a c.s.b.f. $f: B^n \rightarrow B$; and since each of these is the transpose of another, we can be satisfied with $\frac{1}{2}(2^n - 2) = 2^{n-1} - 1$ matrices by viewing them normally and sideways. These matrices (or the more manageable decomposition charts, which we will introduce immediately) will constitute the necessary tools for the application of Ashenhurst's fundamental criterion for deciding whether or not a Boolean function is disjunctively decomposable.

The reader probably feels that the effort involved in the use of any criterion that requires the construction of all $2^{n-1} - 1$ decomposition matrices would be prohibitive, even for moderate values of n. To alleviate this situation, we will make use of standard n-variable "decomposition charts," which are suitable for use with any Boolean function $f(x_n, x_{n-1}, \cdots, x_1)$. One has only to circle the integers in $\mathscr{K}^0(f)$ on these charts in order to have access to the same information as that possessed by the partition matrices.

EXAMPLE 7.5

Observe that the matrix of Example 7.3,

$x_4x_2x_1$	x_5x_3			
	1	0	0	0
	0	0	1	1
	1	0	0	0
	0	1	0	1
	0	1	0	1
	0	0	①	1
	1	1	0	1
	1	0	0	0

or

x_4	x_2	x_1	x_5x_3 00	01	10	11
0	0	0	1	0	0	0
0	0	1	0	0	1	1
0	1	0	1	0	0	0
0	1	1	0	1	0	1
1	0	0	0	1	0	1
1	0	1	0	0	①	1
1	1	0	1	1	0	1
1	1	1	1	0	0	0

simply contains the 32 entries of the truth table for f in an order determined by the rows and columns in the second matrix above. For example, the entry

$$f(1, 1, 0, 0, 1) = 1$$

of Table 8.2 appears at the intersection of

Row: $(x_4, x_2, x_1) = (1,0,1)$
Column: $(x_5, x_3) = (1,0)$

as circled in the second matrix above. By this sort of reasoning, we see that, by circling the integers in $\mathscr{K}^0(f)$ on the predrawn chart,

$x_4x_2x_1$	x_5x_3			
	⓪	4	16	20
	1	5	⑰	㉑
	②	6	18	22
	3	⑦	19	㉓
	8	⑫	24	㉘
	9	13	㉕	㉙
	⑩	⑭	26	㉚
	⑪	15	27	31

we have a record of the same information possessed by the original matrix, where we interpret circled numbers as "1" and uncircled numbers as "0". Moreover, a replica of this same chart could be used with another function, $f: B^5 \longrightarrow B$, by simply circling the integers of its $\mathscr{K}^0(f)$.

In Tables 7.3, 7.4, and 7.5, we have provided all *decomposition charts* for use with functions $f: B^n \longrightarrow B (3 \leq n \leq 5)$. (Often the decomposition chart that represents the partition matrix of f with respect to A will be called the λ_A *chart* of f.) These are to be used as in Example 7.5, in lieu of constructing the partition matrices. (Should the reader have sufficient occasions to use them, he can easily construct his own set of charts for $n > 5$. In any event, a repeated use of these charts makes it necessary that copies be available in quantity. These are the reasons for our not having provided a more extensive collection of decomposition charts.)

	x_1		x_2		x_3
	0 1		0 2		0 4
x_3x_2	2 3	x_3x_1	1 3	x_2x_1	1 5
	4 5		4 6		2 6
	6 7		5 7		3 7

TABLE 7.3   THREE-VARIABLE DECOMPOSITION CHARTS

	x_1		x_2		x_3		x_4
	0 1		0 2		0 4		0 8
	2 3		1 3		1 5		1 9
	4 5		4 6		2 6		2 10
$x_4x_3x_2$	6 7	$x_4x_3x_1$	5 7	$x_4x_2x_1$	3 7	$x_3x_2x_1$	3 11
	8 9		8 10		8 12		4 12
	10 11		9 11		9 13		5 13
	12 13		12 14		10 14		6 14
	14 15		13 15		11 15		7 15

	x_2x_1		x_3x_1		x_3x_2
	0 1 2 3		0 1 4 5		0 2 4 6
x_4x_3	4 5 6 7	x_4x_2	2 3 6 7	x_4x_1	1 3 5 7
	8 9 10 11		8 9 12 13		8 10 12 14
	12 13 14 15		10 11 14 15		9 11 13 15

TABLE 7.4   FOUR-VARIABLE DECOMPOSITION CHARTS

	x_1		x_2		x_3		x_4
	0 1		0 2		0 4		0 8
	2 3		1 3		1 5		1 9
	4 5		4 6		2 6		2 10
	6 7		5 7		3 7		3 11
	8 9		8 10		8 12		4 12
$x_5x_4x_3x_2$	10 11	$x_5x_4x_3x_1$	9 11	$x_5x_4x_2x_1$	9 13	$x_5x_3x_2x_1$	5 13
	12 13		12 14		10 14		6 14
	14 15		13 15		11 15		7 15
	16 17		16 18		16 20		16 24
	18 19		17 19		17 21		17 25
	20 21		20 22		18 22		18 26
	22 23		21 23		19 23		19 27
	24 25		24 26		24 28		20 28
	26 27		25 27		25 29		21 29
	28 29		28 30		26 30		22 30
	30 31		29 31		27 31		23 31

x_5

$x_4x_3x_2x_1$ | x_5 |
|---|
| 0 16 |
| 1 17 |
| 2 18 |
| 3 19 |
| 4 20 |
| 5 21 |
| 6 22 |
| 7 23 |
| 8 24 |
| 9 25 |
| 10 26 |
| 11 27 |
| 12 28 |
| 13 29 |
| 14 30 |
| 15 31 |

x_2x_1 — $x_5x_4x_3$

0	1	2	3
4	5	6	7
8	9	10	11
12	13	14	15
16	17	18	19
20	21	22	23
24	25	26	27
28	29	30	31

x_3x_1 — $x_5x_4x_2$

0	1	4	5
2	3	6	7
8	9	12	13
10	11	14	15
16	17	20	21
18	19	22	23
24	25	28	29
26	27	30	31

x_3x_2 — $x_5x_4x_1$

0	2	4	6
1	3	5	7
8	10	12	14
9	11	13	15
16	18	20	22
17	19	21	23
24	26	28	30
25	27	29	31

x_4x_1 — $x_5x_3x_2$

0	1	8	9
2	3	10	11
4	5	12	13
6	7	14	15
16	17	24	25
18	19	26	27
20	21	28	29
22	23	30	31

x_4x_2 — $x_5x_3x_1$

0	2	8	10
1	3	9	11
4	6	12	14
5	7	13	15
16	18	24	26
17	19	25	27
20	22	28	30
21	23	29	31

x_4x_3 — $x_5x_2x_1$

0	4	8	12
1	5	9	13
2	6	10	14
3	7	11	15
16	20	24	28
17	21	25	29
18	22	26	30
19	23	27	31

x_5x_1 — $x_4x_3x_2$

0	1	16	17
2	3	18	19
4	5	20	21
6	7	22	23
8	9	24	25
10	11	26	27
12	13	28	29
14	15	30	31

x_5x_2 — $x_4x_3x_1$

0	2	16	18
1	3	17	19
4	6	20	22
5	7	21	23
8	10	24	26
9	11	25	27
12	14	28	30
13	15	29	31

x_5x_3 — $x_4x_2x_1$

0	4	16	20
1	5	17	21
2	6	18	22
3	7	19	23
8	12	24	28
9	13	25	29
10	14	26	30
11	15	27	31

x_5x_4 — $x_3x_2x_1$

0	8	16	24
1	9	17	25
2	10	18	26
3	11	19	27
4	12	20	28
5	13	21	29
6	14	22	30
7	15	23	31

TABLE 7.5   FIVE VARIABLE DECOMPOSITION CHARTS

7.4   SIMPLE DISJUNCTIVE DECOMPOSITIONS

Before stating the promised disjunctive decomposability criteria, we introduce a notational device that will be helpful in our subsequent discussions. If $v = (v_n, v_{n-1}, \cdots, v_1) \in B^n$ and $\lambda = \{A, S_n - A\}$ is any primary partition of S_n, the λ *components* of v are the vertices (of $B^{|A|}$ and $B^{|S_n-A|}$, respectively)

$$v^{(1)} = \left(v_{\pi_A^{-1}(n)},\ v_{\pi_A^{-1}(n-1)},\ \cdots,\ v_{\pi_A^{-1}(n-|A|+1)}\right) \tag{7.8}$$

$$v^{(2)} = \left(v_{\pi_A^{-1}(n-|A|)},\ v_{\pi_A^{-1}(n-|A|-1)},\ \cdots,\ v_{\pi_A^{-1}(1)}\right) \tag{7.9}$$

where π_A is the permutation of Sec. 7.3.

EXAMPLE 7.6

If $v = (0,1,1,0,1) \in B^5$ and

$$\lambda = \{\overline{x_4,\, x_2,\, x_1}\,;\, \overline{x_5,\, x_3}\} = \{A,\, S_n - A\}$$

then (cf. Example 7.3)

$$v^{(1)} = (1,0,1)$$
$$v^{(2)} = (0,1)$$

More generally, we will have occasion to use λ components $v^{(1)}$, $v^{(2)}$, $\cdots$, $v^{(p)}$ of $v = (v_n, v_{n-1}, \cdots, v_1)$ when $\lambda = \{A_1, A_2, \cdots, A_p\}$ is an arbitrary partition of S_n. Thus, if $v = (1,1,0,0,1,0,1) \in B^7$ and $\lambda = \{\overline{x_5,\, x_3,\, x_2}\,;\, \overline{x_7,\, x_1}\,;\, \overline{x_6,\, x_4}\} = \{A_1, A_2, A_3\}$, then we have

$$v^{(1)} = (0,1,0)$$
$$v^{(2)} = (1,1)$$
$$v^{(3)} = (1,0)$$

Theorem 7.1. (Due to Ashenhurst): The c.s.b.f. $f: B^n \longrightarrow B$ has a simple disjunctive decomposition

$$f(x_n, x_{n-1}, \cdots, x_1) = F(\varphi(A),\, S_n - A)$$

for suitable functions

$$\varphi : B^{|A|} \longrightarrow B$$
$$F : B^{n-|A|+1} \longrightarrow B$$

if and only if the partition function $f_A : B^{|A|} \longrightarrow B^{2^{n-|A|}}$ resulting from the primary partition $\lambda = \{A,\, S_n - A\}$ is into a 2-element subset of $B^{2^{n-|A|}}$ (which is the same as saying that the partition matrix of f with respect to A has at most two distinct rows.)

PROOF. Suppose that the condition is satisfied—that for a certain 2-element subset $\{a^{(0)}, a^{(1)}\} \subseteq B^{2^{n-|A|}}$ we have

$$f_A(b_{|A|}, b_{|A|-1}, \cdots, b_1) = \begin{cases} a^{(0)} \\ \text{or} \\ a^{(1)} \end{cases} \tag{7.10}$$

for every element of $B^{|A|}$. We then define $\varphi : B^{|A|} \longrightarrow B$ according to

$$\varphi(b_{|A|}, b_{|A|-1}, \cdots, b_1) = b \Longleftrightarrow f_A(b_{|A|}, b_{|A|-1}, \cdots, b_1) = a^{(b)} \tag{7.11}$$

and $F : B^{n-|A|+1} = B \times B^{n-|A|} \to B$ by writing

$$F(u, w) = \tau_{2^{n-|A|}-\partial(w)}(a^{(u)}) \tag{7.12}$$

Here $\tau_j : B^{2^{n-|A|}} \to B$ is the jth coordinate projection of Eq. 0.23 and $\partial : B^{n-|A|} \to Z_{2_{n-|A|}}$ is (essentially binary to decimal base conversion) the mapping of Eq. 0.66.

Now, for any $v = (v_n, v_{n-1}, \cdots, v_1) \in B^n$, we denote (cf. Eqs. 7.8 and 7.9) $u = \varphi(v^{(1)})$ and $w = v^{(2)}$. Then, using Eqs. 7.7, 7.11, 7.12 with the substitution $j = 2^{n-|A|} - \partial(w)$, we have

$$\begin{aligned}
F(\varphi(A), S_n - A) &\equiv F(\varphi(v^{(1)}), v^{(2)}) \\
&= F(u, w) \\
&= \tau_j(a^{(u)}) \\
&= \tau_j(f_A(v^{(1)})) \\
&= \tau_j(f \cdot t_{\pi_A}(v^{(1)}, \overbrace{0, 0, \cdots, 0, 0}^{n-|A|}), \\
&\qquad f \cdot t_{\pi_A}(v^{(1)}, 0, 0, \cdots, 0, 1), \\
&\qquad \qquad \vdots \\
&\qquad f \cdot t_{\pi_A}(v^{(1)}, \overbrace{1, 1, \cdots, 1, 1}^{n-|A|})) \\
&= \tau_j(a_{2^{n-|A|}}, a_{2^{n-|A|}-1}, \cdots, a_j, \cdots, a_1) \\
&= a_j
\end{aligned}$$

where

$$a_j = f \cdot t_{\pi_A}(v^{(1)}, b^j_{n-|A|}, b^j_{n-|A|-1}, b^j_1)$$

and

$$\partial(b^j_{n-|A|}, \cdots, b^j_1) = 2^{n-|A|} - j = \partial(w)$$

Since ∂ is 1-1, we obtain

$$(b^j_{n-|A|}, \cdots, b^j_1) = w$$

and using Eq. 7.6, we obtain the desired conclusion

$$\begin{aligned}
F(\varphi(A), S_n - A) = a_j &= f \cdot t_{\pi_A}(v^{(1)}, v^{(2)}) \\
&= f \cdot t_{\pi_A}(v_{\pi_A^{-1}(n)}, v_{\pi_A^{-1}(n-1)}, \cdots, v_{\pi_A^{-1}(1)}) \\
&= f(v_n, v_{n-1}, \cdots, v_1) \quad \blacksquare
\end{aligned}$$

We leave the converse argument as an exercise for the reader. It should be observed that the parenthetical phrasing of the Ashenhurst criterion (that the partition matrix of f with respect to A have at most two distinct rows) is reminiscent of the criterion for case (2) classification in the tree circuit theorem; in this sense, Ashenhurst's theorem might be considered a generalization of Theorem 6.1(2).

EXAMPLE 7.7

If $A = \{x_4, x_3\}$ in Example 7.4, we observe that the partition matrix of f with respect to A has but two rows

$$a^{(0)} = (1,0,1,0)$$
$$a^{(1)} = (0,0,1,1)$$

According to Eq. 7.11, we define $\varphi : B^{|A|} = B^2 \longrightarrow B$ by

x_4	x_3	φ
0	0	0
0	1	1
1	0	1
1	1	0

that is, $\varphi(0, 0) = 0$, since $f_A(0, 0) = (1, 0, 1, 0) = a^{(0)}$, etc. Using Eq. 7.12, we write

$$F(0,b_2,b_1) = \tau_{4-\partial(b_2,b_1)}(a^{(0)})$$
$$= \tau_{4-\partial(b_2,b_1)}(1,0,1,0)$$
$$F(1,b_2,b_1) = \tau_{4-\partial(b_2,b_1)}(a^{(1)})$$
$$= \tau_{4-\partial(b_2,b_1)}(0,0,1,1)$$

so that F has the truth table

φ	x_2	x_1	F	
0	0	0	1	
0	0	1	0	$a^{(0)}$
0	1	0	1	
0	1	1	0	
1	0	0	0	
1	0	1	0	$a^{(1)}$
1	1	0	1	
1	1	1	1	

that is,

$$F(0,0,0) = \tau_{4-\partial(0,0)}(1,0,1,0) = \tau_4(1,0,1,0) = 1$$
$$F(0,0,1) = \tau_{4-\partial(0,1)}(1,0,1,0) = \tau_3(1,0,1,0) = 0$$

etc. While the proof of Ashenhurst's theorem is constructive in that Eqs. 7.11 and 7.12 provide the necessary definitions for the functions φ, F, it is instructive to observe that φ plays the role of selecting one of the two "vectors" $a^{(0)}$ or $a^{(1)}$; that is $\varphi = 0$ selects $a^{(0)}$ and $\varphi = 1$ selects $a^{(1)}$. This is a convenient way of viewing the truth table for F.

Now

$$\varphi(x_4, x_3) = x_4 \oplus x_3$$
$$F(\varphi, x_2, x_1) = \bar{\varphi}\bar{x}_1 + \varphi x_2$$

as depicted in Fig. 7.2.

EXAMPLE 7.8

We have already indicated that the decomposition charts will be most convenient in testing Ashenhurst's "two-row criterion." As an illustration, suppose $f: B^5 \longrightarrow B$ with

$$\mathcal{K}^0(f) = \{3,5,13,15,16,19,20,24,26,28,30\}$$

One of its decomposition charts,

$$x_4 x_2$$

	0	2	8	10
	1	③	9	11
	4	6	12	14
$x_5 x_3 x_1$	⑤	7	⑬	⑮
	⑯	18	㉔	㉖
	17	⑲	25	27
	⑳	22	㉘	㉚
	21	23	29	31

has but two column patterns (row patterns when viewed sideways). Thus, f has the decomposition

$$f(x_5, x_4, x_3, x_1) = F(\varphi(x_4, x_2), x_5, x_3, x_1)$$

If the first, third, and fourth columns are denoted by $a^{(0)}$ and the second by $a^{(1)}$, we have

x_4	x_2	φ
0	0	0
0	1	1
1	0	0
1	1	0

$\varphi(x_4, x_2) = \bar{x}_4 x_2$

and as mentioned in the preceding example, the function φ plays the role of selecting one of the two functions of x_5, x_3, x_1, which correspond to the columns $a^{(0)}$ and $a^{(1)}$. Thus, one can write the truth table

φ	x_5	x_3	x_1	F	
0	0	0	0	0	
0	0	0	1	0	
0	0	1	0	0	
0	0	1	1	1	$a^{(0)}$
0	1	0	0	1	
0	1	0	1	0	
0	1	1	0	1	
0	1	1	1	0	
1	0	0	0	0	
1	0	0	1	1	
1	0	1	0	0	
1	0	1	1	0	$a^{(1)}$
1	1	0	0	0	
1	1	0	1	1	
1	1	1	0	0	
1	1	1	1	0	

without actually appealing to Eq. 7.12.

By plotting $\mathcal{K}^0(F) = \{3, 4, 6, 9, 13\}$ on the four-variable decomposition charts, we learn that F is not disjunctively decomposable, since none of the decomposition charts has only a two row (or column)-pattern:

Circled entries are shown in parentheses, e.g. (3) denotes a circled 3.

$\varphi x_5 x_3$ — x_1:

0	1
2	(3)
(4)	5
(6)	7
8	(9)
10	11
12	(13)
14	15

$\varphi x_5 x_1$ — x_3:

0	2
1	(3)
(4)	(6)
5	7
8	10
(9)	11
12	14
(13)	15

$\varphi x_3 x_1$ — x_5:

0	(4)
1	5
2	(6)
(3)	7
8	12
(9)	(13)
10	14
11	15

$x_5 x_3 x_1$ — φ:

0	8
1	(9)
2	10
(3)	11
(4)	12
5	(13)
(6)	14
7	15

φx_5 — $x_3 x_1$:

0	1	2	(3)
(4)	5	(6)	7
8	(9)	10	11
12	(13)	14	15

φx_3 — $x_5 x_1$:

0	1	(4)	5
2	(3)	(6)	7
8	(9)	12	(13)
10	11	14	15

φx_1 — $x_5 x_3$:

0	2	(4)	(6)
1	(3)	5	7
8	10	12	14
(9)	11	(13)	15

But by using the methods of Chapter 6, we can choose to implement F with a tree circuit; Fig. 7.3 is representative of the results of these techniques. Combining the results with the knowledge that $\varphi = \bar{x}_4 x_2$, we obtain the two-input-per-gate circuit of Fig. 7.4.

This example gives an indication as to the way in which the decomposition theory can be effectively combined with the tree circuit theory of the preceding chapter.

Having not yet given the criterion for the most general (Eq. 7.5) or multiple disjunctive decomposition, we immediately correct this deficiency and offer at the same time a preview of the subject of the next section with the following corollary.

Corollary 7.2. (Ashenhurst's Disjunctive Decomposition Theorem): The c.s.b.f. $f: B^n \longrightarrow B$ has the disjunctive decomposition

$$f(x_n, x_{n-1}, \cdots, x_1) = F(\varphi_p(A_p), \varphi_{p-1}(A_{p-1}), \cdots, \varphi_1(A_1))$$

for suitable functions

$$\varphi_i : B^{|A_i|} \longrightarrow B \qquad (i = 1, 2, \cdots, p)$$

$$F : B^p \longrightarrow B$$

if and only if the partition $\lambda = \{A_1, A_2, \cdots, A_p\}$ is nontrivial and the partition matrices of f with respect to A_i have at most two distinct rows $(i = 1, 2, \cdots, p)$.

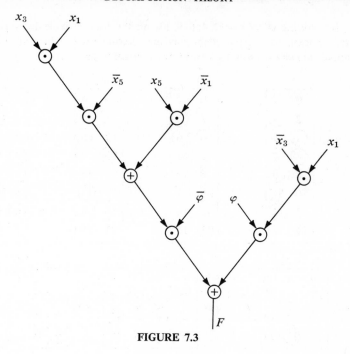

FIGURE 7.3

We have stated this corollary without proof, assuming that the reader can infer as much from our detailed treatment of the simple

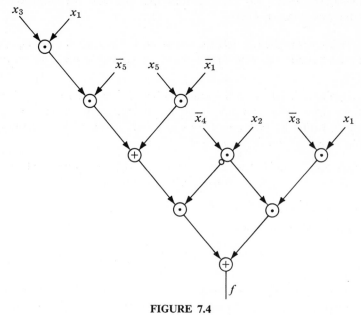

FIGURE 7.4

decomposition criterion. Moreover, there seems to be no immediate need for an additional example; we will have ample opportunity to study more examples as we proceed. But, for the time being, the reader is reminded that the simple disjunctive decompositions considered thus far are themselves examples of the corollary; simply refine $\gamma = \{A, S_n - A\}$ by writing $\lambda = \{A, A_2, A_3, \cdots, A_p\}$ with $A_j = \{x_{\rho_j}\}$ to appreciate this remark. Since we have always had $|A| \geq 2$, λ is nontrivial. Moreover, the partition matrix of f with respect to A has at most two distinct rows because we are assuming that $f = F(\varphi(A), S_n - A)$. That the partition matrices of f with respect to the A_j $(j = 2, 3, \cdots, p)$ have this property is obvious, for they have only two rows to begin with! Taking $\varphi_j(A_j) = x_{\rho_j}$, we obtain Eq. 7.5; that is,

$$f(x_n, x_{n-1}, \cdots, x_1) = F(\varphi(A), S_n - A)$$
$$= F(\varphi(A), \varphi_2(A_2), \cdots, \varphi_p(A_p))$$

7.5   MULTIPLE DISJUNCTIVE DECOMPOSITIONS

Consider again the general (multiple) disjunctive decomposition (Eq. 7.5)

$$f(x_n, x_{n-1}, \cdots, x_1) = F(\varphi_p(A_p), \varphi_{p-1}, (A_{p-1}), \cdots, \varphi_1(A_1))$$

for any partition $\lambda = \{A_1, A_2, \cdots, A_p\}$ of S_n. We say that the decomposition (Eq. 7.5) is of *type* II if

(A) $F(\varphi_p, \varphi_{p-1}, \cdots, \varphi_1) = \varphi_p + \varphi_{p-1} + \cdots + \varphi_1$, or

(B) $F(\varphi_p, \varphi_{p-1}, \cdots, \varphi_1) = \varphi_p \cdot \varphi_{p-1} \cdot (\cdots) \cdot \varphi_1$, or

(C) $F(\varphi_p, \varphi_{p-1}, \cdots, \varphi_1) = \varphi_p \oplus \varphi_{p-1} \oplus \cdots \oplus \varphi_1$.

Otherwise it is said to be of *type* I.

We now give a theorem that expresses (as with Ashenhurst's theorem) a criterion based on the partition matrices (or the decomposition charts) for deciding whether a c.s.b.f. f admits a type II decomposition.

Theorem 7.3.   The c.s.b.f. $f : B^n \longrightarrow B$ has a type II disjunctive decomposition

$$f(x_n, x_{n-1}, \cdots, x_1) = F(\varphi_p(A_p), \varphi_{p-1}(A_{p-1}), \cdots, \varphi_1(A_1))$$

for suitable functions

$$\varphi_i : B^{|A_i|} \longrightarrow B \qquad (i = 1, 2, \cdots, p)$$

if and only if for each A_i in the partition $\lambda = \{A_1, A_2, \cdots, A_p\}$ the partition matrices of f with respect to A_i have at most two distinct rows,

(a) one of which is the row $\overbrace{(1, 1, \cdots, 1)}^{2^n-|A_i|}$, or

(b) one of which is the row $\overbrace{(0, 0, \cdots, 0)}^{2^n-|A_i|}$, or

(c) that are complementary.

PROOF. Suppose first that for each $A_i \in \lambda$, the partition matrix of f with respect to A_i satisfies property (a). In this event, we define functions

$$\varphi_p : B^{|A_p|} \longrightarrow B$$

$$\tilde{\varphi}_p : B^{|S_n-A_p|} \longrightarrow B$$

as follows (cf. Prob. 7.24):

$$\varphi_p(u) = 1 \Longleftrightarrow f_{A_p}(u) = \overbrace{(1, 1, \cdots, 1)}^{2^{n-|A_p|}} \qquad (7.13)$$

$$\tilde{\varphi}_p(w) = 1 \Longleftrightarrow f_{S_n-A_p}(w) = \overbrace{(1, 1, \cdots, 1)}^{2^{|A_p|}} \qquad (7.14)$$

Then we take

$$F(\varphi_p, \tilde{\varphi}_p) = \varphi_p + \tilde{\varphi}_p$$

Now consider any vertex $v = (v_n, v_{n-1}, \cdots, v_1) \in B^n$, and for the primary partition $\lambda_p = \{A_p, S_n - A_p\}$, let $u = v^{(1)}$ and $w = v^{(2)}$ be the λ_p components (cf. Eqs. 7.8 and 7.9) of v. Then

$$f(v) = 1 \Longleftrightarrow \begin{cases} f_{A_p}(u) = \overbrace{(1, 1, \cdots, 1)}^{2^{n-|A_p|}} \\ \text{or} \\ f_{S_n-A_p}(w) = \overbrace{(1, 1, \cdots, 1)}^{2^{|A_p|}} \end{cases}$$

$$\Longleftrightarrow \begin{cases} \varphi_p(u) = 1 \\ \text{or} \\ \tilde{\varphi}_p(w) = 1 \end{cases}$$

$$\Longleftrightarrow F(\varphi_p, \tilde{\varphi}_p) = 1$$

where the "or" is inclusive and the first double implication holds because the pattern

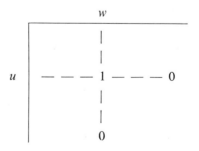

in which neither row u nor column w consists entirely of "ones," would contradict (a).

Now put $S = S_n - A_p$ and consider the partition $\lambda_{p-1} = \{A_{p-1}, S - A_{p-1}\}$ of S. That the partition matrix of f with respect to A_j satisfied (a) implies that the partition matrix of $\tilde{\varphi}_p$ with respect to A_j satisfies (a) for each $j < p$. Therefore, the above process may be repeated, yielding

$$\tilde{\varphi}_p = \varphi_{p-1} + \tilde{\varphi}_{p-1}$$

Continuing, we eventually obtain, for condition (a),

$$f(x_n, x_{n-1}, \cdots, x_1) = \varphi_p + \varphi_{p-1} + \cdots + \varphi_1$$

Conversely, if (A) holds for functions $\varphi_i : B^{|A_i|} \longrightarrow B$, it is easy to see that the partition matrix of f with respect to each A_i satisfies property (a). ∎

The proofs for property (b) or (c) are similar and left as exercises. For synthesis purposes, however, we tabulate the required definitions of the subfunctions in all three instances. For property (a),

$$\varphi_i(u) = 1 \Longleftrightarrow f_{A_i}(u) = \overbrace{(1, 1, \cdots, 1)}^{2^{n-|A_i|}} \qquad (7.15)$$

For property (b),

$$\varphi_i(u) = 1 \Longleftrightarrow f_{A_i}(u) \neq \overbrace{(0, 0, \cdots, 0)}^{2^{n-|A_i|}} \qquad (7.16)$$

For property (c),

$$\varphi_i(u) = 1 \Longleftrightarrow f_{A_i}(u) = a^{(i)} \qquad (7.17)$$

with $a^{(2)}, a^{(3)}, \cdots, a^{(p)}$ arbitrarily chosen between the two complementary rows and $a^{(1)}$ chosen so that for $v = (v_n, v_{n-1}, \cdots, v_1) \in B^n$ having λ components (cf. Example 7.6) $v^{(1)}, v^{(2)}, \cdots, v^{(p)}$, we have

$$f(v) = 1 \Longrightarrow \varphi_i(v^{(i)}) = 1 \text{ for an odd number of indices } i \qquad (7.18)$$

EXAMPLE 7.9

In order to illustrate Theorem 7.3, consider the function $f : B^4 \longrightarrow B$ for which $\mathscr{K}^0(f) = \{7, 13\}$. From the circled four-variable decomposition charts

	x_1			x_2			x_3			x_4	
	0	1		0	2		0	4		0	8
	2	3		1	3		1	5		1	9
	4	5		4	6		2	6		2	10
$x_4 x_3 x_2$	6	⑦	$x_4 x_3 x_1$	5	⑦	$x_4 x_2 x_1$	3	⑦	$x_3 x_2 x_1$	3	11
	8	9		8	10		8	12		4	12
	10	11		9	11		9	⑬		5	⑬
	12	⑬		12	14		10	14		6	14
	14	15		⑬	15		11	15		⑦	15

x_4x_3 \ x_2x_1				
	0	1	2	3
	4	5	6	(7)
	8	9	10	11
	12	(13)	14	15

x_4x_2 \ x_3x_1				
	0	1	4	5
	2	3	6	(7)
	8	9	12	(13)
	10	11	14	15

x_4x_1 \ x_3x_2				
	0	2	4	6
	1	3	5	(7)
	8	10	12	14
	9	11	(13)	15

we see that if $\lambda = \{\overline{x_1}; \overline{x_3}; \overline{x_4, x_2}\} = \{A_1, A_2, A_3\}$, the condition (b) of Theorem 7.3 is satisfied. We therefore define the subfunctions $\varphi_i : B^{|A_i|} \longrightarrow B$ $(i = 1,2,3)$ according to Eq. 7.16; that is,

x_1	φ_1	x_3	φ_2	x_4 x_2	φ_3
0	0	0	0	0 0	0
1	1	1	1	0 1	1
				1 0	1
				1 1	0

Thus,

$$\varphi_1(x_1) = x_1$$
$$\varphi_2(x_3) = x_3$$
$$\varphi_3(x_4, x_2) = x_4 \oplus x_2$$

and

$$f(x_4, x_3, x_2, x_1) = \varphi_3 \cdot \varphi_2 \cdot \varphi_1 = (x_4 \oplus x_2)x_3x_1$$

EXAMPLE 7.10

If

$$\mathscr{K}^0(f) = \{0,3,5,6,8,11,12,15,16,18,21,23,24,26,28,30\}$$

for the function $f: B^5 \longrightarrow B$, we observe from the selected collection of circled five-variable charts

$x_4x_3x_1$ \ x_5x_2				
	(0)	2	(16)	(18)
	1	(3)	17	19
	4	(6)	20	22
	(5)	7	(21)	(23)
	(8)	10	(24)	(26)
	9	(11)	25	27
	(12)	14	(28)	(30)
	13	(15)	29	31

$x_5x_2x_1$ \ x_4x_3				
	(0)	4	(8)	(12)
	1	(5)	9	13
	2	(6)	10	14
	(3)	7	(11)	(15)
	(16)	20	(24)	(28)
	17	(21)	25	29
	(18)	22	(26)	(30)
	19	(23)	27	31

$x_5x_4x_3x_2$ \ x_1		
	(0)	1
	2	(3)
	4	(5)
	(6)	7
	(8)	9
	10	11
	(12)	13
	14	15
	(16)	17
	(18)	19
	20	(21)
	22	(23)
	(24)	25
	(26)	27
	(28)	29
	(30)	31

that when $\lambda = \{\overline{x_5, x_2}; \overline{x_4, x_3}; \overline{x_1}\} = \{A_1, A_2, A_3\}$, we have condition (c) of Theorem 7.3. Using Eq. 7.17, we obtain subfunctions φ_3, φ_2,

x_1	φ_3	x_4	x_3	φ_2
0	0	0	0	1
1	1	0	1	0
		1	0	1
		1	1	1

by making quite arbitrary choices

$$a^{(3)} = (0,1,1,0,0,1,0,1,0,0,1,1,0,0,0,0)$$
$$a^{(2)} = (1,0,0,1,1,0,1,0)$$

between the two complementary columns of the last two matrices (charts). Between the two complementary columns of the first matrix, we *must then* choose

$$a^{(1)} = (0,1,1,0,0,1,0,1)$$

in order that Eq. 7.18 holds:

$$f(v) = 1 \Longrightarrow \varphi_i(v^{(i)}) = 1 \text{ for an odd number of indices } i$$

For example, suppose we take $V = 21 \in \mathscr{K}^0(f)$ so that for

$$v = \partial^{-1}(21) = (1,0,1,0,1) = (v_5, v_4, v_3, v_2, v_1)$$

we have $f(v) = 1$. Then we have the λ components

$$v^{(1)} = (v_5, v_2) = (1,0);$$
$$v^{(2)} = (v_4, v_3) = (0,1); \quad \varphi_2(v^{(2)}) = 0$$
$$v^{(3)} = (v_1) = (1) \quad ; \quad \varphi_3(v^{(3)}) = 1$$

and we need $\varphi_1(v^{(1)}) = 0$ in order that we obtain an odd number of "ones" among the $\varphi_i(v^{(i)})$; this fixes one entry in the truth table

x_5	x_2	φ_1
0	0	
0	1	
1	0	0
1	1	

of φ_1. Thus, if we want Eq. 7.17 for $i = 1$,

$$\varphi_1(u) = 1 \Longleftrightarrow f_{A_1} = a^{(1)}$$

we must *not* choose $a^{(1)}$ to be the third column of the matrix; so we have to take $a^{(1)} = (0,1,1,0,0,1,0,1)$ and complete the definition

x_5	x_2	φ_1
0	0	0
0	1	1
1	0	0
1	1	0

appropriately. Then (see Fig. 7.5)

$$f(x_5, x_4, x_3, x_2, x_1) = \varphi_3 \oplus \varphi_2 \oplus \varphi_1 = x_1 \oplus (x_4 + \bar{x}_3) \oplus (\bar{x}_5 x_2)$$

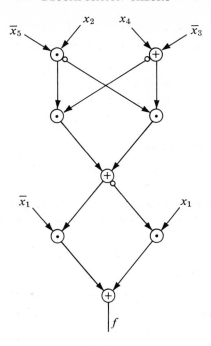

FIGURE 7.5

When Eq. 7.5 is that of a type I disjunctive decomposition, we define the subfunctions $\varphi_i : B^{|A_i|} \longrightarrow B$ in the usual way; that is,

$$\varphi_i(u) = 1 \Longleftrightarrow f_{A_i}(u) = a^{(i)} \tag{7.19}$$

($i = 1, 2, \cdots, p$) for "vectors" $a^{(i)}$, arbitrarily chosen as one or the other of the two rows of the partition matrix of f with respect to A_i. We then have the problem of defining $F : B^p \longrightarrow B$ in such a way that Eq. 7.5 holds. Assuming that the φ_i have already been defined according to Eq. 7.19, consider any $(b_p, b_{p-1}, \cdots, b_1) \in B^p$ and choose elements

$$v^{(i)} \in \varphi_i^{-1}(b_i) \tag{7.20}$$

for each $i = 1, 2, \cdots, p$. This can be done because the subfunctions φ_i are onto B. (Why?) These elements $v^{(i)} \in B^{|A_i|}$ are the λ components (cf. Example 7.6) of a unique vertex $v = (v_n, v_{n-1}, \cdots, v_1) \in B^n$ because λ is a partition. We take

$$F(b_p, b_{p-1}, \cdots, b_1) = f(v) \tag{7.21}$$

Using Eqs. 7.20 and 7.21, it then follows that

$$F(\varphi_p(A_p), \varphi_{p-1}(A_{p-1}), \cdots, \varphi_1(A_1)) = F(\varphi_p(v^{(p)}), \varphi_{p-1}(v^{(p-1)}), \cdots, \varphi_1(v^{(1)}))$$
$$= F(b_p, b_{p-1}, \cdots, b_1)$$
$$= f(v)$$

for every $v \in B^n$.

EXAMPLE 7.11

Suppose $f: B^5 \longrightarrow B$ has

$$\mathcal{K}^0(f) = \{1,2,3,4,7,9,11,12,14,16,18,19,21,22,24,26,29,31\}$$

An inspection of all circled decomposition charts (because of Prob. 7.24 it is necessary to view them only in one fashion, say, by rows) shows that f is not disjunctively decomposable of type II. Nevertheless, the three charts

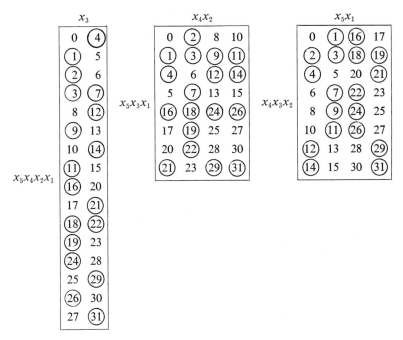

reveal (since each has only two column patterns—this is trivially true of the first chart) that f is disjunctively decomposable (on account of Corollary 7.2) for the partition

$$\lambda = \{\overline{x_3}; \, \overline{x_4, x_2}; \, \overline{x_5, x_1}\} = \{A_1, A_2, A_3\}$$

and we have a multiple decomposition of type I. Choosing

$$a^{(1)} = (1,0,0,1,1,0,1,0,0,1,1,0,0,1,0,1)$$
$$a^{(2)} = (1,1,0,1,1,1,1,0)$$
$$a^{(3)} = (0,1,1,0,0,0,1,1)$$

we obtain the truth tables

x_3	φ_1	x_4	x_2	φ_2	x_5	x_1	φ_3
0	0	0	0	0	0	0	1
1	1	0	1	1	0	1	0
		1	0	0	1	0	0
		1	1	0	1	1	1

for the φ_i, as prescribed by Eq. 7.19. Then $F: B^3 \longrightarrow B$ is uniquely determined by Eq. 7.5; we must have

φ_3	φ_2	φ_1	F
0	0	0	1
0	0	1	0
0	1	0	1
0	1	1	1
1	0	0	0
1	0	1	1
1	1	0	1
1	1	1	0

To illustrate, consider the third entry of the truth table where (b_3, b_2, b_1) $= (0,1,0)$. According to Eq. 7.20, we may take

$$v^{(3)} = (1,0) = (v_5, v_1)$$
$$v^{(2)} = (0,1) = (v_4, v_2)$$
$$v^{(1)} = (0) = (v_3)$$

as λ components of $v = (v_5, v_4, v_3, v_2, v_1) = (1,0,0,1,0)$. Using Eq. 7.21, we take

$$F(0,1,0) = f(1,0,0,1,0) = 1$$

since $\partial(v) = 18 \in \mathcal{K}^0(f)$.

Using a tree circuit for F (since it is not disjunctively decomposable), we obtain Fig. 7.6 according to the methods of Chapter 6. When this result is combined with the knowledge that

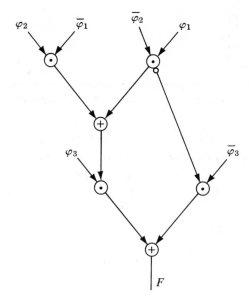

FIGURE 7.6

$$\varphi_3 = \overline{x_5 \oplus x_1}$$
$$\varphi_2 = \bar{x}_4 x_2$$
$$\varphi_1 = x_3$$

we obtain the economical two-input-per-gate realization of f, depicted in Fig. 7.7.

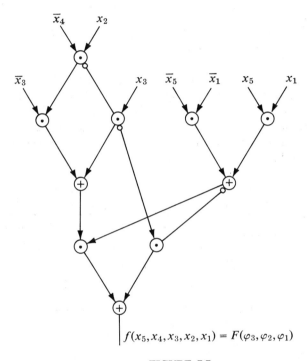

$$f(x_5, x_4, x_3, x_2, x_1) = F(\varphi_3, \varphi_2, \varphi_1)$$

FIGURE 7.7

7.6   ALGORITHM FOR DETERMINING THE DECOMPOSITION STRUCTURE

If the c.s.b.f. $f : B^n \longrightarrow B$ has a simple disjunctive decomposition

$$f(x_n, x_{n-1}, \cdots, x_1) = F(\varphi(A), S_n - A) \qquad (7.22)$$

for the primary partition $\lambda = \{A, S_n - A\}$ of S_n, it is said to be a *maximal* decomposition if f does not have a simple disjunctive decomposition $f = F(\psi(B), S_n - B)$ whenever $B \supseteq A, B \neq A$.

We combine the theory of the two preceding sections with the following theorem.

Theorem 7.4.[†]   (Ashenhurst's Structure Theorem): If the c.s.b.f. $f: B^n \longrightarrow B$ has maximal simple disjunctive decompositions for the primary partitions $\lambda_i = \{A_i, S_n - A_i\}$ ($i = 1, 2, \cdots, p$) and only these, then either

(1) $\lambda = \{A_i; 1 \leq i \leq p\}$ is a partition of S_n and f is of type I, or
(2) $\bar{\lambda} = \{S_n - A_i; 1 \leq i \leq p\}$ is a partition of S_n and f is of type II.

This will allow us to formulate an algorithm for determining the complete decomposition structure of any disjunctively decomposable function.

In this algorithm, we will naturally incorporate Ashenhurst's disjunctive decomposability criterion (cf. Theorem 7.1) and a means for identifying the type (I or II) whenever disjunctive decompositions exist; these constitute *phase* 0 (see the "flow chart" of Fig. 7.8) of the algorithm.

At the conclusion of phase 0, we know which of the three (mutually exclusive) possibilities,

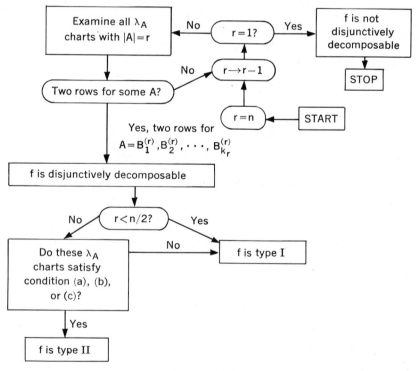

FIGURE 7.8

†A proof appears in Ref. 7-1.

(I) f is of type I,
(II) f is of type II,
(III) f is not disjunctively decomposable,

describes the given function $f: B^n \longrightarrow B$. This information is obtained by applying Ashenhurst's "two row-pattern" criterion to the partition matrices (λ_A charts) of f with respect to $A \subseteq S_n$ for decreasing $|A|$. If for all $|A| \geq n/2$ the "two row-pattern" criterion fails to yield a decomposition, we know that f is not of type II. (Why?) Hence, if it then happens that the "two row-pattern" criterion is satisfied on some λ_A chart with $2 \leq |A| < n/2$, it must be that f is decomposable of type I. On the other hand, if the first success of Ashenhurst's criterion occurs on a λ_A chart with $|A| \geq n/2$, it may yet be that f is of type I. Whether or not this is the case can be determined by examining the two-rowed λ_A charts under consideration, to see if they meet one of the following conditions:

(a)   One of the two rows consists entirely of ones.
(b)   One of the two rows consists entirely of zeros.
(c)   The two distinct rows are complementary.

If they do, f is of type II; otherwise, f is type I. (See Prob. 7.10.)

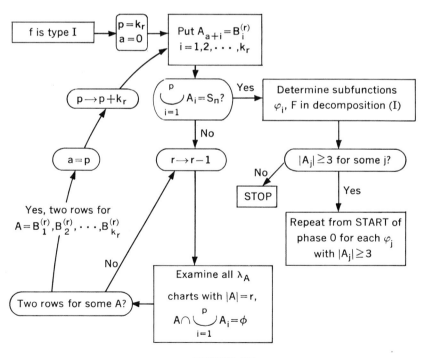

FIGURE 7.9

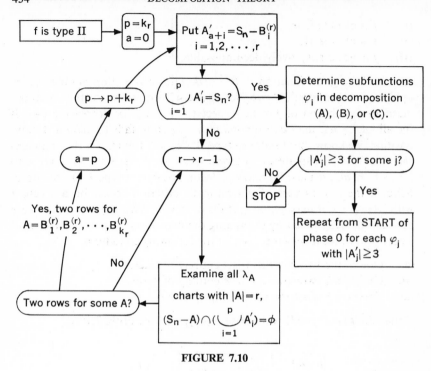

FIGURE 7.10

Assuming that f is found to be disjunctively decomposable in phase 0, we enter the appropriate flow chart (Fig. 7.9 or Fig. 7.10), which describes *phase* I or *phase* II:

Phase I: The determination of the partition $\lambda = \{A_1, A_2, \cdots, A_p\}$ and the subfunctions φ_i, F of the type I decomposition,

$$f = F(\varphi_p(A_p), \varphi_{p-1}(A_{p-1}), \cdots, \varphi_1(A_1))$$

Phase II: The determination of the partition

$$\bar{\lambda} = \{S_n - A_1, S_n - A_2, \cdots, S_n - A_p\} = \{A_1', A_2', \cdots, A_p'\}$$

and the subfunctions φ_i of the appropriate type II decomposition

(A) $f = \varphi_p(A_p') + \varphi_{p-1}, (A_{p-1}') + \cdots + \varphi_1(A_1')$;

(B) $f = \varphi_p(A_p') \cdot \varphi_{p-1}(A_{p-1}') \cdot (\cdots) \cdot \varphi_1(A_1')$;

(C) $f = \varphi_p(A_p') \oplus \varphi_{p-1}(A_{p-1}') \oplus \cdots \oplus \varphi_1(A_1')$;

where the subsets $A_1, A_2, \cdots, A_p$ are those for which (cf. Theorem 7.4)

$$f = F(\varphi(A_i), S_n - A_i)$$

is a maximal decomposition of f.

The determination of the subfunctions φ_i (and F when we are in phase I) is exactly as outlined in Sec. 7.5. The phase (I or II) terminates in one of two situations: Either each subfunction φ_i is of fewer than three variables, or some subfunction φ_i is of three or more variables. With the latter outcome, the entire procedure is to be repeated for each subfunction φ_j of three or more variables, beginning at START of phase 0.

Left chart — x_1, labeled $x_6x_5x_4x_3x_2$ (circled numbers shown in parentheses):

0	(1)
(2)	3
(4)	5
6	(7)
8	(9)
(10)	11
(12)	13
14	(15)
(16)	17
18	(19)
(20)	21
22	(23)
24	(25)
(26)	27
28	(29)
(30)	31
32	(33)
(34)	35
(36)	37
38	(39)
40	41
(42)	43
(44)	45
46	(47)
48	(49)
(50)	51
(52)	53
54	(55)
56	(57)
(58)	59
(60)	61
62	(63)

Right chart — x_2, labeled $x_6x_5x_4x_3x_1$ (circled numbers shown in parentheses):

0	(2)
(1)	3
(4)	6
5	(7)
8	(10)
(9)	11
(12)	14
13	(15)
(16)	18
17	(19)
(20)	22
21	(23)
24	(26)
(25)	27
28	(30)
(29)	31
32	(34)
(33)	35
(36)	38
37	(39)
40	(42)
(41)	43
(44)	46
45	(47)
48	(50)
(49)	51
(52)	54
53	(55)
56	(58)
(57)	59
(60)	62
61	(63)

EXAMPLE 7.12

Consider the c.s.b.f. $f: B^6 \longrightarrow B$ having

$$\mathcal{K}^0(f) = \{1,2,4,7,9,10,12,15,16,19,20,23,25,26,29,30,33,$$
$$34,36,39,41,42,44,47,49,50,52,55,57,58,60,63\}$$

(In order to illustrate the algorithm adequately, one needs to take an example having fairly large n. Although we have not provided six-variable decomposition charts, we *will* provide as many as are required for an understanding of the example.)

In phase 0 (Fig. 7.8) we initially set $r = n = 6$, but we are immediately told ($r \longrightarrow r - 1$) to decrease r by 1. Since $r = 5 \neq 1$, we examine all λ_A charts having $|A| = 5$. Of these, the following two satisfy Ashenhurst's "two row-pattern" criterion, whereas the other four do not. Using the notation of Fig. 7.8, we put

$$B_1^{(5)} = \{x_6, x_5, x_4, x_3, x_2\}$$
$$(k_5 = 2)$$
$$B_2^{(5)} = \{x_6, x_5, x_4, x_3, x_1\}$$

Now $r = 5 \nleq 3 = n/2$, so that we must ask whether these two λ_A charts satisfy condition (a), (b), or (c). Since the two rows are complementary, condition (c), in each case, the answer is "yes" and f is of type II.

Entering phase II (Fig. 7.10), we set

$$p = k_5 = 2$$
$$a = 0$$

$$A_1' = S_6 - B_1^{(5)} = \{x_1\}$$
$$A_2' = S_6 - B_2^{(5)} = \{x_2\}$$

and since

$$\bigcup_{i=1}^{p} A_i' = \{x_1\} \cup \{x_2\} = \{x_1, x_2\} \neq S_6$$

we must decrease r to $r = 4$, and examine all λ_A charts for which

$$|A| = 4$$
$$(S_6 - A) \cap \{x_1, x_2\} = \phi$$

This allows only the subsets of size 4, containing both x_1 and x_2: $\{x_6, x_5, x_2, x_1\}$, $\{x_6, x_4, x_2, x_1\}$, $\{x_6, x_3, x_2, x_1\}$, $\{x_5, x_4, x_2, x_1\}$, $\{x_5, x_3, x_2, x_1\}$, $\{x_4, x_3, x_2, x_1\}$ to be considered as A. If the reader were to construct the corresponding λ_A charts, he would see that none of them satisfies the "two row-pattern" criterion. Hence, we must decrease r to $r = 3$ and consider all λ_A charts having

$$|A| = 3$$
$$(S_6 - A) \cap \{x_1, x_2\} = \phi$$

Again the Ashenhurst criterion is not met for such subsets A.

But when $r = 2$, we find one (and only one) subset

$$A = B_1^{(2)} = \{x_2, x_1\} \qquad (k_2 = 1)$$

for which

$$|A| = 2$$
$$(S_6 - A) \cap \{x_1, x_2\} = \{x_6, x_5, x_4, x_3\} \cap \{x_2, x_1\} = \phi$$

while the λ_A chart (it must be viewed sideways)

$x_2 x_1$

0	①	②	3
④	5	6	⑦
8	⑨	⑩	11
⑫	13	14	⑮
⑯	17	18	⑲
⑳	21	22	㉓
24	㉕	㉖	27
28	㉙	㉚	31
32	㉝	㉞	35
㊱	37	38	㊴
40	㊶	㊷	43
㊸	45	46	㊼
48	㊾	㊿	51
㊾	53	54	55
56	57	58	59
60	61	62	63

$x_6 x_5 x_4 x_3$

has two row-patterns. Following Fig. 7.10, we put

$$a = 2 \qquad \text{(the current value of } p\text{)}$$

and $(p \longrightarrow p + k_r)$ increase p by $k_r = k_2 = 1$ (since r is currently 2):

$$p = 3$$

Then, setting

$$A'_{a+1} = A'_3 = S_6 - B_1^{(2)} = \{x_6, x_5, x_4, x_3\}$$

we have

$$\bigcup_{i=1}^{p} A'_i = A'_1 \cup A'_2 \cup A'_3 = \{x_1\} \cup \{x_2\} \cup \{x_6, x_5, x_4, x_3\} = S_6$$

Thus we are in possession of the partition (2),

$$\overline{\lambda} = \{A'_1, A'_2, A'_3\} = \overline{\{x_1; x_2; x_6, x_5, x_4, x_3\}}$$

described in Theorem 7.4, and the subfunctions $\varphi_1, \varphi_2, \varphi_3$ of the type II (c) decomposition,

$$f = \varphi_3(x_6, x_5, x_4, x_3) \oplus \varphi_2(x_2) \oplus \varphi_1(x_1) \qquad (7.23)$$

may be determined according to the method (Eqs. 7.18 and 7.19) of Sec. 7.5. The reader can verify that the selections

$$a^{(3)} = (0,1,1,0)$$
$$a^{(2)} = (1,0,0, \cdots, 1,0,0,1) \Big\} \text{ arbitrary}$$
$$a^{(1)} = (0,1,1, \cdots, 0,1,1,0)$$

are in agreement with this method. They yield (Eq. 7.17) truth tables

x_6	x_5	x_4	x_3	φ_3	x_2	φ_2	x_1	φ_1
0	0	0	0	1	0	0	0	1
0	0	0	1	0	1	1	1	0
0	0	1	0	1				
0	0	1	1	0				
0	1	0	0	0				
0	1	0	1	0				
0	1	1	0	1				
0	1	1	1	1				
1	0	0	0	1				
1	0	0	1	0				
1	0	1	0	1				
1	0	1	1	0				
1	1	0	0	1				
1	1	0	1	0				
1	1	1	0	1				
1	1	1	1	0				

for the three subfunctions.

Since $|A_3| = 4 \geq 3$, we must repeat the entire process for the subfunction $\varphi_3(x_6, x_5, x_4, x_3)$. When $r = 3$ in phase 0, we observe that none of the λ_A charts with $|A| = r = 3$,

satisfies the "two row-pattern" criterion, so we set $r = 2$ and find that for

$$A = B_1^{(2)} = \{x_6, x_5\} \qquad (k_2 = 1)$$

the Ashenhurst criteria is satisfied:

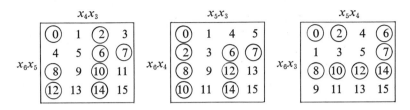

Now $r = 2 \not< 2 = n/2$, but nevertheless the λ_A chart does not meet one of the conditions—(a), (b), or (c)—so that φ_3 is of type I. Thus, we consult Fig. 7.9 in order to execute phase I. There we put

$$p = k_2 = 1$$
$$a = 0$$

$$A_1 = B_1^{(2)} = \{x_6, x_5\}$$

and since

$$\bigcup_{i=1}^{1} A_i = A_1 = \{x_6, x_5\} \neq \{x_6, x_5, x_4, x_3\}$$

we must decrease r to $r = 1$ and examine all λ_A charts for which

$$|A| = 1$$
$$A \cap \{x_6, x_5\} = \phi$$

that is, we consider only $A = \{x_4\}$ and $A = \{x_3\}$. But, trivially, each of these λ_A charts has two rows, so

$$B_1^{(1)} = \{x_4\}$$
$$(k_1 = 2)$$
$$B_2^{(1)} = \{x_3\}$$

and we set

$$a = 1$$
$$p = 1 + 2 = 3$$

$$A_2 = \{x_4\}$$
$$A_3 = \{x_3\}$$

and it is then true that

$$\bigcup_{i=1}^{3} A_i = \{x_6, x_5, x_4, x_3\}$$

so we now synthesize the subfunction $\psi_1(A_1)$ and F in the decomposition

$$\varphi_3 = F(\psi_1(x_6, x_5), x_4, x_3) \tag{7.24}†$$

According to the usual methods, we have truth tables

†Since $|A_3| = |A_2| = 1$, we have $\psi_3(x_3) = x_3$, $\psi_2(x_4) = x_4$.

x_6	x_5	ψ_1	ψ_1	x_4	x_3	F
0	0	0	0	0	0	0
0	1	1	0	0	1	1
1	0	0	0	1	0	0
1	1	0	0	1	1	1
			1	0	0	0
			1	0	1	0
			1	1	0	1
			1	1	1	1

Combining Eqs. 7.23 and 7.24, we have the complete (since $|A_i| < 3$ for $i = 1,2,3$) disjunctive decomposition

$$f(x_6, x_5, x_4, x_3, x_2, x_1) = F(\psi_1(x_6, x_5), x_4, x_3) \oplus \varphi_2(x_2) \oplus \varphi_1(x_1) \quad (7.25)$$

where our truth tables yield

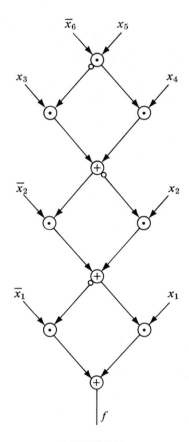

FIGURE 7.11

$$\varphi_1(x_1) = \bar{x}_1$$
$$\varphi_2(x_2) = x_2$$
$$\psi_1(x_6, x_5) = \bar{x}_6 x_5 \qquad (7.26)$$
$$F(\psi_1, x_4, x_3) = \overline{\psi}_1 x_3 + \psi_1 x_4$$

Together, Eqs. 7.25 and 7.26 imply the economical circuit of Fig. 7.11.

7.7 COMPOUND DISJUNCTIVE DECOMPOSITIONS

The examples of the previous sections clearly demonstrate the usefulness of a knowledge of disjunctive decomposition theory to the logical designer. A more quantitative demonstration of this utility can be had if we interpret the following lemma as it applies to the simple disjunctive decomposition.

Lemma 7.5   For all $r, s \geq 2$ (cf. Eq. 6.19),

$$B_T(r) + B_T(s) \leq B_T(r + s - 1)$$

with equality when $r = s = 2$.

PROOF.   A glance at either the first row of Table 6.3 or the third column of Table 6.6 alleviates the need for a complete inductive proof of this inequality. When $r = s = 2$, the inequality becomes an equality,

$$B_T(2) + B_T(2) = 6 + 6 = 12 = B_T(3) \ \blacksquare$$

Now it would seem reasonable to say that the simple disjunctive decomposition ($|A| \geq 2$)

$$f(x_n, x_{n-1}, \cdots, x_1) = F(\varphi(A), S_n - A)$$

is *profitable* if

$$B_T(|A|) + B_T(n - |A| + 1) \leq B_T(n) \qquad (7.27)$$

since the two figures on the left represent tree-circuit upper bounds on the costs of the two boxes appearing in the block diagram of Fig. 7.1. But, taking $r = |A|$ and $s = n - |A| + 1$, it can be seen (since $2 \leq |A| \leq n - 1$) that Lemma 7.5 implies the next theorem.

Theorem 7.6   Every simple disjunctive decomposition is profitable.

In this way, our opening remark about the utility of the disjunctive decomposition theory takes on a more exact (quantitative) meaning. If Eq. 7.27 were generalized properly, one could extend the assertion of Theorem 7.6 to the multiple disjunctive decompositions.

Unfortunately, the percentage of disjunctively decomposable functions in $B(n)$ becomes decreasingly small with increasing n.† Thus, we are naturally led to consider other types of decompositions if our theory is to be generally applicable. In this connection, there are at least two ways in which the theory can be generalized. One of these (see Ref. 7-1) allows for "nondisjunctive" decompositions, the form of which is identical with Eq. 7.5 but whose subsets A_i are members of a covering $\gamma = \{A_1, A_2, \cdots, A_p\}$ of S_n rather than a partition. Another way allows *compound disjunctive decompositions*‡ of the form $(2 \leq k < |A| \leq n - 1)$

$$f(x_n, x_{n-1}, \cdots, x_1) = F(\varphi_k(A), \varphi_{k-1}(A), \cdots, \varphi_1(A), S_n - A) \quad (7.28)$$

where $\lambda_A = \{A, S_n - A\}$ is a primary partition of S_n, as with the simple disjunctive decompositions. We will concentrate on the latter extension because it is more compatible with our previous developments.

The compound decomposition of Eq. 7.28 is said to be *trivial* if $k = 2$ and $|A| = n - 1$. We adopt this terminology because it then reduces, for some variable x_i, to

$$f(x_n, x_{n-1}, \cdots, x_1) = F(\varphi_2(x_n, x_{n-1}, \cdots, \hat{x}_i, \cdots, x_1),$$
$$\varphi_1(x_n, x_{n-1}, \cdots, \hat{x}_i, \cdots, x_1), x_i) \quad (7.29)$$

which is immediately recognized (cf. Eq. 6.7) as the tree circuit equation. Since an entire chapter has been devoted to its study, it is not of particular interest here.

With respect to the existence of compound disjunctive decompositions, we state the following generalization (if $k = 1$, it becomes identical with Ashenhurst's theorem) of Theorem 7.1.

Theorem 7.7   (Curtis-Ashenhurst): The c.s.b.f. $f: B^n \longrightarrow B$ has a compound disjunctive decomposition $(2 \leq k < |A| \leq n - 1)$

$$f(x_n, x_{n-1}, \cdots, x_1) = F(\varphi_k(A), \varphi_{k-1}(A), \cdots, \varphi_1(A), S_n - A)$$

for suitable functions

$$\varphi_i : B^{|A|} \longrightarrow B \qquad (i = 1, 2, \cdots, k)$$
$$F : B^{n - |A| + k} \longrightarrow C$$

if and only if the partition matrix of f with respect to A resulting from the primary partition $\lambda = \{A, S_n - A\}$ has ρ distinct rows for some integer $\rho \leq 2^k$.

PROOF.   As with Ashenhurst's theorem, we will prove only the half of the theorem that shows how to define the subfunctions φ_i and F occurring in Eq. 7.28 when it is assumed that the "ρ row criteria" is satisfied.

---

†In fact, C. E. Shannon has shown that this percentage approaches zero as $n \longrightarrow \infty$.
‡Some authors prefer to call this an "improper multiple decomposition."

Let $\mathscr{A} = \{a^{(0)}, a^{(1)}, \cdots, a^{(\rho-1)}\}$ be the collection of distinct rows of the partition matrix of f with respect to A. Then for each element of $B^{|A|}$, we have

$$f_A(b_{|A|}, b_{|A|-1}, \cdots, b_1) = a^{(r)}$$

for some r, $0 \le r \le \rho - 1$. Since $\rho \le 2^k$, there exist 1–1 mappings[†]

$$\varphi : \mathscr{A} \longrightarrow B^k$$

One such mapping is obtained by setting (cf. Eq. 0.66)

$$\varphi(a^{(r)}) = \partial^{-1}(r)$$

If we then take $\tilde{\varphi} : B^{|A|} \longrightarrow B^k$ to be the function

$$\tilde{\varphi} = \varphi \cdot f_A \tag{7.30}$$

we have defined the k subfunctions φ_i simultaneously; that is,

$$\varphi_i = \tau_i \cdot \tilde{\varphi} = \tau_i \cdot \varphi \cdot f_A \tag{7.31}$$

($i = 1, 2, \cdots, k$), where τ_i is the ith coordinate projection.

Next we take $F : B^{n-|A|+k} = B^k \times B^{n-|A|} \longrightarrow C$ to be the i.s.b.f.:

$$F(u, w) = \begin{cases} I & \text{if } \tilde{\varphi}^{-1}(u) = \varnothing \\ \tau_{2^{n-|A|}-\partial(w)}(a^{(\partial(u))}) & \text{otherwise} \end{cases} \tag{7.32}$$

(Note the similarity to Eq. 7.12 for $\partial(u) = u$ if $u \in B$.) Having defined the subfunctions, the proof that $f = F(\varphi_k(A), \varphi_{k-1}(A), \cdots, \varphi_1(A), S_n - A)$ is too similar to that of Ashenhurst's theorem to bear repeating. ∎

EXAMPLE 7.13

Suppose $f : B^5 \longrightarrow B$ is such that

$$\mathscr{K}^0(f) = \{0,2,7,11,12,17,21,22,25,27,28,29,30\}$$

Although f is not disjunctively decomposable in the sense of our earlier theory, the fact that the decomposition chart

$$x_3 x_2 x_1$$

	⓪	1	②	3	4	5	6	⑦
	8	9	10	⑪	⑫	13	14	15
$x_5 x_4$	16	⑰	18	19	20	㉑	㉒	23
	24	㉕	26	㉗	28	㉙	㉚	31

[†]In fact, there are many such mappings; the situation is not unlike that encountered when choosing a state assignment for a sequential machine.

has but $\rho = 3 \leq 2^2 = 2^k$ distinct column patterns,

$$a^{(0)} = (1,0,0,0)$$
$$a^{(1)} = (0,0,1,1)$$
$$a^{(2)} = (0,1,0,1)$$

shows the existence of a compound disjunctive decomposition,

$$f(x_5, x_4, x_3, x_2, x_1) = F(\varphi_2(x_3, x_2, x_1), \; \varphi_1(x_3, x_2, x_1), \; x_5, x_4)$$

of the form in Eq. 7.28, with $\lambda_A = \{\overline{x_3, x_2, x_1}; \overline{x_5, x_4}\}$ and $k = 2$. Then, using Eq. 7.30, we have (for the most natural choice for φ)

$$
\begin{array}{ll}
f_A(0,0,0) = a^{(0)} & \tilde{\varphi}(0,0,0) = (0,0) \\
f_A(0,0,1) = a^{(1)} & \tilde{\varphi}(0,0,1) = (0,1) \\
f_A(0,1,0) = a^{(0)} & \tilde{\varphi}(0,1,0) = (0,0) \\
f_A(0,1,1) = a^{(2)} & \tilde{\varphi}(0,1,1) = (1,0) \\
f_A(1,0,0) = a^{(2)} & \tilde{\varphi}(1,0,0) = (1,0) \\
f_A(1,0,1) = a^{(1)} & \tilde{\varphi}(1,0,1) = (0,1) \\
f_A(1,1,0) = a^{(1)} & \tilde{\varphi}(1,1,0) = (0,1) \\
f_A(1,1,1) = a^{(0)} & \tilde{\varphi}(1,1,1) = (0,0)
\end{array}
$$

which simultaneously defines (cf. Eq. 7.31) the truth tables

x_3	x_2	x_1	φ_2	φ_1
0	0	0	0	0
0	0	1	0	1
0	1	0	0	0
0	1	1	1	0
1	0	0	1	0
1	0	1	0	1
1	1	0	0	1
1	1	1	0	0

for the subfunctions φ_2 and φ_1.

Using Eq. 7.32 to define $F: B^4 \longrightarrow B$, we have

$$F(0,0,b_2,b_1) = \tau_{4-\partial(b_2, b_1)}(a^{(\partial(0,0))})$$
$$= \tau_{4-\partial(b_2, b_1)}(1,0,0,0)$$
$$F(0,1,b_2,b_1) = \tau_{4-\partial(b_2, b_1)}(0,0,1,1)$$
$$F(1,0,b_2,b_1) = \tau_{4-\partial(b_2, b_1)}(0,1,0,1)$$
$$F(1,1,b_2,b_1) = I \quad \text{since } \tilde{\varphi}^{-1}(1,1) = \varnothing$$

giving the incomplete truth table

φ_2	φ_1	x_5	x_4	F
0	0	0	0	1
0	0	0	1	0
0	0	1	0	0
0	0	1	1	0
0	1	0	0	0
0	1	0	1	0
0	1	1	0	1
0	1	1	1	1
1	0	0	0	0
1	0	0	1	1
1	0	1	0	0
1	0	1	1	1
1	1	0	0	I
1	1	0	1	I
1	1	1	0	I
1	1	1	1	I

Any circuits for F, φ_2, and φ_1 will now yield a circuit for f by the interconnections indicated in Fig. 7.12. Such a circuit can evidently be fabricated at a cost that is at most

$$B_T(3,2) + B_T(4,1) = 18 + 24 = 42$$

Since $B_T(5,1) = 52$, we see that a "profit" is anticipated in making use of this compound decomposition.

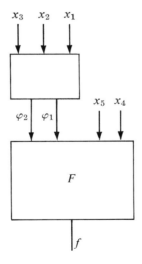

FIGURE 7.12

7.8 THE GENERALIZED DECOMPOSITION ITERATION

Judging from the computations that showed the advantage of the decomposition of Example 7.13, it seems reasonable to generalize Eq. 7.27 in a way that would result in our indicating as "profitable" a simple ($k = 1$) or compound ($k \geq 2$) disjunctive decomposition of the form of Eq. 7.28, provided

$$B_T(|A|, k) + B_T(n - |A| + k) \leq B_T(n, 1) \qquad (7.33)$$

Then the nonnegative difference could be called the "profit" of the decomposition. But, for use with our final algorithm (Sec. 7.9) for constructing economical two-input-per-gate circuits, this estimation technique would amount to an oversimplification; it would not acknowledge that the subfunctions $\varphi_1(A)$, $\varphi_2(A)$, $\cdots$, $\varphi_k(A)$ may be expected to contribute an amount less than $B_T(|A|, k)$ if additional functions of the variables in A need also to be constructed. And if f were but one of a family $\mathscr{F} = \{f_1, f_2, \cdots, f_m\}$ of functions $f_j : B^n \longrightarrow B$ of the same n variables, the right-hand side of Eq. 7.33 should read $B_T(n, m) - B_T(n, m - 1)$. Furthermore, if $k = 1$, so that Eq. 7.28 is a simple disjunctive decomposition, the figure $B_T(n - |A| + 1)$ should be replaced by $2 + B_T(n - |A|)$ or $6 + B_T(n - |A|)$ when the decomposition is type II, depending on which of the conditions (A), (B), or (C) of Sec. 7.5 is satisfied.

These three considerations dramatize the need for a more general definition of "profitable"—particularly when several families of functions are to be synthesized; at the same time, they dictate the revisions of Eq. 7.33, which are required in the more general setting. We suppose that

$$\mathscr{F} = \{f_1, f_2, \cdots, f_m\} \qquad f_j : B^n \longrightarrow B$$
$$\mathscr{G} = \{g_1, g_2, \cdots, g_r\} \qquad g_i : B^{|A|} \longrightarrow B$$

are two given families of functions, that the f_j are each functions of the variables in $S_n = \{x_n, x_{n-1}, \cdots, x_1\}$, and that the g_i are each functions of the variables in $A \subseteq S_n$. Then the simple ($k = 1$) or compound ($k \geq 2$) disjunctive decomposition of Eq. 7.28 for f_j (if it exists),

$$f_j(x_n, x_{n-1}, \cdots, x_1) = F(\varphi_k(A), \varphi_{k-1}(A), \cdots, \varphi_1(A), S_n - A) \qquad (7.34)$$

is called *profitable with respect to $\mathscr{F}$ and $\mathscr{G}$* if

$$\Delta(|A|, r, k) + \partial_A(F) \leq \Delta(n, m - 1, 1) \qquad (7.35)$$

Here the differences, Δ, are defined by

$$\Delta(q, r, s) = B_T(q, r + s) - B_T(q, r) \qquad (7.36)$$

and the figures $\partial_A(F)$ are taken as

$$\partial_A(F) = B_T(n - |A| + 1) \qquad \text{if } k = 1 \quad \text{(type I)} \tag{7.37a}$$

$$\partial_A(F) = 2 + B_T(n - |A|) \qquad \text{if } k = 1 \quad \text{(type II (A), (B))} \quad \text{or}$$
$$6 + B_T(n - |A|) \qquad \text{if } k = 1 \quad \text{(type II(C))} \tag{7.37b}$$

$$\partial_A(F) = B_T(n - |A| + k) \qquad \text{if } 2 \le k < |A| < n - 1 \tag{7.37c}$$

$$\partial_A(F) = d_i(f_j) \qquad \text{if } |A| = n - 1 \quad \text{so that } S_n - A = \{x_i\} \tag{7.37d}$$

When the decomposition (Eq. 7.34) is profitable with respect to $\mathscr{F}$ and $\mathscr{G}$, the nonnegative difference

$$P(f_j, A) = \Delta(n, m - 1, 1) - \Delta(|A|, r, k) - \partial_A(F) \tag{7.38}$$

is called the *profit* of the decomposition. Note in Eqs. 7.37 that we allow (when $k = 1$) for simple disjunctive decompositions and (when $|A| = n - 1$) for trivial compound disjunctive decompositions (alias tree circuits), whence we take $\partial_A(F)$ from Eq. 6.20.

EXAMPLE 7.14

By way of illustration, suppose $\mathscr{F} = \{f_1, f_2, f_3\}$ is a family of functions $f_j : B^5 \longrightarrow B$ of the Boolean variables in $S_5 = \{x_5, x_4, x_3, x_2, x_1\}$ and that $\mathscr{G} = \{g_1, g_2, g_3, g_4\}$ is a collection of functions $g_i : B^3 \longrightarrow B$ of the variables in $A = \{x_3, x_2, x_1\} \subseteq S_5$. Now, if f_1 is the function f of Example 7.13, its λ_A chart shows the existence of a compound decomposition

$$f = f_1(x_5, x_4, x_3, x_2, x_1) = F(\varphi_2(x_3, x_2, x_1), \varphi_1(x_3, x_2, x_1), x_5, x_4) \tag{7.39}$$

Taking $n = 5$, $m = 3$, $r = 4$, $k = 2$, $|A| = 3$, we compute from Eqs. 7.36 and 7.37c:

$$\Delta(|A|, r, k) = \Delta(3, 4, 2)$$
$$= B_T(3, 6) - B_T(3, 4)$$
$$= 46 - 34 = 12$$

$$\Delta(n, m - 1, 1) = \Delta(5, 2, 1)$$
$$= B_T(5, 3) - B_T(5, 2)$$
$$= 136 - 94 = 42$$

$$\partial_A(F) = B_T(n - |A| + k) = B_T(4) = 24$$

Thus, according to Eqs. 7.35 and 7.38, the decomposition (Eq. 7.39) is profitable with respect to $\mathscr{F}$ and $\mathscr{G}$, having the profit

$$P(f_1, A) = 42 - 12 - 24 = 6$$

Note, as we did in Example 7.13, that Eq. 7.33 would imply a profit of 10 rather than 6. The presence of the family $\mathscr{G}$ and the fact that f_1 is itself one of a family of functions alters (as it should) our estimate.

EXAMPLE 7.15

With f the same as in Example 7.13, but $\mathscr{F} = \{f\}$ and $\mathscr{G} = \{g_1, g_2, g_3, g_4$ $g_5\}$, a family of functions $g_i : B^4 \longrightarrow B$ of the variables in $A = \{x_5, x_4, x_3, x_1\}$, we find for the λ_A chart of f that the Ashenhurst-Curtis "ρ row-pattern criterion" is trivially satisfied for $\rho = 4 = 2^2$; that is, it is trivially true that f has the compound decomposition

$$f(x_5, x_4, x_3, x_2, x_1) = F(\varphi_2(x_5, x_4, x_3, x_1), \varphi_1(x_5, x_4, x_3, x_1), x_2)$$

(This is the claim of the tree circuit theorem!) Since we have case 4 of the tree circuit theorem we would not ordinarily (neglecting $\mathscr{G}$) expect this decomposition to have a positive profit; Eq. 6.22 gives

$$\sigma_2(f) = 6 + B_T(4,2) = 6 + 46 = 52 = B_T(5,1)$$

But, taking $n = 5$, $m = 1$, $r = 5$, $k = 2$, $|A| = 4$, we have

$$\Delta(|A|,r,k) = B_T(4,7) - B_T(4,5)$$
$$= 136 - 100 = 36$$

$$\Delta(n, m - 1,1) = B_T(5,1) - B_T(5,0) = 52 - 0 = 52$$

and from Eq. 7.37d, with $|A| = n - 1$, $S_n - A = \{x_2\}$, we have

$$\partial_A(F) = d_2(f) = 6$$

Thus, Eq. 7.38 shows that

$$P(f, A) = 52 - 36 - 6 = 10$$

so that a substantial saving is expected by merely applying the tree circuit theorem to f with respect to x_2.

As already indicated, provision must be made in our final algorithm (Sec. 7.9) for discussing a system

$$X = \{X_\alpha = (S^{(\alpha)}, F^{(\alpha)}); \alpha = 1, 2, \cdots, p\}$$

of pairs $X_\alpha = (S^{(\alpha)}, F^{(\alpha)})$ where each

$$S^{(\alpha)} = \{x_{1\alpha}, x_{2\alpha}, \cdots, x_{n_\alpha \alpha}\}$$

is a set of Boolean variables and the corresponding

$$F^{(\alpha)} = \{f_{1\alpha}, f_{2\alpha}, \cdots, f_{m_\alpha \alpha}\}$$

is a family of functions $f_{j\alpha} : B^{n_\alpha} \longrightarrow B$ of the variables in $S^{(\alpha)}$. The system X, whose various pairs $(S^{(\alpha)}, F^{(\alpha)})$ are assumed to have distinct variable sets, forms a partially ordered set $(X, \geq)$ under the relation

$$X_\alpha \geq Y_\alpha \longleftrightarrow S^{(\alpha)} \supseteq T^{(\alpha)} \tag{7.40}$$

for pairs $X_\alpha = (S^{(\alpha)}, F^{(\alpha)})$, $Y_\alpha = (T^{(\alpha)}, G^{(\alpha)})$. In order that the situations where $S^{(\alpha)} \supseteq T^{(\alpha)}$ be exploited to best advantage in the profit equation (Eq. 7.38), it would seem desirable to first decompose functions selected from among families $F^{(\alpha)}$ for which $X_\alpha = (S^{(\alpha)}, F^{(\alpha)})$ is maximal in $(X, \geq)$. We now describe a decompositional iteration that has this characteristic.

Let $(X, \geq)$ be a partially ordered set of the type just introduced.

(1)   Using Eq. 7.38, test for profitable decompositions (simple and

compound (trivial or not)) of each function $f \in F^{(\alpha)}$ for which X_α is maximal in $(X, \geq)$.

(2)　If positive profits exist in (1), choose $f \in F^{(\alpha)}$ and $A \subseteq S^{(\alpha)}$ for which $P(f, A)$ is a maximum. If not, proceed to (4).

(3)　Perform the decomposition selected in (2). The decomposition will create subfunctions (cf. Eqs. 7.37):

(a)　Simple, Type I

$$\varphi : B^{|A|} \longrightarrow B \qquad X_{p+1} = (A, \{\varphi\})$$
$$F : B^{n-|A|+1} \longrightarrow B \qquad X_{p+2} = (S^{(\alpha)} - A \cup \{\varphi\}, \{F\})$$

(b)　Simple, type II

$$\varphi : B^{|A|} \longrightarrow B \qquad X_{p+1} = (A, \{\varphi\})$$
$$\psi : B^{n-|A|} \longrightarrow B \qquad X_{p+2} = (S^{(\alpha)} - A, \{\psi\})$$

(c)　Nontrivial compound

$$\varphi_i : B^{|A|} \longrightarrow B \, (i = 1, 2, \cdots, k) \quad X_{p+1} = (A, \{\varphi_i\})$$
$$F : B^{n-|A|+k} \longrightarrow B \qquad\qquad X_{p+2} = (S^{(\alpha)} - A \cup \{\varphi_i\}, \{F\})$$

(d)　Tree circuit

$$g_j, h_j : B^{n-1} \longrightarrow B \qquad X_{p+1} = (S^{(\alpha)} - \{x_j\}, \{g_j, h_j\})$$

and the system X is to be modified accordingly by

(i)　deleting f from $F^{(\alpha)}$,

(ii)　augmenting $F^{(\beta)}$ whenever $S^{(\beta)} = S^{(p+q)}$ $(q = 1, 2)$,

(iii)　augmenting X by the new pairs $X_{p+q} = (S^{(p+q)}, F^{(p+q)})$ unaccounted for in (ii),

thus assuring that the new system X has the same property (that its variable sets $S^{(\alpha)}$ are distinct) as it originally possessed. The iteration is then complete.

(4)　Perform a *generalized* (multiple-output) *tree circuit iteration* of maximal X_α, which differs from that of Sec. 6.11 only in that the "profit"

$$B_T(n, m) - B_T(n - 1, \rho_i) - \sum_{j=1}^{m} d_i(f_j)$$

resulting from a strict interpretation of Eq. 6.22 is to be replaced by

$$P(F, x_i) = B_T(n, m) - \Delta(n - 1, r, \rho_i) - \sum_{j=1}^{m} d_i(f_j) \qquad \textbf{(7.41)}$$

This profit equation acknowledges (as does Eq. 7.38) that there may exist a pair $X_\beta = (S^{(\beta)}, F^{(\beta)})$ in X with

$$S^{(\beta)} = S^{(\alpha)} - \{x_i\}$$
$$F^{(\beta)} = \{f_{1\beta}, f_{2\beta}, \cdots, f_{r\beta}\}$$

and it alters the estimated cost of the tree circuit subfunctions accordingly. Having chosen $x_i \in S^{(\alpha)}$ and $F = F^{(\alpha)}$, which maximizes Eq. 7.41 among all maximal $X_\alpha = (S^{(\alpha)}, F^{(\alpha)})$ in $(X, \geq)$, and having performed the corresponding tree circuit decomposition of *each $f \in F^{(\alpha)}$* with respect to this variable x_i, the system X is then modified as in (3) to account for the deletion of X_α and the appearance of the tree circuit subfunctions. The iteration is then complete.

EXAMPLE 7.16

In Example 7.14 we have the system

$$X = \{(S_5, \mathscr{F}), (A, \mathscr{G})\} = \{X_1, X_2\}$$

and the partially ordered set $(X, \geq)$ in which $(S_5, \mathscr{F}) > (A, \mathscr{G})$. Supposing in (1) that the decomposition of Eq. 7.39 has maximum profit among all those $P(f_i, B)$ with $i = 1,2,3$ and $B \subseteq S_5$, we would in (2) choose f_1 and A. Performing this decomposition in (3), we would obtain subfunctions (c):

$$\varphi_1 : B^3 \longrightarrow B \qquad X_3 = (A, \{\varphi_2, \varphi_1\})$$

$$\varphi_2 : B^3 \longrightarrow B \qquad X_4 = (\{x_5, x_4, \varphi_2, \varphi_1\}, \{F\})$$

$$F : B^4 \longrightarrow B$$

The system X then has to be modified as follows:

$$X = \{X_1, X_2, X_4\}$$

where
$$X_1 = (S_5, \{f_2, f_3\})$$
$$X_2 = (A, \{g_1, g_2, g_3, g_4, \varphi_2, \varphi_1\})$$
$$X_4 = (\{x_5, x_4, \varphi_2, \varphi_1\}, \{F\})$$

The new system will have two maximal elements, X_1 and X_4.

7.9 PROGRAM FOR SYNTHESIZING ECONOMICAL TWO-INPUT-PER-GATE CIRCUITS

The final and all-encompassing program that climaxes the theory of the preceding two chapters is depicted in the flow chart of Fig. 7.13. Even a casual glance at this chart reveals that all important synthesis procedures:

(1) The tree circuit algorithm (Sec. 6.11)
(2) The decomposition structure algorithm (Sec. 7.6)
(3) The synthesis of compound disjunctive decompositions (Sec. 7.7)
(4) The minimal two-variable circuit algorithm (Sec. 3.16)
(5) The generalized decomposition iteration (Sec. 7.8)

$$X = \left\{ X_\alpha = (S^{(\alpha)}, F^{(\alpha)}), \alpha = 1, 2, \cdots, p \right\}$$

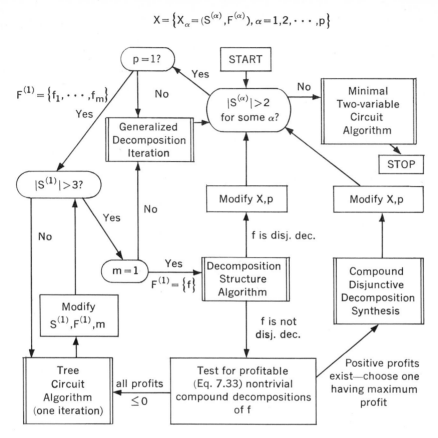

FIGURE 7.13

are employed. We have not bothered to give detailed instruction as to the way in which the system X should be modified when procedures (1), (2), or (3) have been employed. We have already done this with (5), and the reader should be able to generalize from the instructions given there. Owing to the presence of (5), the procedures are embedded in a selection process that treats (as it must) a system X of families of functions, choosing from among those families having maximal subsets a function having a decomposition with profit that is maximal. Except when X consists of only one family of functions of three or fewer variables, or of only one function, it is the iteration (5) that is repeated until we finally obtain only functions of two variables, whence (4) is employed to complete the synthesis. While we do not guarantee that the resulting circuit will be minimal in its cost (even among two-input-per-gate circuits), we can expect it to be quite economical.

EXAMPLE 7.17

To illustrate this final program, consider the two functions $f_1, f_2: B^5 \longrightarrow B$, having

$$\mathscr{K}^0(f_1) = \{0,5,6,7,8,9,11,12,15,16,20,26,28,30\}$$
$$\mathscr{K}^0(f_2) = \{0,1,6,7,12,13,14,15,17,18,20,23,24,26,29,31\}$$

We have a system $X = \{X_1 = (S^{(1)}, F^{(1)})\}$ with

$$S^{(1)} = \{x_5, x_4, x_3, x_2, x_1\} = S_5 \quad \text{and} \quad F^{(1)} = \{f_1, f_2\}$$

Since $|S^{(1)}| = 5$, $p = 1$, $m = 2 \neq 1$, we arrive (in Fig. 7.13) at the box labeled "Generalized Decomposition Iteration."

Even though the partition matrix of f_1 with respect to $A = \{x_4, x_3, x_2\}$ has but four rows

$$x_5 x_1$$

$$x_4 x_3 x_2 \quad \begin{array}{|cccc|}
\hline
⓪ & 1 & ⑯ & 17 \\
2 & 3 & 18 & 19 \\
4 & ⑤ & ⑳ & 21 \\
⑥ & ⑦ & 22 & 23 \\
⑧ & ⑨ & 24 & 25 \\
10 & ⑪ & ㉖ & 27 \\
⑫ & 13 & ㉘ & 29 \\
14 & ⑮ & ㉚ & 31 \\
\hline
\end{array}$$

the computation

$$P(f_1, A) = \Delta(5,1,1) - \Delta(3,0,2) - B_T(4)$$
$$= (94 - 52) - (18 - 0) - 24$$
$$= 0$$

shows that a positive profit is not anticipated from the corresponding compound decomposition. A similar analysis of the other λ_A charts for f_1 reveals no positive profits.

But the same chart for f_2

$$x_5 x_1$$

$$x_4 x_3 x_2 \quad \begin{array}{|cccc|}
\hline
⓪ & ① & 16 & ⑰ \\
2 & 3 & ⑱ & 19 \\
4 & 5 & ⑳ & 21 \\
⑥ & ⑦ & 22 & ㉓ \\
8 & 9 & ㉔ & 25 \\
10 & 11 & ㉖ & 27 \\
⑫ & ⑬ & 28 & ㉙ \\
⑭ & ⑮ & 30 & ㉛ \\
\hline
\end{array}$$

shows that Ashenhurst's "two-row pattern" criterion is met and that f_2 has the type II (C), Sec. 7.5, disjunctive decomposition

$$f_2(x_5, x_4, x_3, x_2, x_1) = \varphi(x_4, x_3, x_2) \oplus \psi(x_5, x_1) \qquad (7.42)$$

with the profit

$$\begin{aligned} P(f_2, A) &= \Delta(5,1,1) - \Delta(3,0,1) - (6 + B_T(2)) \\ &= (94 - 52) - (12 - 0) - (6 + 6) \\ &= 42 - 24 = 18 > 0 \end{aligned}$$

Further examination of the charts for f_2 reveals that this is the most profitable decomposition.

The subfunctions φ and ψ in Eq. 7.42 have truth tables

x_4	x_3	x_2	φ		x_5	x_1	ψ
0	0	0	1		0	0	0
0	0	1	0		0	1	0
0	1	0	0		1	0	1
0	1	1	1		1	1	0
1	0	0	0				
1	0	1	0				
1	1	0	1				
1	1	1	1				

as found by the methods of Sec. 7.5.

Having chosen this decomposition, the system X must be modified:

$$X = \{X_1, X_2, X_3\}$$

where

$$X_1 = \{S_5, \{f_1\}\}$$
$$X_2 = \{\{x_4, x_3, x_2\}, \{\varphi\}\}$$
$$X_3 = \{\{x_5, x_1\}, \{\psi\}\}$$

Since we then have $|S^{(1)}| = 5$, $p = 3$, we return to the "Generalized Decomposition Iteration."

This time, the aforementioned compound decomposition of f_1 will be profitable, for with $A = \{x_4, x_3, x_2\}$

$$\begin{aligned} P(f_1, A) &= \Delta(5,0,1) - \Delta(3,1,2) - B_T(4) \\ &= (52 - 0) - (26 - 12) - 24 \\ &= 14 \end{aligned}$$

Since this decomposition proves to be the only profitable decomposition of f_1, the program selects this decomposition on this second iteration. By the methods of Sec. 7.7 we write

$$f_1(x_5, x_4, x_3, x_2, x_1) = F(\varphi_2(x_4, x_3, x_2), \varphi_1(x_4, x_3, x_2), x_5, x_1) \qquad (7.43)$$

for the truth tables

x_4	x_3	x_2	φ_2	φ_1
0	0	0	0	0
0	0	1	0	1
0	1	0	1	0
0	1	1	1	1
1	0	0	1	1
1	0	1	1	0
1	1	0	0	0
1	1	1	1	0

φ_2	φ_1	x_5	x_1	F
0	0	0	0	1
0	0	0	1	0
0	0	1	0	1
0	0	1	1	0
0	1	0	0	0
0	1	0	1	0
0	1	1	0	0
0	1	1	1	0
1	0	0	0	0
1	0	0	1	1
1	0	1	0	1
1	0	1	1	0
1	1	0	0	1
1	1	0	1	1
1	1	1	0	0
1	1	1	1	0

The modified system becomes $X = \{X_1, X_2, X_3\}$, with

$$X_1 = \{\{\varphi_2, \varphi_1, x_5, x_1\}, \{F\}\}$$
$$X_2 = \{\{x_4, x_3, x_2\}, \{\varphi, \varphi_2, \varphi_1\}\}$$
$$X_3 = \{\{x_5, x_1\}, \{\psi\}\}$$

The reader should now verify that the program next selects a type II (C) disjunctive decomposition

$$F(\varphi_2, \varphi_1, x_5, x_1) = \psi_2(\varphi_2, x_5) \oplus \psi_1(\varphi_1, x_1) \tag{7.44}$$

and that a fourth pass will select a (multiple-output) tree circuit for the family $F^{(2)} = \{\varphi, \varphi_2, \varphi_1\}$ with respect to the variable x_2.

Since the subfunctions ψ_2 and ψ_1 have truth tables

φ_2	x_5	ψ_2	φ_1	x_1	ψ_1
0	0	0	0	0	1
0	1	0	0	1	0
1	0	1	1	0	0
1	1	0	1	1	0

the reader has only to construct the tree circuit for the family $F^{(2)}$ with respect to x_2 in order to obtain the two-input-per-gate circuit derived by the program (see Fig. 7.14).

We have purposely chosen here an example for which the program tends to utilize the generalized decomposition iteration because this is its only new feature employed; examples that illustrate the intracacies of the other algorithms have already been given.

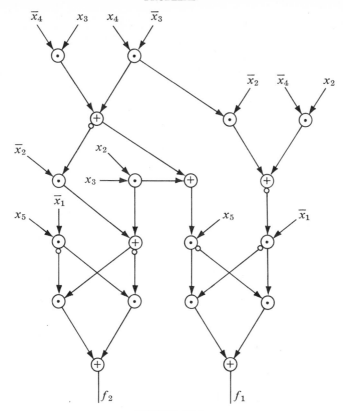

FIGURE 7.14

PROBLEMS

7.1 Give nontrivial decompositions of the following mappings:

(a) $f: C \longrightarrow R$, where $f(z) = \overline{z^2}$.

(b) $f: R \longrightarrow R$, where $f(x) = e^{x^2}$.

7.2 For the c.s.b.f.'s $f: B^3 \longrightarrow B$, as shown,

(a)   (b)

x_3	x_2	x_1	f		x_3	x_2	x_1	f
0	0	0	0		0	0	0	0
0	0	1	1		0	0	1	1
0	1	0	1		0	1	0	1
0	1	1	0		0	1	1	1
1	0	0	0		1	0	0	1
1	0	1	0		1	0	1	0
1	1	0	0		1	1	0	0
1	1	1	0		1	1	1	0

and the partition $\lambda = \{A_1, A_2\} = \{\overline{x_3}; \overline{x_2, x_1}\}$, exhibit decompositions of the form

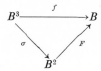

where $\sigma = \varphi_2 \times \varphi_1$, $\varphi_1 : B \longrightarrow B$, $\varphi_2 : B^2 \longrightarrow B$.

7.3 By appealing directly to the definition of Sec. 7.2, show that the functions f of Prob. 7.2 are disjunctively decomposable.

7.4 Show (using Ashenhurst's theorem) that a c.s.b.f. $f : B^n \longrightarrow B$ whose ith partial expansion (for some $i = 1, 2, \cdots, n$) leads to Case 2 of the tree circuit theorem is disjunctively decomposable. Show also that the converse is not true.

7.5 Obtain the partition function $f_A : B^3 \longrightarrow B^4$ of f with respect to A if $f : B^5 \longrightarrow B$ is such that
$$\mathscr{K}^0(f) = \{0,1,3,4,7,9,11,15,16,21,25,26,27,30,31\}$$
and $A = \{x_4, x_2, x_1\}$; $A = \{x_5, x_4, x_2\}$; $A = \{x_5, x_2, x_1\}$.

7.6 Prove the half of Ashenhurst's theorem (Theorem 7.1) that was not proved in the text.

7.7 For the functions $f : B^4 \longrightarrow B$
(a) Determine whether f is disjunctively decomposable, or not;
(b) For subfunctions φ_j and F in the decompositions (wherever f is decomposable) which are functions of more than two variables, repeat step (a);
(c) Determine the most economical tree circuits for f, if it is not disjunctively decomposable, and for subfunctions of more than two variables which are not disjunctively decomposable.

Thus synthesize economical two-input-per-gate circuits when

(i) $\qquad\qquad\qquad \mathscr{K}^0(f) = \{0,5,7,9,11,12\}$
(ii) $\qquad\qquad\qquad \mathscr{K}^0(f) = \{0,1,2,7,11,13\}$
(iii) $\qquad\qquad\qquad \mathscr{K}^0(f) = \{0,3,5,6,8,10,12,14\}$

7.8 Prove that a disjunctively decomposable function $f : B^3 \longrightarrow B$ is necessarily type II.

7.9 Prove Theorem 7.3(b) and (c).

*7.10 Show that if $f : B^n \longrightarrow B$ is a c.s.b.f. whose partition matrix with respect to some $A \subseteq S_n$ satisfies one of the (mutually exclusive) conditions (a), (b), and (c) of Theorem 7.3 and if the partition matrix of f with respect to A' ($|A'| > 1$) has but two rows, the same condition, (a), (b), or (c), is met for this matrix.

7.11 For the following disjunctively decomposable functions $f : B^5 \longrightarrow B$, determine

    (a)   whether the decomposition is type I or type II;

    (b)   the subfunctions (φ_j and F) of the decomposition resulting from one pass through Figs. 7.8 through 7.10.

    (i) $\mathscr{K}^0(f) = \{0,3,4,7,8,9,12,13,17,18,20,23,26,27,28,29\}$

    (ii) $\mathscr{K}^0(f) = \{0,1,2,3,6,7,9,10,11,15,18,19,25,26,27,31\}$

    (iii) $\mathscr{K}^0(f) = \{3,4,5,6,7,8,9,10,11,15,16,20,21,22,23,24,25,26,27,28\}$

    (iv) $\mathscr{K}^0(f) = \{2,3,6,7,10,11,19,23,27\}$

    (v) $\mathscr{K}^0(f) = \{0,1,2,3,4,5,6,7,8,9,11,24,25,26,27,28,29,30,31\}$

7.12   Construct a set of six-variable decomposition charts.

7.13   Use the algorithm of Sec. 7.6 to determine the complete decomposition structure of $f : B^6 \longrightarrow B$ (cf. Prob. 7.12), where

    (a) $\mathscr{K}^0(f) = \{1,2,3,5,6,7,8,11,12,15,16,19,20,23,24,25,27,28,29,$
                  $31,33,34,35,36,39,40,43,44,45,47,48,51,53,54,55,56,$
                                           $57,59,60,63\}$

    (b) $\mathscr{K}^0(f) = \{0,2,5,7,8,11,13,14,16,17,18,19,24,25,30,31\}$

*7.14 Complete the proof of the Curtis-Ashenhurst theorem by showing that

    (a)   The definitions of Eqs. 7.31 and 7.32 have as consequence:

$$f(x_n, x_{n-1}, \cdots, x_1) = F(\varphi_k(A), \varphi_{k-1}(A), \cdots, \varphi_1(A), S_n - A).$$

    (b)   Conversely, if the decomposition of (a) exists for some $A \subseteq S_n$, then the partition matrix of f with respect to A has ρ distinct rows for some integer $\rho \leq 2^k$.

*7.15 (a)   Show that if $f, g \in B(n)$ and $f \cong g$, then f is disjunctively decomposable iff g is disjunctively decomposable.

    (b)   Using the class decomposition (cf. Sec. 2.11) of $B(3)$, determine among the 256 functions of $B(3)$ the number of decomposable functions.

7.16 (a)   By using the tree circuit algorithm (cf. Sec. 6.11) on the family $\mathscr{H} = \{\varphi_1, \varphi_2\}$ and the function $F : B^4 \longrightarrow B$ of Example 7.13, obtain an economical two-input-per-gate circuit for $f : B^5 \longrightarrow B$ as defined in that example.

    (b)   If f is considered as belonging to a family $\mathscr{F} = \{f, f'\}$ where $f, f' : B^5 \longrightarrow B$ are functions of the variables in $S_5 = \{x_5, x_4, x_3, x_2, x_1\}$ and $\mathscr{G} = \{g_1, g_2, g_3, g_4, g_5\}$ is a family in which the $g_i : B^{|A|} \longrightarrow B$ $(i = 1,2,3,4,5)$ are functions of the variables in $A = \{x_3, x_2, x_1\}$, compute $P(f, A)$, the profit of the decomposition in Eq. 7.28.

*7.17 (a)   If $f : B^n \longrightarrow B$ and $A \subseteq S_n$, show that f has the decomposition

$$f(x_n, x_{n-1}, \cdots, x_1) = F(\psi(\varphi(A), S_n - A), A)$$

if and only if the partition matrix of f with respect to A has at most six distinct rows and these consist of not more than two "nontrivial" rows and their complements, together with the trivial rows $(0,0, \cdots, 0)$ and $(1,1, \cdots, 1)$.

    (b)   Derive a "profit" formula for this type of decomposition.

(c) Describe a means for incorporating this type of decomposition within the program of Sec. 7.9.

7.18 (a) For $A = \{x_3, x_2, x_1\} \subseteq S_5$ and $f : B^5 \longrightarrow B$ for which

$$\mathcal{K}^0(f) = \{4,6,7,8,10,11,13,14,16,18,19,21,22,26,29,30,31\}$$

show that a decomposition of the type described in Prob. 7.17 exists; determine the subfunctions F, ψ, φ and the "profit" of the decomposition.

(b) Obtain an economical two-input-per-gate circuit for f by constructing tree circuits for (1) F with respect to the variable ψ, yielding two subfunctions, $G(x_3, x_2, x_1)$ and $H(x_3, x_2, x_1)$; (2) the family $\{G, H, \varphi\}$ of functions of the variables in A; (3) the function ψ.

(c) How should the profit formula of Prob. 7.17(b) be revised if we take advantage (as in b) of the tree circuit of F with respect to ψ to obtain three functions G, H, and φ of the same $|A|$ variables?

7.19 Use the program of Sec. 7.9 to determine economical two-input-per-gate circuits for (a) the family $F = \{f_1, f_2\}$, where $f_1, f_2 : B^5 \longrightarrow B$ are such that

$$\mathcal{K}^0(f_1) = \{1,3,4,6,8,9,11,12,13,14,16,18,21,23,24,26,31\}$$
$$\mathcal{K}^0(f_2) = \{1,2,3,4,7,8,9,11,13,14,17,19,20,22,25,26,27,28,31\}$$

and (b) the family $F = \{f_1, f_2, f_3\}$, where $f_1, f_2, f_3 : B^4 \longrightarrow B$ are such that

$$\mathcal{K}^0(f_1) = \{0,1,6,7,8,9,10,14,15\}$$
$$\mathcal{K}^0(f_2) = \{2,3,4,5,6,7,8,10,11,12,13,14,15\}$$
$$\mathcal{K}^0(f_3) = \{2,4,5,6,7,8,12,13,14,15\}$$

and (c) the function $f : B^6 \longrightarrow B$ (cf. Prob. 7.12) for which

$$\mathcal{K}^0(f) = \{2,3,4,6,7,8,9,12,13,16,18,19,21,22,23,24,25,28,29,$$
$$32,33,37,42,43,44,46,47,49,52,56,58,59,61,62,63\}$$

and (d) the function $f : B^6 \longrightarrow B$ for which

$$\mathcal{K}^0(f) = \{0,1,3,5,6,9,10,13,14,15,18,20,21,25,26,29,31,36,$$
$$37,38,40,41,42,43,44,45,46,50,54,55,59,60,62,63\}$$

7.20 Compare the cost of the circuits obtained in Prob. 7.19 with that obtained by the methods of Chapter 3.

7.21 (a) State a generalization of Ashenhurst's theorem to incompletely specified functions.

(b) Do the same for the Curtis-Ashenhurst theorem.

*7.22 Prove Ashenhurst's structure theorem.

7.23 Show that if $\lambda = 0$, the decomposition of Eq. 7.4 is trivial and that if $\lambda = I$, then $\sigma = t_\pi^b$ for some permutation $\pi : n^+ \longrightarrow n^+$ and some $b = (b_n, b_{n-1}, \cdots, b_1) \in B^n$.

7.24 Show that the partition matrix of f with respect to A satisfies property (a), (b), or (c) of Theorem 7.3 iff the partition matrix of f with respect to $S_n - A$ satisfies the same property.

SUGGESTED REFERENCES

7-1   CURTIS, H. A., *A New Approach to the Design of Switching Circuits* (Princeton, New Jersey: D. Van Nostrand Co.), 1962.

7-2   HU, SZE-TSEN, *Threshold Logic* (Berkeley, California: University of California Press), 1965.

7-3   ASHENHURST, R. L., *The Decomposition of Switching Functions*, April 2-5, 1957. Annals of the Harvard Computational Laboratory (Harvard University Press), XXIX, pp 74–116, 1959.

APPENDIX

TABLE I

$\eta(f)$	$[f]$	$\eta(f)$	$[f]$	$\eta(f)$	$[f]$	$\eta(f)$	$[f]$
0	0_1	48	II_1	96	II_2	144	II_2
1	I_1	49	III_1	97	III_3	145	III_2
2	I_1	50	III_1	98	III_2	146	III_3
3	II_1	51	IV_1	99	IV_4	147	IV_4
4	I_1	52	III_2	100	III_2	148	III_3
5	II_1	53	IV_3	101	IV_4	149	IV_4
6	II_2	54	IV_4	102	IV_5	150	IV_6
7	III_1	55	V_1	103	V_3	151	V_2
8	I_1	56	III_2	104	III_3	152	III_2
9	II_2	57	IV_4	105	IV_6	153	IV_5
10	II_1	58	IV_3	106	IV_4	154	IV_4
11	III_1	59	V_1	107	V_2	155	V_3
12	II_1	60	IV_5	108	IV_4	156	IV_4
13	III_1	61	V_3	109	V_2	157	V_2
14	III_1	62	V_3	110	V_3	158	V_3
15	IV_1	63	VI_1	111	VI_2	159	VI_2
16	I_1	64	I_1	112	III_1	160	II_1
17	II_1	65	II_2	113	IV_2	161	III_2
18	II_2	66	II_3	114	IV_3	162	III_1
19	III_1	67	III_2	115	V_1	163	III_3
20	II_2	68	II_1	116	IV_3	164	III_2
21	III_1	69	III_1	117	V_1	165	IV_5
22	III_3	70	III_2	118	V_3	166	IV_4
23	IV_2	71	IV_3	119	VI_1	167	V_3
24	II_3	72	II_2	120	IV_4	168	III_1
25	III_2	73	III_3	121	V_2	169	IV_4
26	III_2	74	III_2	122	V_3	170	IV_1
27	IV_3	75	IV_4	123	VI_2	171	V_1
28	III_2	76	III_1	124	V_3	172	IV_3
29	IV_3	77	IV_2	125	VI_2	173	V_3
30	IV_4	78	IV_3	126	VI_3	174	V_1
31	V_1	79	V_1	127	VII_1	175	VI_1
32	I_1	80	II_1	128	I_1	176	III_1
33	II_2	81	III_1	129	II_3	177	IV_3
34	II_1	82	III_2	130	II_2	178	IV_2
35	III_1	83	IV_3	131	III_2	179	V_1
36	II_3	84	III_1	132	II_2	180	IV_4
37	III_2	85	IV_1	133	III_2	181	V_3
38	III_2	86	IV_4	134	III_3	182	V_2
39	IV_3	87	V_1	135	IV_4	183	VI_2
40	II_2	88	III_2	136	II_1	184	IV_3
41	III_3	89	IV_4	137	III_2	185	V_3
42	III_1	90	IV_5	138	III_1	186	V_1
43	IV_2	91	V_3	139	IV_3	187	VI_1
44	III_2	92	IV_3	140	III_1	188	V_3
45	IV_4	93	V_1	141	IV_3	189	VI_3
46	IV_3	94	V_3	142	IV_2	190	VI_2
47	V_1	95	VI_1	143	V_1	191	VII_1

TABLE I (Cont'd)

$\eta(f)$	$[f]$	$\eta(f)$	$[f]$	$\eta(f)$	$[f]$	$\eta(f)$	$[f]$
192	II_1	208	III_1	224	III_1	240	IV_1
193	III_2	209	IV_3	225	IV_4	241	V_1
194	III_2	210	IV_4	226	IV_3	242	V_1
195	IV_5	211	V_3	227	V_3	243	VI_1
196	III_1	212	IV_2	228	IV_3	244	V_1
197	IV_3	213	V_1	229	V_3	245	VI_1
198	IV_4	214	V_2	230	V_3	246	VI_2
199	V_3	215	VI_2	231	VI_3	247	VII_1
200	III_1	216	IV_3	232	IV_2	248	V_1
201	IV_4	217	V_3	233	V_2	249	VI_2
202	IV_3	218	V_3	234	V_1	250	VI_1
203	V_3	219	VI_3	235	VI_2	251	VII_1
204	IV_1	220	V_1	236	V_1	252	VI_1
205	V_1	221	VI_1	237	VI_2	243	VII_1
206	V_1	222	VI_2	238	VI_1	254	VII_1
207	VI_1	223	VII_1	239	VII_1	255	VIII_1

TABLE II

Case	Type	① G_i	② H_i	③ F_i	④ $T(F_i)$	⑤ $\tau_i(f)$
2	(i) 00 / 01	0 / g_i	h_i / 0	$H_i x_i$ / $G_i\bar{x}_i$	2 / 2	$2+T(H_i)$ / $2+T(G_i)$
	(ii) 00 / 10	$g_i=h_i$ / $g_i=\bar{h}_i$	$h_i=g_i$ / $h_i=\bar{g}_i$	$G_i=H_i$ / $G_i\bar{x}_i+\bar{G}_i x_i=\bar{H}_i\bar{x}_i+H_i x_i$	0 / 6	$T(G_i)=T(H_i)$ / $6+\min\{T(G_i),T(H_i)\}$
	(iii) 00 / 11	(see above)				
	(iv) 01 / 10					
	(v) 01 / 11	g_i	0	G_i+x_i	2	$2+T(G_i)$
	(vi) 10 / 11	0	h_i	$H_i+\bar{x}_i$	2	$2+T(H_i)$

Case	Type	① G_i	② H_i	③ F_i	④ $T(F_i)$	⑤ $\tau_i(f)$
2 (i)	00	0	h_i	$H_i x_i$	2	$2+T(H_i)$
	01	g_i	0	$G_i\bar{x}_i$	2	$2+T(G_i)$
2 (ii)	00	$g_i=h_i$	$h_i=g_i$	$G_i=H_i$	0	$T(G_i)=T(H_i)$
	10	$g_i=\bar{h}_i$	$h_i=\bar{g}_i$	$G_i\bar{x}_i+\bar{G}_i x_i=\bar{H}_i\bar{x}_i+H_i x_i$	6	$6+\min\{T(G_i),T(H_i)\}$
2 (v)	01	g_i	0	G_i+x_i	2	$2+T(G_i)$
2 (vi)	11	0	h_i	$H_i+\bar{x}_i$	2	$2+T(H_i)$

Case 3

Type	① G_i	② H_i	③ F_i	④ $T(F_i)$	⑤ $\tau_i(f)$
(i) 00 / 01 / 10	$g_i\le G_i'\le g_i+\bar{g}_i\bar{h}_i$; $G_i''=g_i+h_i$; g_i	$H_i''=g_i+h_i$; $h_i\le H_i'\le h_i+\bar{g}_i\bar{h}_i$; h_i	$H_i''\cdot(G_i'\bar{x}_i+\bar{G}_i'x_i)$; $G_i''\cdot(\bar{H}_i'\bar{x}_i+H_i'x_i)$; $G_i\bar{x}_i+H_i x_i$	8 ; 8 ; 6	$\min\begin{cases}8+T(G_i')+T(H_i'')\\8+T(G_i'')+T(H_i')\\6+T(G_i)+T(H_i)\end{cases}$
(ii) 00 / 01	$g_i\bar{h}_i\le G_i'\le g_i$; g_i	$\bar{g}_i h_i\le H_i'\le h_i$; h_i	$G_i'+x_i H_i'$; $H_i(x_i+G_i')$	4	$4+\min\begin{cases}T(G_i')+T(H_i')\\T(G_i')+T(H_i)\end{cases}$
(iii) 10 / 11	$g_i\bar{h}_i\le G_i'\le g_i$; g_i	$\bar{g}_i h_i\le H_i'\le h_i$; h_i	$H_i+\bar{x}_i G_i'$; $G_i(\bar{x}_i+H_i')$	4	$4+\min\begin{cases}T(G_i')+T(H_i)\\T(G_i)+T(H_i')\end{cases}$
(iv) 01 / 10 / 11	$G_i''=g_i h_i$; $g_i\bar{h}_i\le G_i'\le g_i$; g_i	$\bar{g}_i h_i\le H_i'\le h_i$; $H_i''=g_i h_i$; h_i	$G_i''+(\bar{H}_i'\bar{x}_i+H_i'x_i)$; $H_i''+(G_i'\bar{x}_i+\bar{G}_i'x_i)$; $G_i\bar{x}_i+H_i x_i$; $(G_i'\bar{x}_i+H_i'x_i)+K_i'$†	8 ; 8 ; 6 ; 8	$\min\begin{cases}8+T(G_i'')+T(H_i')\\8+T(G_i')+T(H_i'')\\6+T(G_i)+T(H_i)\\8+T(G_i')+T(H_i')+T(K_i')\end{cases}$

Case 4

Type	① G_i	② H_i	③ F_i	④ $T(F_i)$	⑤ $\tau_i(f)$
00	g_i	h_i	$G_i\bar{x}_i+H_i x_i$	6	$6+T(G_i)+T(H_i)$
01 / 10 / 11	$g_i\bar{h}_i\le G_i'\le g_i$	$\bar{g}_i h_i\le H_i'\le h_i$	$(G_i\bar{x}_i+H_i'x_i)+K_i'$†	8	$\min\begin{cases}6+T(G_i)+T(H_i)\\8+T(G_i')+T(H_i')+T(K_i')\end{cases}$

†Technically, this form (since $f = F_i(G_i', H_i', K_i', x_i)$) should not be regarded as a part of Theorem 6.1. The reason for including it here becomes apparent in a proof of Theorem 6.4.

TABLE II
(Cont'd)

Case	Type	⑥ $t_i(f)$	⑦‡ $M(f)$	⑧‡ $\mu_1(f)$
2	(i) 00 / 01	$2+M'(H_i)$	$\mu_1(H_i)+M(H_i)$	$\mu_1(H_i)$
	(ii) 00 / 10	$2+M'(G_i)$	$\mu_1(G_i)+M(G_i)$	$\mu_1(G_i)$
	(iii) 00 / 11	$M'(G_i)=M'(H_i)$	$M(G_i)+M(H_i)$	$\mu_1(G_i)=\mu_1(H_i)$
	(iv) 01 / 10	$6+\min\{M'(G_i),M'(H_i)\}$	$\mu_1(G_i)+\mu_1(H_i)$ $+M(G_i)+M(H_i)$	$\mu_1(G_i)+\mu_1(H_i)$
	(v) 01 / 11	$2+M'(G_i)$	$2+M(G_i)$	$1+\mu_1(G_i)$
	(vi) 10 / 11	$2+M'(H_i)$	$2+M(H_i)$	$1+\mu_1(H_i)$
3	(i) 00 / 01 / 10	$\min\begin{cases}8+M'(G_i')+M'(H_i'')\\8+M'(G_i')+M'(H_i')\\6+M'(G_i)+M'(H_i)\end{cases}$	$\mu_1(G_i)+\mu_1(H_i)$ $+M(G_i)+M(H_i)$	$\mu_1(G_i)+\mu_1(H_i)$
	(ii) 00 / 01 / 11	$4+\min\begin{cases}M'(G_i)+M'(H_i')\\M'(G_i)+M'(H_i)\end{cases}$	$\mu_1(H_i')+M(G_i)+M(H_i')$	$\mu_1(G_i)+\mu_1(H_i')$
	(iii) 00 / 10 / 11	$4+\min\begin{cases}M'(G_i)+M'(H_i)\\M'(G_i)+M'(H_i)\end{cases}$	$\mu_1(G_i')+M(G_i')+M(H_i)$	$\mu_1(G_i')+\mu_1(H_i)$
	(iv) 01 / 10 / 11	$\min\begin{cases}8+M'(G_i')+M'(H_i')\\8+M'(G_i')+M'(H_i'')\\6+M'(G_i)+M'(H_i)\end{cases}$	$\mu_1(G_i')+\mu_1(H_i')+M(G_i')$ $+M(H_i)+M(K_i')$	$\mu_1(G_i')+\mu_1(H_i')$ $+\mu_1(K_i')$
4	00 / 01 / 10 / 11	$\min\begin{cases}6+M'(G_i)+M'(H_i)\\8+M'(G_i')+M'(H_i')+M'(g_ih_i)\end{cases}$	$\mu_1(G_i')+\mu_1(H_i')+M(G_i')$ $+M(H_i')+M(K_i')$	$\mu_1(G_i')+\mu_1(H_i')$ $+\mu_1(K_i')$

‡Columns 7 and 8 should be interpreted as follows: There exists G_i, H_i, G_i', H_i' satisfying columns 1 and 2 such that $M(f)$ and $\mu_1(f)$ have the values claimed. (See Probs. 3.3 through 3.8.)

TABLE I₁ CHARACTERISTIC NUMBERS FOR CLASS I_1

b \ π	1	(12)	(23)	(123)	(132)	(13)
111	1	1	1	1	1	1
110	2	4	2	16	4	16
101	4	2	16	2	16	4
100	8	8	32	32	64	64
011	16	16	4	4	2	2
010	32	64	8	64	8	32
001	64	32	64	8	32	8
000	128	128	128	128	128	128

TABLE II₁ CHARACTERISTIC NUMBERS FOR CLASS II_1

b \ π	1	(12)	(23)	(123)	(132)	(13)
111	3	5	3	17	5	17
110	3	5	3	17	5	17
101	12	10	48	34	80	68
100	12	10	48	34	80	68
011	48	80	12	68	10	34
010	48	80	12	68	10	34
001	192	160	192	136	160	136
000	192	160	192	136	160	136

TABLE II₂ CHARACTERISTIC NUMBERS FOR CLASS II_2

b \ π	1	(12)	(23)	(123)	(132)	(13)
111	9	9	33	33	65	65
110	6	6	18	18	20	20
101	6	6	18	18	20	20
100	9	9	33	33	65	65
011	144	144	132	132	130	130
010	96	96	72	72	40	40
001	96	96	72	72	40	40
000	144	144	132	132	130	130

TABLE II₃ CHARACTERISTIC NUMBERS FOR CLASS II_3

b \ π	1	(12)	(23)	(123)	(132)	(13)
111	129	129	129	129	129	129
110	66	36	66	24	36	24
101	36	66	24	66	24	36
100	24	24	36	36	66	66
011	24	24	36	36	66	66
010	36	66	24	66	24	36
001	66	36	66	24	36	24
000	129	129	129	129	129	129

TABLE III$_1$ CHARACTERISTIC NUMBERS FOR CLASS III$_1$

b \ π	1	(12)	(23)	(123)	(132)	(13)
111	7	7	19	19	21	21
110	11	13	35	49	69	81
101	13	11	49	35	81	69
100	14	14	50	50	84	84
011	112	112	76	76	42	42
010	176	208	140	196	138	162
001	208	176	196	140	162	138
000	224	224	200	200	168	168

TABLE III$_2$ CHARACTERISTIC NUMBERS FOR CLASS III$_2$

b \ π	1	(12)	(23)	(123)	(132)	(13)
111	67	37	67	25	37	25
110	131	133	131	145	133	145
101	28	26	52	38	82	70
100	44	74	56	98	88	100
011	52	82	28	70	26	38
010	56	88	44	100	74	98
001	193	161	193	137	161	137
000	194	164	194	152	164	152

TABLE III$_3$ CHARACTERISTIC NUMBERS FOR CLASS III$_3$

b \ π	1	(12)	(23)	(123)	(132)	(13)
111	41	73	41	97	73	97
110	22	22	22	22	22	22
101	134	134	146	146	148	148
100	73	41	97	41	97	73
011	146	148	134	148	134	146
010	97	97	73	73	41	41
001	104	104	104	104	104	104
000	148	146	148	134	146	134

TABLE IV$_1$ CHARACTERISTIC NUMBERS FOR CLASS IV$_1$

b \ π	1	(12)	(23)	(123)	(132)	(13)
111	15	15	51	51	85	85
110	15	15	51	51	85	85
101	15	15	51	51	85	85
100	15	15	51	51	85	85
011	240	240	204	204	170	170
010	240	240	204	204	170	170
001	240	240	204	204	170	170
000	240	240	204	204	170	170

TABLE IV₂ CHARACTERISTIC NUMBERS FOR CLASS IV_2

b \ π	1	(12)	(23)	(123)	(132)	(13)
111	23	23	23	23	23	23
110	43	77	43	113	77	113
101	77	43	113	43	113	77
100	142	142	178	178	212	212
011	113	113	77	77	43	43
010	178	212	142	212	142	178
001	212	178	212	142	178	142
000	232	232	232	232	232	232

TABLE IV₃ CHARACTERISTIC NUMBERS FOR CLASS IV_3

b \ π	1	(12)	(23)	(123)	(132)	(13)
111	39	71	27	83	29	53
110	27	29	39	53	71	83
101	141	139	177	163	209	197
100	78	46	114	58	116	92
011	114	116	78	92	46	58
010	177	209	141	197	139	163
001	216	184	228	172	226	202
000	228	226	216	202	184	172

TABLE IV₄ CHARACTERISTIC NUMBERS FOR CLASS IV_4

b \ π	1	(12)	(23)	(123)	(132)	(13)
111	135	135	147	147	149	149
110	75	45	99	57	101	89
101	45	75	57	99	89	101
100	30	30	54	54	86	86
011	120	120	108	108	106	106
010	180	210	156	198	154	166
001	210	180	198	156	166	154
000	225	225	201	201	169	169

TABLE IV₅ CHARACTERISTIC NUMBERS FOR CLASS IV_5

b \ π	1	(12)	(23)	(123)	(132)	(13)
111	195	165	195	153	165	153
110	195	165	195	153	165	153
101	60	90	60	102	90	102
100	60	90	60	102	90	102
011	60	90	60	102	90	102
010	60	90	60	102	90	102
001	195	165	195	153	165	153
000	195	165	195	153	165	153

TABLE IV$_6$ CHARACTERISTIC NUMBERS FOR CLASS IV$_6$

π b	1	(12)	(23)	(123)	(132)	(13)
111	105	105	105	105	105	105
110	150	150	150	150	150	150
101	150	150	150	150	150	150
100	105	105	105	105	105	105
011	150	150	150	150	150	150
010	105	105	105	105	105	105
001	105	105	105	105	105	105
000	150	150	150	150	150	150

DATE DUE

GAYLORD   PRINTED IN U.S.A.